THE

RAY SOCIETY

Instituted 1844

This volume (No. 137 of the series) is issued to members of the Ray Society for the Year 1951, and is sold at a price of 30/-

LONDON
1953

Printed by
Metchim & Son Limited,
8 Storey's Gate,
London, S.W.1.

BRITISH SPIDERS

by

G. H. LOCKET, M.A. (Oxon.), M.Sc. (Lond.), F.Z.S.
& A. F. MILLIDGE, Ph.D., B.Sc. (Lond.)

VOL. II

with 254 figures in the text

Dedicated to Enid Locket and Josephine Millidge, without whose constant patience and encouragement this work could never have been undertaken or completed.

PREFACE

IN this, the second and final volume of our work on British spiders, we present the descriptions of the species of the families AGELENIDÆ, MIMETIDÆ, THERIDIIDÆ, NESTICIDÆ, TETRAGNATHIDÆ, ARGIOPIDÆ and LINYPHIIDÆ ; the treatment of the latter family has been almost entirely the work of one of us (A. F. M.). We have kept as far as possible to the methods and layout which were employed in Volume I. We think it may be worth emphasising, in view of some enquiries which have been made, that the descriptions given in both volumes apply only to the adult spiders, and that the characters of the genera which have been selected are based on the British species only.

Since Volume I was published a few species new to Britain have come to our notice, and accounts of these are added in the present volume, so that, on going to press, we shall have dealt with all the current British species.

We wish to acknowledge once more our deep gratitude for much help willingly given from many quarters. Mr. A. A. D. La Touche has not only lent us further specimens, but has allowed us to describe his *Drassodes sörenseni* (Strand) and *Micaria silesiaca* L. Koch which are new to Britain and are thus recorded as such for the first time. Mr. E. Duffey, while working with the Bureau of Animal Population at Oxford, has captured and sent us *Pirata uliginosus* (Thorell), which is new to Britain, as well as other rarities. We are indebted also to Mr. A. D. Blest for specimens of *Wideria polita* (Simon) and *Lophocarenum radicicola* (L. Koch), both new to Britain, and for other rarities. Mr. A. M. Wild has sent us *Xysticus acerbus* Thorell and *Lycosa paludicola* (Clerck).

Dr. W. J. Gertsch, of the American Museum of Natural History, has helped us greatly by the loan of specimens, and has discovered from our first volume that the genus *Scotophaeus* E. Simon, 1893, should give place to *Herpyllus* Hentz 1832. We are grateful to him also for keeping us in touch with relevant work at present going on in the United States, as well as for the gift of specimens. Dr. Å. Holm, of Uppsala, has helped us by the loan and gift of specimens from Sweden for comparison and drawing. Dr. Jacques Denis, of Denain, has rendered us much assistance by confirming the identities of species not hitherto found in this country. Prof. P. Bonnet has provided us with useful information on points of nomenclature.

We are again grateful to the authorities and workers of several museums for the loan of specimens freely made : to Prof. G. C. Varley

v

and his assistants at the Hope Department of the University Museum at Oxford, who have the keeping of the Pickard-Cambridge collection ; to Mr. W. K. Ford, of the Liverpool City Museum, where the Falconer collection is lodged ; to Miss G. Lynch, of the Dublin Museum of Natural History, and to Dr. Marc André, of the Museum d'Histoire Naturelle of Paris. We are especially grateful to the authorities of the British Museum (Natural History), who have made available to us all of Dr. Jackson's material, as well as for the loan of other specimens. We again owe a debt of gratitude to Mr. E. Browning for his help in the matter of specimens, and for carrying out many enquiries on our behalf.

We acknowledge with thanks the permission given by the Linnaean Society of London to reproduce Text-figs. 96 ; 97 ; 98 ; 99 ; 100 ; 152 ; 244, C ; 246, 247, 249., and likewise permission from the Editors of the *Annals and Magazine of Natural History* to reproduce Text-fig. 115.

Finally we wish to express our best thanks to Dr. Maurice Burton for kindly advice and information, which have helped to relieve us of anxiety on many practical matters.

CONTENTS : VOLUME II

I. DESCRIPTION OF THE SPECIES

18. Family AGELENIDÆ.

CHARACTERS OF FAMILY. CARAPACE: Oval, attenuated in front (except in *Amaurobius* and *Cicurea*) with a longitudinal fovea (repre-

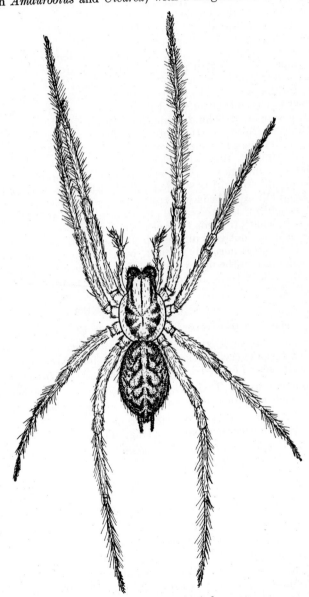

TEXT-FIG. 1.—*Tegenaria larva.*

sented by a mark in *Argyroneta*). EYES : Not very different in size (except in *Cryphœca, Tetrilus, Tuberta* and *Hahnia*). ABDOMEN : Oval. A transverse slit near the spinners (usually difficult to see) marks the tracheal spiracles, except in *Argyroneta*, where it is near the epigastric fold (Text-fig. 4, A), and in *Antistea* and *Hahnia*, where it is well in advance of the spinners. SPINNERS : Anteriors cylindrical or conical, separated to a varying degree ; medians of the same form or smaller. Posteriors usually recognisably biarticulate (see however *Argyroneta*) ; apical segments of varying length, with fusules arranged along the inner side. In *Antistea* and *Hahnia* the spinners lie in a transverse row (Text-fig. 2, F). STERNUM : Wide, heart-shaped, sometimes pointed behind, sometimes projecting between coxæ IV. CHELICERÆ : Nearly vertical, often markedly convex, especially at the base. Outer margin usually with 3 teeth, inner with 2–8. PALPS : ♀, with a claw. ♂, tibia with one or more external apophyses ; patella and femur sometimes with an apophysis. The embolus of the palpal organs usually long. LEGS : Generally bearing spines, more numerous on III and IV. Apical edges of trochanters without a notch ; no regular tarsal scopulæ ; three toothed tarsal claws. Tarsal trichobothria increase in length towards the apical end of tarsus.

The males are not very different from the females in size and coloration. The web is normally a sheet, with a retreat at one corner, and the spiders run on the upper surface of it. In closed spaces (e.g. under stones or bark of trees) it may take a tubular form.

KEY TO THE GENERA

1. Spinners in a transverse line (Text-fig. 2, F) . . . 9

——Spinners as in Text-fig. 2, A, B. Anteriors contiguous ; posteriors very like them. Tracheal spiracles recognisable just behind epigastric fold (Text-fig. 4, A) (1) **Argyroneta**

——Spinners as in Text-figs. 2, C–E, with two segments. Tracheal spiracle close to spinners and not easily seen . 2

2. Apical segment of posterior spinners clearly recognisable, not much shorter than basal, or longer (Text-fig. 2, C, D) . 3

——Apical segment of posterior spinners much shorter than basal, not so clearly recognisable (Text-fig. 2, E) . . 6

3. Posterior eyes in a strongly recurved row (Text-fig. 3, C)
(3) **Textrix**

——Posterior row of eyes straight or procurved 4

4. Both rows of eyes strongly procurved . . (2) **Agelena**

——Both rows of eyes not, or only slightly, procurved . . 5

5. Cephalic region of carapace narrowed (Text-fig. 1). Legs long and slender. Cheliceræ not very convex ; inner margin with 4–8 teeth. ♂ palpal patella with no apophysis . . . . . . (4) **Tegenaria**

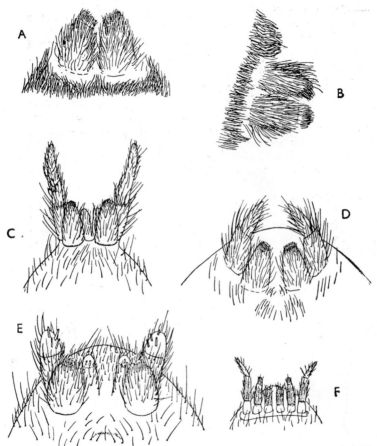

TEXT-FIG. 2.—Spinners: A, B, *Argyroneta;* C, *Agelena;* D, *Tegenaria;* E, *Cicurina;* F, *Hahnia.*

——Cephalic region of carapace much broader (Text-fig. 3, A). Legs short and stout. Cheliceræ very convex; inner margin with 3 teeth. ♂ palpal patella with an apophysis (Text-fig. 15, A, B) . . (5) **Amaurobius**

6. Anterior row of eyes strongly procurved (as seen from front)
(7) **Cryphœca**

——Anterior row of eyes straight or nearly so. 7

7. Eyes nearly equal in size. Inner margin of cheliceræ with 7 teeth. Length about 6 mm. Male palpal organs of normal size and construction (Text-fig. 16, A) (6) **Cicurina**

——Anterior median eyes smaller, usually much smaller than the the rest. Inner margin of cheliceræ with 2–3 teeth. Length 3½ mm. or less. Male palpal organ very abnormal (Text-figs. 17, A, 18, B).   8

8. Inner row of cheliceræ with 3 teeth. No clear abdominal pattern . . . . (8) **Tetrilus**

——Inner row of cheliceræ with 2 teeth. A clear abdominal pattern like that of *Cryphœca silvicola* . (9) **Tuberta**

9. Anterior median eyes equal to or slightly greater than the posterior medians (Text-fig. 19, A). Tracheal spiracle approximately half way from spinners to epigastric fold. Male palpal femur with an apophysis (Text-fig. 19, C)
(10) **Antistea**

——Anterior median eyes smaller than posterior medians (Text-fig. 20, A). Tracheal spiracle 1/3 to 1/4 of way from spinners to epigastric fold. Male palpal femur without an apophysis . . . . . (11) **Hahnia**

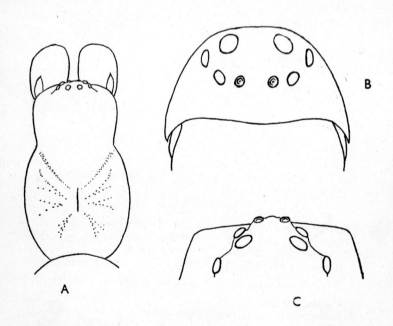

Text-fig. 3.—A, Carapace of *Amaurobius*; B, C, Eyes of *Textrix*.

1. Genus **ARGYRONETA** P. A. Latreille 1804.

CHARACTERS OF GENUS. CARAPACE : Cephalic area long and somewhat attenuated. Fovea not distinct, represented by a longitudinal narrow dark streak. Faint radiating striæ visible. EYES : Anterior row slightly recurved ; medians the smallest, 0·5 diameter apart and 1·5 diameters from laterals. Posterior row slightly recurved, eyes almost equidistant. ABDOMEN : Thickly clothed with rather short hairs. Tracheal spiracles situated far from spinners (indicated by a fold just behind the epigastric fold (Text-fig. 4, A)). SPINNERS : Anteriors conical, placed close together (Text-fig. 2, A). Posteriors about the same length, but rather more slender (Text-fig. 2, B). STERNUM : Heart shaped, pointed behind, projecting a little between coxæ IV. CHELICERÆ : Strong, convex at the base. ♀ : nearly vertical ; inner row with two nearly equal teeth. ♂ : longer than in ♀ and projecting more in front ; fangs also longer. The two teeth in the inner row widely

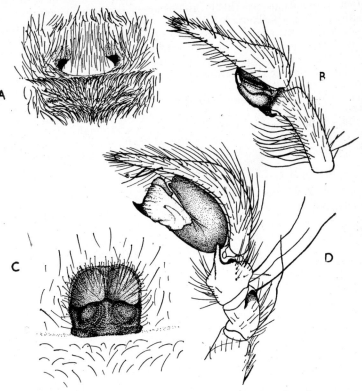

TEXT-FIG. 4.—*Argyroneta aquatica:* A, epigyne ; B, male palp.
Agelena labyrinthica: C, epigyne ; D, male palp.

separated. MAXILLÆ : Rather short, broad and with nearly parallel sides. LABIUM : Slightly longer than broad ; reaching much further than mid point of maxillæ. LEGS : Rather thickly clothed with short, and also in places with long, hairs ; retrolateral sides of III and IV largely clear of hairs. I and II with few spines (except for ventral, usually paired, spines on tibiæ and metatarsi). III and IV with many spines on tibiæ and metatarsi.

This genus falls in E. Simon's sub-Family CYBÆINÆ (1897, p. 224).

There is one British species, *Argyroneta aquatica* (Clerck), the well-known water spider.

Argyroneta aquatica (Clerck).

(=*Argyroneta aquatica* (Linnaeus))
(Text-figs. 2, A, B ; 4, A, B)

Araneus aquaticus C. Clerck, 1757, p. 143. *Argyroneta aquatica* Recent authors.

DESCRIPTION. LENGTH : ♀ : about 8–15 mm. ♂ : about 9–12 mm. (Greater variations are likely to occur ; specimens from different localities show considerable differences in size.) CARAPACE : Light yellow brown with faint darker striæ ; with only a few hairs, mostly along striæ in cephalic area. ABDOMEN : Uniform mouse-grey ; thickly and evenly covered with rather short hairs. CHELICERÆ : Red-brown, darker than carapace. EPIGYNE : Text-fig. 4, A. MALE PALP : Text-fig. 4, B.

The male spider is usually larger than the female.

OCCURRENCE : Locally abundant in ponds and ditches and distributed all over the British Isles. The species, though air-breathing, is entirely aquatic and rarely leaves the water. (For the biology of the species reference may be made to E. Nielsen, 1932, I, p. 98.)

2. Genus AGELENA C. A. Walckenaer 1805.

CHARACTERS OF GENUS. CARAPACE : Rather long, the cephalic region narrowed. EYES : Nearly equal in size ; anterior medians not noticeably different from the rest. Both rows markedly procurved (as seen from above and from in front). Medians form a trapezium, nearly a rectangle, a little longer than broad. Laterals narrowly separated. Width of clypeus two–three times diameter of an anterior lateral eye. ABDOMEN : Oval, tapering somewhat behind. SPINNERS : Anteriors clearly separated (Text-fig. 2, C). Posteriors much longer and very clearly of two segments ; the apical segment longer than the basal and tapering (very noticeably when viewed from side or above). STERNUM : Almost circular with a narrow pointed piece projecting a little between coxæ IV. CHELICERÆ : Strong and nearly vertical. Each row with three teeth. LEGS : Long and narrow towards extremities, very hairy ; spines mostly long and aculeate. MALE PALP : An apophysis occurs on the patella, in addition to those on the tibia.

There is one British species, *Agelena labyrinthica* (Clerck).

Agelena labyrinthica (Clerck).

(=Agelena labyrinthica (Linnaeus))
(Text-figs. 2, C ; 4, C, D)

Araneus labyrinthicus C. Clerck, 1757, p. 79. *Aranea labyrinthica* C. Linnaeus, 1758, page 620. *Agelena labyrinthica* C. A. Walckenaer, 1825, p. 226 and recent authors.

DESCRIPTION. LENGTH : ♀ : about 8–12 mm. ♂ : about 8–9 mm. (greater variations may very well occur). CARAPACE : A median light brown band, almost parallel sided and width of the ocular area, runs the whole length. It is flanked in the thoracic region by chocolate brown areas, outside which are light lateral bands with a very thin dark borderline. ABDOMEN : Dark sooty grey with a lighter longitudinal median region mottled with the darker colour, and on each side of this is a series of dusky brown lighter curved transverse bars. CHELICERÆ : Deep brown, becoming reddish on preservation. LEGS : All segments with long hairs. Light brown with faint, dusky, wide annulations on tibiæ and metatarsi. EPIGYNE : Text-fig. 4, C. MALE PALP : Text-fig. 4, D.

OCCURRENCE : Common and locally abundant in the southern counties. It occurs widely in Wales and Eire but appears not to be recorded from Scotland. The large sheet web, with a tubular retreat, found amongst grass and heather, is a familiar sight. Mating occurs in July and the male is found living with the female even after the eggs are laid. The female remains with these in a closed silken cell until she dies.

3. Genus **TEXTRIX** C. J. Sundevall 1833.

CHARACTERS OF GENUS. CARAPACE : Cephalic region rather narrow and long with parallel sides. EYES : Text-fig. 3 B, C. Posterior row strongly recurved. ABDOMEN : Anterior spinners separated by about one-and-a-half diameters of one of them. Posterior spinners about twice as long as anterior, the tapering apical segment a little longer than the basal. STERNUM : As in *Agelena*. CHELICERÆ : Inner margin with two teeth. LEGS : Relatively short ; length of I about same as body length. MALE PALP : With a tibial apophysis, but none on patella.

There is one British species, *Textrix denticulata* (Olivier).

Textrix denticulata (Olivier).
(Text-figs. 3, B, C ; 5)

Aranea denticulata A. G. Olivier, 1789, p. 213. *Agelena lycosina* C. J. Sundevall, 1832, p. 130. *Textrix lycosina* J. Blackwall, 1861–4, p. 172. *T. denticulata* O. P.-Cambridge, 1879–81, p. 66 ; C. Chyzer and L. Kulczynski, 1891–7, II, p. 175 ; M. Dahl, 1931, p. 18 ; E. Simon, 1937, p. 1017.

DESCRIPTION. LENGTH : ♀ ♂ : about 6–7 mm. CARAPACE : Dark brown, grey or black with deeper radiating markings. A median light band, in marked contrast, runs from posterior eyes nearly to posterior edge of carapace. There is a trace of sub-marginal lateral bands (a lightening of the darker areas) and there is a thin black borderline.

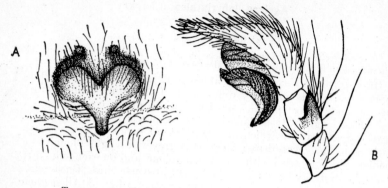

TEXT-FIG. 5.—*Textrix denticulata:* A, epigyne; B, male palp.

(The light regions are covered to a varying extent with light yellow or cream hairs, particularly conspicuous in the living spider.) EYES: Text-fig. 3, B, C. ABDOMEN: A light yellow or red-brown median dentate band runs the whole length; a reddish lanceolate stripe, flanked by dark patches, lies within its anterior half. The dentate band is edged with dark grey or black and the rest of the dorsal region and sides are either black or covered with dark mottling on a brown field. There is a good deal of variation, but the essentials of the pattern are preserved. STERNUM: Brown, grey or black; no pattern. LEGS: Very clearly annulated. In living spiders whitish rings sometimes occur in the lighter regions. EPIGYNE: Text-fig. 5, A. MALE PALP: Text-fig. 5, B. This is a pretty little spider; the carapace and abdominal markings, as well as the disposition of the eyes (when seen from above), give it rather the appearance of a *Lycosa*, until one notices the long projecting spinners.

OCCURRENCE: Distributed all over the British Isles. Often abundant locally. Found under loose stones, in crevices in rocks and on close-trimmed bushes, such as holly; it spins a small sheet web.

4. Genus **TEGENARIA** P. A. Latreille 1804.

CHARACTERS OF GENUS. CARAPACE: Like *Agelena*. EYES: Anterior row procurved (as seen from in front); eyes equal or medians smaller than laterals. Posterior row a little longer, slightly procurved; eyes nearly equal and nearly equally spaced. Laterals narrowly separated. CLYPEUS: Wider than twice the diameter of an anterior median eye. ABDOMEN: Pattern of type shown in Text-fig. 1. SPINNERS: Of same type as in *Agelena*, but anteriors set rather closer and apical segment of posteriors shorter, or very little longer than basal (cf. *Agelena* and *Textrix*). STERNUM: Pattern of type shown in Text-fig. 11. (The lateral paired light patches sometimes suppressed or absent, e.g. *T. parietina*, *T. agrestis*). LABIUM: Longer than broad (at the base).

Cheliceræ : Not very convex ; inner margin with 4–8 teeth. Legs :
Long and thin ; spines aculeate, hairs numerous and long. Male
palp : Tibial apophyses present, but none on patella.

The web is a sheet, the familiar cob-web being an example, with a
more or less tubular retreat at one side. The spider runs on the upper
surface of the sheet.

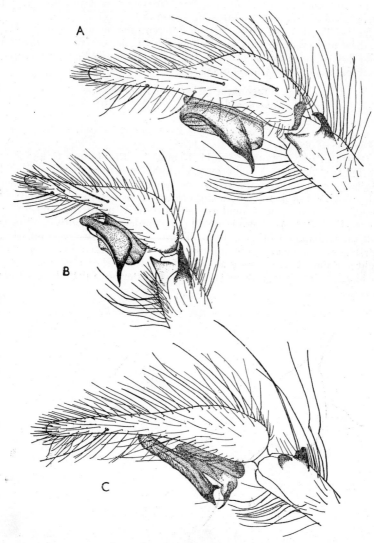

Text-fig. 6.—Male palps : A, *Tegenaria atrica;* B, *T. larva;* C, *T. parietina.*

There are seven species recorded in the British Isles. All except
T. agrestis and *T. silvestris* occur in domestic buildings, houses, sheds
etc., but they may also be found further afield. They all have the
same general appearance, but the larger species have relatively longer
legs and are darker in colour, presenting indeed a sinister aspect which,
with their rapid movements, may cause people considerable alarm. The
males, of *T. atrica* especially, are frequently seen in late summer and
autumn wandering about houses in search of females.

Note.—The lengths given for the different species are generally the
smallest and greatest for the specimens available, but there is often a
good deal of variation in size, and specimens may well be found having
total lengths outside these limits.

Tegenaria atrica C. L. Koch.
(Text-figs. 6, A ; 7, A ; 9, A ; 11, B)

Tegenaria atrica C. L. Koch, 1843, X, p. 105.   *T. sæva* J. Blackwall, 1844, p. 179.
T. atrica J. Blackwall, 1861–64, p. 165 ; O. P.-Cambridge, 1879–81, p. 62 ; M. Dahl,
1931, p. 35.   *T. sæva* E. Simon, 1937, p. 1003.

DESCRIPTION. LENGTH : ♀ : 11–15 mm. ♂ : 13–14 mm. CARAPACE :
As in Text-fig. 1. A light grey or light brown median band and
similarly coloured lateral bands are separated by a much darker
(almost black) broken region ; this colour sometimes invades the lateral
bands. (The markings tend to fade in spirit more than on other
parts of the body.) There is a thin dark borderline. Width of clypeus
2–3 times diameter of an anterior lateral eye. ABDOMEN : Somewhat
variable ; a median light longitudinal area is flanked by a series of
light and dark bars disposed as in Text. fig. 1. Darker areas sooty grey
or black. SPINNERS : Apical segment of posteriors a little longer than

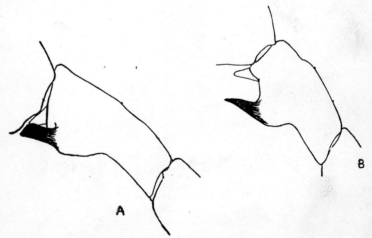

TEXT-FIG. 7.—Tibiæ of male palps : A, *Tegenaria atrica;* B, *T. larva* (viewed
dorsally and a little from the outside).

the basal. STERNUM : Pattern characteristic of the genus (Text-fig. 11, B). CHELICERÆ : ♀, inner margin with 7–8 teeth (the basal tooth very small or absent). LEGS : Rather dark brown (fading in spirit to colour of light parts of carapace), without annulations in mature spiders. This is a very long legged species ; ratio Leg I/body length :—♀. about 2 ; ♂, nearly 3. EPIGYNE : Text-fig. 9, A. MALE PALP : Text-fig. 6, A. This differs from that of *T. larva* especially in the form of the tibial apophysis (see also Text-fig. 7, A).

This species is easily distinguished from the others of the genus, with the possible exception of *T. larva* ♀ (q.v. for the differences).

OCCURRENCE : Very common, usually in cellars, outhouses etc., but also among roots under overhanging banks and in similar situations out of doors. Recorded over England and Wales and in Lanarkshire and Forfar in Scotland. In Eire it is replaced, at all events in houses, by *T. larva.*

Tegenaria larva Simon.
(Text-figs. 1 ; 6, B ; 7, B ; 9, C)

Tegenaria larva E. Simon 1875, II, p. 86 ; F. Muller and E. Schenkel, 1894, p. 753. *T. hibernica* O. P.-Cambridge, 1891, p. 86 ; 1893, p. 150 ; 1908, p. 168. *T. larva* M. Dahl, 1931, p. 37. *T. atrica* E. Simon, 1937, p. 1003.

DESCRIPTION. LENGTH : ♀ : 15–16 mm. ♂ : 10–14 mm. CARAPACE AND ABDOMEN : Text-fig. 1 ; like *T. atrica.* Apical segment of posterior spinners a little longer than the basal. STERNUM : Pattern, especially in ♀, less distinct than in *T. atrica* ; lateral paired light patches sometimes scarcely visible, and median stripe usually wider than in *T. atrica.* CHELICERÆ : ♀ : inner margin with 7 teeth. LEGS : No annulations. Ratio Leg I/Body-length as in *T. atrica.* EPIGYNE : Text-fig. 9, C. This requires careful comparison with that of *T. atrica.* MALE PALP : Text-fig. 6, B. This may be distinguished with certainty from that of *T. atrica* by the shape of the tibial apophysis, especially if this is viewed as in Text-fig. 7, B.

OCCURRENCE : Recorded from Southport (Lancashire) and from Cumberland. Widespread in Ireland, where it replaces *T. atrica* in houses.

Tegenaria parietina (Fourcroy).
(Text-figs. 6, C ; 8 ; 9, B)

Aranea parietina + phalangioides A. F. de Fourcroy, 1785, pp. 533 and 525. *Aranea domestica* C. A. Walckenaer, 1802, p. 216. *A. guyoni* F. E. Guerin, 1837, p. 7. *Tegenaria domestica* J. Blackwall, 1861–4, p. 163. *T. guyonii* O. P.-Cambridge, 1879–81, p. 473. *T. parietina* C. Chyzer and L. Kulczynski, 1891–7, II, p. 166 ; M. Dahl, 1931, p. 45 ; E. Simon, 1937, p. 1005.

DESCRIPTION. LENGTH : ♀ : about 14 mm. ♂ : about 11 mm. General appearance as in Text-fig. 8. CARAPACE : Similar to that of *T. atrica.* Width of clypeus about 4 times diameter of an anterior lateral eye. ABDOMEN : Pattern less well defined than in *T. atrica.* STERNUM : Pattern obscure or absent ; the central light area, when present, rather wide. CHELICERÆ : ♀, inner margin with 3–4 teeth

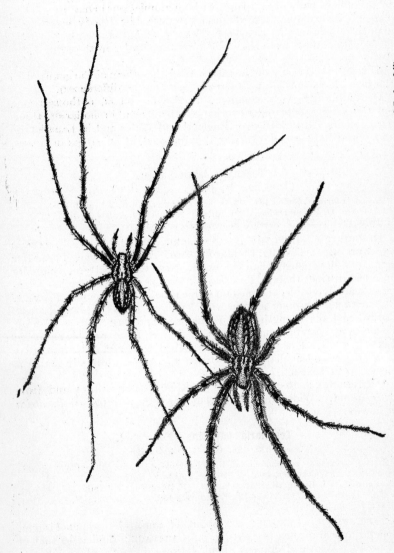

TEXT-FIG. 8.—*Tegenaria parietina* (from J. Blackwall's " Spiders of Great Britain and Ireland ").

(one specimen had three on one chelicera, four on the other). ; LEGS, Not noticeably annulated. Ratio Leg I/body-length : ♀, 2·9 ; ♂, 5. This is our most long-legged species. EPIGYNE : Text-fig. 9, B. MALE PALP : Text-fig. 6, C. The species has a superficial resemblance to *T. atrica*, but has relatively longer legs (see Text-fig. 8) and the sexual organs are quite distinct.

OCCURRENCE : Found in situations similar to those inhabited by *T. atrica*, but more rarely. In England as far north as Staffordshire and in Ireland. Not recorded from Wales or Scotland.

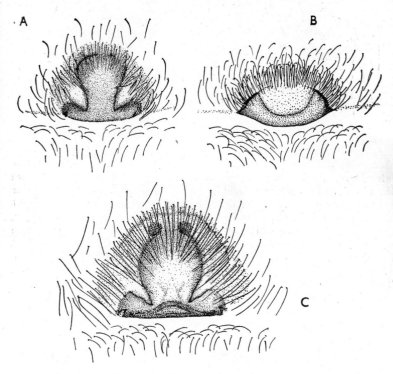

TEXT-FIG. 9.—Epigynes : A, *Tegenaria atrica;* B, *T. parietina;* C, *T. larva.*

Tegenaria agrestis (Walckenaer).
(Text-fig. 10, A, B)

Aranea agrestis C. A. Walckenaer, 1802, p. 216. *Tegenaria agrestis* M. Dahl, 1931, p. 42 ; E. Simon, 1937, p. 1000.

DESCRIPTION. LENGTH : ♀ 11–14 mm. ♂ : about 7 mm. (probably often longer). CARAPACE : Similar to *T. atrica*, the darker region taking the general form of the radiating streaks ; these markings sometimes

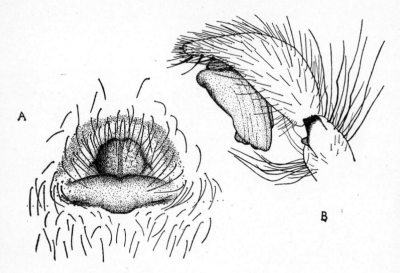

TEXT-FIG. 10.—*Tegenaria agrestis:* A, epigyne ; B, male palp.

obscure. Width of clypeus about 4 times diameter of an anterior lateral eye. ABDOMEN : Pattern typical of the genus, but more obscure than in *T. atrica* (better defined in males). Apical segment of posterior spinners very slightly longer than the basal. STERNUM : Central light area wide ; the lateral paired patches very faint or absent in females, occasionally just discernible in males. CHELICERÆ : ♀, inner margin with 7 teeth. LEGS : Colour as light parts of carapace : without annulations. Ratio Leg I/body-length : ♀, 1·4–1·6 ; ♂, about 2·6. EPIGYNE : Text-fig. 10, A. This is very distinct. MALE PALP : Text-fig. 10, B.

OCCURRENCE : In a gravel pit, Wilverley Plain (Hampshire).

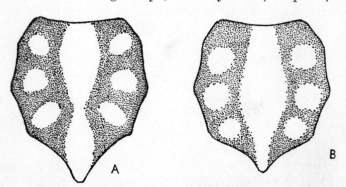

TEXT-FIG. 11.—Sternum : A, *Tegenaria domestica;* B, *T. atrica.*

Tegenaria domestica (Clerck).
(= *T. domestica* (Linnaeus))
(Text-figs. 11, A ; 12, A, B)

Araneus domesticus C. Clerck, 1757, p. 76. *Aranea domestica* C. Linnaeus, 1758, p. 620. *A. derhami* J. A. Scopoli, 1763, p. 400. *A. civilis* C. A. Walckenaer, 1802, p. 216. *Tegenaria civilis* J. Blackwall, 1861–4, p. 166. *T. derhamii* O. P.-Cambridge, 1879–81, p. 63 ; C. Chyzer and L. Kulczynski, 1891–7, II, p. 170 ; M. Dahl, 1931, p. 39, B. J. Kaston, 1948, p. 279. *T. domestica* E. Simon, 1937, p. 1009.

DESCRIPTION. LENGTH : ♀ : 9–10 mm. ♂ : 6–9 mm. CARAPACE : In some specimens nearly uniform light brown with faint radiating streaks, especially at junction of cephalic and thoracic regions. In well-marked specimens there is a pair of light lateral bands (with a dark borderline) and a light median stripe ; between these is a pair of wide darker bands (not broken up as much as in *T. atrica*) which extend to the head. Width of clypeus 2 to 3 times diameter of an anterior lateral eye. EYES : Anterior medians about 2/3 diameter of anterior laterals ; separated from each other and from laterals by less than half diameter. ABDOMEN : The pattern sometimes quite indiscernible,

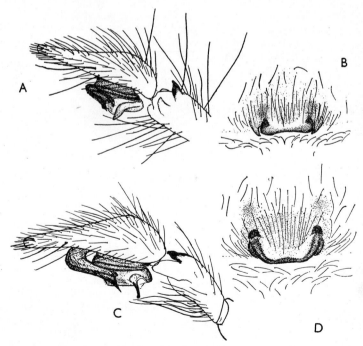

TEXT-FIG. 12.—*Tegenaria domestica:* A, male palp ; B, epigyne.
T. pagana: C, male palp ; D, epigyne.

the whole dorsal region being light brown. When present, pattern of same general character as in *T. atrica*, but made up of dark sooty patches on a light brown background. Apical segment of posterior spinners a little shorter than the basal. STERNUM : Pattern of type shown in Text-fig. 11, A, but variation in the size of the light round patches occurs and in some specimens pattern is quite absent. CHELICERÆ : ♀ : Inner margin with 4 teeth. LEGS : Some specimens have distinct annulations on femora, others have them faint or quite absent. Ratio Leg I/body-length : ♀, 1·8–1·9 ; ♂, 2–2·5. EPIGYNE : Text-fig. 12, B. MALE PALP : Text-fig. 12, A. The whole spider is sometimes almost uniform yellow brown without any definite markings.

OCCURRENCE : Found almost always in houses, sheds and cellars. Very common, and distributed all over the British Isles.

Tegenaria pagana C. L. Koch.
(Text-fig. 12, C, D)

Tegenaria pagana C. L. Koch, 1841, VIII, p. 31 ; C. Chyzer and L. Kulczynski, 1891–7, II, p. 169 ; M. Dahl, 1931, p. 43 ; E. Simon, 1937, p. 1010. (All British records up to 1901 refer to *T. domestica* (Cl). See W. S. Bristowe 1939, p. 48).

DESCRIPTION. This species resembles *T. domestica* very closely. Both sexes can be distinguished from that species by a careful inspection of the sexual organs. In addition the basal segment of the posterior spinners is darkened (especially outside) in *T. pagana*, but not in *T. domestica*. This darkening seems to persist after long preservation and to be a reliable character. The sternum patterns on the other hand vary in both species and we do not find them to be reliable as a distinguishing character. EPIGYNE : Text-fig. 12, D. MALE PALP : Text-fig. 12, C.

OCCURRENCE : Dublin (Castleknock).

Tegenaria silvestris L. Koch.
(Text-fig. 13, A, B, C)

Tegenaria silvestris L. Koch, 1872, p. 288. *T. campestris* O. P.-Cambridge, 1879–81, p. 64. *T. silvestris* C. Chyzer and L. Kulczynski, 1891–7, II, p. 169 ; M. Dahl, 1931, p. 33 ; E. Simon, 1937, p. 1007. (W. S. Bristowe (1939, p. 48) calls this species *T. silvestris* C. L. Koch, and identifies it with *T. campestris* C. L. K.)

DESCRIPTION. LENGTH : ♀ : 5–7 mm. ♂ : 5–6 mm. CARAPACE : Marking similar to *T. agrestis*. Borderline distinct, with some dark colour diffusing inwards from it. Width of clypeus about 1½ times diameter of an anterior lateral eye. EYES : Anterior medians almost touching anterior laterals ; posterior medians closer to laterals than to each other. ABDOMEN AND STERNUM : Patterns typical of genus. CHELICERÆ : ♀, inner margin with 5 teeth. LEGS : Distinctly annulated, especially on femora ; tibiæ and metatarsi I and II less distinctly annulated. Ratio Leg I/total length : ♀, about 2 ; ♂, 2·2–2·4. EPIGYNE : Text-fig. 13, C. MALE PALP : Text-fig. 13, A, B.

OCCURRENCE : Found not infrequently under stones, logs, bark of trees, etc. Recorded widely over England and Wales.

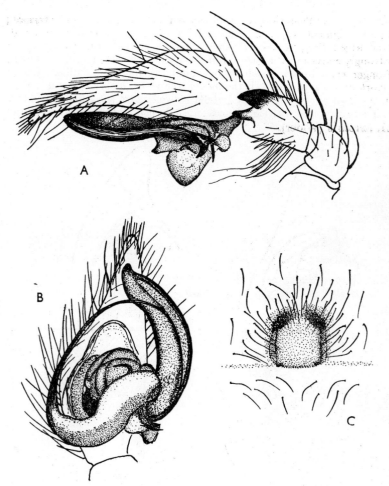

TEXT-FIG. 13.—*Tegenaria silvestris:* A, male palp (from side); B, ditto (ventrally); C, epigyne.

5. Genus **AMAUROBIUS** C. L. Koch 1836.

CHARACTERS OF GENUS. CARAPACE: Cephalic region very broad and rounded in front, not narrowed as in the other genera (Text-fig. 3, A). Width of clypeus little more than diameter of an anterior lateral eye. EYES: Not very different in size; anterior medians the smallest. Anterior row very slightly procurved or straight. Posterior row a little longer, nearly straight; eyes almost equidistant. ABDOMEN: Widest in posterior half (not tapering towards spinners). Spinners rather short; anteriors separated by little less than a diameter of

one of them. Posteriors a little less than twice the length of anteriors ;
apical segment tapering, shorter, or not longer, than the basal.
STERNUM : Shaped as in *Tegenaria*, having no pattern. CHELICERÆ :
Strongly convex at the base. Inner margin with three teeth. LABIUM :
Longer than broad, reaching beyond mid point of maxillæ. LEGS :
Short and stout (leg I little longer than the body). MALE PALP :
Having an apophysis on the patella as well as on the tibia.

There are two British species : *Amaurobius atropos* (Walck.) and
A. terrestris (Wider).

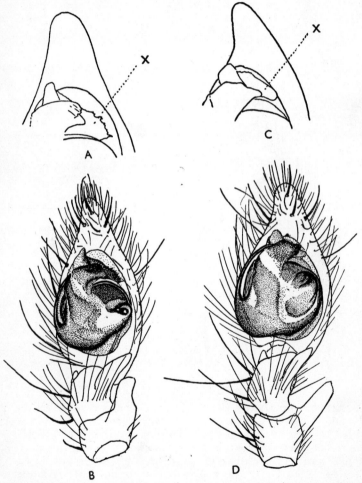

TEXT-FIG. 14.—Male palps (below) : A, B, *Amaurobius atropos; C, D, A.
terrestris.*

Amaurobius atropos (Walckenaer).
(Text-figs. 14, A, B ; 15, A, C)

Drassus atropos C. A. Walckenaer, 1825, p. 170. *Cœlotes saxatilis* J. Blackwall, 1861–4, p. 169. *C. atropos* O. P.-Cambridge, 1879–81, p. 60 ; C. Chyzer and L. Kulczynski, 1891–7, II, p. 160 ; M. Dahl, 1931, p. 22 (who considers this and *C. terrestris* to be the same species) ; E. Simon, 1937, p. 990. *Amaurobius atropos* L. Kulczynski, 1906, p. 434.

DESCRIPTION. LENGTH : ♀ : 9–12 mm. ♂ : 7–9 mm. CARAPACE : Rather deep reddish brown ; front of head, junction of cephalic and thoracic area, and radiating striæ darker. Head and cheliceræ almost black in some living specimens. ABDOMEN : Mottled with dark grey or black, the lighter parts dull yellow or brown. A dark stripe runs the whole length ; it is widest in front, where it sometimes has a light centre and, as it tapers towards the spinners, almost to a line, it becomes broken into a series of little △'s in the posterior half. Running from each of these is a pair of rather narrow dark bars (sloping backwards) alternating with light patches, the general make-up of the

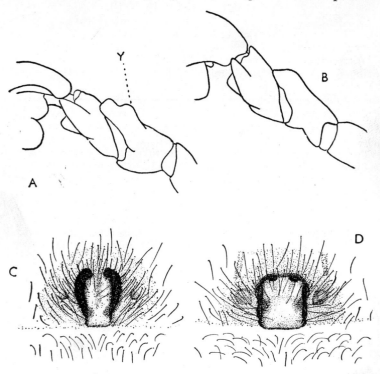

TEXT-FIG. 15.—Patella and tibia of male palp : A, *Amaurobius atropos;* B, *A. terrestris.*
Epigynes : C, *A. atropos;* D, *A. terrestris.*

pattern being reminiscent of *Agelena*. CHELICERÆ : Black or very
deep reddish brown. LEGS : Reddish brown, without annuli. EPIGYNE:
Text-fig. 15, C. This needs to be compared carefully with that of
A. terrestris. The dark parts of each may vary, but in *A. atropos* the
central region is much longer than broad. MALE PALP : Text-fig. 14,
A, B. This may be distinguished from that of *A. terrestris* by considering : (*a*) the general proportions of the parts of the sexual organs
seen ventrally (Text-fig. 14, B) ; (*b*) the part marked " X " (Text-
fig. 14, A) which in this species is distinctly serrated, not smooth ;
(*c*) the shape of the base of the apophysis on the patella (" Y " in
Text-fig. 15, A).

OCCURRENCE : Distributed all over England and Wales, recorded for
Scotland. Locally abundant in northern England, Devon and Wales,
especially in mountainous districts and over 3,000 ft. Less frequent
in most southern counties.

Amaurobius terrestris (Wider).
(Text-figs. 14, C, D ; 15, B, D)

Aranea terrestris Wider, 1834, p. 215. *Cœlotes pabulator* O. P.-Cambridge, 1889,
p. 113. *C. terrestris* C. Chyzer and L. Kulczynski, 1891–7, II, p. 161 ; O. P.-Cambridge.
1905, p. 44 ; E. Simon 1937, p. 991. *Amaurobius terrestris* L. Kulczynski, 1906, p. 443.

DESCRIPTION. LENGTH : ♀ : 10–13 mm. ♂ : 8–10 mm. This species
resembles *A. atropos* closely, and differs from it in the following respects.
ABDOMEN : The anterior part has more suffused dark colour, on which
is a lighter median lanceolate stripe (corresponding to the light inside
of the dark stripe in *A. atropos*). In the posterior half is usually a
series of wide dark bars, forming chevrons, wider than the corresponding more broken bars of *A. atropos*. Although these differences
seem generally to persist, in specimens taken from widely separated
regions, variation of such patterns is likely to occur and they are not
thought to be of much value for diagnostic purposes. EPIGYNE :
Text-fig. 15, D. The dark parts may vary somewhat but the central
area is not much longer than broad. MALE PALP : Text-fig. 14, C, D.
This may be distinguished from that of *A. atropos* by considering (*a*)
the general proportions of the parts of the sexual organs seen ventrally
(Text-fig. 14, D) ; (*b*) the part marked " X " in Text-fig. 14, C, which
is smooth, not serrated ; (*c*) the shape of the apophysis on the patella
(Text-fig. 15, B).

OCCURRENCE : Frequent locally in southern counties of England, but
also from Yorkshire and Berwickshire.

6. Genus CICURINA A. Menge 1869.

CHARACTERS OF GENUS. CARAPACE : Rather long ; head relatively
broad. Width of clypeus about twice diameter of an anterior eye.
EYES : Both rows nearly straight, the posterior slightly longer ; eyes
nearly equal in size. ABDOMEN : Without a pattern (in the British
species). SPINNERS : Anteriors separated by about two diameters.
Apical segment of posteriors short and conical (Text-fig. 2, E).

STERNUM : As in *Tegenaria*, but with no pattern. CHELICERÆ : Nearly vertical and only slightly swollen at the base. Inner margin with 7 teeth (the three basal ones smaller and close together). LABIUM : Slightly wider than long, not quite reaching mid-point of maxillæ. LEGS : With rather large spines on all segments except tarsi.

There is one British species.

Cicurina cicur (Fabricius).
(Text-fig. 16, A, B)

Aranea cicurea J. C. Fabricius, 1793, p. 410 (*cicurea* altered by A. Menge, 1871, p. 272 to *cicur*). *Cicurina cicur* A. Menge, 1871, p. 272. *Aranea cinerea* G. W. F. Panzer, 1793, p. 23. *Tegenaria cinerea* O. P.-Cambridge, 1879–81, p. 65. *Cicurina cicur* C. Chyzer and L. Kulczynski, 1891–7, II, p. 155 ; M. Dahl, 1931, p. 7. *C. cicurea* E. Simon, 1937, p. 1018 ; W. S. Bristowe, 1939, p. 48. (We accept the conclusions of P. Bonnet (1949) on the naming of this species.)

DESCRIPTION. LENGTH : ♀♂ : 5–7 mm. CARAPACE : Light brown with very faint marks radiating from a thin dark foveal streak. ABDOMEN : Uniform mouse grey, without a pattern. LEGS : Femora

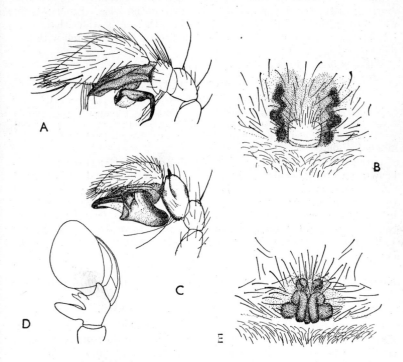

TEXT-FIG. 16.—*Cicurina cicur:* A, male palp : B, epigyne.
  Cryphœca silvicola: C, male palp ; D, ditto (seen dorsally), showing shape of tibial apophyses ; E, epigyne.

coloured as carapace, other segments usually a little darker, but without annulations. EPIGYNE : Text-fig. 16, B. MALE PALP : Text-fig. 16, A.

OCCURRENCE : Rather rare. Recorded in England as far north as Northumberland and as far west as Dorsetshire, not from other parts of the British Isles. Found in rather damp and dark places, under stones, amongst low plants and moss. Adult in spring and early summer and in autumn (and possibly at other seasons).

7. Genus **CRYPHOECA** T. Thorell 1869.

CHARACTERS OF GENUS. CARAPACE : Oval, attenuated in front. Clypeus not wider than diameter of a lateral anterior eye. EYES : Anterior row strongly procurved (as seen from in front) ; medians much smaller than laterals, which are sub-equal to all the remaining eyes. Posterior row nearly straight, eyes nearly equidistant. ABDOMEN : With a distinct pattern (in the British species). SPINNERS : Anteriors separated by about a diameter of one of them. Posteriors with apical segments distinct and pointed, but much shorter than basal. STERNUM : Almost circular, pointed behind. CHELICERÆ : Nearly vertical, distinctly but moderately swollen at the base. Inner margin with 5 teeth (in British species). LABIUM : Distinctly wider than long. LEGS : Short and robust. Tibiæ and metatarsi I and II each with 3–4 pairs of strong ventral spines.

There is one British species.

Cryphoeca silvicola (C. L. Koch).
(Text-fig. 16, C, D, E)

Tegenaria silvicola C. L. Koch, 1834, p. 125 ; J. Blackwall, 1861–4, p. 168. *Hahnia silvicola* C. L. Koch, 1845, XII, p. 158. *Cryphœca silvicola* O. P.-Cambridge, 1879–81, p. 474 ; C. Chyzer and L. Kulczynski, 1891–7, II. p. 157 ; M. Dahl 1931, p. 5 ; E. Simon, 1937, p. 1021.

DESCRIPTION. LENGTH : ♀♂ : 2·5–3 mm. CARAPACE : Light brown with sooty radiating streaks and, sometimes, a dark V-shaped mark immediately in front of the fovea, at junction of head and thoracic region. ABDOMEN : Dull black or sooty grey with a pattern in lighter colour of the type found in *Tegenaria* (see Text-fig. 1). STERNUM : Light brown, becoming darker towards edges. LEGS : Light brown, annulated with black. EPIGYNE : Text-fig. 16, E. MALE PALP : Text-fig. 16, C, D.

OCCURRENCE : Among leaves in woods, but also in open places and moors. Locally abundant. Distributed all over the British Isles.

8. Genus **TETRILUS** E. Simon 1886.

CHARACTERS OF GENUS. CARAPACE : Shaped as in *Cryphœca*. EYES : Anterior row nearly straight (as seen from in front) ; medians smaller than laterals. Posterior row straight or procurved, with eyes equal. ABDOMEN : Pattern usually faint or absent. SPINNERS : Anteriors separated by about twice the diameter of one of them (the medians can be seen distinctly between them). Posteriors with apical segment pointed and about half length of the basal. STERNUM : Heart shaped. CHELICERÆ : Nearly vertical, a slight swelling at base just perceptible. Inner margin with 3–4 teeth. LABIUM : Wider than long. LEGS : Longer and more slender than in *Cryphoeca*. Tibiæ I and II with 5–6 pairs of strong ventral spines ; metatarsi I and II with 3 pairs (in British species).

There are two British species : *Tetrilus macrophthalmus* (Kulczynski) and *T. arietinus* (Thorell).

Note.—There has been some doubt as to whether these two species should be recognised as quite separate. W. S. Bristowe (1939, pp. 46 and 167) considers that *T. macrophthalmus* Kulcz. is no more than a sub-species of *T. arietinus ;* while Kulczynski himself (1891–7, II, p. 156) first described the former as a variety of the latter. E. Simon (1937, p. 1022–1023) considers them as separate species. The epigynes of the two females appear to be indistinguishable ; no males of *T. arietinus* are available to us and Simon had none of *T. macrophthalmus*, but from Kulczynski's remarks (loc. cit) about the small differences in the male palps, which accompany a difference in arrangement, as well as the size, of the eyes, we prefer to regard them as separate species, at least until intermediate forms are recorded.

Tetrilus macrophthalmus (Kulczynski).
(Text-fig. 17, A, B, C)

Tuberta arietina var. *macrophthalma* L. Kulczynski in C. Chyzer and L. Kulczynski, 1891–7, II, p. 156. *Tetrilus arietinus* O. P.-Cambridge, 1900, p. 20. *Cryphœca recisa* O. P.-Cambridge, 1907, p. 136 ; J. W. Carr, 1907, p. 48. *Tetrilus recisus* A. R. Jackson, 1913, p. 23. *Tetrilus macrophthalmus* E. Simon, 1937, p. 1023.

DESCRIPTION. LENGTH : ♀ ♂ : about 3·5 mm. CARAPACE : Uniform light yellow brown. EYES : Text-fig. 17, C. ABDOMEN : Coloured as carapace with faint traces of darker markings, (on available specimens) which sometimes appear to form a pattern. O. P.-Cambridge (1907, p. 137) mentions an indistinct longitudinal central yellowish brown stripe, followed to the spinners by several indistinct chevrons. A fresh immature specimen (from Sherwood Forest) had a discernible light pattern, on a sooty background, consisting of a longitudinal stripe on the anterior half, flanked by a pair of small light patches ; these were followed by a pair of wide light transverse bars which ran right round the sides. On the posterior half was a succession of transverse light bars, diminishing in size to the spinners. LEGS : Coloured as carapace or, sometimes, a little darker. EPIGYNE : Text-fig. 17, B. MALE PALP : Text-fig. 17, A. This is remarkable for the great length of the whip-like style and its fantastic accompanying lamella, which is divided close to its base, one branch being directed downwards and backwards, while the other, beginning in a forward direction, sweeps in an arc around the palp as shown in the figure.

OCCURRENCE : Very rare. Recorded from Somerset, Surrey, Berkshire, Leicester, Nottinghamshire (Sherwood Forest), Glamorgan. Found under the dead bark of old trees in Sherwood Forest, but also as a guest of the ants *Acanthomyops fuliginosus*, *A. umbratus*, *Formica rufa* (See H. St. J. Donisthorpe (1927 p. 182) and W. S. Bristowe (1939, p. 163)).

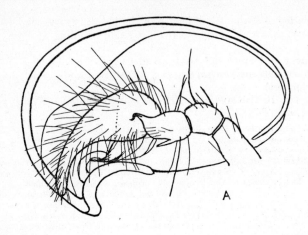

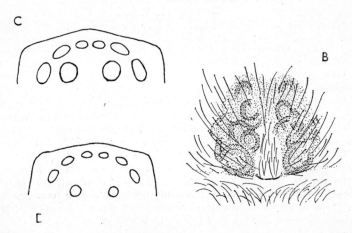

TEXT-FIG. 17.—*Tetrilus macrophthalmus:* A, male palp; B, epigyne; C, eyes. *Tetrilus arietinus:* D, eyes.

Tetrilus arietinus (Thorell).
(Text-fig. 17, D)

Cryphœca arietina T. Thorell, 1870–3, II, p. 165. *Tuberta arietina* C. Chyzer and L. Kulczynski, 1891–7, II, p. 156. *Cryphœca diversa* O. P.-Cambridge, 1893, p. 148.; 1905, p. 44; 1907, p. 124. *Tetrilus arietinus* E. Simon, 1937, p. 1022.

DESCRIPTION. This species differs from *T. macrophthalmus* in the following respects. LENGTH : ♀ about 3·25 mm. EYES : Text-fig. 17, D. (The arrangement and size of these constitute the most marked difference.) ABDOMEN : No pattern visible on available specimens, but Simon (1937, p. 1022) mentions markings which would seem to be similar to those of *T. macrophthalmus*. CHELICERÆ: Inner row with four teeth (but this is not considered to be a reliable diagnostic character). MALE PALP: No specimen is available, but from accounts of Simon (loc. cit.) and Kulczynski (1891–7, II p. 156) it appears that the external lamella of the palpal organ sweeps round further than in *T. macrophthalmus*, passing the apical end of the femur, and that there are other small differences.

OCCURRENCE: Very rare. It seems to be entirely myrmecophilous, the host being *Acanthomyops fuliginosus*. Recorded from Surrey, Berkshire, Cumberland and Durham. (See H. St. J. Donisthorpe, 1927 p. 182).

9. Genus **TUBERTA** E. Simon 1884.

CHARACTERS OF GENUS. The genus is very close to *Tetrilus*, from which it differs in the following respects. CHELICERÆ: Inner margin with 2 teeth. LEGS: Shorter and more robust. Femur I with a large prolateral spine close to the apex. Tibia I with 3 pairs of strong ventral spines. ABDOMEN: That of the single British species, *Tuberta mœrens* (Camb.) bears a very distinct pattern similar to that of *Cryphœca silvicola*.

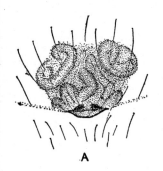 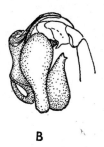

TEXT-FIG. 18.—*Tuberta mœrens:* A, epigyne; B, male palp (after Kulczynski).

Tuberta mœrens (O. P.-Cambridge).
(Text-fig. 18, A, B)

Cœlotes mœrens O. P.-Cambridge, 1863, p. 8572 (♀). *Cryphœca mirabilis* T. Thorell, 1870–3, p. 166. *C. mœrens* E. Simon, 1875, **5**, p. 53 (♀). *Tuberta insignipalpis* id, 1884, **5**, p. 869. f. 806 (♂). *Cryphœca mœrens* O. P.-Cambridge, 1879–81, pp. 59 and 571. *Tuberta mirabilis* C. Chyzer and L. Kulczynski, 1891–7, II, p. 156; M. Dahl, 1937, p. 117. *Tuberta mœrens* E. Simon, 1937, p. 1023.

C

DESCRIPTION. LENGTH : ♀ : about 2 mm. CARAPACE : Very like *Cryphœca silvicola*, with ill-defined dusky radiating streaks on a yellow-brown ground. Width of clypeus about half diameter of an anterior lateral eye. EYES : Anterior row straight, medians much smaller than laterals (about one quarter diameter), which are a little larger than posteriors. Posterior row straight ; eyes nearly equal, medians a little nearer to laterals than to each other. ABDOMEN : A light pattern, of the type found in *Cryphœca silvicola*, very clear on an almost black background. Spinners as in *Tetrilus*. STERNUM : Shaped as in *Tetrilus* ; dusky mottling on a yellow-brown ground, with a narrow median light stripe in anterior half. LEGS : Light yellow brown, suffused with a dusky grey, except on patellæ and tarsi. EPIGYNE : Text-fig. 18, A. There is a small chitinised portion as shown, and the seminal coils appear irregularly. MALE PALP : Text-fig. 18, B. (After Kulczynski.)

The above description was taken from the single specimen in Dr. Jackson's collection. It has the general appearance of a *Cryphœca silvicola*, for which it might well be mistaken in the field. No males have been taken in this country.

OCCURRENCE : Bloxworth (Dorsetshire) ; Bagley Wood (Berkshire). Only one immature and two adult females have as yet been collected in Britain.

10. Genus **ANTISTEA** E. Simon 1897.

CHARACTERS OF GENUS. CARAPACE : Oval, narrowed in front ; foveal streak distinct. Clypeus equal to or slightly wider than the diameter of an anterior lateral eye. EYES : Anterior row strongly procurved (seen from in front) ; posterior row procurved. All eyes sub-equal, but anterior medians equal to or slightly larger than posterior medians (Text-fig. 19, A). ABDOMEN : With a pattern, sometimes indistinct. Tracheal spiracle approximately half way between spinners and epigastric fold. SPINNERS : In a transverse row. STERNUM : Heart-shaped, projecting in a blunt point between coxæ IV. CHELICERÆ : Fairly weak. LABIUM : Wider than long. LEGS : Short and robust, with few spines. MALE PALP : The femur, patella and tibia each bear an apophysis. There is one British species.

Antistea elegans (Blackwall).
(Text-fig. 19, A, B, C)

Agelena elegans J. Blackwall, 1841, p. 619 ; 1861–4, p. 155. *Hahnia elegans* O. P.-Cambridge, 1879–81, p. 69 ; C. Chyzer and L. Kulczynski, 1891–7, II, p. 177. *Antistea elegans* M. Dahl, 1937, p. 101 ; E. Simon, 1937, p. 1032.

DESCRIPTION. LENGTH : ♀ ♂ : about 2·5–3 mm. CARAPACE : Orange to bright yellow-brown, with fovea and radiating striæ black or dark brown. A row of bristles runs forward from fovea, and ocular area has numerous bristles. ABDOMEN : Dark greyish brown, with lighter chevrons running from middle down to spinners ; covered in long hairs.

STERNUM AND LEGS : Coloured as carapace. EPIGYNE : Text-fig. 19, B.
MALE PALP : Text-fig. 19, C.

OCCURRENCE : In wet places, where it forms its small sheet web in
depressions in the ground. Distributed all over the British Isles, but
local. Adult in summer.

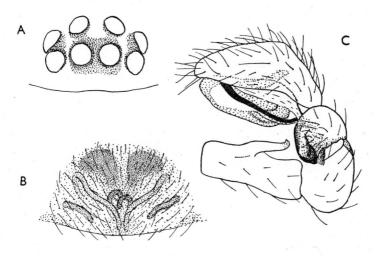

TEXT-FIG. 19.—*Antistea elegans:* A, eyes (from in front) ; B, epigyne ; C, male
palp.

11. Genus **HAHNIA** C. L. Koch 1841.

CHARACTERS OF GENUS. CARAPACE : Oval, narrowed in front ;
foveal streak usually clear. Clypeus wider or narrower than diameter
of an anterior lateral eye. EYES : Anterior row strongly procurved
(seen from in front), posterior row procurved. Anterior medians
distinctly smaller than remaining eyes (Text-fig. 20, A). ABDOMEN :
With or without a pattern. Tracheal spiracle about one quarter to
one third of way from spinners to epigastric fold. SPINNERS : In a
transverse row. STERNUM : Heart-shaped, broadly truncate between
coxæ IV. CHELICERÆ : Weak. LABIUM : Wider than long. LEGS :
Short and robust, with only a few spines. MALE PALP : Patella and
tibia each with an apophysis, that on tibia being long and curved.

There are five British species, which may be separated as follows :

1. Clypeus much wider than diameter of anterior lateral eye .   2

——Clypeus narrower, or scarcely wider than, diameter of
anterior lateral eye 3

2. Metatarsi III and IV with several spines apically. A dark
coloured species, usually approx. 2 mm. in length

H. montana

——Metatarsi III and IV spineless. Pale coloured species usually about 1·4 mm. in length . . . **H. candida**

3. Metatarsi III and IV with several stout spines
H. nava (dark coloured)
and **H. helveola** (light coloured)

——Metatarsi III and IV spineless. . . . **H. pusilla**

The species are separable (females readily, males less readily) by their genitalia.

Hahnia montana (Blackwall).
(Text-fig. 20, B, C, D)

Agelena montana J. Blackwall, 1841, p. 622; 1861–4, p. 157. *Hahnia montana* O. P.-Cambridge, 1879–81, p. 70; M. Dahl, 1937, p. 113; E. Simon, 1937, p. 1026.

DESCRIPTION. LENGTH: ♀: 1·8–2 mm. ♂: 1·5–1·7 mm. CARAPACE: Yellow-brown to brown with blackish fovea and broad black radiating striæ. There is a central longitudinal row of bristles, and some bristles in the ocular area. Clypeus much wider than diameter of an anterior lateral eye. ABDOMEN: Brown, tinged with yellowish or greenish brown. Chevrons, if visible at all, very faint. STERNUM: Yellow-brown, margined with black. LEGS: Brown to dark brown, with

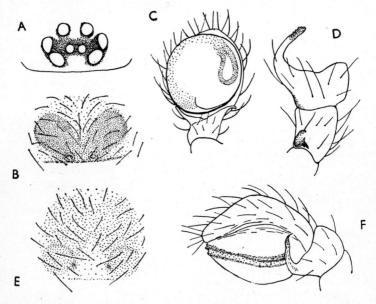

TEXT-FIG. 20.—A, *Hahnia nava*, eyes (from in front).
Hahnia montana: B, epigyne; C, male palp (below); D, male palpal patella and tibia (from side).
Hahnia candida: E, epigyne; F, male palp (side).

patellæ rather paler. EPIGYNE : Text-fig. 20, B. MALE PALP : Text-fig. 20, C, D. The species is readily distinguished from *H. candida* by its size and darker colour.

OCCURRENCE : In undergrowth of woods and in heather, etc. Distributed throughout the British Isles ; common. Adults at all seasons.

Hahnia candida, Simon.
(Text-fig. 20 E, F)

Hahnia candida E. Simon, 1875, **2,** p. 142 ; O. P.-Cambridge, 1879–81, p. 71 ; M. Dahl, 1937, p. 108 ; E. Simon, 1937, p. 1028.

DESCRIPTION. LENGTH : ♀ ♂ : 1·3–1·4 mm. CARAPACE : Pale yellow-brown, with fovea and striæ scarcely visible. Central row of bristles, and some bristles in ocular area. Clypeus much wider than

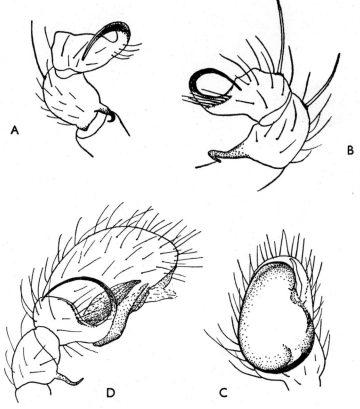

TEXT-FIG. 21.—Male palps : A, *Hahnia nava* (right palp from side) ; B, *H. helveola* (from side and below) ; C, ditto (tarsus from below) ; D, *H. pusilla* (right palp from side).

diameter of anterior lateral eye. ABDOMEN : Pale whitish yellow, covered in numerous fine hairs. STERNUM : Pale whitish yellow, margined narrowly with black. LEGS : Pale brown. EPIGYNE : Text-fig. 20, E. Rather indefinite in outline. MALE PALP : Text-fig. 20, F.

OCCURRENCE : Under stones, in a few localities in Dorsetshire only. (The Scottish record is dubious.) Adults in summer.

Hahnia nava (Blackwall).
(Text-figs. 20, A ; 21, A ; 22, A)

Agelena nava J. Blackwall, 1841, p. 623 and 1861–4, p. 158. *Hahnia nava* O. P.-Cambridge, 1879–81, p. 69 and 1907, p. 124 ; C. Chyzer and L. Kulczynski, 1891–7, II, p. 178 ; M. Dahl, 1937, p. 111 ; E. Simon, 1937, p. 1031.

DESCRIPTION. LENGTH : ♀♂ : 1·6–2 mm. The species is a dull greyish black in the field. CARAPACE : Dark brownish black, with black fovea and radiating striæ. A line of bristles runs forward from fovea, and a few bristles are present in ocular area. Clypeus narrower than diameter of an anterior lateral eye. ABDOMEN : Blackish, covered with fairly long hairs. STERNUM : Yellow-brown. LEGS : Dark brown to black, with bases of segments sometimes yellowish. EPIGYNE : Text-fig. 22, A. MALE PALP : Text-fig. 21, A. The species is readily distinguished from *H. helveola* and *H. pusilla* by its dark colour.

OCCURRENCE : In moss and grass, under stones ; not in woods. Distributed throughout the British Isles, but local. Adults in summer.

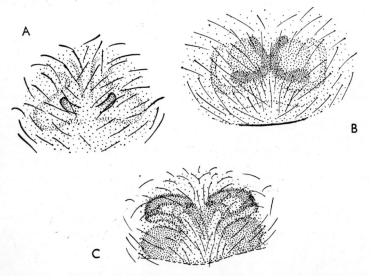

TEXT-FIG. 22.—Epigynes : A, *Hahnia nava;* B, *H. helveola;* C, *H. pusilla.*

Hahnia helveola Simon.
(Text-figs. 21, B, C ; 22, B)

Hahnia helveola E. Simon, 1875, **2,** p. 139 ; O. P.-Cambridge, 1879–81, p. 72 ; E. Simon, 1937, p. 1032. *H. bressica* M. Dahl, 1937, p. 106.

DESCRIPTION. LENGTH : ♀: 2·5–3 mm. ♂ : about 2·25 mm. CARAPACE : Yellow-brown, with darker fovea and radiating striæ. There is a central row of fine bristles, and some bristles in ocular area. Clypeus narrower than diameter of anterior lateral eye. ABDOMEN : Pale yellow, with broad blackish chevrons from front to back, of varying distinctness. Covered with fine hairs. STERNUM : Pale yellow-brown, with numerous fine hairs. LEGS : Coloured as carapace, or slightly darker. EPIGYNE : Text-fig. 22, B. MALE PALP : Text-fig. 21, B, C.

OCCURRENCE : In undergrowth, often in woods. Distributed throughout the British Isles, but local (though often then abundant). Adults in autumn and winter.

Hahnia pusilla C. L. Koch.
(Text-figs. 21, D ; 22, C)

Hahnia pusilla C. L. Koch, 1841, VIII, p. 61 ; and *H. bressica* E. Simon, 1875, **2,** p. 141. *H. pusilla* A. R. Jackson, 1907, p. 2 ; 1908, p. 68 ; O. P.-Cambridge, 1907, p. 138 ; M. Dahl, 1937, p. 112 ; E. Simon, 1937, p. 1032.

DESCRIPTION. LENGTH : ♀ ♂ : 1·4–1·5 mm. CARAPACE : Pale yellow-brown, with fovea and striæ scarcely visible. There are a few stout bristles between region of fovea and eyes, and in ocular area. Clypeus narrower than diameter of anterior lateral eye. ABDOMEN : Pale whitish yellow, covered in numerous fine hairs. STERNUM : Pale whitish yellow to yellow, with a number of fairly stout hairs. Rounder behind and projecting less between coxæ IV than in *H. helveola*. LEGS : Pale brown to whitish. EPIGYNE : Text-fig. 22, C. MALE PALP : Text-fig. 21, D.

OCCURRENCE : Found only in a few localities ; in Cheshire, Lancashire, Yorkshire and Derbyshire. In detritus and under stones.

19. Family MIMETIDÆ.

CHARACTERS OF FAMILY. CARAPACE : Elevated in the middle in Genus *Ero* (Text-fig. 23, A), with a small circular depression in thoracic region. EYES : Heterogeneous, anterior medians the darkest. Laterals on eminences. Median trapezium generally a little wider in front (almost a rectangle in *Ero*). ABDOMEN : Convex ; sparsely covered with strong hairs or spines (Text-fig. 23, A). STERNUM : Longer than wide, separating coxæ IV. CHELICERÆ : Rather long, vertical and parallel-sided, with no lateral condyle. Outer margin with 4–8 teeth (of a peculiar type, appearing articulated at the base, see Text-fig. 23, D). Inner margin with none, or one very small tooth. MAXILLÆ : Long, narrow, sub-acuminate and converging. FEMALE PALP : With a claw. LEGS : Bearing many spines. Anterior metatarsi strongly curved (Text-fig. 23, B). Anterior tibiæ and metatarsi with series of strong dorso-prolateral spines (appearing dorsal from the side, Text-fig. 23, B, C), with smaller spines between, all curving forward. There are three tarsal claws, the paired claws with 2–4 teeth.

Genus **ERO** C. L. Koch 1837.

CHARACTERS OF GENUS. CARAPACE : Elevated in the middle (Text-fig. 23, A), with a circular depression in the middle of the thoracic region. Clypeus very concave, about as wide as ocular area. EYES : Posterior row very slightly recurved ; eyes equal ; medians nearer to each other than to laterals. Anterior row very slightly recurved (as seen from in front), nearly straight ; medians darker, and a little larger, than laterals, slightly nearer to each other than to laterals. Laterals on eminences. Median trapezium a very little longer than broad ; width equal in front and behind. ABDOMEN : Text-fig. 23, A. Humped ; bearing dorsally one, or two, pairs of tubercles, which may be flattened, but which are almost always discernible. STERNUM : Tapering, and pointed behind, separating coxæ IV. LABIUM : Triangular, not rebordered, reaching a little beyond mid point of maxillæ. CHELICERÆ : With stridulating ridges on outer surface ; having 4–5 teeth in outer row (Text-fig. 23, D) ; inner row with none. LEGS : Rather slender. Tibiæ and metatarsi I and II with dorso-prolateral spines as in Text-fig. 23, B, C. The sexes are alike in general appearance.

It has been shown by Bristowe (1941, p. 378) that these spiders are predaceous on other spiders.

The three British species *Ero cambridgei* Kulcz., *E. furcata* (Villers) and *E. tuberculata* (Degeer) are very similar, but they can be distinguished by their sexual organs.

Ero cambridgei Kulczynski.
(Text-figs. 24, A ; 25, B)

Ero cambridgei L. Kulczynski, 1911, p. 61 ; O. P.-Cambridge, 1912, p. 80 and pl. A, figs. 30–33 ; E. Simon, 1932, p. 774.

DESCRIPTION. LENGTH : ♀ : 2·5–3·25 mm. ♂ : about 2·5 mm. CARAPACE : Light yellow-brown with deep brown markings. There is a

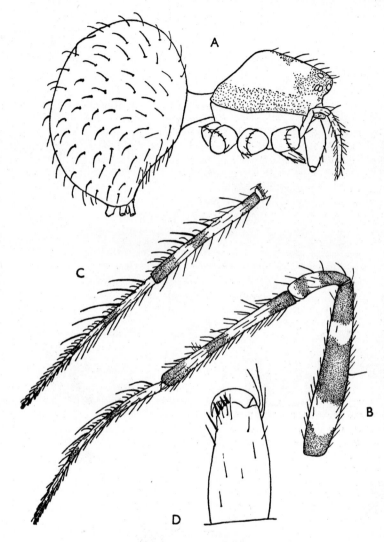

TEXT-FIG. 23.—*Ero:* A, profile of carapace and abdomen ; B, Leg I (left), seen from side ; C, ditto, tibia, metatarsus and tarsus, seen from above ; D, right chelicera from in front, ♀.

dark border varying very much in width (Text-fig. 23, A), sometimes passing across clypeus, sometimes including ocular area (but often not). A median dark line, dilated at junction of cephalic and thoracic regions, varies a good deal in width. Some strong spines occur on head, some forming a median line, and on clypeus. ABDOMEN : Shaped as in Text-fig. 23, A, covered with short spines and mottled with dark brown, or black and creamy white, with, sometimes, a reddish tinge. There are two rather flat tubercles on the anterior half (Text-fig. 23, A) and behind these is a triangular region, almost constituting a folium, lighter than the rest of the dorsal area and tapering to the spinners. STERNUM : Dark brown, an irregular patch in the centre being light yellowish. CHELICERÆ : As darker parts of carapace. LEGS : Light yellow-brown, with deep brown annulations. EPIGYNE : Text-fig. 24, A. MALE PALP : Text-fig. 25, B.

OCCURRENCE : Found rather commonly amongst grass, low plants and bushes. Distributed throughout most of the British Isles (but not recorded from Wales). Adult from about August onwards, also in spring and summer.

Ero furcata (Villers).
(Text-figs. 24, B ; 25, C)

Aranea furcata Villers, 1789, p. 129. *Theridion thoracicum* Wider, 1834, p. 218. *Ero variegata* C. L. Koch, 1836, p. 138, 5–6. *Theridion variegatum* J. Blackwall, 1861–4, p. 203. *Ero thoracica* T. Thorell, 1870, p. 77 ; (in part) O. P.-Cambridge, 1879–81, p. 233. *Ero furcata* C. Chyzer and L. Kulczynski, 1891–7, II, p. 13 ; O. P.-Cambridge, 1912, p. 80 and Pl. A. figs. 34–36 ; E. Simon, 1932, p. 774. (This and *E. cambridgei* were confused in British records, under the name *E. thoracica* Wid. or *E. furcata* Vill. until 1912, see O. P.-Cambridge, loc. cit.)

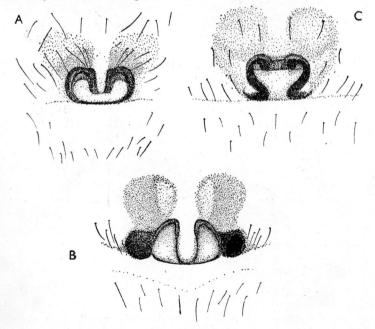

TEXT-FIG. 24.—Epigynes : A, *Ero cambridgei;* B, *E. furcata;* C, *E. tuberculata.*

DESCRIPTION. This species is very like *E. cambridgei*, but can be distinguished from it without difficulty by the sexual organs. EPIGYNE : Text-fig. 24, B. MALE PALP : Text-fig. 25, C.

OCCURRENCE : Found as frequently as the last species, or more so, and in similar situations. Distributed throughout the British Isles. Adult August to October.

Ero tuberculata (Degeer).
(Text-figs. 24, C ; 25, A)

Aranea tuberculata C. Degeer, 1778, p. 226. *Ero tuberculata* O. P.-Cambridge, 1879–81, p. 235 ; C. Chyzer and L. Kulczynski, 1891–7, II, p. 13 ; E. Simon, 1932, p. 775.

DESCRIPTION. LENGTH : ♀ : 3·5–4 mm. ♂ : about 3 mm. This species is very like the last two in general appearance, but can be

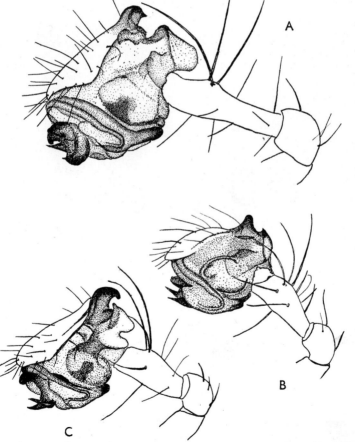

TEXT-FIG. 25.—Male palps : A, *Ero tuberculata;* B, *E. cambridgei;* C, *E. furcata.*

distinguished by its sexual organs and by its having an additional pair of tubercles on the abdomen. The first pair are larger and more prominent and pointed than in the last two species ; the second pair lie posteriorly to them and farther apart. The light region behind the first tubercles is usually clearer and better defined in this species. EPIGYNE : Text-fig. 24, C. MALE PALP : Text-fig. 25, A.

OCCURRENCE : Rare, in the southern counties of England. Adult in June and probably at other times.

20. Family THERIDIIDÆ.

CHARACTERS OF FAMILY. CARAPACE : Variable in profile ; sometimes flat, head sometimes elevated. Clypeus variable in width ; usually wider than in ARGIOPIDÆ. EYES : Heterogeneous ; anterior medians dark, the rest light. ABDOMEN : Variable in shape (see Text-figs. 28, 39, 45). Males, and many females, possess a stridulating

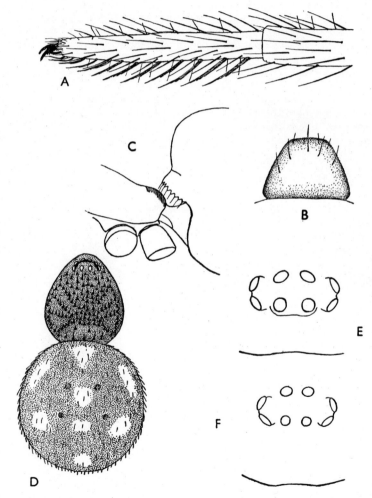

TEXT-FIG. 26.—THERIDIIDÆ : A, tarsus IV ; B, labium ; C, stridulating organ of male *Lithyphantes;* D, *Crustulina guttata,* carapace and abdomen ; E, *Lithyphantes,* eyes from in front ; F, *Asagena,* ditto.

organ (Text-fig. 26, C), but in some genera this is poorly developed
and difficult to see. CHELICERÆ : Usually vertical and not very large
(except in some males, e.g. *Enoplognatha, Theridion ovatum, T. bellicosum, T. instabile*) ; usually, but not always, without teeth, or with
only small teeth. MAXILLÆ AND LABIUM : Variable, the latter not
rebordered (Text-fig. 26, B). FEMALE PALP : With a claw. LEGS :
Bearing bristles and hairs, but few spines ; there is one spine on each
patella, and one to two on tibia I at least. Tibiæ with two rows of
trichobothria. Tarsal claws three, pectinate or smooth. Tarsus IV
with a row of serrated bristles (Text-fig. 26, A) ; the serrations are
much reduced in some of the small species and difficult to recognise ;
in the larger species they are a useful character. MALE PALP : Tibia
and patella with no apophysis ; paracymbium absent. Palpal organs
relatively simple.

The webs of THERIDIIDÆ, at least in Europe, can be divided into two
classes. One type, as made by most species of the genus *Theridion* for
instance, enables the spider to deal with flying insects. The web
consists of a mass of criss-cross threads, on the outside of which are
spun viscid threads (Nielsen, 1932, **2**, pp. 520–572). In the other type,
made by species of *Dipœna, Steatoda, Teutana* and *Lithyphantes* for
example, there is a tendency for a sheet structure to develop in the
middle of the web, and lines reaching down from this sheet are sticky
at their lower ends and serve to entangle such prey as ants (Wiehle,
1931 (2), p. 394).

The method of attacking prey by throwing viscid threads with a
" hand-over-hand " motion of the IVth legs is very characteristic.
Although the chelicerae are weak, the poison is extremely powerful,
at least to invertebrates.

Attempts to produce a key for this family have not, in the past, been
particularly successful, partly because some of the most characteristic
structures are developed only in one sex. For instance the " stridulating organ " (Text-fig. 26, C), consisting of a chitinous ridge, or row
of teeth, on the abdomen, which works against a series of ridges on the
back of the carapace when the spider is sexually excited and, no doubt,
gives rise to a characteristic vibration in the web, is well developed
in the males of a number of species, but is often only vestigial in
females. This organ was regarded as important by Simon (1892–1903,
I. p. 493) who used it to characterise a large group of genera, the
ASAGENEÆ, which includes our *Asagena, Lithyphantes, Teutana,Steatoda,
Crustulina, Enoplognatha*. In the other species of the family it is
present, but often so poorly developed as to be hardly discernible.

The accepted genera probably require revision, but this is not possible
here with our limited representation in Britain. However, A. Archer,
in 1950, published an extremely interesting paper describing a revision
of the families THERIDIIDÆ and MIMETIDÆ. His proposals are far-
reaching and important ; they are based primarily on considerations
of the male palps, and in this he is probably on firm ground, although he
deliberately lays aside the question of the female genitalia for future

consideration (1. c., p. 11). Nevertheless past revisions of the group based on many different characters have needed continuous amendments and we feel that further study of the European fauna is needed before we can adopt Archer's scheme of classification for practical purposes, and that in the present work it will serve the most useful purpose to adhere to the traditional classification.

Our species fall into two of Archer's sub-families. Of these the first, EPISININÆ, includes our *Episinus*, *Euryopis*, together with *Theridion tepidariorum*, *T. formosum* (= *lunatum*), *T. saxatile* and *T. aulicum*. A new genus, *Parasteatoda*, is created for *Theridion tepidariorum* and *T. formosum*; while *Theridion saxatile* is placed in a new genus *Cryptachœa* and *T. aulicum* in a new genus *Kochiura*. *Enoplognatha* is made congeneric with *Theridion* (as typified by *Theridion ovatum*), a decision which has much to recommend it, if genitalia are the sole considerations, and a new genus, *Allotheridion*, is created for the species of the kind included in our Groups III, IV and V of *Theridion* (see p. 59).

In our descriptions we have chosen for mention those characters which seem to us to be reliable and easily discernible, while emphasising once more that the sexual organs provide the best guides in almost every case. The generic key is wholly artificial. It should be noted that some species (particularly in the genus *Theridion*) are extremely variable in coloration, and collectors are likely to find specimens to which the descriptions given are not altogether applicable. As far as possible we have attempted to convey a picture of the most usual appearance of each species as it occurs in this country.

KEY TO THE GENERA

Note.—In the key and the descriptions of the species the following symbols will be used :—

MT I/tI : Length of metatarsus I/length of tarsus I.

l/d : Length of a leg segment/width of same segment.

Tm I : This is explained on p. 175. It applies to the female spider in accounts of species of the THERIDIIDÆ.

1. (*a*) Carapace, sternum and cheliceræ covered with numerous " warts " (Text-fig. 26, D). See Note (1) (4) **Crustulina**
   (*b*) Abdomen : Text-fig. 28 ; legs III relatively short (1) **Episinus**
   (*c*) Tarsi longer than metatarsi : very small spider (13) **Theonoë**
   (*d*) Eyes : Text-fig. 59, A. ♂ abdomen with a scutum (Text-fig. 59, C) . . . . . (12) **Pholcomma**
   (*e*) Not as (*a*)—(*d*) 2

2. Anterior median larger than posterior median eyes *and* further apart 3
——Anterior median not larger than posterior median eyes, or if so, not further apart 4

3. Abdomen pointed posteriorly (Text-fig. 30, A). Tm I : 0·75
                                                (2) **Euryopis**
——Abdomen not so pointed ; Tm I < 0·5. Clypeus very wide
                                                (3) **Dipoena**
4. Lateral eyes clearly separated (Text-fig. 26, E, F) . .   5
——Lateral eyes touching. (See Note (2))   6

5. Sternum and carapace with punctures (especially ♂).
   Median ocular trapezium (Text-fig. 26, F) longer than
   broad, a little narrower in front. Width of clypeus about
   twice that of ocular area. Abdominal pattern of single
   British species : Text-fig. 36, A . .   (5) **Asagena**
——Sternum and carapace without punctures. Median ocular
   trapezium a square (Text-fig. 26, E). Width of clypeus
   about equal to that of ocular area. Abdominal pattern of
   single British species : Text-fig. 37, A . (6) **Lithyphantes**

6. Anterior median eyes much larger than anterior laterals.
   ♂ carapace and sternum covered with punctuations.
   Abdominal pattern of single British species : Text-
   fig. 38, A . . . . . .   (7) **Steatoda**
——Anterior eyes less unequal, or medians smaller than
   laterals. ♂ carapace and sternum without punctuations .   7

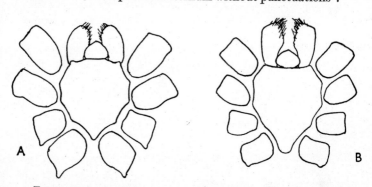

TEXT-FIG. 27.—Sternum : A, *Robertus lividus;* B, *Theridion vittatum.*

7. Abdomen unicolorous, black to grey (see however *Enoplognatha thoracica*, p. 83). Sternum not produced between
   coxæ IV (Text-fig. 27, A). Tm I : about 0·5 (11) **Robertus**
——Abdomen with a dorsal pattern (except *Enoplognatha
   thoracica* and *Theridion ovatum*, p. 76). Sternum
   produced between coxæ IV. (Text-fig. 27, B) . . .   8

8. ♂ with well developed stridulating organ. Single British
   species with characteristic abdomen pattern (Text-
   fig. 39, A). Tm I : 0·67. Large spider (5–6 mm.)
                                                (8) **Teutana**

——♂ stridulating organ less well developed (often difficult to
see). Abdomen patterns different. Tm I usually less
than 0.67 (Note (3)). Smaller spiders   9

9. Tm I > 0·5 (but < 0·9). ♂ cheliceræ large and divergent,
with large conspicuous teeth .   .   . (10) **Enoplognatha**

——Tm I < 0·5 (or 0·9 in *T. ovatum* and *T. tinctum*). Cheliceræ
rarely large and divergent (Note (4)) .   (9) **Theridion**

Note (1).—*Steatoda* and *Asagena* have punctuations on carapace and
sternum, but these are somewhat different from those in *Crustulina*,
and in any case the single species in each of these two genera are much
larger spiders, differ in other respects and are distinctively marked.
Text-figs. 36, A ; 38, A.

Note (2).—The laterals in *Teutana* are sometimes not quite touching.
The species occurring in Britain, *T. grossa*, is very distinctly marked
(Text-fig. 39, A).

Note (3).—Tm I is 0·67 in *Enoplognatha schaufussi* (p. 83) and 0·9
in *Theridion ovatum* and *T. tinctum* (pp. 76, 75).

Note (4).—The cheliceral teeth of males of *Enoplognatha* are characteristic (Text-fig. 56). The males of some species of *Theridion* have
enlarged cheliceræ, which also bear an apophysis and teeth (e.g.
T. ovatum, *T. bellicosum*, *T. instabile* ; Text-figs. 50, B ; 51, C, D)
but they will be seen to be of diff rent form from those characteristic
of *Enoplognatha*.

1. Genus **EPISINUS** P. A. Latreille 1809.

CHARACTERS OF GENUS. EYES : Not very different in size ; median
trapezium a little longer than broad. Laterals separated. ABDOMEN :
Long, and truncated behind (Text-fig. 28). LEGS : Long and rather
robust ; III notably shorter than the others.

There are two British species, *Episinus angulatus* (Bl.) and *E. truncatus*
Latr., which are superficially very alike, and there has been a good deal
of confusion in their nomenclature and recording in this country up to
1906. O. P.-Cambridge then recognised that there were two indigenous
species (1906, p. 83), but the species he then called " *E. truncatus*
Walck.'' (Pl. A. fig. 3) was in fact *E. angulatus* (Bl.) and the one he
called " *E. lugubris* Sim." (Pl. A. fig. 2) was *E. truncatus* Latr.

Episinus angulatus (Blackwall).
(Text-figs. 28 ; 29, A, B)

Theridion angulatum J. Blackwall, 1836, p. 483 ; 1861–4, p. 202. *Episinus truncatus*
O. P.-Cambridge, 1906, p. 83, and Pl. A. fig. 3. *E. angulatus* L. Kulczynski, 1905 (2),
p. 430 ; E. Simon, 1914, p. 245 ; H. Wiehle, 1937, p. 130.

DESCRIPTION. LENGTH : ♀ : 3·75–4·5 mm. ♂ : about 4 mm.
CARAPACE : Text-fig. 28. The pattern dark brown on a yellowish
ground. ABDOMEN : Text-fig. 28. Dark parts of folium sepia or
blackish grey, light regions yellowish. The angles at the posterior end

D

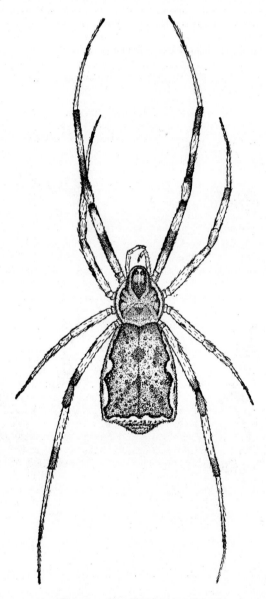

TEXT-FIG. 28.—*Episinus angulatus* ♀.

may be developed into conical tubercles, especially in large specimens. Ventrally : a light mark present just in front of spinners, varying in shape, but usually triangular, the apex pointing backwards. STERNUM : Uniform dark brown. LEGS : Light yellow with dark brown markings, as in Text-fig. 28. EPIGYNE : Text-fig. 29, A. This is somewhat variable and not always easy to distinguish from that of *E. truncatus*. MALE PALP : Text-fig. 29, B. It can be distinguished without difficulty from that of *E. truncatus* by examining the tip.

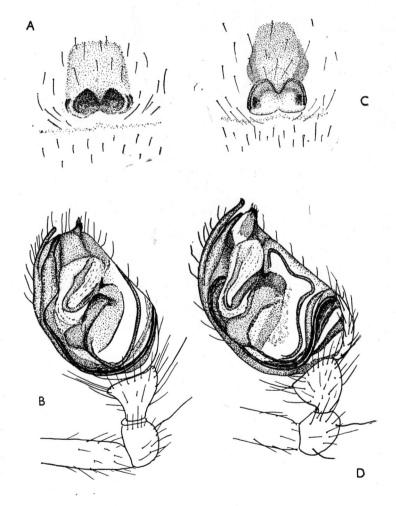

TEXT-FIG. 29.—*Episinus angulatus:* A, epigyne ; B, male palp.
E. truncatus: C, epigyne ; D, male palp.

The female needs to be distinguished from the rarer *E. truncatus*. The most reliable characters are the markings of the carapace, and of the legs.

OCCURRENCE : Fairly common amongst grass and low plants and bushes. Distributed throughout England and Eire, recorded from Wales. (The Scottish record is doubtful.)

Episinus truncatus Latreille.
(Text-fig. 29, C, D)

Episinus truncatus P. A. Latreille, 1809, p. 371. *E. lugubris* E. Simon, 1873, p. 123 ; 1881, **5**, p. 42 ; O. P.-Cambridge, 1906, p. 83 and Pl. A. fig. 2. *E. truncatus* L. Kulczynski, 1905 (2), p. 430 ; E. Simon, 1914, p. 245 ; H. Wiehle, 1937, p. 128.

DESCRIPTION. LENGTH : ♀ : 3·5–4 mm. ♂ : 3·25–4 mm. This species bears a close superficial resemblance to *E. angulatus*, but differs in the following respects. CARAPACE : No well defined pattern ; dark margin, and light border within it, absent or only just discernible. ABDOMEN : Folium of same shape, but border less distinct. Ventrally : There is almost always a series of light spots from spinners to epigastric fold. (The first of these spots, immediately in front of the spinners, is very like the triangular white mark found in *E. angulatus* and that is perhaps not such a reliable distinguishing character as has sometimes been supposed.) LEGS : Femora and tibiæ I and II quite uniformly dark, and also tibia IV. The dark colour often a rusty brown, as opposed to the chocolate brown of *E. angulatus*. EPIGYNE : Text-fig. 29, C. Variable, usually lighter than in *E. angulatus*. MALE PALP : Text-fig. 29, D.

OCCURRENCE : Much less common than *E. angulatus*. In southern counties of England. Recorded from Eire (Carlow).

2. Genus **EURYOPIS** A. Menge 1868.

CHARACTERS OF GENUS. EYES : Anterior medians greater than posterior medians and further apart. CLYPEUS : Wide ; approximately equal to cheliceral length (♂) or rather less (♀). ABDOMEN : Rather pointed posteriorly (Text-fig. 30, A). STERNUM : Pointed posteriorly and projecting between coxæ IV. CHELICERÆ : Short and weak, but with long fang. LEGS : Stout, with tibia I :—1/d ca.4 ; TmI 0·75–0·8. Stridulating organs not present in ♂.

There is one British species.

Euryopis flavomaculata (C. L. Koch).
(Text-fig. 30)

Micryphantes flavomaculatus C. L. Koch, 1836, p. 67. *Theridion flavomaculatum* J. Blackwall, 1861–4, p. 201. *Euryopis flavomaculata* O. P.-Cambridge, 1879–81, p. 100 ; C. Chyzer and L. Kulczynski, 1891–7, II, p. 21 ; E. Simon, 1914, p. 247 ; H. Wiehle, 1937, p. 132.

DESCRIPTION. LENGTH : ♀ : 3·5–4 mm. ♂ : about 3 mm. CARAPACE : Orange brown, with ocular area suffused with black. Some bristles on head and clypeus. EYES : Large, with anterior medians equal to, or very slightly greater than, posterior medians, and further apart. ABDOMEN : Rather pointed posteriorly, grey to black, with four yellow-brown impressed dots, and with pattern of yellow-white to golden blotches and angular bars (Text-fig. 30, A) more clearly developed in ♂ than in ♀. STERNUM : Yellow, edged with black ; point projecting between coxæ IV. LEGS : Orange-brown, with metatarsi and tarsi sometimes suffused with dark brown. Tibiæ I

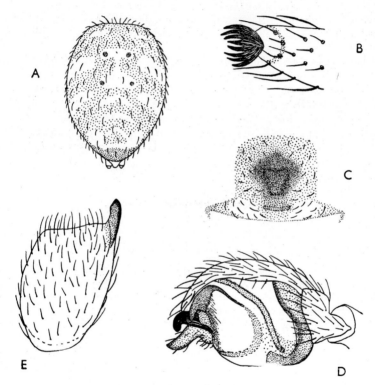

TEXT-FIG. 30.—*Euryopis flavomaculata:* A, abdomen (♀) ; B, female palpal claw (from above and in front) ; C, epigyne ; D, male palp ; E, male palpal tarsus (from above and slightly in front).

and II with two dorsal spines ; tibiæ III and IV with one dorsal spine. MT I/t I about 1·35. Tm I : 0·75–0·80 ; trichobothrium clearly visible (cf. *Dipœna*). Tarsal claws with a number of large teeth. ♀ PALP : with a peculiar claw (Text-fig. 30, B). EPIGYNE : Text-fig. 30, C. MALE PALP : Text-fig. 30, D, E.

OCCURRENCE : In moss, etc. ; usually in damp places. Rare. From the west and south of England. Recorded from Scotland and Eire.

3. Genus **DIPŒNA** T. Thorell 1869.

CHARACTERS OF GENUS. CARAPACE : Very high anteriorly ; clypeus wide and concave (Text-fig. 31, A), wider than length of cheliceræ. EYES : Large and fairly close together in a small group. Anterior medians greater than posterior medians and further apart. ABDOMEN : Rather globular. Stridulating apparatus weakly developed in the male. CHELICERÆ : Feeble ; shorter than width of clypeus. STERNUM : Broadly produced between coxæ IV. LEGS : Spineless, with metatarsi appreciably longer than tarsi (e.g. MT I / t I about 1·5–2·5). Tarsi rather acuminate, with tarsal claws small, having a few (not very distinct) teeth. Tm I : 0·3–0·5 ; trichobothrium very difficult to see.

The species can be split into groups according to the following key :

1. Metatarsus I about twice (or more than twice) as long as tarsus I (dark coloured species) **D. tristis, D. melano-gaster, D. torva**
——Metatarsus I about 1·5–1·6 times as long as tarsus I . . 2

2. Dark coloured species, almost wholly black **D. coracina**
——Lighter coloured species **D. inornata, D. prona, D. erythropus**

The species within the groups can be separated fairly readily by the sex organs.

Dipœna erythropus (Simon).
(Text-figs. 31, C ; 32, B)

Laseola erythropus, E. Simon, 1881, p. 141 ; C. Chyzer and L. Kulczynski 1891–7, II, p. 24 ; W. Falconer, 1914, p. 55. *Laseola proxima* O. P.-Cambridge, 1895, p. 102. *Dipœna erythropus* E. Simon, 1914, pp. 276, 301 ; H. Wiehle, 1937, p. 188.

DESCRIPTION. LENGTH : ♀ : about 2·5 mm. ♂ : 2–2·5 mm. CARAPACE : Dusky yellow, suffused with some black, particularly on head and sides. Some bristly hairs on head and clypeus. ABDOMEN : Brownish grey to black. STERNUM : Brown, suffused with some black. LEGS : Pale yellow to yellow brown. MT I/t I : about 1·6. EPIGYNE : Text-fig. 32, B. Small and insignificant. MALE PALP : Text-fig. 31, C.

OCCURRENCE : Rare. Recorded from Cornwall, Kent and Warwickshire.

Dipœna prona (Menge).
(Text-figs. 31, A, B ; 32, A)

Pachydactylus prona A. Menge, 1868, p. 177. *Euryopis prona* O. P.-Cambridge, 1879–81, p. 481. *Laseola prona* C. Chyzer and L. Kulczynski, 1891–7, II, p. 25 ; W. Falconer, 1914, p. 58. *Dipœna prona* E. Simon, 1914, pp. 277, 302 ; H. Wiehle, 1937, p. 186.

DESCRIPTION. LENGTH : ♀ : about 2·5 mm. ♂ : about 2 mm. CARAPACE : Yellow-brown, suffused with black on head. ABDOMEN : Brownish to blackish. STERNUM : Yellow-brown, blackish on edges. LEGS : Yellow-brown, suffused with black. MT I/t I about 1·5–1·6. EPIGYNE : Text-fig. 32, A. MALE PALP : Text-fig. 31, B.

OCCURRENCE : On gorse bushes and in undergrowth, in summer. Rare. From Dorset, Kent and the Isle of Wight.

Dipœna inornata (O. P.-Cambridge).
(Text-figs. 31, D, E ; 32, C)

Theridion inornatum O. P.-Cambridge, 1861, p. 433 ; J. Blackwall, 1861–64, p. 196. *Euryopis inornata* O. P.-Cambridge, 1879–81, p. 100. *Laseola inornata* C. Chyzer and L. Kulczynski, 1891–7, II, p. 25 ; W. Falconer, 1914, p. 58. *Dipœna inornata* E. Simon, 1914, p. 278 ; H. Wiehle, 1937, p. 187.

DESCRIPTION. LENGTH : ♀ : 2·25 mm. ♂ : 1·5–1·7 mm. CARA-PACE : Yellow-brown to yellow, with head suffused with some black.

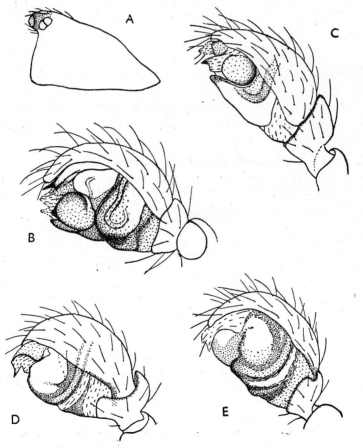

TEXT-FIG. 31.—A, *Dipœna prona* ♂, carapace.
  Male palps: B, *Dipœna prona;* C, *D. erythropus;* D, *Dipœna inornata* (side) ; E, ditto (from side and below).

Numerous long bristles on head. ABDOMEN : Brownish to black.
STERNUM : Yellow-brown, blackish on margins. LEGS : Yellow to
yellow brown ; tibiæ suffused with brownish black. MT I/t I about
1·5–1·6. EPIGYNE : Text-fig. 32, C., characteristic. MALE PALP :
Text-fig. 31, D, E.

OCCURRENCE : In heather and detritus and under stones. Adult in
May and June. Rare. From the southern half of England.

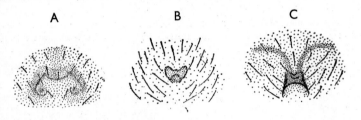

TEXT-FIG. 32.—Epigynes : A, *Dipœna prona;* B, *Dipœna erythropus;* C, *Dipœna
inornata.*

Dipœna tristis (Hahn).
(Text-fig. 33, A, D)

Theridion triste C. W. Hahn, 1831, p. 89. *Laseola tristis* C. Chyzer and L. Kulczynski
1891–7, II, p. 23 ; O. P.-Cambridge, 1895, p. 102 ; W. Falconer, 1914, p. 58. *Dipœna
tristis* E. Simon, 1914, p. 276 ; H. Wiehle, p. 182.

DESCRIPTION. LENGTH : ♀ : about 3 mm. ♂ : about 2·5 mm.
CARAPACE : Very dark brown to black, bearing numerous black
bristles, particularly on head. ABDOMEN : Glossy black, with
numerous hairs. STERNUM : Dark brown to blackish. LEGS :
Dark brown to black, with tarsi yellow (sometimes suffused with
black), and base of femora III and IV yellow to orange. Base of
tibiæ III and IV likewise yellow to orange at times in male. MT I/t I :
2·0. EPIGYNE : Text-fig. 33, D. Very insignificant. MALE PALP :
Text-fig. 33, A.

OCCURRENCE : On low bushes and trees, in woods. Very local, but
frequent in one or two places. Isle of Wight, Hampshire and Dorsetshire ; also recorded from Eire.

Dipœna coracina (C. L. Koch).
(Text-fig. 33, B, E)

Theridion coracinum C. L. Koch, 1841, p. 84. *Steatoda coracina* O. P.-Cambridge,
1879–81, p. 98. *Euryopis coracina* O. P.-Cambridge, ibid, p. 573. *Laseola nigrina*
C. Chyzer and L. Kulczynski, 1891–7, II, p. 26 ; W. Bosenberg, 1902, p. 123. *Dipœna
coracina* E. Simon, 1914, p. 277 ; H. Wiehle, 1937, p. 185.

DESCRIPTION. LENGTH : ♀ : 2–2·5 mm. ♂ : 1·75–2 mm. The
species is stated by Pickard-Cambridge (1879–81, p. 98) to be a uniform
sooty black in colour, save the extremities of the legs, which are white.
The species has not been taken in Britain for many years and the only

specimens available were dark brown in colour. LEGS : MT I/t I : 1·5.
EPIGYNE : Text-fig. 33, E. Very indefinite and possibly nothing is
visible in fresh specimens. MALE PALP : Text-fig. 33, B. Very similar
to *D. prona*, from which its colour should distinguish it.

OCCURRENCE : In heather, near Bloxworth (Dorsetshire) in May
" and summer months ", and in a swamp near Bloxworth in May ;
also from Suffolk.

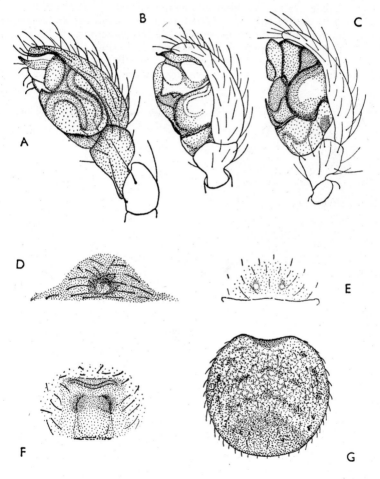

TEXT-FIG. 33.—Male palps : A, *Dipœna tristis;* B, *Dipœna coracina;* C, *Dipœna melanogaster.*
Epigynes : D, *Dipœna tristis;* E, *Dipœna coracina;* F, *Dipœna melanogaster.*
G, Abdomen of *D. melanogaster.*

Dipœna melanogaster (C. L. Koch).
(Text-fig. 33, C, F, G)

Atea melanogaster C. L. Koch, 1845, p. 143. *Dipoena melanogaster* O. P.-Cambridge, 1879–81, p. 478 ; C. Chyzer and L. Kulczynski, 1891–7, II, p. 26 ; E. Simon, 1914, p. 274 ; H. Wiehle, 1937, p. 181.

DESCRIPTION. LENGTH : ♀ : 2·5–3 mm. ♂ : about 2·5 mm. As the specimens available were all very old, the colours given here are based on Pickard-Cambridge's description (1879–81, p. 478). CARAPACE : Deep black-brown ; some long bristles on head. ABDOMEN : Very globular and broad, slightly indented anteriorly (Text-fig. 33, G). Yellowish dorsally, thickly mottled with yellow-brown and marked with numerous black blotches forming obscure chevrons. Sides black, with a whitish yellow patch on either side anteriorly. Black ventrally. ♀ with numerous strong black bristles dorsally. ♂ with numerous minute black tubercles, dorsally, bearing some long bristles. STERNUM :

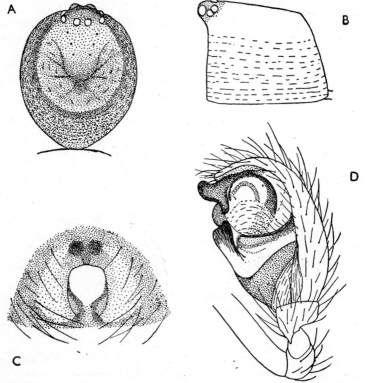

TEXT-FIG. 34.—*Dipœna torva:* A, ♂ carapace (from above) ; B, ditto (side) ; C, epigyne ; D, male palp.

Dark brown. Legs : Pale yellow, blotched and annulated with black and yellow-brown. MT I/t I about 2–2·2. Epigyne : Text-fig. 33, F, characteristic. Male palp : Text-fig. 33, C.

Occurrence : On gorse bushes, and possibly other low herbage. Extremely rare (Dorset and Hampshire only).

Dipœna torva (Thorell).
(Text-fig. 34)

Steatoda torva T. Thorell, 1875 (3), p. 58–9 (♀). *Laseola procax* A. Förster and P. Bertkau, 1883, p. 242 (♂♀). *L. torva* C. Chyzer and L. Kulczynski, 1891–7, I, p. 25 (♀). *Dipœna torva* H. Wiehle, 1937, p. 189 (♀). *Euryopis procax* E. Simon, 1879, p. 254. *Dipœna procax* E. Simon, 1914, p. 275. *D. procax* and *D. torva* A. Tullgren, 1949, pp. 52, 54.

Description. Length : ♀ : 3·5–4 mm. ♂ : about 2·75 mm. Carapace : ♀ : dark brown with black striæ ; black bristles on head and clypeus. ♂ : dark brown, extremely high (Text-fig. 34, B) with a horse-shoe shaped depression on top (Text-fig. 34, A). Abdomen : Black, with a glistening metallic sheen ; bearing numerous short black bristles. Sternum : Dark brown, with some black bristles. Epigyne : Text-fig. 34, C. Very characteristic. Male palp : Text-fig. 34, D.

Occurrence : Found by Mr. A. A. D. La Touche on pine trunks in the Black Wood of Rannoch (Perthshire). This is the first record of the species in Britain and we are very grateful to Mr. La Touche for the loan of his specimens.

4. Genus CRUSTULINA A. Menge 1868.

Characters of Genus. Carapace, Sternum and Cheliceræ with numerous " warts " (small crescent shaped elevations, each at one side of a puncture). Sternum : Very broad and truncated between coxæ IV. Abdomen : ♀ : base with a horny ring around the pedicel, in the same place as the stridulating teeth of ♂, which are well developed. Cheliceræ : Weak. Legs : Fairly stout, with tibia I : 1/d about 5–6 ; Tm I about 0·33 ; all metatarsi with a trichobothrium. Metatarsi only slightly longer than tarsi, with MT I/t I : 1·1–1·2.

The two British species are distinguished by the abdominal patterns, which, though they may vary, are still not confusable, and by the sex organs.

Crustulina guttata (Wider).
(Text-figs. 26, D ; 35, A, B, C)

Theridion guttata Wider, 1834, p. 241 ; J. Blackwall, 1861–4, p. 200. *Steatoda guttata* O. P.-Cambridge, 1879–81, p. 99. *Crustulina guttata* C. Chyzer and L. Kulczynski, 1891–7, II, p. 38 ; E. Simon, 1914, p. 279 ; H. Wiehle, 1937, p. 191.

Description. Length : ♀♂ : 1·5–2 mm. Carapace : Brown to dark brown, covered (including clypeus) with numerous warts (Text-fig. 26, D). Eyes : Anterior medians about one diameter apart and about 0·5 diameter from laterals ; posteriors 1·25–1·5 diameters

apart. Median ocular trapezium practically square. ABDOMEN:
Dark brown to black with, dorsally, a well defined pattern of glistening
white blotches (Text-fig. 26, D) and four reddish impressed dots.
Furnished with fairly long hairs. STERNUM: Brown to dark brown,

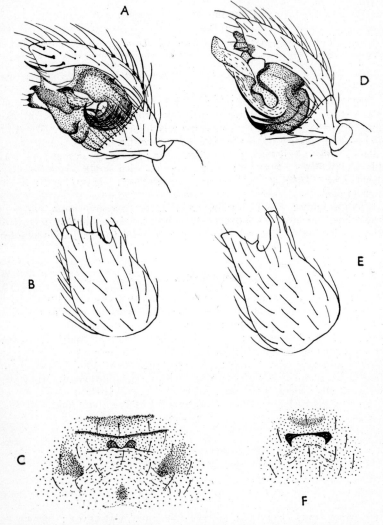

TEXT-FIG. 35.—*Crustulina guttata:* A, male palp; B, male palpal tarsus (from
above); C, epigyne.
Crustulina sticta: D, male palp; E, male palpal tarsus (from above); F,
epigyne.

broad between coxæ IV. With numerous warts like carapace. CHELI-
CERÆ : Weak, with warts anteriorly. LEGS : Yellow-brown to brown,
with apices of femora, tibiæ, metatarsi and tarsi dark brown (particularly femora and tibiæ I and II). Femora I and II with small warts,
each bearing a short hair. Tibiæ I and II with two spines dorsally ;
tibiæ III and IV and one spine dorsally. MT I/t I about 1·1. Tm I :
0·3 ; a trichobothrium present on metatarsus IV. EPIGYNE : Text-
fig. 35, C. MALE PALP : Text-fig. 35, A. This has a few warts on the
tarsus. Patella enlarged and " gouty ". Tarsus (cymbium) bears
mesally, towards the apex a small apophysis (Text-fig. 35, B).

OCCURRENCE : Found, though not very commonly, amongst grass,
and other herbage, in drier situations than *C. sticta*. Found all over
England ; recorded for Scotland and Wales.

Crustulina sticta (O. P.-Cambridge).
(Text-fig. 35, D, E, F)

Theridion stictum O. P.-Cambridge, 1861, p. 432 ; J. Blackwall 1861–4, p. 196.
Steatoda sticta O. P.-Cambridge 1879–81, p. 97. *Crustulina sticta* E. Simon, 1914,
p. 279.

DESCRIPTION. LENGTH : ♀♂ : about 2·5 mm. CARAPACE : As
C. guttata. EYES : Anterior medians 1–1·25 diameter apart, and 0·5
diameter from laterals ; posterior medians 1–1·25 diameter apart and
about 1 diameter from laterals. ABDOMEN : Whitish fawn dorsally
with four reddish impressed dots (larger in ♂). Sides brown, with two
brown blotches anteriorly. Occasionally the whole abdomen is black.
STERNUM and CHELICERÆ : As in *C. guttata*. LEGS : Pale yellow-brown
with no annulations. Femora I and II with small warts. All tibiæ
with only one spine dorsally (reduced or scarcely visible in ♂). MT I/t I
about 1·2. Tm I : 0·34 ; metatarsus IV with a trichobothrium.
EPIGYNE : Text-fig. 35, F. MALE PALP : Text-fig. 35, D. With no
warts on tarsi. Patella enlarged and gouty apically. Tarsal apophysis
(Text-fig. 35, E) larger than in *C. guttata*.

OCCURRENCE : In wet swampy places. Generally rare, but frequent
at Wicken Fen (Cambridgeshire). Other records from Dorsetshire,
Sussex, Norfolk, Suffolk, Staffordshire.

5. Genus ASAGENA C. J. Sundevall 1833.

CHARACTERS OF GENUS. CARAPACE : Covered with granulations.
EYES : Median trapezium longer than broad, a little narrower in
front than behind. Laterals on tubercles and not touching (Text-
fig. 26, F). Clypeus about twice as wide as trapezium. ABDOMEN :
♀ : Text-fig. 36, A. ♂ : with a well developed stridulating organ.
STERNUM : Covered with punctuations, especially marked in males.
LEGS : Stout ; tibia I *d/l*=about 0·3. ♂ : Femora with a series of
teeth on ventral side, especially prominent at apical end in II. Tm I :
0·67. There is one British species.

Asagena phalerata (Panzer).
(Text-fig. 36)

Phalangium phaleratum G. W. F. Panzer, 1801, **78**, 21. *Aranea signata* C. A. Walckenaer, 1802, p. 209. *Theridion signatum* J. Blackwall, 1861–4, p. 205. *Asagena phalerata* O. P.-Cambridge, 1879–81, p. 102 and recent authors.

DESCRIPTION. LENGTH : ♀ : 3·5–5 mm. ♂ : 4–4·5 mm. CARAPACE : Text-fig. 36, A. Dark brown, with darker streaks, almost black in some specimens; covered with small punctures. ABDOMEN : Text-fig. 36, A. Black with yellow marks (becoming white or cream on

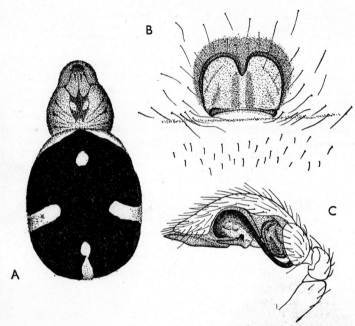

TEXT-FIG. 36.—*Asagena phalereta:* A, carapace and abdomen, ♀; B, epigyne; C, male palp.

preservation) ; these vary and are sometimes reduced or even absent. STERNUM : Dark brown or black, deeply punctured all over. LEGS : Femora I and II usually dark brown, III and IV yellow-brown to orange. Patellæ lighter brown or orange. Tibiæ I and II dark, sometimes light at the base or with two longitudinal light streaks dorsally; III and IV variable, apical half to two thirds often darkened. Metatarsi and tarsi unicolorous or darkened apically. EPIGYNE : Text-fig. 36, B. MALE PALP : Text-fig. 36, C.

OCCURRENCE : Rather rare but widespread, in England, Scotland and Wales. Usually found in heather or dry places.

6. Genus **LITHYPHANTES** T. Thorell 1869.

CHARACTERS OF GENUS. CARAPACE : Without granulations. EYES : Text-fig. 26, E. Median trapezium almost a square. Laterals on tubercles and not touching. Clypeus about as wide as median trapezium. ABDOMEN : ♂, with a well developed stridulating organ. STERNUM : Without punctuations. LEGS : Moderately long and slender ; tibia I $d/l=0·19$. Tm I$=0·41$.

There is one British species.

Lithyphantes albomaculatus (Degeer).
(Text-fig. 37)

Aranea albomaculata C. Degeer, 1778, p. 257. *Phrurolithus corollatus* C. L. Koch, 1839, VI, p. 100. *Steatoda corollata* T. Thorell, 1856, p. 85. *Lithyphantes corollatus* C. Chyzer and L. Kulczynski, 1891–7, II, p. 41. *L. albomaculatus* E. Simon, 1914, p. 282 ; H. Wiehle, 1937, p. 200 ; B. J. Kaston, 1948, p. 78.

DESCRIPTION. LENGTH : ♀ : 3·5–6 mm. ♂ : about 5 mm. CARAPACE : Text-fig. 37, A. Light brown to black, with little definite marking. ABDOMEN : Text-fig. 37, A. Black, with white or cream flecks. (The pattern is variable, the light flecks shown here may be smaller, fused with one another or, occasionally, quite absent.) Ventrally : black, with a light mark shaped like a Ψ (the side arms of which are sometimes absent). LEGS : Brown or yellow, with apical halves of all

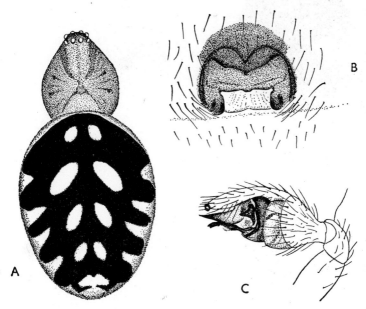

TEXT-FIG. 37.—*Lithyphantes albomaculata:* A, carapace and abdomen, ♀ ; B, epigyne; C, male palp.

segments deeper brown. Most of femora I and II and all of tibiæ I and II are sometimes deep brown, but this is variable. EPIGYNE : Text-fig. 37, B. MALE PALP : Text-fig. 37, C.

OCCURRENCE : Rare, in southern counties. Found in heathery stony places, the web being on, or close to, the ground.

7. Genus **STEATODA** C. J. Sundevall 1833.

CHARACTERS OF GENUS. CARAPACE : ♂ : covered with punctuations ; these scarcely perceptible in ♀. EYES : Anterior medians considerably larger than anterior laterals. Median trapezium almost a square, a little wider in front. Laterals touching. Clypeus about as wide as ocular area. ABDOMEN : ♂ stridulating organ well developed. STERNUM : ♂, punctuated ; ♀, only slightly. Projects narrowly between coxæ IV. LEGS : Rather short. Tibia I d/l about 0·16. Tm I : 0·45.

There is one British species.

Steatoda bipunctata (Linnaeus).
(Text-fig. 38)

Aranea bipunctata C. Linnaeus, 1758, p. 620. *A.* 4-*punctata* C. A. Walckenaer, 1802, p. 210. *Theridion quadripunctatum* C. W. Hahn, 1831, p. 78 ; J. Blackwall, 1861–4, p. 177. *Steatoda bipunctata* O. P.-Cambridge, 1879–81, p. 96 and recent authors.

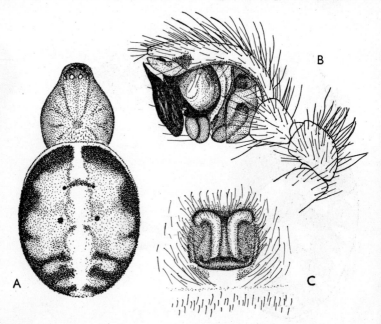

TEXT-FIG. 38.—*Steatoda bipunctata:* A, carapace and abdomen ♀; B, male palp ; C, epigyne.

DESCRIPTION. LENGTH : ♀ : 4·5–7 mm. ♂ : 4–5 mm. CARAPACE:
♀ : Text-fig. 38, A. Medium brown ; punctuations scarcely discernible.
♂ : Deep brown, almost black ; covered with punctuations. ABDOMEN :
Text-fig. 38, A. Dark parts chocolate brown, the light parts coffee
coloured. In spite of long, sparse, black hairs (not shown in the figure),
has a glossy, shiny appearance. Ventrally : A dark " V ", based on
the spinners, encloses a light triangle. Spinners surrounded by a
similar dark colour. STERNUM : Coloured as carapace ; covered with
punctuations, rather widely spaced, each one with a hair pointing
forwards and inwards (these punctuations much diminished in female).
LEGS : Yellow-brown, sometimes with annulations, or darkenings,
especially on III and IV. EPIGYNE : Text-fig. 38, C. MALE PALP :
Text-fig. 38, B. This is large and conspicuous.

OCCURRENCE : Common in houses, and found occasionally out of
doors. Distributed over England, Wales, Scotland. Recorded from
Dublin.

8. Genus **TEUTANA** E. Simon 1881.

CHARACTERS OF GENUS. CARAPACE : With no punctuations. EYES :
Median trapezium almost a square, a little narrower in front than behind.
Laterals not on tubercles and very nearly touching. Clypeus about

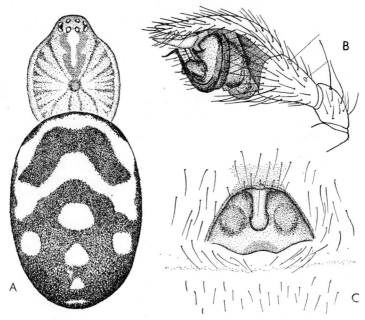

TEXT-FIG. 39.—*Teutana grossa:* A, carapace and abdomen ♀; B, male palp;
C, epigyne.

E

1·25 times as wide as median trapezium. ABDOMEN : Stridulating
organ well developed in ♂. LEGS : Relatively long. Tibia I d/l =0·12.
Tm I : 0·75.

There is one British species.

Teutana grossa (C. L. Koch).
(Text-fig. 39)

Theridium grossum C. L. Koch, 1838, IV, p. 112. *Theridion versutum* J. Blackwall,
1846, p. 302 and 1861–4, p. 193. *T. hamatum* N. Westring, 1851, p. 39 and 1861, p. 181.
Steatoda versuta T. Thorell, 1871, II, p. 89 ; O. P.-Cambridge 1879–81, p. 479. *Teutana
grossa* E. Simon, 1881, V, p. 164 and 1914, p. 280 ; C. Chyzer and L. Kulczynski
1891–7, II, p. 36 ; H. Wiehle, 1937. p. 196 ; B. J. Kaston, 1948, p. 86.

DESCRIPTION. LENGTH : ♀ : about 6·5 mm. (with abdomen fully
distended it might reach to 9–10 mm). ♂ : 4–6 mm. CARAPACE :
Text-fig. 39, A. Yellowish-brown without very definite markings, except
faint radiating striæ. ABDOMEN : Text-fig. 39, A. Variable ; ground
colour purplish violet to almost black. The light spots also vary and
may be nearly absent. LEGS : Coloured as carapace or lighter,
unmarked. EPIGYNE : Text-fig. 39, C. MALE PALP : Text-fig. 39, B.

OCCURRENCE : Rather rare in southern counties ; found as far north
as Staffordshire, and in Eire. Usually in the corners of disused rooms
and out-houses.

9. Genus THERIDION C. A. Walckenaer 1805.

CHARACTERS OF GENUS. EYES : Anterior medians equal to or
smaller than posterior medians and usually a little wider apart.
Laterals contiguous. ABDOMEN : Globular in females, and often in
males ; usually bearing a distinct pattern. Stridulating organs sometimes discernible in males, but usually not well developed or not
discernible. STERNUM : Rounded behind (not truncated), projecting
somewhat between coxæ IV (Text-fig. 27, B). CHELICERÆ : Usually
weak ; some males have them large and divergent. LEGS : Relatively
long and thin ; MT I/tI : 1.6 to 3.6, generally increasing with the
size of the spider. Tm I < 0.54 (except *T. ovatum* and *T. tinctum*
where it is 0.9).

The colouration of some of the species is very variable and, although
abdominal patterns are sometimes characteristic and useful guides,
different parts of these may be emphasized or suppressed, thus changing
the superficial appearance of the abdomen. (Mention is made of such
variation where it is known to occur.) The markings on the ventral
side of the abdomen are often useful, and these have been described in
such cases.

The Genus is divided conveniently into the following groups.

Group I.—The abdomen pattern of the type shown in Text-fig. 40, B.
♂ Metatarsus I with bristles having thickened bases (Text-fig. 40, A).
Theridion vittatum, T. pulchellum, T. aulicum.

Group II.—The abdomen having a profile as in Text-fig. 42. *Theridion
lunatum, T. saxatile, T. tepidariorum.*

Group III.—Two very similar species, with abdomen patterns as in Text-fig. 45, A. *Theridion sisyphium*, *T. impressum*.

Group IV.—Five species with rather similar sexual organs. *Theridion pictum*, *T. simile*, *T. varians*, *T. denticulatum*, *T. familiare*.

Group V.—*Theridion blackwalli*.

Group VI.—*Theridion tinctum*. ♂ cheliceræ narrowed, and divergent apically. Tm I : 0.9.

Group VII—♂ cheliceræ enlarged and bearing an apophysis and teeth (Text-figs. 50, B ; 51, C, D.) *Theridion ovatum*, *T. instabile*, *T. bellicosum*.

Group VIII—*Theridion bimaculatum*.

Group IX.—*Theridion pallens*.

These last two species are peculiar in colouration and structure. See descriptions.

It should be understood that although these groups are convenient (in the same way that an artificial key is convenient) for classifying the British species for identification, they are somewhat arbitrary as regards taxonomy. *Theridion aulicum* and *T. saxatile* could well stand by themselves, and members of Groups III–VI are closely related if one is considering male genitalia alone. It is very possible that A. Archer's revision of the genus (1950) may prevail, and this is based primarily on the male genitalia.

GROUP I.

Theridion vittatum C. L. Koch.
(Text-fig. 40, A, B, C, D)

Theridion vittatum C. L. Koch, 1836, III, p. 65. *T. pulchellum* J. Blackwall, 1861–4, p. 191 ; O. P.-Cambridge, 1879–81, p. 90. *T. vittatum* E. Simon, 1881, p. 98 and 1914, p. 249 ; C. Chyzer and L. Kulczynski, 1891–7, II, p. 36 ; H. Wiehle, 1937, p. 137.

DESCRIPTION. LENGTH : ♀ : 3–3·5 mm. ♂ : 2·5–3·5 mm. CARAPACE : Text-fig. 40, B. Light brown with a fine dark borderline ; median stripe chocolate brown (greyish black in living spiders). ABDOMEN : Text-fig. 40, B. ♀ : Light areas cream or light brown ; median stripe chocolate or a rusty red brown. (This stripe is usually continuous, but may be broken into chevrons posteriorly.) ♂ : Light regions darker than in female, but median stripe, which also is darker, may have a cream border. ♀♂ : Ventrally : A dark brown rectangular region extends from median spinners to the epigastric fold (and this pigmentation may extend anteriorly beyond the fold). Sides light with a somewhat darker reddish brown region along the middle. STERNUM : Dark brown, shading off to a large light yellow central region. LEGS : Light brown or yellow. Apices of segments darkened (femora rarely). Some specimens show faint traces of annulations about the middle of each segment. MT I/tI : 2·3. Tm I : 0·46. ♂ : Metatarsi I and II with ventral bristles, enlarged at their bases

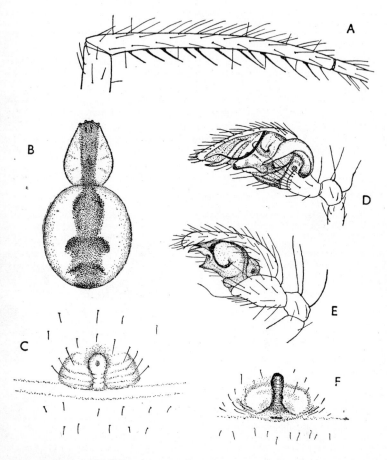

TEXT-FIG. 40.—*Theridion vittatum:* A, male metatarsus I ; B, carapace and abdomen ♀ ; C, epigyne ; D, male palp.
Theridion pulchellum: E, male palp ; F, epigyne.

(Text-fig. 40, A). EPIGYNE : Text-fig. 40, C. This is light and, in preserved specimens, has a waxy appearance. MALE PALP : Text-fig. 40, D.

OCCURRENCE : Frequent on trees, especially oak. Distributed all over England. Recorded from Eire, but not Wales nor Scotland. Adult in May.

Theridion pulchellum (Walckenaer).
(Text-fig. 40, E, F)

Aranea pulchella C. A. Walckenaer, 1802, p. 208. *Theridion pulchellum* C. Chyzer and L. Kulczynski, 1891–7, II, p. 35 ; E. Simon, 1881, p. 97 and 1914, p. 249 ; H. Wiehle, 1937, p. 139. (British records before 1938 refer to *T. vittatum* C. L. K. See W. Falconer, 1938, p. 182.)

DESCRIPTION. LENGTH : ♀ : 2·5–3 mm. ♂ : 3–3·5 mm. (measured from specimens from France). This spider is similar in general appearance to *T. vittatum* but differs from it as follows. CARAPACE : Median stripe less well defined at the edges. LEGS : Femora clear light brown. Patellæ with a dark mark apically. Tibiæ and metatarsi annulated apically and, on I and II, at mid point. Tm I : 0.27. EPIGYNE : Text-fig. 40, F. The finger-like process projecting from the posterior border is not dilated as in *T. vittatum*. MALE PALP : Text-fig. 40, E. (This is drawn from a French specimen).

OCCURRENCE : Bagley Wood (Berkshire), near Oxford. No males can be found in British collections.

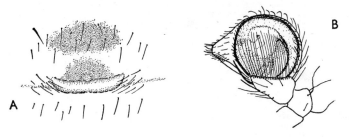

TEXT-FIG. 41.—*Theridion aulicum:* A, epigyne ; B, male palp (from side and a little in front).

Theridion aulicum C. L. Koch.
(Text-fig. 41)

Theridion aulicum C. L. Koch, 1838, IV, p. 115. *T. rufolineatum* H. Lucas, 1846, p. 260 ; O. P.-Cambridge, 1879–81, p. 89. *T. spirifer* O. P.-Cambridge, 1863, p. 8574 ; 1872, p. 280. *T. aulicum* E. Simon, 1914, p. 249 ; H. Wiehle, 1937, p. 139.

DESCRIPTION. LENGTH : ♀ : about 3 mm. ♂ : 2·5–3 mm. The species resembles *T. vittatum* in general appearance but is not very closely related to it structurally. CARAPACE : Median stripe less distinct than in *T. vittatum*, the darkening sometimes confined to cephalic area. Dark border wider, its inside edge less distinct than in *T. vittatum*. ABDOMEN : Variable. Lighter than in *T. vittatum*, with median stripe usually narrower, almost disappearing in some specimens ; usually better defined in males. Sides brown, speckled with white spots. Ventrally : A dark rectangle no wider than area of spinners, extends from epigastric fold to spinners. On each side of this is an equally broad white band. There are often two very distinct spots each side of spinners (less distinct in ♂). STERNUM : As in *T. vittatum*. LEGS : ♀, as in *T. vittatum* but apices of femora almost always darkened. Tm I : 0·27. ♀, I and II without darkening of segments. Ventral bristles on I and II not easily recognisable as analogous to those of *T. vittatum*. EPIGYNE : Text-fig. 41, A. Colour of the transverse bar often very faint in preserved specimens. MALE PALP : Text-fig. 41, B. This is quite unmistakable.

The above description was made from the few specimens available, which had been preserved for a long time. The species seems to be particularly variable in colour, and E. Simon (1881, p. 96) gives a list of five colour varieties which he recognised at that time.

OCCURRENCE : Rare. Found in gorse bushes and the lower branches of trees. In the southern part of England. Adult in early summer.

GROUP II.

Theridion lunatum (Clerck).
(=*Theridion lunatum* (Olivier))
(Text-figs. 42 ; 43, A, B, G)

Araneus lunatus and *A. formosus* C. Clerck, 1757, pp. 52, 56. *Aranea lunata* and *formosa* A. G. Olivier, 1789, p. 210. *A. sisyphia* C. A. Walckenaer, 1802, p. 206. *Theridion sisyphium* id. 1806–8, III, f. 9. *T. sisyphum* J. Blackwall, 1861–4, p. 179. *T. formosum* O. P.-Cambridge, 1879–81, p. 83 ; C. Chyzer and L. Kulczynski, 1891–7, II, 35. *T. lunatum* E. Simon, 1914, p. 260 ; H. Wiehle, 1937, p. 158.

DESCRIPTION. LENGTH : ♀ : 2·5–3 mm. ♂ : about 2·5 mm. CARAPACE : Text-fig. 43, A. Yellow to red-brown ; in some specimens probably black. No definite markings beyond faint radiating streaks. ABDOMEN : Text-fig. 42 shows the shape as seen from the side. Basic pattern as in Text-fig. 43, A, but very variable. Colour brown or black ; light parts white or cream, those on anterior half may be

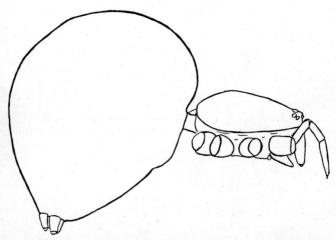

TEXT-FIG. 42.—*Theridion lunatum* ♀, carapace and abdomen (profile).

reduced to a pair of spots and specimens may occur in which they are absent. Reddish streaks may also be present. Ventrally : Depth of colour variable, but usually with two light patches or transverse bars between spinners and epigastric fold (often indistinct in males). STERNUM : Very variable in depth of colouring, yellow-brown to black ; darker in males. Sometimes with lighter markings anteriorly. LEGS : Light brown or yellow, all segments except tarsi darkened apically ; metatarsi III and IV darkened a little also at the base, tibia IV on the apical half. MT I/t I : 2·7. Tm I : 0·41. EPIGYNE : Text-fig. 43, G. MALE PALP : Text-fig. 43, B.

OCCURRENCE : Rather uncommon. It is beaten from bushes and lower branches of trees, particularly in darker parts of woods. Adult in May. In England as far north as Staffordshire.

Theridion saxatile C. L. Koch.
(Text-fig. 43, C, E)

Theridion saxatile C. L. Koch, 1834, 7–8. *T. riparium* J. Blackwall, 1834, p. 354 and 1861–4, p. 182. O. P.-Cambridge, 1879–81, p. 84 ; C. Chyzer and L. Kulczynski, 1891–7, II, p. 35. *T. saxatile* E. Simon, 1914, p. 261 ; H. Wiehle, 1937, p. 160.

DESCRIPTION. LENGTH : ♀ : about 3·5 mm. ♂ : 3–3·25 mm. CARAPACE : Dark brown with light radiating reticulate markings. ABDOMEN : Shaped as in *T. lunatum* (Text-fig. 42) as seen from the side. Pattern deep red-brown, with light parts cream, not well defined and very variable in emphasis of different parts ; of the same general make-up as in *T. lunatum* (Text-fig. 43, A) but more vague. Ventrally : anterior part dark ; a light transverse band, narrowest at its middle, occurs just in front of the spinners, sometimes reduced to a pair of light patches (especially in males). STERNUM : Coloured as carapace. Generally with no pattern, but sometimes with darker patches opposite coxæ. ♂ : similar but darker. LEGS : Light yellow with brown annulations on apical ends of all segments and sometimes on middle of tibiæ. (In some males annulations less well defined or absent on I and II.) MT I/t I : 2·4. Tm I : 0·44. EPIGYNE : Text-fig. 43, E. This being simple, the summary of other distinguishing characters for similar species on p. 73 should be referred to. MALE PALP : Text-fig. 43, C.

OCCURRENCE : Rather rare ; chiefly in southern counties, but recorded from Cumberland. Amongst grass and roots under overhanging banks ; under stones and at the bases of walls. The female spins a long tubular retreat (the entrance opening downwards) which is covered with pieces of twig, grass, stone or earth, etc. The prey seems largely to consist of ants. Adult in late May and early June.

Theridion tepidariorum C. L. Koch.
(Text-fig. 43, D, F)

Theridion tepidariorum C. L. Koch, 1841, VIII, p. 75 and recent authors.

DESCRIPTION. LENGTH : ♀ : 5–7 mm. ♂ : 3·5–4 mm. CARAPACE : Medium to light brown with faint radiating striæ. ABDOMEN : Outline,

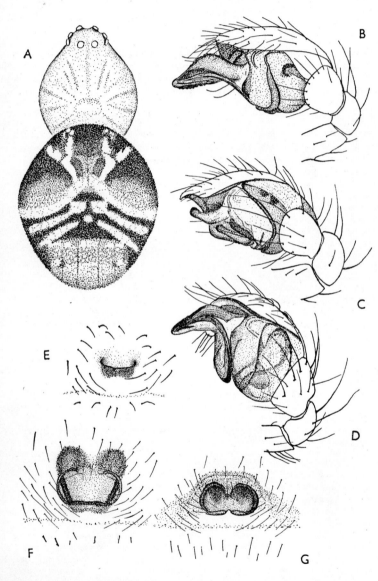

TEXT-FIG. 43.—A, *Theridion lunatum*, carapace and abdomen.
Male palps : B, *Theridion lunatum;* C, *T. saxatile;* D, *T. tepidariorum.*
Epigynes : E, *T. saxatile;* F, *T. tepidariorum;* G, *T. lunatum.*

seen from the side, as in Text-fig. 42). Pattern variable, occasionally approaching that of *T. lunatum* (Text-fig. 43, A). Colouration also variable, the most usual being a " pepper and salt " mottling. Ventrally : a dark area lies immediately in front of spinners ; between this and epigastric fold is a white square in which is a dark chevron (apex backwards). STERNUM : Brown, often darker round edges. LEGS : ♀ : Light brown, frequently annulated with deeper brown. MT I/t I : 3·4. Tm I : 0·32. ♂ : Light brown to orange, annulations frequently (but not always) absent. EPIGYNE : Text-fig. 43, F. MALE PALP : Text-fig. 43, D.

OCCURRENCE : This species, which is cosmopolitan, occurs with great regularity in heated greenhouses, but has been found occasionally out of doors, especially in southern counties. (The life history and distribution are treated in detail by P. Bonnet (1935).)

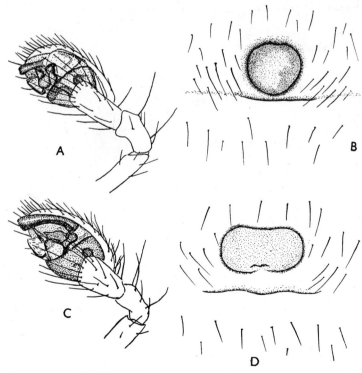

TEXT-FIG. 44.—*Theridion sisyphium:* A, male palp ; B, epigyne.
T. impressum: C, male palp ; D, epigyne.

Theridion tepidariorum simulans Thorell.

Theridion formosum var *simulans* T. Thorell, 1875, p. 55. L. Kulczynski (1898, p. 63) pointed out that this was a variety of *T. tepidariorum* (not of *T. formosum-lunatum*). *T. simulans* W. Bosenberg, 1903, tab. VIII, fig. 117 ; J. Denis, 1944, p. 111.

The status of this sub-species, or variety, is, in our opinion, somewhat doubtful, the epigyne being indistinguishable from that of *T. tepidariorum*, and no males being available. Kulczynski (1898, p. 63) gave as a character for distinguishing it from the latter species the ratio $\dfrac{\text{length tibia I}}{\text{carapace length}}$ which for females lies between 1·13 and 1·27 for *T. simulans* and between 1·42 and 1·48 for *T. tepidariorum*. A number of females, at first thought to be small specimens of *T. tepidariorum*, have been collected by us and by Mr. A. A. D. La Touche far from buildings (from Box Hill and the New Forest), whose measurements agree with those given above for *T. simulans*. A plot of these with Kulczynski's measurements, together with more of *T. tepidariorum*, show that they are consistent with the assumption that there is one species in which tibia I is growing allometrically as regards the carapace, and that if in the formula $y = b\, x^{\alpha}$, y is length tibia I and x is carapace length (b being constant), then α is about 1·65. Hitherto a male has not been taken in this country, and it has not been possible to see whether the small difference in the palp claimed by Bosenberg (1903, tab. VIII, fig. 117) can be used to establish the status of this small form. Occasionally large, typical specimens of *T. tepidariorum* have been taken out of doors, but usually not very far from buildings. It is perhaps noteworthy that these are larger than our other *Theridia*, and it may well be that *T. simulans* is a smaller variety of *T. tepidariorum* better adapted to survival in our climate and conditions, but a decision must await the collection of more material.

GROUP III.

Theridion sisyphium (Clerck).
(Text-figs. 44, A, B ; 45, A)

Araneus sisyphius C. Clerck, 1757, p. 54. *Aranea notata* C. Linnaeus 1758, p. 621, *A. nervosa* A. G. Oliver, 1789, p. 210. *Theridion nervosum* J. Blackwall 1861-4, p. 183. *T. sisyphium* O. P.-Cambridge, 1879–81, p. 85 ; C. Chyzer and L. Kulczynski, 1891–7. II, p. 33 ; E. Simon, 1914, p. 257. *T. notatum* H. Wiehle, 1937, p. 151.

DESCRIPTION. LENGTH : ♀ : 3–4 mm. ♂ : about 3 mm. CARAPACE : Text-fig. 45, A. Light brown, with chocolate median stripe and border. ABDOMEN : Text-fig. 45, A. Dark parts black ; central darker region rusty brown or reddish ; lighter parts white with darker reticulations. (There is variation in the relative extent of the coloured areas, but the general make-up of the pattern is preserved.) Ventrally : Light brown or yellow, with a conspicuous black patch immediately in front of spinners. STERNUM : Light brown or yellow, with a thin darker, reddish borderline. LEGS : Light yellowish brown, darkened at the apices of each segment. (♀ : femora I and II sometimes darker than the rest.) MT I/t I : 2·8–3·1. Tm I : 0·29. EPIGYNE : Text-fig. 44, B. This is almost circular and will appear thus when viewed in the correct position. It is necessary to distinguish it carefully from that of *T. impressum* (Text-fig. 44, D) which is broader than long, and never appears circular seen from any position. MALE PALP : Text-fig. 44, A.

The species needs to be distinguished from *T. impressum*, which it resembles closely in general appearance.

OCCURRENCE : Common, and distributed all over the British Isles. On gorse bushes, brambles, hedges and low plants. Adult at the end of May and beginning of June. The young remain with the mother for some time and are fed by her. (Locket, 1926, p. 1128.)

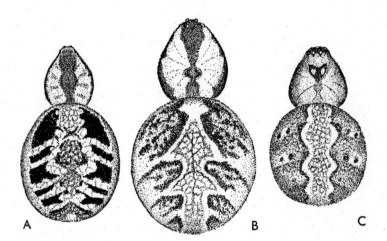

TEXT-FIG. 45.—A, *Theridion sisyphium;* B, *T. pictum;* C, *T. denticulatum.*

Theridion impressum L. Koch.

(Text-fig. 44, C, D)

Theridion impressum L. Koch, 1881, p. 45 ; C. Chyzer and L. Kulczynski, 1891–7, II, p. 33 ; O. P.-Cambridge, 1903, p. 152 ; E. Simon, 1914, p. 257 ; H. Wiehle, 1937, p. 152 ; A. Tullgren, 1949, p. 38.

DESCRIPTION. LENGTH : ♀ : 4–4·5 mm. ♂ : 2·5–3·5 mm. This species resembles *T. sisyphium* closely in markings and colouration ; the most usual differences are as follows. CARAPACE : Marginal dark border is wider. ABDOMEN : Ventrally there is the same black patch as in *T. sisyphium* immediately in front of the spinners, but between this and the epigastric fold is another larger brown patch, often in the form of a triangle with blunted corners, the apex forwards, but some-times less well defined in its outline. STERNUM : Margin generally darker and wider. LEGS : Similar, but apical annulations usually darker. MT I/t I : 3·3–3·5. Tm I : 0·28. EPIGYNE : Text-fig. 44, D.

This never appears circular, always broader than long, and constitutes the most reliable distinguishing character. MALE PALP : Text-fig. 44, C.

OCCURRENCE : Less common than *T. sisyphium*, but found in similar places. It becomes adult about the middle of July in southern counties ; in this species also the young are fed by the female.

GROUP IV.

Theridion pictum (Walckenaer).
(Text-figs. 45, B ; 46, A ; 47, A)

Aranea picta C. A. Walckenaer, 1802, p. 207. *T. ornatum* C. W. Hahn, 1831, p. 6; A. Tullgren, 1949, p. 45. *T. pictum* J. Blackwall, 1861–64, p. 184 ; O. P.-Cambridge, 1879–81, p. 476 ; C. Chyzer and L. Kulczynski, 1891–7, II, p. 34 ; E. Simon, 1914, p. 266 ; H. Wiehle, 1937, p. 168.

DESCRIPTION. LENGTH : ♀ : 3·5–4·75 mm. ♂ : 2·25–3·5 mm. CARAPACE : Text-fig. 45, B. Light yellow brown, with sepia markings. ABDOMEN : Text-fig. 45, B. Central band usually red edged with white. The rest white with black, brown, or grey, mottling. The lateral teeth of the light central band extend as shown (cf. *T. simile*, and in contrast to *T. denticulatum*). Ventrally : Frequently a light, nearly white area (yellow-green in living spiders), between the spinners and epigastric fold, has a dark patch in the middle of it and is flanked by darker areas ; but the whole region is very variable in colour, sometimes all dark, or with a pair of light patches just behind the epigastric fold (especially so in males). The spinners are surrounded usually by dark or black pigment ; this is sometimes intensified immediately in front of the spinners, appearing then as a black spot. ♂ : the epigastric region greatly swollen. STERNUM : Coloured as carapace, with a darker border of very varying width. LEGS : Light yellow-brown, clearly annulated in black, except femora, which have black patches. MT I/tI=2·6. Tm I=0·42. EPIGYNE : Text-fig. 47, A. (This is not always as well defined as indicated here, but the parts can be made out.) MALE PALP : Text-fig. 46, A. This bears some resemblance to that of *T. varians* (Text-fig. 46, C).

OCCURRENCE : Widespread throughout England and Scotland, but of rather local occurrence. Usually in damp places, on low bushes, nettles, etc. Adult in late May or early June. We have observed that the young feed communally on prey caught by the mother, as in *T. sisyphium* and *T. impressum*.

Theridion simile C. L. Koch.
(Text-figs. 46, B ; 47, C)

Theridion simile C. L. Koch 1836, p. 62 ; J. Blackwall, 1861–4, p. 187 ; O. P.-Cambridge, 1879–81, p. 88, and recent authors.

DESCRIPTION. LENGTH : ♀♂ : 2–2·25 mm. CARAPACE : Light to medium dark brown, with no very definite pattern, usually a little darker along the edges. ABDOMEN : Very variable, the pattern

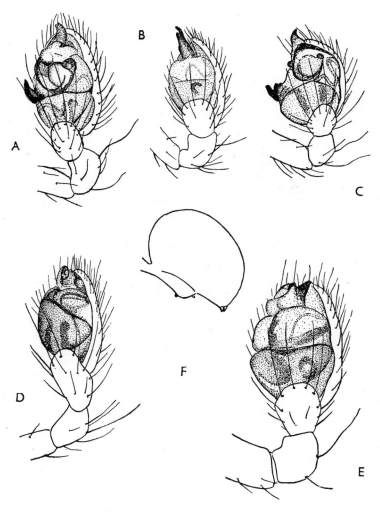

TEXT-FIG. 46.—Male palps : A, *Theridion pictum;* B, *T. simile;* C, *T. varians;* D, *T. denticulatum;* E, *T. familiare;* F, *T. varians,* ♂ : abdomen, showing swollen epigastric region.

essentially as in *T. pictum* ; the first, anterior, enlargement of the dentate median band being often emphasized, and then forming a conspicuous light triangle. But this, and the subsequent enlargements, may be obscure or even quite absent. The dark parts are usually made up of brown mottlings on an almost white ground and are very variable in depth of colour. Ventrally : There is a transverse light band on a slightly darker ground, and this band often has a dark posterior margin. STERNUM : Light brown, usually darkening towards the edges. LEGS : Coloured as lighter parts of carapace, with dark brown annulations, which vary in intensity but are especially clear on apices of segments, rarely complete on femora ; less well defined in males. MT I/tI=2·2. Tm I=0·27. EPIGYNE : Text-fig. 47, C. This being simple, the summary of other distinguishing characters for similar species on p. 73 should be referred to. MALE PALP : Text-fig. 46, B. The apical apophysis is notched and is characteristic. The male is generally coloured as the female, but is usually darker.

OCCURRENCE : Found, though not commonly, on bushes and low plants, more especially in southern counties, though occurring in Yorkshire and recorded from Scotland and Eire. Adult towards the end of May and beginning of June.

Theridion varians Hahn.

(Text-figs. 46, C, F ; 47, B)

Theridion varians C. W. Hahn, 1831, p. 93 ; J. Blackwall, 1861–4, p. 88 ; O. P.-Cambridge, 1879–81, p. 87, and recent authors.

DESCRIPTION. LENGTH : ♀ : 2·5–3·5 mm. ♂ : 2·25–2·75 mm. CARAPACE : Light yellow or cream, with a dark median band, which encloses the eyes, and a thin dark borderline. ABDOMEN : Pattern of type of *T. denticulatum* (Text-fig. 45, C), but usually much lighter and less well defined, and the points of the denticulations of the central band are generally sharper. Ventrally : whole region between spinners and epigastric fold light as a rule, but variation occurs. (There is no conspicuous light triangle as in *T. denticulatum*.) ♂: The epigastric region greatly swollen (Text-fig. 46, F). STERNUM : Very variable; generally coloured as carapace with a dark border, which varies greatly in width, sometimes covering the whole sternum. LEGS : Coloured as carapace, flecked or tinted with black to a varying extent and very like *T. tinctum*. Some males have faint brown annulations. MT I/tI= 2·8, Tm I=0·40. EPIGYNE : Text-fig. 47, B. MALE PALP : Text-fig. 46, C. Both these are characteristic and enable the spider to be identified without difficulty.

OCCURRENCE : Common on trees, bushes, buildings, and occurring all over the British Isles. Males adult towards the end of May ; females have been found as late as October.

Theridion denticulatum (Walckenaer).
(Text-figs. 45, C ; 46, D ; 47, D)

Aranea denticulata C. A. Walckenaer, 1802, p. 208. *Theridion melanurum* C. W. Hahn, 1831, p. 6 ; A. Tullgren, 1949, p. 41. *T. denticulatum* J. Blackwall, 1861–4, p. 185 ; O. P.-Cambridge, 1879–81, p. 86 ; C. Chyzer and L. Kulczynski, 1891–7, II, p. 34 ; E. Simon, 1914, p. 267 ; H. Wiehle, 1937, p. 165.

DESCRIPTION. LENGTH : ♀ : 2·5–3·75 mm. ♂ : 2·25–3·75 mm. CARAPACE : Text-fig. 45, C. Dark brown with an almost black median mark. Darkening of border regions variable in width. ABDOMEN : Text-fig. 45, C. Black or grey ; depth of colour very variable as well as emphasis of different parts of the pattern. Shape of light median

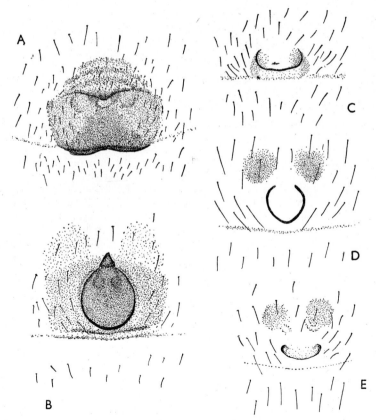

TEXT-FIG. 47.—Epigynes : A, *Theridion pictum;* B, *T. varians;* C, *T. simile;* D, *T. denticulatum;* E, *T. familiare.*

band characteristic, the dentations not extended as in *T. pictum* and *T. simile*. Ventrally : dark brown or black, with a conspicuous triangular cream patch mid-way between spinners and epigastric fold, with its apex forwards. ♂ : epigastric region markedly swollen. STERNUM : Coloured as carapace. LEGS : Light brown or cream, usually annulated clearly in black, but annulations sometimes incomplete or reduced to blotches, sometimes absent on femora. MT I/tI= 2·4–2·7, Tm I=0·44. EPIGYNE : Text-fig. 47, D. This consists of a fine chitinous ring and if the appearance of this is not familiar, reference to the table on p. 73 is advisable. According to Tullgren (1949, p. 42) some variation occurs in the epigyne and vulva. MALE PALP : Text-fig. 46, D. Some females of *T. familiare* resemble those of this species at first sight and, as they are sometimes found in similar situations, the distinguishing characters should be noted (p. 73).

OCCURRENCE : Common in buildings and found on trees and bushes. Distributed all over the British Isles.

Theridion familiare O. P.- Cambridge.

(Text-figs. 46, E ; 47, E)

Theridion familiare O. P.-Cambridge, 1871, p. 418 and 1879–81, p. 86 ; E. Simon, 1914, p. 264 ; H. Wiehle, 1937, p. 170.

DESCRIPTION. LENGTH : ♀ : 1·5–2 mm. ♂ : about 1·5 mm. CARAPACE : Brown, variable in depth, darker towards edges. Cephalic area sometimes darker than the rest (not always). Thoracic area sometimes with darker radiations, sometimes with a marbled appearance, but usually no definite pattern. ABDOMEN : Pattern of the type of *T. denticulatum*, the dorsal median light stripe similar in shape and often having a well marked dark margin. Remaining dorsal pattern usually not definite and made up of mottlings. Colour more reddish brown than in *T. denticulatum* (which tends to be black or grey). Ventrally : A cream patch, as in *T. denticulatum*, but not so well defined. ♂ : epigastric region noticeably swollen. STERNUM : Coloured as carapace ; unmarked or with some obscure blotches. LEGS : Annulated, sometimes faintly, with dark sooty colour. MT I/tI=ca 1·8, Tm I=0·41. EPIGYNE : Text-fig. 47, E. The chitinous ring is somewhat variable in shape, but broader, relative to its length, than in *T. denticulatum*, and the slight thickening of the outside edges is characteristic. MALE PALP : Text-fig. 46, E. This needs careful comparison with *T. denticulatum*. (See table on p. 73).

OCCURRENCE : Rare. Found in lofts and outhouses and unused rooms, but a specimen has been beaten from gorse and it may occur occasionally far from buildings. Most records are from southern counties, but it has occurred in Staffordshire and Lincolnshire.

In view of the variation of colouring which can occur, and of the similarity of the epigynes, the following summary of other characters may be useful in checking the identity of the female species given below. (The markings on the ventral sides of the abdomen seem to vary less than those on the dorsal side and are generally reliable.)

	Abdomen (ventral)	Eyes	Length	Tm I	MTI/tI
T. denticulatum	Dark, with a conspicuous white Δ	Ant. meds. separated by nearly two diams. Much wider apart than posterior meds, which are nearer each other than to post. lats.	2.5–3.75 mm.	0.44	2.6
T. familiare	Similar mark, but less well defined.	Ant. meds. separated by little more than one diam. Slightly wider apart than posterior meds.* Posteriors nearly equidistant.	1.5–2 mm.	0.41	1.8
T. simile	Transverse light band on a darker ground.	Ant. meds. separated by about 1¾ diam. Little wider apart than post. meds.* Posteriors almost equidistant.	2–2.25 mm.	0.27	2.2
T. saxatile	Transverse light band, narrowest in middle (or divided into 2 light patches) on dark ground, darker in front.	Ant. meds. separated by about 1½ diam. Little wider apart than post. meds.* Posteriors almost equidistant.	about 3.5 mm.	0.44	2.4

*Median ocular trapezium almost a square.

Theridion tinctum is usually easily distinguishable, especially since in this species Tm I=about 0.9, and MT I/tI=3.0

GROUP V.

Theridion blackwalli O.P. - Cambridge.
(Text-figs. 48, A, B ; 49, A)

Theridion blackwalli O. P.-Cambridge, 1871, p. 419, and 1889, Pl. A. fig. 3. *Euryopis blackwalli id.* 1879–81, p. 481. *Theridion blackwalli* C. Chyzer and L. Kulczynski, 1891–7, II, p. 33 ; E. Simon, 1914, p. 263 ; H. Wiehle, 1937, p. 176.

DESCRIPTION. LENGTH : ♀ : about 2·75 mm. ♂ : about 2·25 mm. CARAPACE : Text-fig. 49, A. Medium brown with sooty markings ; ♂ lighter. ABDOMEN : Text-fig. 49, A. Folium fairly dark brown with

F

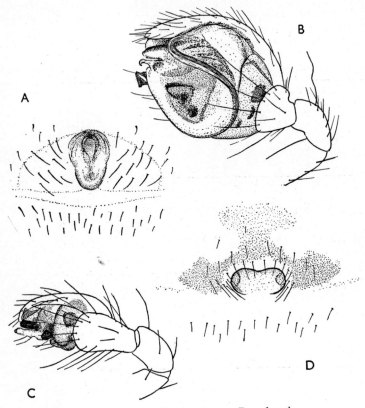

TEXT-FIG. 48.—*Theridion blackwalli:* A, epigyne ; B, male palp.
    T. tinctum: C, male palp ; D, epigyne.

deeper parts a sooty black, depth of colour variable, the whole region
sometimes almost black. The ground colour and sides a marbled white.
Ventrally : two small white spots occur half way between epigastric
fold and spinners (reduced or absent in some males). STERNUM : Dark
brown or black, with sometimes fainter patches. ♂ : lighter and having
a dark borderline. LEGS : Yellow-brown ; femora (except IV), tibiæ
and sometimes metatarsi with a black patch on ventral side of basal
half. Tibiæ and metatarsi with a similar patch on ventral side at the
tips of each. Femora sometimes with complete annulations at apices
(except III). MT I/tI=1·8, Tm I=0·54. ♂ : markings often reduced
to small spots, or absent. EPIGYNE : Text-fig. 48, A. MALE PALP :
Text-fig. 48, B.
    OCCURRENCE : Very rare. Amongst grasses and low plants. Records
are mostly from southern and midland counties, but it has been taken
in Cheshire and in Durham.

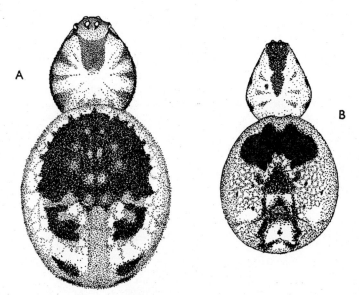

TEXT-FIG. 49.—A, *Theridion blackwalli;* B, *T. tinctum.*

GROUP VI.

Theridion tinctum (Walckenaer).
(Text-figs. 48, C, D ; 49, B)

Aranea tincta C. A. Walckenaer, 1802, p. 208. *Theridion tinctum* J. Blackwall,
1861–4, p. 190 ; O. P.-Cambridge, 1879–81, p. 88 ; C. Chyzer and L. Kulczynski,
1891–7, II, p. 34 ; E. Simon, 1914, p. 258 ; H. Wiehle, 1937, p. 154.

DESCRIPTION. LENGTH : ♀ : 2·5–3·5 mm. ♂ : about 2.5 mm.
CARAPACE : Text-fig. 49, B. Grey, with black patches along the
margin and a black bar along anterior edge of clypeus (often reduced to
a narrow patch in males). Median dark mark characteristic, but not
always reaching the eyes. Radiating streaks often not present.
ABDOMEN : Text-fig. 49, B. This is extremely variable. The dark
anterior patch shown is usually present in some form, though often
reduced or enlarged ; the markings which follow this are sometimes
absent, or very different from those shown. Light parts sometimes
lemon-yellow, with some pink marks on sides. Ventrally : very
variable. If the region between spinners and epigastric fold is light, it
frequently bears a black triangle (apex forwards), on each side of
which is a black transverse band, coming in from the sides. Often
the bands and triangle are fused to give a single dark transverse band.
STERNUM : Again very variable ; usually light yellow-brown (as
carapace) with dark wide borders (except anteriorly) and a median
dark patch, sometimes broken in the middle, which nearly reaches the
anterior edge. In some specimens (especially males) the whole sternum

black. CHELICERÆ : Coloured as carapace with dark patches along inner margins near the base.♂ : elongated and divergent apically ; fang longer than in ♀. LEGS : Coloured as carapace, with black annulations, distinct on III and IV, less so on I and II. In some specimens annulations are replaced by spots or patches, which do not go right round the limb. MT I/tI=2·8–3·1, Tm I=0·89. EPIGYNE : Text-fig. 48, D. (The pigmentation shown seems fairly constant.) MALE PALP : Text-fig. 48, C. The coloration of this species is perhaps more variable than in any other of the Genus. Some males are almost black.

OCCURRENCE : Very abundant locally on low trees, especially yew and box. In England as far north as Cheshire and Lincolnshire, and in Wales. Adults are found from May and June to October.

GROUP VII.

Theridion ovatum (Clerck).

(=*Theridion redimitum* (Linnaeus))

(Text-fig. 50)

Araneus ovatus C. Clerck, 1757, p. 58. *A. redimitus* p. 59 *A. lineatus*, p. 60. *Aranea redimita* C. Linnaeus, 1758, p. 621. *Phyllonethis lineata* T. Thorell, 1870, p. 78 ; O. P.-Cambridge, 1879–81, p. 94. *Theridion lineatum* J. Blackwall, 1861–4, p. 176 ; C. Chyzer and L. Kulczynski, 1891–7, II, p. 32. *T. ovatum* E. Simon, 1914, p. 251. *T. redimitum* H. Wiehle, 1937, p. 140 ; B. J. Kaston, 1948, p. 111.

DESCRIPTION. LENGTH : ♀ : 5–5·5 mm. ♂ : 3–4 mm. (further variation in size is likely). CARAPACE : Text-fig. 50, A. Light yellow-brown with (usually) a fine black borderline and a dark median streak. ABDOMEN : Dorsally covered with light carmine (Clerck's *ovatum*) or with a pair of wide longitudinal carmine stripes (Clerck's *redimitum*) or (most frequently) entirely creamy-white with 4–5 pairs of black spots (Text-fig. 50, A) (Clerck's *lineatum*) ; these spots are usually larger and more conspicuous in males, and may become very small in females whose abdomens are distended. Ventrally : White, with a black median rectangular wedge from epigastric fold to spinners. On each side of spinners is a white spot with a black one immediately behind it. The frequency of occurrence of the colour varieties has been studied by Bristowe (1931, p. 466), and their interbreeding by Gerhardt (1921, p. 161). STERNUM : Colour as carapace, with a black border and black longitudinal median line. CHELICERÆ : Enlarged in ♂ (Text-fig. 50, B), their growth being allometric (G. H. Locket, 1932). There is a large apophysis, easily seen, and two teeth in the inner row. LEGS : Light brown, sometimes nearly white, or with a greenish tinge. Tibia I darkened at apex. MT I/tI=3·6, Tm I=0·95. EPIGYNE : Text-fig. 50, C. MALE PALP : Text-fig. 50, D.

OCCURRENCE : This is perhaps the commonest spider of the genus. Found by sweeping herbage, particularly nettles, and low bushes, such as bramble. Distributed all over the British Isles. Adult in June. The female makes a retreat by rolling up living leaves and produces a blue-green egg cocoon.

Theridion instabile O.P.-Cambridge.
(Text-fig. 51, A, C, E, F)

Theridion instabile O. P.-Cambridge, 1870, p. 416. *Phyllonethis instabilis* id., 1879–81, p. 95. *Theridion instabile* A. R. Jackson, 1914, p. 122, Pl. II, figs. 8, 10, 12, 13 ; E. Simon, 1914, p. 256 ; H. Wiehle, 1937, p. 146.

DESCRIPTION. LENGTH : ♀ : 2–2·5 mm. ♂ : 1·75–2·25 mm. CARAPACE : Variable ; usually light brown or yellow, with cephalic area, including ocular area, darker. (Sometimes this dark area extends backwards as a dark band to just short of the posterior margin of the

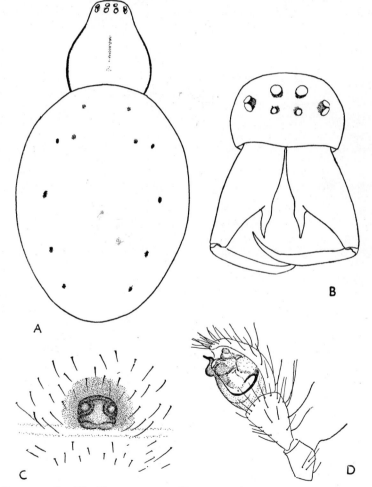

TEXT-FIG. 50.—*Theridion ovatum* var. *lineatum ;* A, carapace and abdomen, ♀ ; B, head and cheliceræ, ♂ (from in front) ; C, epigyne ; D, male palp.

thoracic area. In darker specimens the mark may be nearly absent, but is usually more distinct in light and old specimens). ABDOMEN :

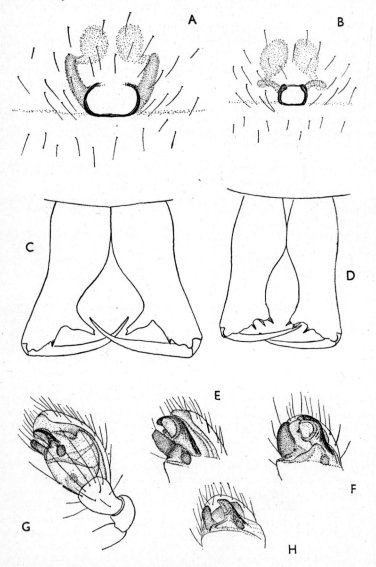

TEXT-FIG. 51.—*Theridion instabile:* A, epigyne; C, male cheliceræ (from in front); E, tip of male palp (side); F, ditto (below).
Theridion bellicosum: B, epigyne; D, male cheliceræ (from in front); G, male palp; H, tip of male palp (below).

Very variable. A common arrangement is a dark ill-defined folium with dentated, deeply cut, edges, and bearing a light median stripe, also with wavy or dentate edges. But the whole dorsal region may be almost white or the folium may be nearly uniform dark brown (especially in males). Anything between these extremes may occur. Ventrally : Either uniform light brown or yellow, or with a sooty patch, sometimes as a transverse bar, but variable in shape, often better defined in males. Area of spinners usually surrounded by a narrow darkish ring. STERNUM : Uniform light brown. CHELICERÆ : ♂. Text-fig. 51, C. These grow allometrically (G. H. Locket, 1932). LEGS : Uniform light yellow. MT I/tI=2·8, Tm I=0·40. EPIGYNE : Text-fig. 51, A. The epigynal orifice extends to about the edges of the seminal sacs ; the finger-like appearance of the ducts at the sides is characteristic, and the chitinized ring is thinner, relatively, than in *T. bellicosum*. MALE PALP : Text-fig. 51, E, F.

OCCURRENCE : A rather rare species. Found usually in marshes in southern counties, but extending as far north as Cumberland. Considerable numbers have sometimes been found together, on nettle and other low plants. Males adult in the second week in May ; both sexes have also been taken in October.

Theridion bellicosum Simon.
(Text-figs. 51, B, D, G, H)

Theridion bellicosum E. Simon, 1873, p. 106 ; A. R. Jackson, 1914, p. 123, Pl. II, figs. 9, 11, 7. *T. instabile bellicosum* E. Simon, 1914, p. 256. *T. bellicosum* H. Wiehle, 1937, p. 144. (Jackson (loc. cit., p. 124) considered that *T. lepidum* of Chyzer and Kulczynski (1891-7, II, p. 32) and of de Lessert (1910, p. 98) was referable to this species.)

DESCRIPTION. LENGTH : ♀ : 1·5–2 mm. ♂ : about 1·75 mm. CARAPACE : Usually yellow-brown, sometimes greyish olive with radiating lighter streaks. In some specimens there is a darker quadrilateral or triangle having its base at the thoracic juncture, the apex forwards. (This area does not reach the eyes.) ABDOMEN : Brown, variable in depth, usually light. Pattern, if present, usually consists of 2–3 pairs of sooty blotches. Sometimes the anterior pair extend, tapering, down and round the sides. Ventrally : Light yellow-brown, often with a sooty blotch or transverse bar. STERNUM : Yellow-brown, often suffused with darker brown or sooty colouration, especially round the edges. CHELICERÆ : ♂ : Text-fig. 51, D. These again show allometric growth. In large specimens three teeth occur, arranged as shown in the figure ; the middle tooth may be absent on small specimens. LEGS : Clear yellow-brown. MT I/tI : 2·1, Tm I : 0·39. EPIGYNE : Text-fig. 51, B. The outside edges of the epigynal orifice are well within the edges of the seminal sacs. The course of the ducts at the sides is different from those of *T. instabile*, as also the thickness of the chitinized ring. MALE PALP : Text-fig. 51, G, H.

OCCURRENCE : Rare. Among stones on the sides of mountains ; in Wales, the north of England and in Scotland.

GROUP VIII.

Theridion bimaculatum (Linnaeus).
(Text-fig. 52)

Aranea bimaculata C. Linnaeus, 1767, p. 1033. *A. carolina* C. A. Walckenaer, 1802, p. 208. *Theridion carolinum* J. Blackwall, 1861–4, p. 192. *T. bimaculatum* O. P.-Cambridge, 1879–81, p. 91 ; C. Chyzer and L. Kulczynski, 1891–7, II, p. 32 ; E. Simon, 1914, p. 252 ; H. Wiehle, 1937, p. 149.

DESCRIPTION. LENGTH : ♀ : 2·5–3·25 mm. ♂ : 2·5–3 mm. CARAPACE : Often uniform rather light brown, sometimes with faint radiating streaks. Sometimes with darkening of the cephalic area, but not quite

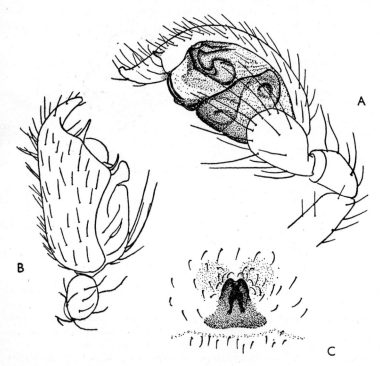

TEXT-FIG. 52.—*Theridion bimaculatum:* A, male palp ; B, right palp (from above and outside) ; C, epigyne.

as far as the eyes ; this darkening may be extended backwards forming a median band, constricted in the middle and flanked, at this point, by two lighter areas. ABDOMEN : ♀ : globular ; reddish brown and shiny, with a cream, longitudinal, tapering, median stripe, variable in width, sometimes occupying almost the whole dorsal area. ♂ : cylindrical ; colouration similar, but light median stripe represented by a few very small white spots. STERNUM : Usually uniform brown, as carapace, but sometimes with a lighter central region, which may occupy more than half the area. LEGS: Uniform light yellow. MT I/tI : 2·9. Tm I : 0·39. EPIGYNE : Text-fig. 52, C. MALE PALP : Text-fig. 52, A, B. There is a characteristic tooth and an apophysis on the cymbium ; the tarsus is larger, relatively, than in most species, and dark. The spider holds the palps out in front of it in a characteristic manner while running. The female carries her cocoon under her body.

OCCURRENCE : Common in grass and low herbage. Distributed throughout the British Isles. Adult in May, June and July ; females are found mature in October.

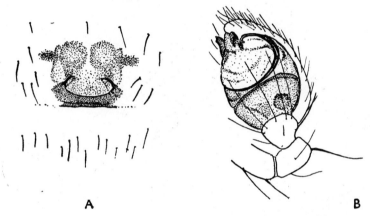

TEXT-FIG. 53.—*Theridion pallens:* A, epigyne ; B, male palp.

GROUP IX.

Theridion pallens Blackwall.
(Text-fig. 53)

Theridion pallens J. Blackwall, 1834, p. 357 and 1861–4, p. 194 ; O. P.-Cambridge, 1879–81, p. 92, and recent authors.

DESCRIPTION. LENGTH : ♀ : about 1·75 mm. ♂ : 1·25–1·5 mm. CARAPACE : ♀ : Yellowish white to light brown. ♂ : Similar ground colour, but cephalic area dark brown (including ocular area) with, sometimes, a light region in centre of this. ABDOMEN : ♀ : Globular, almost spherical. Colouration variable. Markings often faint or absent, but there is sometimes a darkening of the anterior dorsal surface with a yellow, or white, transverse band, or sometimes a cross, in the middle. Ventrally : Uniform brown, light yellow or white. ♂ : Part or whole of dorsal surface black or deep brown, often mottled with cream and lighter brown. Ventrally : usually more or less suffused with sooty grey colour. STERNUM : Heart-shaped ; rounded behind, coxæ IV being widely separated (by about two diameters). LEGS : ♀ : coloured, uniformly, as carapace. MT I/tI : 1·6. ♂ : femora and tarsi similar, but tibiæ and metatarsi darkened with sooty grey (becoming brown on preservation) ; femora with occasional blotches of similar colour. EPIGYNE : Text-fig. 53, A. MALE PALP : Text-fig. 53, B.

OCCURRENCE : This little spider is common and can be obtained, often in abundance, by beating trees, especially evergreens ; but it is also found amongst low plants and even fallen leaves. Distributed all over the British Isles. Males are mature in April and May. Females are found throughout the summer and into September.

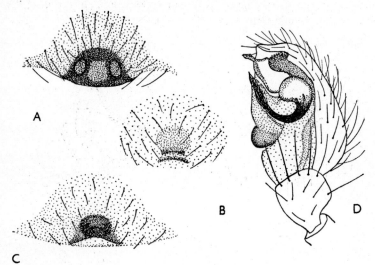

TEXT-FIG. 54.—Epigynes : A, *Enoplognatha thoracica;* B, *E. schaufussi;* C, *E. mandibularis.* D, male palp of *E. thoracica.*

10. Genus **ENOPLOGNATHA** Pavesi 1880.

CHARACTERS OF GENUS. EYES : Fairly small, with median ocular trapezium narrower in front than behind ; anterior medians smaller than or equal to posterior medians. ABDOMEN : Often with a folium (not so in our commonest species, *E. thoracica*). STERNUM : Prolonged narrowly between coxæ IV. CHELICERÆ : Large and divergent in ♂, with large and conspicuous teeth. Less developed in ♀, but with one tooth on inner margin. LEGS : Tm I=about 0·6–0·67. MT I/tI= 1·6–2·2. (These last values are considerably lower than those for *Theridion*, considering the sizes of the species.) Tibia I with two long fine spines dorsally ; tibiæ II to IV with one or two long spines dorsally. Tarsal claws large with numerous large teeth, clearly visible. ♀ palpal claw pectinate.

The males can be distinguished readily by the palpal organs and the cheliceral teeth. The females can be separated by the abdominal patterns, the proportions of the legs, and, less readily, by the epigynes.

There are three British species.

Enoplognatha thoracica (Hahn).
(Text-fig. 54, A, D)

Theridion thoracicum C. W. Hahn, 1831, p. 88. *Neriene albipunctata* O. P.-Cambridge, 1879–81, p. 122. *Neriene hispida* id., *ibid*, p. 137. *Enoplognatha thoracica* C. Chyzer and L. Kulczynski, 1891–7, II, p. 45 ; E. Simon, 1914, p. 284 ; H. Wiehle, 1937, p. 205.

DESCRIPTION. LENGTH : ♀ : 3·5–4 mm. ♂ : 2·5–3 mm. CARAPACE : Yellow-brown. ABDOMEN : Black, with no pattern. STERNUM : Yellow-brown, reticulated with black ; pointed posteriorly. CHELICERÆ : ♂ : considerably developed, with large teeth. Front and sides with numerous little warts, particularly near the base. Fang with a small tooth. LEGS : Yellow-brown. Tm I = 0·58. All tibiæ with two long fine spines dorsally. MT I/tI about 1·6. Legs fairly stout,

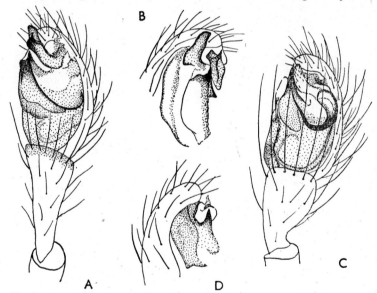

TEXT-FIG. 55.—Male palps : A, *Enoplognatha schaufussi;* B, ditto (at tip from inside) ; C, *E. mandibularis;* D, ditto (at tip from inside).

with MT I : l/d about 7·5 (♀). ♂ : Tibia and metatarsus I with, ventrally, two rows of small warts, each bearing a bristle. EPIGYNE : Text-fig. 54, A. MALE PALP : Text-fig. 54, D.

OCCURRENCE : Fairly common ; in grass, under stones, etc. Distributed all over the British Isles. Adult in summer.

Enoplognatha schaufussi (L. Koch).
(Text-figs. 54, B ; 55, A, B ; 56, A, C)

Meta schaufussi L. Koch, 1882, p. 628. *Enoplognatha maritima* E. Simon, 1884, V, p. 189 ; C. Chyzer and L. Kulczynski, 1891–7, II, p. 43. *E. caricis* O. P.-Cambridge, 1889, p. 114. *E. mandibularis* idem, 1907, p. 126. *E. maritima* E. Simon, 1914, p. 284 ; A. R. Jackson, 1924, p. 112 ; H. Wiehle, 1937, p. 207.

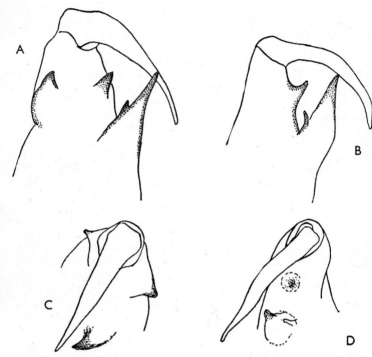

TEXT-FIG. 56.—Male chelicera, posterior (inner) side : A, *Enoplognatha schaufussi;*
B, *E. mandibularis nigrocincta.*
Male chelicera, seen from inside, looking at apex : C, *E. schaufussi;* D, *E.
mandibularis nigrocincta.*

DESCRIPTION. LENGTH : ♀: 3·5–4·5 mm. ♂: about 3–3·5 mm.
CARAPACE : Yellow to yellow-brown. ABDOMEN : ♀: dorsally greyish-
yellow, with numerous shining white blotches ; the folium is outlined
in black and has a central black longitudinal line. (The folium rather
resembles that of *Zygiella*, Text-fig. 108, A.) Ventrally : black, with
two white lines running back from epigastric furrow. ♂: similar, but
with rather more white and black. STERNUM : Yellow-brown, with
black margins and suffused with some black ; pointed posteriorly.
CHELICERÆ : ♂ : with very large teeth ; distinguished from *E. mandibularis* when viewed from below (Text-fig. 56). Fang without a tooth.
LEGS : Yellow-brown. Tm I=0.67. Tibia I with two long fine spines
dorsally ; tibiæ II to IV with only one spine dorsally. Legs much
thinner than in *E. thoracica* or *E. mandibularis*, with MT I : l/d (at
mid point) about 15 (♀).   MT I/tI=about 2·1—2·2. EPIGYNE :
Text-fig. 54, B. Rather indefinite, not distinguishable with much
certainty from that of *E. mandibularis*. MALE PALP : Text-fig. 55, A.
Distinguished from that of *E. mandibularis* by the palpal organs viewed
from inside at the tip (Text-fig. 55, B).

Occurrence : In sandy localities, under stones, in grass, etc. Rare ; in Hampshire, Dorsetshire and Staffordshire. Adult from May to July.

Enoplognatha mandibularis (Lucas).
(Text-figs. 54, C ; 55, C, D ; 56, B, D)

Theridion mandibulare H. Lucas, 1840, p. 266. *E. mandibularis* E. Simon, 1914, p. 286 ; A. R. Jackson, 1924, p. 112. *E. mandibularis* W. Falconer, 1919, p. 296.

DESCRIPTION. LENGTH : ♀ : 3–3·5 mm. ♂ : 2·5–3 mm. CARAPACE : Brown to dusky yellow-brown, blackish at margins, and with faint dark striæ. ABDOMEN : ♀ : dorsally greyish, with numerous white blotches and an obscure folium. On either side is a row of large black blotches. Centrally there is a broken black stripe, followed by obscure black chevrons posteriorly. Ventrally : a large speckled white blotch (sometimes obscure) fills the area between epigastric fold and spinners. ♂ : Dorsally white, with a central irregular black band and black edges. Ventrally : a pale area with white blotches fills the area between epigastric fold and spinners. STERNUM : Dark brown, pointed posteriorly. CHELICERÆ : ♂ : with very large teeth, readily distinguished from *E. schaufussi* when viewed from below (Text-fig. 56). LEGS : Yellow-brown to brown, often dusky and suffused with black. Tm I = 0·58–0·62. Tibial spines like *E. schaufussi*. MT I : l/d (at mid point) about 8–10 (♀♂) (cf. *E. schaufussi*). MT I/t I about 1·7 (♀♂). EPIGYNE : Text-fig. 54, C not readily distinguishable from that of *E. schaufussi*. MALE PALP : Text-fig. 55, C. Distinguished from that of *E. schaufussi* by the palpal organs viewed from inside at the tip (Text-fig. 55, D).

The female is distinguishable from *E. schaufussi* by the position of the trichobothrium on MT I, by the proportions of the metatarsi and tarsi, and by the abdominal pattern. The male is distinguished by the palpal organs, the cheliceræ and proportions of metatarsi to tarsi.

Occurrence : In dry sandy places, under stones and in grass, etc., in a few of the more southern counties : rare. Adult from May to July. (The specimens of *E. mandibularis* (Lucas) taken in Britain seem to belong to the small form *nigrocincta* Simon (1884, p. 193).)

11. Genus **ROBERTUS** O. P.-Cambridge 1879.

CHARACTERS OF GENUS. EYES : Width of posterior median pair greater than width of anterior median pair. ABDOMEN : Unicolorous, grey to black, with usually four reddish impressed dots visible dorsally. Stridulating organ not much developed in males. STERNUM : Pointed posteriorly, but not projecting between coxæ IV, which are close together. (Text-fig. 27, A). CHELICERÆ : Stout, similar in both sexes ; toothed on inner margin. LEGS : Tm I about 0·5, slightly more or less. Tibiæ each with one fine dorsal spine. Legs fairly stout, with tibia I : l/d about 4–5. Ratio MT I/t I varies from about 1·5 in *R. lividus* to about 1·0 in *R. neglectus* and *R. scoticus*. Tarsal claws with numerous large teeth.

The females are separated very readily by the epigynes. The males are divisible into two groups by the palpal organs :

 (*a*) Palpal organs with projecting apophyses (Text-fig. 58, B, D)
  R. neglectus, R. scoticus, R. insignis

 (*b*) Palpal organs without projecting apophyses. (Text-fig. 58, A, C)
  R. lividus, R. arundineti.

Horse shoe Pass

Robertus lividus (Blackwall).
(Text-figs. 57, A ; 58, A)

Neriene livida J. Blackwall, 1836, p. 486, and 1861–4, p. 252 ; O. P.-Cambridge, 1879–81, p. 122. *Pedanostethus lividus* C. Chyzer and L. Kulczynski, 1891–7, II, p. 48. *Robertus lividus* E. Simon, 1914, p. 288 ; H. Wiehle, 1937, p. 212.

DESCRIPTION. LENGTH : ♀♂ : 2·5–4 mm. CARAPACE : Brown, shiny. EYES : Anterior medians slightly less than one diameter

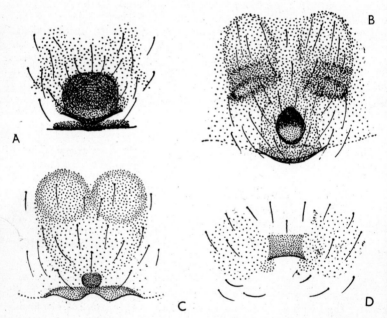

TEXT-FIG. 57.—Epigynes : A, *Robertus lividus;* B, *R. arundineti;* C, *R. scoticus;* D, *R. neglectus.*

apart and one diameter from laterals. Posteriors all about 1·25–1·5 diameters apart. Anterior medians about one diameter from corresponding posterior medians. ABDOMEN : Grey to black with four faint reddish impressed dots. STERNUM : Brown, pointed posteriorly. LEGS : Orange to brown, with tarsi usually somewhat darker. Furnished with numerous long stout hairs, with one fine dorsal spine on each tibia. MT I/t I and MT IV/t IV about 1·45–1·5. Tm I=0·54. EPIGYNE : Text-fig. 57, A. MALE PALP : Text-fig. 58, A.

This species is rather similar to *R. arundineti*, from which it is distinguished by its larger size, its genitalia (most clearly in the female), the eyes and the proportions of the metatarsi and tarsi.

OCCURRENCE : Common, but perhaps even more frequent in the north than in the south. In detritus, moss, grass, etc., particularly in woods. Distributed all over the British Isles. Adult at all seasons.

Robertus arundineti (O. P.-Cambridge).
(Text-figs. 57, B ; 58, C)

Neriene arundineti O. P.-Cambridge 1871, p. 441 (♀); idem. 1879–81, p. 135. *N. clarkii* idem. 1871, p. 441 (♂); idem. 1879–81, p. 119. *Pedanostethus clarkii* C. Chyzer and L. Kulczynski, 1891–7, II, p. 47 ; W. Bösenberg, 1902, p. 138. *Robertus arundineti* E. Simon, 1914, p. 287 ; H. Wiehle, 1937, p. 214.

DESCRIPTION. LENGTH : ♀: about 2·5 mm. ♂ : 2–2·25 mm. CARAPACE : Yellow-brown to brown. EYES : Anteriors as in *R. lividus* ; posteriors one diameter (or scarcely more) apart. Anterior medians rather less than one diameter from corresponding posterior medians. ABDOMEN : As *R. lividus*. STERNUM : Brown, reticulated with black, and with a narrow black margin. LEGS : Yellow-brown, with tarsi slightly darker. With numerous hairs, rather finer than in *R. lividus*, and with one fine dorsal spine on each tibia. Coxæ IV close together. MT I/tI and MT IV/t IV about 1·25. Tm I=0·54. EPIGYNE : Text-fig. 57, B. MALE PALP : Text-fig. 58, C. Rather similar to *R. lividus* (q.v.).

OCCURRENCE : In undergrowth of woods, amongst heather and grass on open moors and mountain sides. Rare, but widespread over the British Isles.

Robertus neglectus (O. P.-Cambridge).
(Text-figs. 57, D ; 58, B)

Neriene neglecta O. P.-Cambridge, 1871, p. 443 ; idem, 1879–81, p. 121. *Neriene aspera* idem, 1879–81, p. 136. *Robertus astutus* idem, p. 103. *Pedanostethus neglectus* C. Chyzer and L. Kulczynski, 1891–7, II, p. 47. *Robertus neglectus* O. P.-Cambridge, 1905, p. 46 ; E. Simon, 1914, p. 287 ; H. Wiehle, 1937, p. 215.

DESCRIPTION. LENGTH : ♀ : 2–2·25 mm. ♂ : about 1·75 mm. CARAPACE : Brown to orange-brown. EYES : Anterior medians about 1·5 diameters apart and one diameter from laterals ; posteriors 1–1·5 diameters apart. Anterior medians more than one diameter from posterior medians. ABDOMEN : As *R. lividus*. STERNUM : Brown, sometimes reticulated with black, and with a fine black margin. LEGS : Yellow-brown, with numerous fine hairs. One fine dorsal spine (not greatly differentiated from a hair) on each tibia. MT I/t I : 1–1.1 ; MT IV/t IV : 1–1·2. Tm I slightly less than 0·5. EPIGYNE : Text-fig. 57, D. MALE PALP : Text-fig. 58, B ; a prominent process projects from the palpal organs.

OCCURRENCE : Rare. Recorded chiefly from the north of England and from Wales, Scotland and Eire.

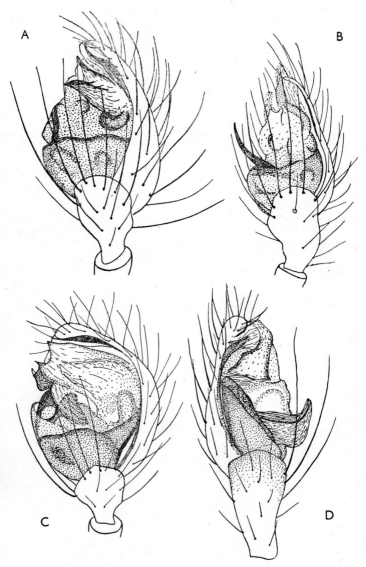

TEXT-FIG. 58.—Male palps : A, *Robertus lividus;* B, *R. neglectus;* C, *R. arundineti;* D, *R. insignis* (right palp).

Robertus scoticus Jackson.
(Text-fig. 57, C)

Robertus scoticus A. R. Jackson, 1914, p. 120 (♀); E. Schenkel, 1923, pp. 84–86 (♂); A. R. Jackson 1924, p. 11; H. Wiehle, 1937, p. 217. *Robertus monticola* E. Simon, 1914, p. 287.

DESCRIPTION. LENGTH : ♀ : 2 mm. (No male was available, this sex not having yet been taken in Britain.) CARAPACE : Brown, with darker striæ. EYES : Anteriors about 0.5 diameter apart ; posteriors less than one diameter apart. ABDOMEN : As *R. lividus*. STERNUM : Yellow-brown, with blackish margins. LEGS : Brown, rather short, with numerous hairs. Tibial spines apparently as *R. lividus*, but specimen not in very good condition. MT I/t I about 1·0 ; MT IV/t IV about 1·1. Tm I slightly less than 0·5. EPIGYNE : Text-fig. 57, C.

OCCURRENCE : One female specimen taken by Dr. A. R. Jackson (1913) in moss at Rannoch (Perthshire).

Robertus insignis O. P.-Cambridge.
(Text-fig. 58, D)

Robertus insignis O. P.-Cambridge, 1907, p. 138.

DESCRIPTION. LENGTH : ♂ : 2·5 mm. (The female is unknown). CARAPACE : Orange brown, with slightly darker striæ. EYES : Anteriors about half a diameter apart ; posterior medians about one diameter apart and more than one diameter from laterals. ABDOMEN : As *R. lividus*. STERNUM : Orange-brown. LEGS : Brown. Most of leg segments missing in the unique specimen. MALE PALP : Text-fig. 58, D.

OCCURRENCE : A single male, taken at Norwich, is the only example known.

12. Genus **PHOLCOMMA** T. Thorell 1869–70.

CHARACTERS OF GENUS. EYES : Rather like *Pholcus* (Text-fig. 59, A). ABDOMEN : Very globular. ♂ : with scutum in the form of a ring circling the abdomen. STERNUM : Very broad posteriorly. LEGS : Short. All tibiæ with two fine dorsal spines. Tm I : 0·2–0·25.

Pholcomma gibbum (Westring). *Horse shoe Pass.*
(Text-fig. 59)

Erigone gibba N. Westring, 1851, p. 44 and 1861, p. 279. *Pholcomma gibbum* O. P.-Cambridge, 1879–81, p. 82 ; C. Chyzer and L. Kulczynski, 1891–7, II, p. 49 ; E. Simon, 1914, p. 289 ; H. Wiehle, 1937, p. 218.

DESCRIPTION. LENGTH : ♂ ♀ : 1·25–1·5 mm. This spider has a very squat appearance, with a globular abdomen and short legs. CARAPACE : Yellow-brown to reddish brown ; broad. EYES : Text-fig. 59, A. ABDOMEN : Brown ; with scutum in male (Text-fig. 59, C). ♀ : with four reddish impressed dots. STERNUM : Yellow to brown, with narrow black margin ; reticulated. Very broad posteriorly. LEGS : Yellow-brown to orange. All tibiæ with two fine dorsal spines.

G

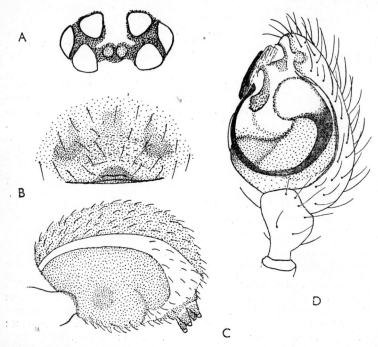

TEXT-FIG. 59.—*Pholcomma gibbum:* A, eyes (♀), seen from in front ; B, epigyne ; C, abdomen (♂), showing scutum ; D, male palp.

MT I/t I about 1·25 ; Tm I=0·2–0·25.   Serrated bristles on tarsus IV very indistinct. EPIGYNE : Text-fig. 59, B ; indistinct. MALE PALP : Text-fig. 59, D.

OCCURRENCE : In detritus, in the open and under trees (especially conifers), on heaths, sandhills, marshes, etc. Fairly common, and distributed all over the British Isles. Adults in autumn to spring.

13. Genus **THEONOË** E. Simon 1881.

CHARACTERS OF GENUS. EYES : Arranged rather like *Pholcomma* (Text-fig. 60, A). Median ocular trapezium much wider behind than in front. STERNUM : Very broad between coxæ IV. LEGS : Tm I about 0.33. Tarsi longer than metatarsi. Tibiæ spineless. The male has stridulating organs. The only species is very small.

Theonoë minutissima (O. P.-Cambridge).
(Text-fig. 60)

Walckenaera minutissima O. P.-Cambridge, 1879, p. 203 ; idem, 1879–81, p. 500. *Theonoë minutissima* G. H. Carpenter 1898, p. 160 ; E. Simon, 1926, p. 311 ; H. Wiehle, 1937, p. 219. *Onesinda minutissima* O. P.-Cambridge, 1895, p. 104.

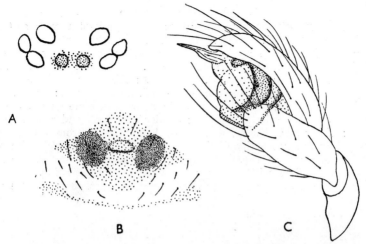

TEXT-FIG. 60.—*Theonoë minutissima* : A, eyes, seen from in front ; B, epigyne ; C, male palp.

DESCRIPTION. LENGTH : ♂♀ : 1–1·25 mm. CARAPACE : Yellow-brown to brown. EYES : Somewhat like *Pholcus* in arrangement, with anterior medians slightly smaller than the rest (Text-fig. 60, A). Median ocular trapezium much narrower in front than behind. Posterior median eyes about two diameters apart. ABDOMEN : Grey to black, rather globular ; four large impressed dots sometimes visible dorsally. STERNUM : Brown, with narrow blackish margins. Broader than long, very broad between coxæ IV. With numerous minute pits over the surface, each bearing a bristle. LEGS : Yellow-brown to brown. Tibiæ spineless. Tarsi longer than metatarsi, with e.g. t I/MT I about 1·3. Tm I 0·3–0·35 ; Tm IV absent. FEMALE PALP : Claw on tarsus not pectinate. EPIGYNE : Text-fig. 60, B. MALE PALP : Text-fig. 60, C.

OCCURRENCE : In vegetable debris, under stones ; in lowlands and on mountain tops. Widespread over the British Isles, but rare.

21. Family NESTICIDÆ.

CHARACTERS OF FAMILY. CLYPEUS : Wide (at least as wide as the median ocular area). EYES : Anterior medians darker and smaller than the rest, which are nearly equal in size. Anterior row very slightly procurved (as seen from in front). Posterior row procurved, the eyes nearly equally spaced. STERNUM : About as broad as long, projecting somewhat between coxæ IV. CHELICERÆ : Vertical, moderately strong, with three teeth in outer row, none on the inner (in the British species). LABIUM : Wider than long and rebordered. LEGS : Long and slender, with many long bristles (from which the few spines are not easily distinguished). Those on ventral sides of tarsi stronger than those on dorsal sides, especially on IV (as in THERIDIIDÆ, but without clear serrations). Tarsal claws, three ; the paired ones long and toothed, the median short. FEMALE PALP : With a long claw. MALE PALP : With a large paracymbium (Text-fig. 61, A).

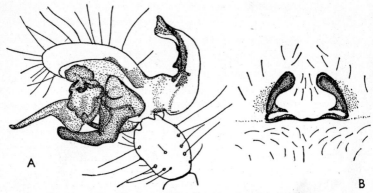

TEXT-FIG. 61.—*Nesticus cellulanus:*   A, male palp ;   B, epigyne.

Genus **NESTICUS** T. Thorell 1869.

There is one British representative of the Genus.

Nesticus cellulanus (Clerck).
(=*N. cellulanus* (Olivier))
(Text-fig. 61)

Araneus cellulanus C. Clerck, 1757, p. 62.   *Aranea cellulana* A. G. Olivier, 1789, p. 211.   *Linyphia crypticolens* C. A. Walckenaer, 1802, p. 207 ; J. Blackwall, 1861–4, p. 224.   *Nesticus cellulanus* O. P.-Cambridge, 1879–81, p. 93 and recent authors.

DESCRIPTION. LENGTH : ♀ : 3·5–6 mm. ♂ : 3–5 mm. CARAPACE : Light brownish yellow, with a thin dark borderline and a dark median band which extends to the ocular area (and in some specimens across the clypeus) ; it narrows immediately behind the eyes, then expands and narrows again to form a V at the junction of thoracic and cephalic areas, and expands once more towards the posterior margin. ABDOMEN : Almost globular. A clear light brown-yellow median band (sometimes broken) is flanked by sooty grey paired patches which vary greatly in shape and disposition, sometimes forming angular bars or loops or sometimes ovals which enclose areas of lighter colour. Ventrally : variable. A pair of dark bars often converge from the anterior half of the sides towards the spinners, but stop short before reaching them. Sometimes the area is clear of markings. STERNUM : Uniform light yellow-brown. LEGS : Coloured as carapace, generally with dusky annulations, but sometimes having none. EPIGYNE : Text-fig. 61, B. The parts are somewhat variable in shape and depth of colouring, but there is usually little difficulty in identifying it. MALE PALP : Text-fig. 61, A. This, with its large paracymbium, is very distinct.

OCCURRENCE : Distributed throughout the British Isles, but confined to damp and dark localities, such as cellars, crevices under stones in woods and wet places. Often many are found together. It is probable that mating occurs out of doors in August and September ; adults are found at varying seasons (e.g. April, August, September) indoors.

22. Family TETRAGNATHIDÆ.

CHARACTERS OF FAMILY. CARAPACE : Text-figs. 66, B ; 71. EYES : Text-figs. 62, A ; 72, A. ABDOMEN : Oval in *Pachygnatha* (Text-fig. 71) ; more or less elongated and tapering in *Tetragnatha* and *Eugnatha* (Text-fig. 63). CHELICERÆ : Text-figs. 64, 68, 72, A ; with strong teeth ; longer and specially developed in males for locking those of the female during copulation. (See W. S. Bristowe 1941, pp. 495, 496). LABIUM : Text-figs. 62, C ; 72, C. Distinctly rebordered. LEGS : Greatly elongated in *Tetragnatha* and *Eugnatha* (Text-fig. 63). Femora with a series of trichobothria on dorsal side near the base (apart from any others which may occur on the segment) : Text-fig. 62, B ; 72, D. Auxiliary foot-claws (cf. Text-fig. 74, D) present in orb weavers *Tetragnatha* and *Eugnatha*, not in *Pachygnatha*. EPIGYNE : Strictly speaking there is no epigyne. The epigastric fold is strongly procurved (Text-figs. 67 ; 73, D, E) and the genital orifice occurs at the posterior margin, well behind the branchial opercula. MALE PALP : Simple (e.g. Text-figs. 69, A ; 73, A) ; paracymbium, originating from base of tarsus, distinct and hairy (Text-fig. 73, A, B, C).

Three genera are represented in Britain. The species of *Tetragnatha* and *Eugnatha* are long-legged orb weavers. Those of *Pachygnatha* are of more normal proportions ; they are found near or on the ground among vegetation and do not spin webs when adult.

1. Genus **TETRAGNATHA** P. A. Latreille 1804.

CHARACTERS OF GENUS. EYES : Text-fig. 62, A. ABDOMEN : Long and narrow ; somewhat humped up anteriorly in *T. obtusa* and in

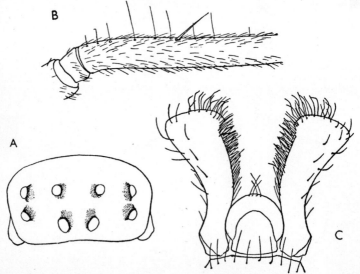

TEXT-FIG. 62.—*Tetragnatha:* A, eyes (seen from in front) ; B, femur, showing trichobothria ; C, maxillæ and labium.

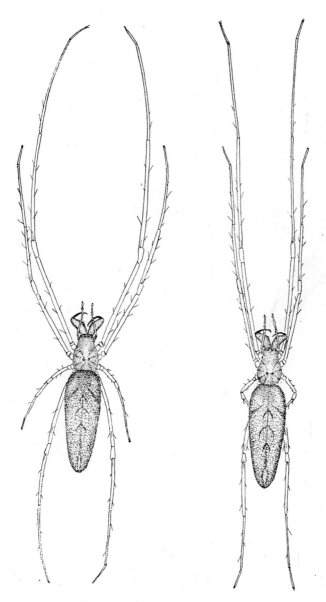

Text-fig. 63.—*Tetragnatha extensa.* ♀

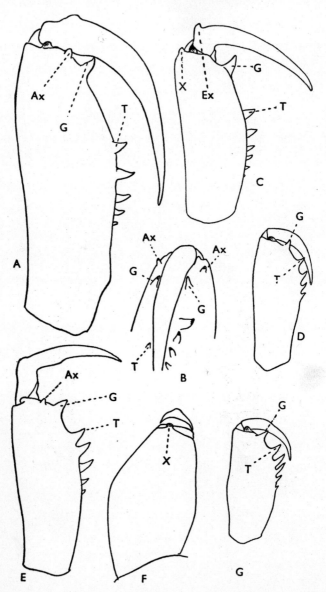

TEXT-FIG. 64.—*Tetragnatha*. Females. Left cheliceræ: A, B, *Tetragnatha extensa*; C, *T. montana*; D, *T. pinicola*; E, *T. nigrita*; F, *T. montana*, right chelicera from side; G, *T. obtusa*.

gravid females of other species. STERNUM : Shaped as in Text-fig. 66, A.
CHELICERÆ : Long and divergent with two rows of teeth (see descriptions of species). Narrower and usually longer in males, and with an
apophysis (Text-fig. 68 " a ") used in locking the female's fang during
copulation (see W. S. Bristowe, 1941, p. 496, fig. 94). MAXILLÆ and
LABIUM : Text-fig. 62, C. LEGS : Long, as in Text-fig. 63, bearing
long spines. Tarsi with auxiliary tarsal claws (as in ARGIOPIDÆ,
Text-fig. 74, D). EPIGYNE AND MALE PALP : Simple in structure (see
descriptions of species). Spinners of orb webs.

There are five British species : *Tetragnatha extensa* (L.), *T. pinicola*
L. K., *T. montana* Sim., *T. obtusa* C. L. K., and *T. nigrita* Lendl.
The genitalia of the species are all very similar ; identification must
therefore be supported by other characters. Parts of the colouring
and pattern are of some assistance, but a consideration of the teeth,
and other prominences, on the cheliceræ is the most reliable method

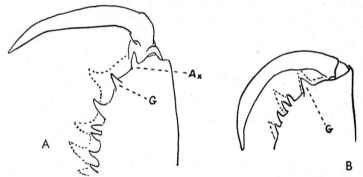

TEXT-FIG. 65.—Female left cheliceræ ; posterior (inner) side : A, *Tetragnatha
nigrita;* B, *T. obtusa.*

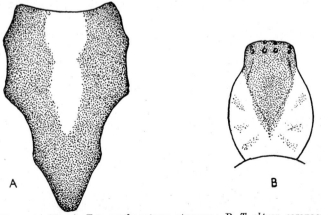

TEXT-FIG. 66.—A, *Tetragnatha extensa,* sternum ; B, *T. obtusa,* carapace.

of procedure in almost every case. (It is, however, applicable only to *adult* specimens.)

Colouration of the abdomen is determined very largely by the arrangement of many light silvery areas separated by narrow dark lines, which are seen as reticulations under the microscope. If the separating lines are wide, a darker appearance will result, and considerable variation may occur in a single species. Thus we do not consider colouration of the abdomen by itself to be reliable.

H. Wiehle (1939) has made a very careful study of the German species (which are also ours) and has reviewed critically the use made by previous authors of various characters for identification. His own method, based primarily on the cheliceral armature, has been found by us to be generally reliable and convenient and we have followed it closely. (A. Tullgren (1947) in criticising Wiehle's work, has pointed out that Wiehle appears to have figured a small specimen of *T. extensa* ♂ for *T. pinicola* ♂, and *T. dearmata* Thor.♂ instead of *T. obtusa* ♂, and, judging from the drawings by the two authors, and from actual specimens, this would certainly seem to be the case.)

Wiehle points out that the most apical of the main teeth are somewhat different from the rest and act as guides for bringing the fang to rest,

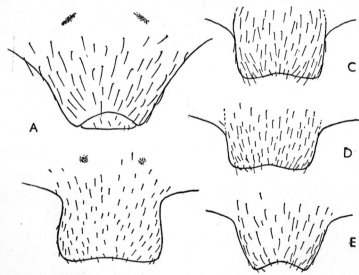

TEXT-FIG. 67.—Epigynal folds: A, *Tetragnatha extensa*; B, *T. montana*; C, *T. nigrita*; D, *T. obtusa*; E, *T. pinicola*.

when it folds into the cheliceral groove between the two rows of teeth. We shall refer to the teeth, apophyses and other prominences as follows in all our figures :

Male and Female. G=the guide teeth.

Ax=the " auxiliary " guide teeth, present in some species. (These are sometimes difficult to make out when the chelicera is viewed from in front, but if it is looked at from the inside (Text-fig. 64, B) or straight down onto the apex, then the teeth are seen clearly enough).

T=the first (largest) tooth of the row proper.

Males.

a=an apophysis, used for locking the female's fang during copulation.

Sl=a tooth which usually slopes towards the base of the segment.

t=a small tooth or prominence, found in some species.

Females.

Ex=an excrescence found on the outer edge of the fang, near its base, in some species.

Except where stated otherwise, attention will be confined to the armature as seen when the cheliceræ are viewed from in front, with the whole length of the segment lying in the plane of focus of the microscope. Thus only the outer row of teeth will be considered as a rule.

The following tables summarise the points to be looked for and have been found reliable. (The marking on the sternum in *T. extensa* and *T. pinicola* persists after long preservation in spirit and we have no hesitation in following Wiehle and others in making use of it.) It should be noted that the number of teeth present in either row is *not* a reliable character and may vary for a single species.

FEMALES

	Median light patch on sternum	Auxiliary guides to fang (Ax)	Excrescence on fang (Ex)	Other distinguishing characters
T. extensa	Present	Present	Absent (except in largest specimens)	
T. pinicola	Present	Absent	Absent	Dorsal side of abdomen silvery white.
T. montana	Absent	Absent	Present	A blunt excrescence, X, on apical edge of outside of basal segment of chelicera (Text-fig. 64, C, F).
T. obtusa	Absent	Absent	Absent	Cephalic region of carapace darker than thoracic (Text-fig. 66, B).
T. nigrita	Absent	†Present	‡Present	Carapace pattern sometimes nearly that of *T. obtusa*, sometimes absent.

†In some specimens (Ax) is very small on the outer margin of the fang groove and is then difficult to see; but on the inner margin it is prominent, and it here constitutes probably the most reliable feature for distinguishing this species from *T. obtusa* (Text-fig. 65).

‡Not as pronounced as in *T. montana*, and sometimes reduced so as to be scarcely visible.

MALES

	Median light patch on sternum	Auxiliary fang guide (Ax.)	Tooth (t) between apophysis (a) and slanting tooth (Sl.)	Other distinguishing characters.
T. extensa	Present	Present	Absent	Distinguished by the tip of conductor of embolus, Text-fig. 69, B, C.
T. pinicola	Present	Present	Absent	
T. montana	Absent	Absent	Present (blunt)	
T. obtusa	Absent	Absent	†Absent	Cephalic region of carapace darker than thoracic (as ♀).
T. nigrita	Absent	Absent	Present (pointed)	Carapace markings may be like *T. obtusa*. Blunt protuberance Y, on inner cheliceral margin.‡

†The tooth (Sl) (Text-fig. 68, D) which in this species is not sloping, should not be mistaken for this.

‡This obscures view of first two teeth of inner row, and is not present in other species. It must be viewed in profile, otherwise it sometimes becomes nearly invisible.

EPIGYNES. The TETRAGNATHIDÆ are usually said to possess no epigyne, and this is true in the sense in which the term epigyne is used in this book. Nevertheless there is some specialisation of the integument in this region in adult specimens, covering to some extent the epigastric fold, which is procurved. The shapes of the posterior margins of these specialised areas differ from one species to another and provide additional checks to identification. We shall refer to them as the " epignal folds ". MALE PALPS : These are simple in structure and all rather similar. The form of the conductor of the style is often the most useful part to examine.

Tetragnatha extensa (Linnaeus).
(Text-figs. 64, A, B ; 66, A ; 67, A ; 68, A ; 69, B)

Aranea extensa C. Linnaeus, 1785, p. 621. *Tetragnatha extensa* E. Simon, 1874, p. 155, and 1929, pp. 648, 651 ; C. Chyzer and L. Kulczynski, 1891–7, I, p. 144 ; H. Wiehle, 1939, p. 376 ; A. Tullgren, 1947, p. 130.

DESCRIPTION. LENGTH : ♀ : 8–11 mm. ♂ : 6–9 mm. (The range of size may well be greater than this.) CARAPACE : Light brown or yellowish brown, sometimes with slightly darker radiations from foveal area. ABDOMEN : Colouration usually light whitish green with a metallic sheen. A slightly darker region running longitudinally constitutes something of the nature of a folium, whose edges are nearly straight. Ventrally : a narrow dark band runs from epigastric fold to spinners, being flanked by a pair of narrow silvery bands, which

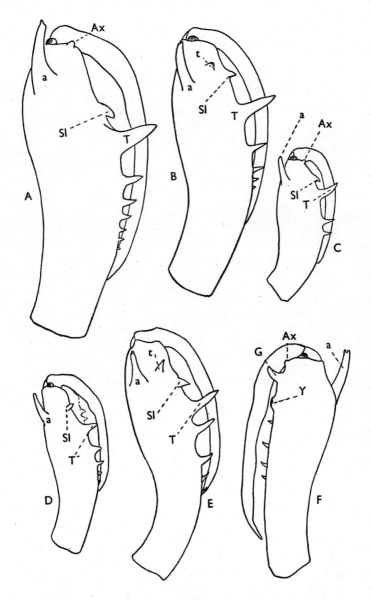

TEXT-FIG. 68.—*Tetragnatha*. Males. Left cheliceræ: A, *Tetragnatha extensa;* B, *T. montana;* C, *T. pinicola;* D, *T. obtusa;* E, *T. nigrita;* F, ditto, posterior (inner) side.

are usually clearly defined. The sides are usually somewhat darker than these bands in their lower halves, light or silvery in their upper halves. STERNUM : Dark brown, often darker towards edges, with a yellow mark starting from the anterior border (Text-fig. 66, A). CHELICERÆ : Coloured as carapace. ♀ : Text-fig. 64, A, B. ♂ : Text-fig. 68, A. LEGS : Coloured as carapace (somewhat darker in males), without annulations or markings. EPIGYNAL FOLD : Text-fig. 67, A. MALE PALP : Text-fig. 69, B. Small specimens need to be distinguished carefully from T. pinicola. For the male, the shape of the tip of the conductor to the embolus (Text-fig. 69, B, C) is the most reliable character.

OCCURRENCE : Very abundant locally, especially in reeds and bushes close to water. Distributed all over the British Isles. Adult in June and July and sometimes later.

Tetragnatha pinicola L. Koch.
(Text-figs. 64, D ; 67, E ; 68, C ; 69, C)

Tetragnatha pinicola L. Koch, 1870, p. 11 ; C. Chyzer and L. Kulczynski, 1891–7, I, p. 144 ; E. Simon, 1929, pp. 648, 651 ; H. Wiehle, 1939, p. 376 ; A. Tullgren, 1947, p. 130.

DESCRIPTION. LENGTH : ♀ : 5–6 mm. ♂ : 4·5–5 mm. CARAPACE : Light yellow-brown, sometimes with darker radiating lines from the foveal area, which sometimes have light flecks placed irregularly towards their marginal ends. ABDOMEN : Like *T. extensa*, except that the silvery sheen on the dorsal side is here more marked. Ventrally : the dark median band may have on it some silvery spots which make up the light colouration of the other parts ; the pair of light bands flanking the median dark band are not quite so well defined as in *T. extensa* and outside them is a darker region before the silvery colour of the rest of the abdomen begins. STERNUM : As in *T. extensa*. CHELICERÆ : ♀ : Text-fig. 64, D. ♂ : Text-fig. 68, C. LEGS : Light yellow or brown, coloured uniformly as carapace. EPIGYNAL FOLD : Text-fig. 67, E. MALE PALP : Text-fig. 69, C. The species needs to be distinguished from small specimens of *T. extensa*. In the male the shape of the tip of the conductor to the embolus is the most reliable character (Text-fig. 69, B, C).

OCCURRENCE : On trees. A rather rare species, but distributed over the British Isles and recorded from Eire.

Tetragnatha montana Simon.
(Text-figs. 64, C, F ; 67, B ; 68, B ; 69, A, E)

Tetragnatha montana E. Simon, 1874, I, p. 157, and 1929, pp. 648, 649 ; H. Wiehle, 1939, p. 377. *T. extensa* forma *solandri* T. Thorell, 1870–3, III, p. 459. *T. solandri* C. Chyzer and L. Kulczynski, 1891–7, I, p. 145 ; A. Tullgren, 1947, p. 144.

DESCRIPTION. LENGTH : ♀ : 6·5–10 mm. ♂ : 6·5–8 mm. (The range of size may well be greater than this.) CARAPACE : Light brown ; darker in some specimens. ABDOMEN : Dorsally very like *T. extensa*, but usually somewhat darker. Ventrally : a median longitudinal black, or deep brown, band is flanked by a pair of silvery bands which are much less well defined than in *T. extensa*, and sometimes very faint. The sides are silvery on their dorsal parts, dark brown on the ventral half, with a wavy edge separating the two regions. STERNUM : Dark brown, sometimes darker along the margins, sometimes with light patches opposite coxæ, but always without the median light mark (cf. *T. extensa* and *T. pinicola* Text-fig. 66, A). CHELICERÆ : ♀ : Text-fig. 64, C, F. ♂ : Text-fig. 68, B. LEGS : Coloured as cara-

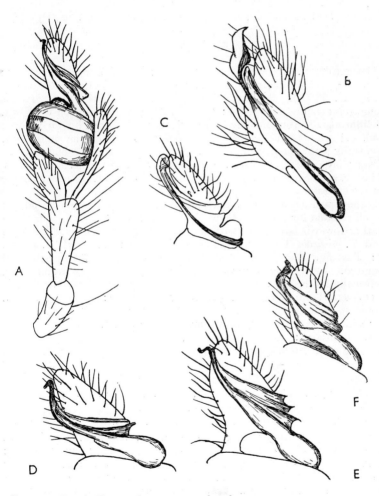

TEXT-FIG. 69.—A, *Tetragnatha montana*, male palp.
Tip of male palp : B, *Tetragnatha extensa;* C, *T. pinicola;* D, *T. obtusa;* E, *T. montana;* F, *T. nigrita.*

pace. EPIGYNAL FOLD : Text-fig. 67, B. (The hairs are shorter than
in *T. extensa*.) MALE PALP : Text-fig. 69, A, E.

OCCURRENCE : Probably the commonest species. On bushes, low
herbage and trees. In the same localities as *T. extensa*, but often found
further from water than that species and sometimes in more shady
places. Distributed all over the British Isles. Adult towards the end
of May and June.

Tetragnatha obtusa C. L. Koch.
(Text-figs. 64, G ; 65, B ; 66, B ; 67, D ; 68, D ; 69, D)

Tetragnatha obtusa C. L. Koch, 1837, I, p. 5; C. Chyzer and L. Kulczynski, 1891–7, I,
p. 145; E. Simon, 1929, pp. 648, 650; H. Wiehle, 1939, p. 376; A. Tullgren, 1947,
p. 134.

DESCRIPTION. LENGTH : ♀ : 5–7 mm. ♂ : 3·5–5·5 mm. CARAPACE :
Thoracic region light greyish brown, cephalic region distinctly darker
(Text-fig. 66, B). Borders often darker, and radiating dark wedges
sometimes occur. ABDOMEN : Colour variable, silvery green to brown.
Folium usually (but not always) distinct, with a dark brown border ;
widened and then strongly constricted at about the mid-point.
Ventrally : the median dark band lies on a lighter area which may be
silvery or quite dull brown. The sides variable, sometimes silvery
all over, sometimes with dark patches. (The abdomen in many female
specimens appears humped when viewed sideways ; but gravid females
of other species often look like this, and the character is not considered
at all reliable for identification.) STERNUM : Dark brown, sometimes
darker towards edges, but with no median light region (cf. *T. extensa*
and *T. pinicola* Text-fig. 66, A.) CHELICERÆ : ♀ : Text-fig. 64, G.
♂ : Text-fig. 68, D. The tooth (Sl) is not sloping, but upright and
pointed. LEGS : Light to dark brown, with some dark annulations,
especially at the joints (these are faint or quite absent in some males).
EPIGYNAL FOLD : Text-fig. 67, D. MALE PALP : Text-fig. 69, D.
Some specimens require care in distinguishing them from *T. nigrita*,
for which purpose the cheliceral armature is most reliable.

OCCURRENCE : Locally abundant, on trees especially. Recorded
from all over England and from Eire, but not from Wales or Scotland.

Tetragnatha nigrita Lendl.
(Text-figs. 64, E ; 65, A ; 67, C ; 68, E, F ; 69, F)

Tetragnatha nigrita A. Lendl, 1886, p. 88 ; C. Chyzer and L. Kulczynski, 1891–7, I,
p. 144 ; H. Wiehle, 1939, p. 377 ; A. Tullgren, 1947, p. 147.

DESCRIPTION. LENGTH : ♀ : 7–9·5 mm. ♂ : 5–8 mm. This species
resembles *T. obtusa*, but the colouration is usually much darker ;
living specimens are sometimes almost black. It is almost always
larger, and the annulations and dark marks on the legs are usually less
distinct than in *T. obtusa*. However specimens are occasionally met
with which require careful comparison with that species, and the
cheliceral armature is the most reliable guide (see table on pp. 99, 100.)

EPIGYNAL FOLD: Text-fig. 67, C. MALE PALP: Text-fig. 69, F.
OCCURRENCE: Rather rare, in southern counties of England (recorded
as far north as Staffordshire), also in Eire.

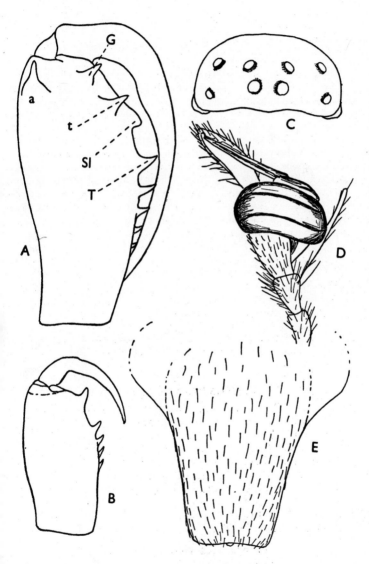

TEXT-FIG. 70.—*Eugnatha striata:* A, left chelicera (♂); B, ditto (♀); C, Eyes
(♀, seen from in front); D, male palp; E, epigynal fold.

H

2. Genus **EUGNATHA** V. Audouin 1827.

The single species, *Eugnatha striata* differs from those of the previou
genus in the following respects.

EYES : Text-fig. 70, C. The laterals are further from each other tha
in *Tetragnatha*. CHELICERÆ : ♂ : the apophysis (a) (Text-fig. 70, A
is pointed and not blunt or bifid. MALE PALP : The bulb is relative
bigger (Text-fig. 70, D) and the paracymbium (when viewed from th
inside as the palp is normally held by the spider) tapers to a poin

Eugnatha striata (L. Koch).
(Text-fig. 70)

Tetragnatha striata L. Koch, 1862, p. 79 ; E. Simon, 1929, p. 651. *Eugnatha stria*
C. Chyzer and L. Kulczynski, 1891–7, I, p. 146 ; H. Wiehle, 1939, p. 378 ; A. Tullgre
1931 (1), p. 119.

DESCRIPTION. LENGTH : ♀ : 8·5–10 mm. ♂ : about 8·5 mr
CARAPACE : Yellow to brown with no clear markings, but some pr
served specimens have a faint sub-marginal dark line. ABDOMEN
Folium dark brown, with sometimes a faint light stripe down the midd
of it and with a light edge. Ventrally : a median dark brown region
flanked by a pair of silvery stripes. The sides greenish or yellow brow
(All these markings vary and are usually clearer in males). STERNUM
Yellowish brown, with no markings. CHELICERÆ : ♀ : Text-fig. 70, I
♂ : Text-fig. 70, A. The apophysis (a) is pointed (cf. *Tetragnatha*
(Sl.) is blunt ; a tooth (t) (between (G) and (T)) is as big as (G) c
larger. LEGS : Uniform yellow to brown. EPIGYNAL FOLD : Tex
fig. 70, E. MALE PALP : Text-fig. 70, D. This is distinct from *Tetra
natha* and serves to identify the species.

OCCURRENCE : Rare. Found amongst reeds standing in or ver
close to water. England (as far north as Durham) and Eire. Matu
from May to August. Wiehle (1939, p. 381) mentions two reproducti
periods, from the end of May to the beginning of July, and the beginnin
of August.

3. Genus **PACHYGNATHA** C. J. Sundevall, 1823.

The spiders of this genus differ from those of the genus *Tetragnath*
in the following respects. GENERAL APPEARANCE : Text-fig. 7
ABDOMEN : Oval, never elongated. STERNUM : Text-fig. 72, B ; wi
punctuations. CHELICERÆ : ♂ : Text-figs. 72, A. ♀ : markedly conve
Text-fig. 72, E. MAXILLÆ : Text-fig. 72, C. LEGS : Not great
elongated ; without spines. Tarsi without auxiliary tarsal claw
The spiders do not spin regular webs for catching prey when adul
although J. I. Balogh (1934) showed that the young spin small orb web
There are three British species. *Pachygnatha clercki* Sund., 1
listeri Sund., *P. degeeri* Sund.

Pachygnatha clercki Sundevall
(Text-figs. 71 ; 72 ; 73, A, D.)

Pachygnatha clercki C. J. Sundevall, 1830, p. 209, and recent authors.

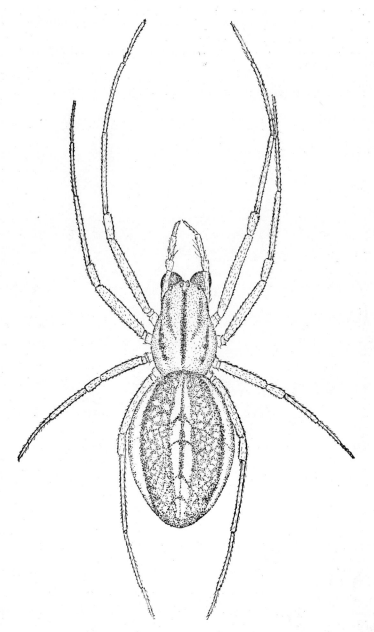

Text-fig. 71.—*Pachygnatha clercki* ♀.

DESCRIPTION. LENGTH : ♀ : about 6 mm. ♂ : 5–6 mm. CARAPACE :
Light brown with a dark brown median and, less well defined, lateral
stripes (Text-fig. 71). There is sometimes a darkening at junction of
cephalic and thoracic regions, especially in males. Faint punctuations
occur along the margins and may form lines radiating from foveal
area. ABDOMEN : ♀ : olive brown with a darker folium (Text-fig. 71).
♂ : colours often more contrasting, e.g. cream with dark brown folium

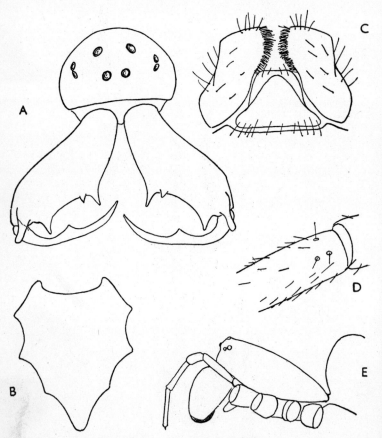

TEXT-FIG. 72.—*Pachygnatha clercki :* A, Head and cheliceræ of male ; B, sternum ;
C, maxillæ and labium(♀) ; D, trichobothria (dorsal side of femur I) ; E,
carapace and cheliceræ (♀).

bearing a cream median stripe. Ventrally : ♀ : uniform olive brown,
with no markings. ♂ : sometimes darker and sometimes with a pair
of white, or light yellow, parallel stripes running from epigastric fold
often to the spinners. STERNUM : Light brown with, sometimes, a

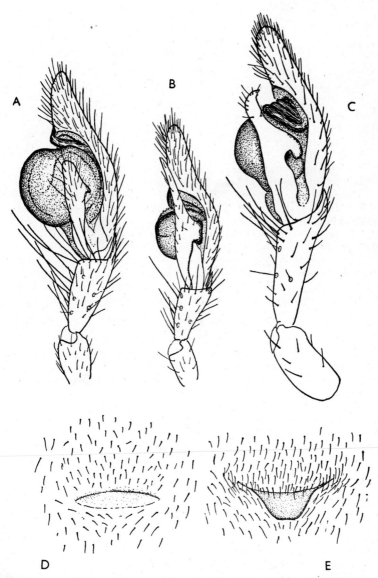

TEXT-FIG. 73.—Male palps : A, *Pachygnatha clercki;* B, *P. degeeri;* C, *P. listeri.*
Epigynal folds: D, *P. clercki;* E, *P. listeri.*

darker border. Usually darker in males. Covered with shallow punctuations. LEGS : Light yellow or brown. EPIGYNAL FOLD : Text-fig. 73, D. MALE PALP : Text-fig. 73, A. The paracymbium is characteristic.

OCCURRENCE : Common among grass and plant stems throughout the British Isles. Adult probably at all seasons.

Pachygnatha listeri Sundevall.
(Text-fig. 73, C, E)

Pachygnatha listeri C. J. Sundevall, 1830, p. 210, and recent authors.

DESCRIPTION. LENGTH : ♀ : 3·5–5 mm. ♂ : 3–4·5 mm. This species differs from *P. clercki* in the following respects. CARAPACE : Markings may be absent ; parts of the median stripe sometimes present, especially in cephalic area, and occasionally traces of lateral bands. There is sometimes a darkening of junction of cephalic and thoracic regions. ABDOMEN : ♀ : folium very variable in depth of colour, and with edges more wavy than in *P. clercki*. The median light stripe broken up into a series of paired light blotches, which vary in size, but are almost always present. ♂ : similar, but folium almost black ; the white blotches persist. Ventrally : depth of colour variable ; two longitudinal lines of white spots sometimes extend from epigastric fold to spinners. EPIGYNAL FOLD : Text-fig. 73, E. This is quite distinct and is the most reliable character for distinguishing the female from *P. clercki*. MALE PALP : Text-fig. 73, C. The paracymbium is characteristic.

OCCURRENCE : Rare, but widespread. Recorded as far north as Edinburgh. In similar situations to those inhabited by *P. clercki*.

Pachygnatha degeeri Sundevall.
(Text-fig. 73, B)

Pachygnatha degeeri C. J. Sundevall, 1830, p. 211, and recent authors.

DESCRIPTION. LENGTH : ♀♂ : 2·5–3 mm. This is a smaller, more darkly coloured species than the two foregoing. CARAPACE : Deep brown, sometimes almost black, especially in males. Pattern, when visible, approaching that of *P. listeri*. Surface partly covered with punctuations, especially on head and along margins ; in thoracic area they form lines radiating from foveal area. ABDOMEN : The general pattern as in *P. clercki*, but folium usually darker, especially along the edges, which are more wavy, and the margin of the median light stripe, which varies a good deal in extent and definition. There is much variation in depth of colouring, as also on ventral side, which sometimes has white spots as in *P. listeri*. STERNUM : Deep brown, as carapace ; densely punctate. LEGS : Light brown or yellow. EPIGYNAL FOLD : Very similar to that of *P. clercki* (Text-fig. 73, D.) MALE PALP : Text-fig. 73, B. The paracymbium is again characteristic. This species is readily distinguished from the others of the genus by its smaller size and its deep brown carapace and sternum.

OCCURRENCE : The commonest species of the genus. Found all over the British Isles, amongst grass stems, etc., usually abundantly.

23. Family ARGIOPIDÆ.

CHARACTERS OF FAMILY. CARAPACE : Usually rather flat ; thoracic region oval or nearly circular, separated from head by an oblique depression. EYES : Not very different in size. Medians may form either a square or a trapezium ; laterals close to one another and often projecting. Clypeus narrower than the ocular area (cf. THERIDIIDÆ) and usually not wider than twice the diameter of an eye (except *Cercidia* and *Theridiosoma*). STERNUM : Heart-shaped or triangular, coxæ IV being nearly contiguous. CHELICERÆ : Strong and vertical, never divergent, and with a lateral condyle (Text-figs. 74, B, C. It is vestigial in *Meta*, and absent in *Theridiosoma*). There are two rows of teeth closely set ; the outer row has 3–5, often strong, teeth, the inner has 2–3. LABIUM : Wider than long (about as long as broad in *Meta*), thickened anteriorly (Text-fig. 74, E). MAXILLÆ : Widest at their extremities (Text-figs. 74, A ; 76, A) ; not or scarcely, longer than wide (except in *Meta*). PALPS : Female with a claw (except in *Theridiosoma*). LEGS : Furnished with numerous spines ; with three tarsal claws and auxiliary foot-claws (Text-fig. 74, D). Without exception spinners of orb-webs.

KEY TO THE GENERA.

1. Maxillæ longer than broad (Text-fig. 76, A). Lateral condyle only vestigial. ♂ : paracymbium with two well-developed branches, one bearing hairs (Text-figs. 78, A, B) . . . . . . (1) **Meta**

——Maxillæ not longer, or scarcely longer, than broad (Text-fig. 74, A). Lateral condyle more fully developed (except *Theridiosoma*). ♂ : paracymbium of a different structure 2

2. Clypeus much wider than diameter of an anterior median eye (Text-fig. 113, A, B). Anterior medians clearly darker than other eyes. No lateral condyle. ♀: palp without a claw. Small spider (both sexes about 2 mm.)

(10) **Theridiosoma**

——Clypeus not wider than twice the diameter of an anterior median eye (except *Cercidia*). Anterior median eyes not noticeably darker than the rest. Lateral condyle present. ♀ : palp with a claw. Larger spiders 3

3. Posterior row of eyes rather strongly procurved (Text-fig. 112, A). Legs I : Metatarsus + tarsus longer than tibia + patella. Abdominal markings as in Text-fig. 112, A. ♂ very much smaller than ♀ . (9) **Argiope**

——Posterior row of eyes never so strongly procurved. Legs I : Metatarsus + tarsus shorter than tibia + patella. Abdominal markings of a different kind. ♂ larger relative to ♀ 4

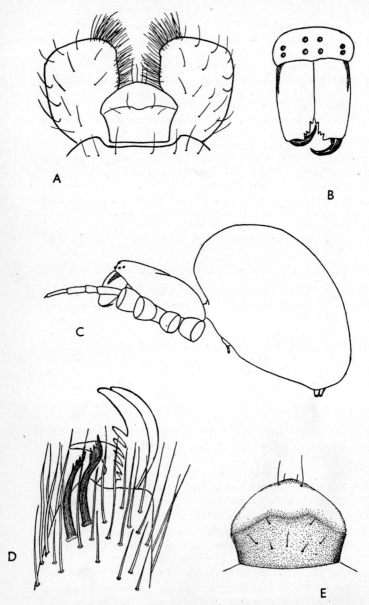

TEXT-FIG. 74.—ARGIOPIDÆ. *Araneus:* A, maxillæ and labium; B, head and cheliceræ (seen from in front); C, carapace and abdomen; D, auxillary foot claws; E, labium.

4. Carapace having a U-shaped junction between head and thoracic region. Both rows of eyes strongly recurved. Abdomen shaped as in Text-fig. 111 . . (8) **Cyclosa**

——Carapace with junction between head and thoracic region not of this shape. Posterior row of eyes, at least, not strongly recurved. Abdomen of a different shape . . 5

5. Carapace with a narrow longitudinal furrow (best seen from slightly in front). Abdominal markings as in Text-fig. 110, A. ♀ : Tibia III with a number of long trichobothria on the prolateral side near the base (Text-fig. 110, D) which on close examination are seen to have a plumose structure . . . . . . (7) **Mangora**

——Carapace without a narrow longitudinal furrow. Abdominal markings of a different type. ♀ : Tibia III without trichobothria of this type near the base . . . 6

6. Width of clypeus 4–5 times diameter of an anterior median eye. Abdomen furnished along anterior margin with a series of short spines, almost like teeth (Text-fig. 106, B) (5) **Cercidia**

——Width of clypeus not more than twice the diameter of an anterior median eye. Abdomen without such spines along anterior border 7

7. Posterior median eyes *not* closer to one another than to the adjacent laterals. Adult spiders spin a web with a sector missing (Text-fig. 107) . . . . . (6) **Zygiella**

——Posterior median eyes closer to one another than to the adjacent laterals. Spiders spinning a complete orb web with no sector missing 8

8. Abdomen shiny ; pattern of type shown in Text-fig. 102 (or coloured uniformly brown in some specimens). Legs relatively shorter . . . . . . (4) **Singa**

——Abdomen not shiny, covered more densely with short hairs. Patterns of a different type (coloured uniformly green in some species). Legs relatively longer. . (2) **Araneus**

——Differing from *Araneus* and *Singa* in the ♂ palpal tibia bearing only one large curved spine. (Abdominal pattern Text-fig. 101, A) . . . . . (3) **Zilla**

1. Genus **META** C. L. Koch 1836.

CHARACTERS OF GENUS. CARAPACE : The fovea deep and long, often trifid posteriorly. Clypeus not much wider than anterior median eyes. EYES : Posterior row slightly procurved or straight. Posterior medians slightly closer to each other than to the adjacent laterals.

ABDOMEN : Oval, a little enlarged in front and usually tapering behind (Text-fig. 75). CHELICERÆ : With traces only of a lateral condyle. ♂ : basal segments longer and narrower than in ♀. MAXILLÆ : Longer than broad (Text-fig. 76, A) ; a distinctive character of the genus. LABIUM : About as long as broad. EPIGYNES : Of a simple and (in

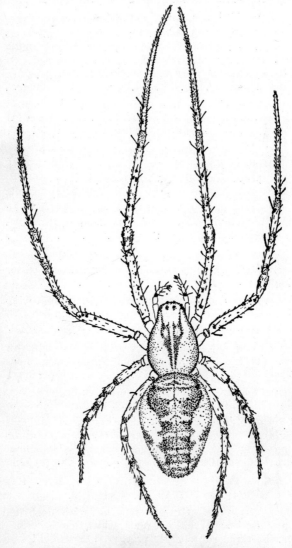

TEXT-FIG. 75.—*Meta segmentata* ♀.

British species) rather uniform type. MALE PALPS : Simpler in structure than in the other genera. Paracymbium divided into two branches (a) a hairy one ; (b) a non-hairy one of varying shape and of use in identification. The two sexes not very different in size and appearance.

Of the British species, *Meta segmentata* (Cl.) and *M. segmentata mengei* (Bl.) are abundant, *M. merianæ* (Scop.) is frequent and locally abundant, whilst *M. menardi* (Latr.) is confined to caves, hollow trees dark cellars and outhouses, and *M. bourneti* Sim. is found in similar situations, but hitherto very rarely.

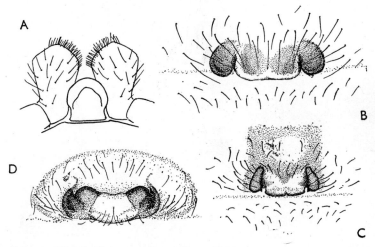

TEXT-FIG. 76.—A, *Meta menardi*, maxillæ and labium.
   Epigynes : B, *Meta segmentata;* C, *M. segmentata mengei;* D, *M. merianae.*

Meta segmentata (Clerck).
(=*Meta reticulata* (Linnaeus))
(Text-figs. 75 ; 76, B ; 77, A, D)

Araneus segmentatus C. Clerck, 1757, p. 45. *Aranea reticulata* C. Linnaeus, 1758, p. 619. *A. inclinata* C. A. Walckenaer, 1802, p. 201. *Epeira inclinata* J. Blackwall, 1861–4, p. 354. *Meta segmentata* O. P.-Cambridge, 1879–81, p. 239 ; C. Chyzer and L. Kulczynski, 1891–7, I, p. 138 ; E. Simon, 1929, p. 653. *Meta reticulata* H. Wiehle, 1931 (1), p. 119.

DESCRIPTION : LENGTH : ♀ : 5–8 mm. ♂ : 5–6 mm. CARAPACE : Text-fig. 75. Light brown with chocolate markings roughly in form of a V. ABDOMEN : Text-fig. 75. Pattern usually characteristic, but colouring and emphasis of different parts extremely variable. Brown, grey, red, yellow, black may all be present in one specimen. STERNUM : Dark brown. LEGS : Yellow-brown ; sometimes faintly annulated,

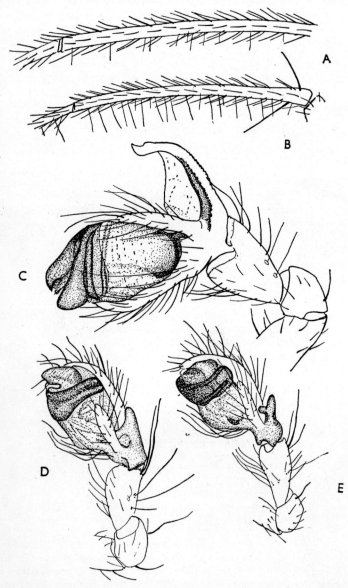

TEXT-FIG. 77.—A, Ventral hairs on metatarsus I, *Meta segmentata*, ♂ ; B, ditto
M. segmentata mengei, ♂.
Male palps : C, *Meta merianœ;* D, *M. segmentata;* E, *M. segmentata mengei.*

especially III and IV. EPIGYNE : Text-fig. 76, B. MALE PALP : Text-fig. 77, D. The species needs to be distinguished from *M. segmentata mengei* (Bl.) (q.v. for differences).

OCCURRENCE : Very abundant on trees, bushes, low plants, window frames of sheds and houses. Adult in late summer and autumn ; some specimens occur in spring, possibly after hibernation as adults.

Meta segmentata mengei (Blackwall).
(Text-figs. 76, C ; 77, B, E)

Epeira mengei J. Blackwall, 1869, p. 398. *Meta segmentata* var. *mengei* T. Thorell, 1870, p. 39 ; C. Chyzer and L. Kulczynski, 1891–7, I, p. 139 ; H. Wiehle, 1931 (1), p. 123. *Meta segmentata mengei* E. Simon, 1929, p. 654.

DESCRIPTION. LENGTH : ♀♂ : 3·5–5 mm. Whether this form should be regarded as a variety of *M. segmentata* (Cl.), or as a subspecies, is in some doubt. The male can be distinguished from the typical form quite easily, apart from its size, (a) by the ventral hairs on metatarsus I (Text-fig. 77, B), (b) by the paracymbium of the palp (Text-fig. 77, E). It is very difficult to find really reliable characters for distinguishing the females. The chitinised areas on either side of the median septum of the epigyne (Text-fig. 76, C) are of some help, but are inclined to vary in appearance. The pigmented area, anterior to the epigyne, varies in extent and depth, but seems always to be present. In *M. segmentata* it is absent or represented, at the most, by extremely faint markings. (This difference would not perhaps be expected to be reliable, but has proved to be so on all specimens so far examined.) The markings, in both sexes, are usually (but not always) more distinct than in the typical form, though disposed in the same way.

OCCURRENCE : Very common in the same situations as *M. segmentata* and probably distributed equally widely, although collectors have not usually distinguished it in their records. Adult in spring and early summer, but it has been recorded in the autumn (see E. Simon, 1929, p. 654, footnote).

Meta merianæ (Scopoli).
(Text-figs. 76, D ; 77, C)

Aranea merianæ J. A. Scopoli, 1763, p. 395. *A. fusca* C. Degeer, 1778, p. 235. *A. antriada* C. A. Walckenaer, 1802, p. 201. *Epeira celata* J. Blackwall, 1861–4, p. 353. *E. antriada* id. 1861–4, p. 351. *Meta merianæ* O. P.-Cambridge, 1879–81, p. 241 ; C. Chyzer and L. Kulczynski, 1891–7, I, p. 139 ; E. Simon, 1929, p. 656 ; H. Wiehle, 1931 (1), p. 125.

DESCRIPTION. LENGTH : ♀ : 5·5–8·5 mm. ♂ : 4·5–7·5 mm. (size variation may well exceed these limits). CARAPACE : Light brown with a thin black borderline, within which is a dark brown marginal band of varying width. Foveal region dark, with radiating dark streaks. Cephalic region dark, with a pair of light patches half way between fovea and ocular area. There is another light region just behind the eyes. Area of median eyes sometimes darkened. ABDOMEN : General design similar to that of *M. segmentata*, but pattern much less distinct, more uniform grey or brown, but depth of colour extremely

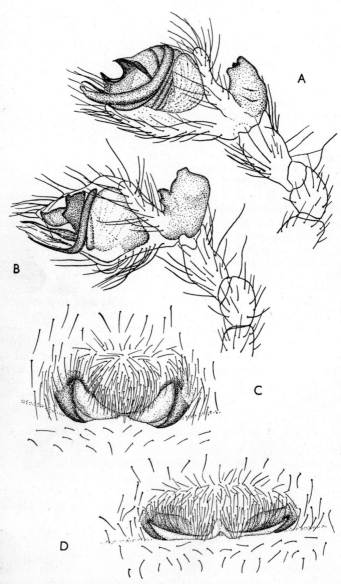

TEXT-FIG. 78.—*Meta menardi:* B, male palp; C, epigyne.
Meta bourneti: A, male palp; D, pigyne.

variable. Ventrally : A rectangular almost black region is flanked by a pair of light streaks curving inwards ; two elongated light patches occur each side of spinners. STERNUM : Dark brown. : LEGS : Light brown or yellow ; annulated in some specimens. Femora with dark spots. EPIGYNE : Text-fig. 76, D. MALE PALP : Text-fig. 77, C. The depth of colour varies greatly and seems to depend on surroundings. Almost black specimens have been taken amongst blackened rocks by lochs in Eire.

OCCURRENCE : In cellars, culverts and caves (not far from the entrances), also on trees and low plants, and amongst rocks, especially when close to water.

Meta merianæ var. *celata* (Blackwall) (J. Blackwall 1841, p. 668 and 1861–4. p. 353) is met with occasionally in similar situations and has normal markings except for a wide cream coloured band running the length of the dorsal side of the abdomen.

Meta menardi (Latreille).
(Text-fig. 78, B, C)

Aranea menardi P. A. Latreille, 1804 (2), p. 266. *Epeira fusca* C. A. Walckenaer, 1805, p. 63 ; J. Blackwall, 1861–4, p. 349. *Meta menardi* O. P.-Cambridge, 1879–81, p. 528 ; C. Chyzer and L. Kulczynski, 1891–7, I, p. 139 ; E. Simon, 1929, p. 656 ; H. Wiehle, 1931 (1), p. 128 ; B. J. Kaston, 1948, p. 233.

DESCRIPTION. LENGTH : ♀ : up to about 13 mm. ♂ : up to about 11 mm. CARAPACE : Light brown, with cephalic region usually darker, especially at junction with thoracic region. Fovea darker, expanding in front and behind. Radiating dark streaks faint or absent. ABDOMEN: General colouration mostly chestnut brown to black. In the fore half is a dark region, on a lighter ground, and within it a lighter median area consisting of a longitudinal bar with two transverse bars across it (the directions taken by these bars variable). On posterior half is a tapering dark region crossed by diminishing light transverse bars. (The distinctness of all parts of pattern very variable, increasing in old specimens as lighter parts become bleached.) Sides have wavy streaks on a lighter ground. Ventrally : Design like *M. merianæ*, but depth of colour very variable. LEGS : Variable in colour ; light to deep rusty brown, obscurely annulated. EPIGYNE : Text-fig. 78, C. MALE PALP : Text-fig. 78, B. The living spiders have a glossy, polished appearance.

OCCURRENCE : In caves, damp cellars or out-buildings, well away from the light. Distributed all over the British Isles.

Meta bourneti Simon.
(Text-fig. 78, A, D)

Meta bourneti E. Simon, 1922, p. 199 ; 1929, p. 657 ; E. Browning and W. Tams, 1944, p. 95.

DESCRIPTION. In size and appearance this species is indistinguishable from the last, although the specimens examined lack the dusky annulations on the legs, usually present in *M. menardi*. EPIGYNE : Text-fig. 78, D. This is wider than and clearly distinct from that of *M. menardi*. MALE PALP : Text-fig. 78, A. The best distinction from that of *M. menardi* lies in the shape of the non-hairy part of the para-cymbium.

OCCURRENCE : Gedding (Suffolk), in a culvert ; Rendcombe (Gloucestershire), in a conduit carrying water pipes, and in a neigh-bouring air-raid shelter ; Moor Park (Hertfordshire), in a tunnel near the Mansion. The species may be expected to occur in situations similar to those occupied by *M. menardi*.

2. Genus **ARANEUS** C. Clerck 1757.

CHARACTERS OF GENUS. CARAPACE : Shape as in Text-fig. 74, C. Towards the posterior part of the thoracic region is a trapezoid area with a transverse slit along its anterior side (not always easy to see).

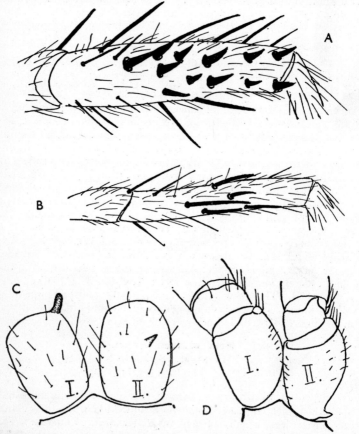

TEXT-FIG. 79.—A, Male tibia II (prolateral side), *Araneus marmoreus;* B, ditto *Araneus redii;* C, coxa I and II, *A. diadematus;* D, ditto *A. marmoreus.*

Clypeus narrow, one–two times diameter of an anterior median eye.
EYES : Text-fig. 74, B. Trapezium formed by median eyes not, or
not much, longer than broad. Laterals touching, or nearly touching.
Posterior row slightly procurved. ABDOMEN : Text-figs. 80, 84, 88,
93, 94. Pattern and folium very variable, sometimes absent. The
surface not shiny (cf. *Singa*). LEGS : Not very long, and rather stout.
♂ : Tibia II furnished inside with thickened or dentiform spines
(Text-fig. 79, A, B) (except in the members of Group IX below).
Coxa I with a small protuberance on apical margin (Text-figs. 79, C ;
100, A, B) (except in Group VIII below and *A. quadratus*). EPIGYNE :
In most species a median appendage, called the *scape* (e.g. Text-fig. 85)
reaches backwards, to a varying extent, from the anterior margin,
sometimes obscuring the view of much of the rest of the organ. MALE
PALP : Patella with two strong curving spines (e.g. Text-fig. 81).
Paracymbium a simple projection with a knob, which may be enlarged
or elongated.

It is convenient to divide the 20 British species into the following
groups for purposes of identification (even though in some cases a
Group may be represented by a single British species.)

Group I.—*Araneus bituberculatus* (Walck.), *A. gibbosus* (Walck.),
A. angulatus Cl. These all have well-defined tubercles or lumps on
the anterior part of the abdomen (Text-fig. 80).

Group II.—*Araneus diadematus* Cl., *A. quadratus* Cl., *A. marmoreus* Cl.,
A. alsine (Walck). These species are closely allied, having rather
similar genitalia, and abdominal folium (except *A. alsine*). Large
specimens of *A. diadematus* have traces of the abdominal tubercles
characteristic of Group I.

Group III.—*Araneus cornutus* Cl., *A. patagiatus* Cl., *A. sclopetarius* Cl.
These again resemble one another and differ from Group II in their
genitalia, especially the median apophysis of the male palp (Text-
fig. 90 (m.)) and in the relatively small scape of the epigynes (Text-
fig. 89).

Group IV.—*Araneus ceropegius* (Walck). This species has some
affinities with those of Group I. It is characterised by the shape and
design of the abdomen (Text-fig. 91, A), which has a light median
ventral stripe reaching from the epigyne to about three quarters of
the way to the spinners. The scape of the epigyne is large, tapering
away posteriorly (but this is frequently missing).

Group V.—*Araneus umbraticus* Cl. A species with a very flat abdomen.
Epigyne : Text-fig. 92, A, with a chitinous process originating
from the posterior border.

Group VI.—*Araneus redii* (Scop.). A species with the abdomen at
least as broad as long, Text-fig. 93, A. Epigyne : Text-fig. 93, C.
The male palp bears a long spine on the tibia, Text-fig. 93, B.

Group VII.—*Araneus adiantus* (Walck). A species with the abdomen
of characteristic shape and pattern (Text-fig. 93, E).

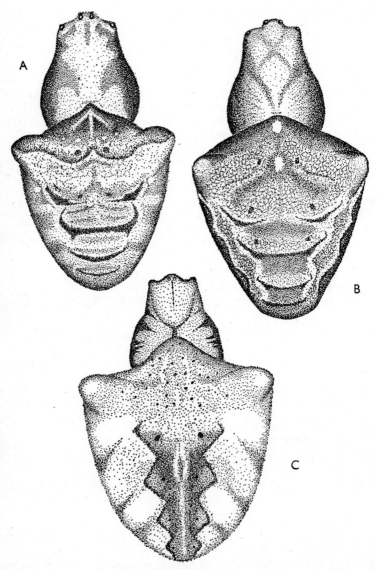

TEXT-FIG. 80. —Carapace and abdomen : A, *Araneus bituberculatus;* B, *Araneus gibbosus;* C, *Araneus angulatus.*

Group VIII.—*Araneus triguttatus* (Fabr.) and *A. sturmi* (Hahn). Two very similar species with characteristic epigynes (Text-figs. 94, B, D) and abdominal patterns. (Text-figs. 94, A, C) and male palps, having the end of the median apophysis trifid (Text-fig. 95, A).

Group IX.—*Araneus cucurbitinus* Cl. (and its variety *opistographus* Kulcz.), *A. alpicus* (L. Koch), *A. inconspicuus* Sim., *A. displicatus* var. *westringi* Thor. These species are very alike, the first three having the abdomen bright green, the last a rusty red ; none has a proper folium. The genitalia of all four are very similar, and identification has caused some trouble in the past. They all spin small, inclined or horizontal webs, sometimes within the hollow of a single leaf.

At the time of writing the genus *Araneus*, as here constituted, is the subject of an interesting and important revision at the hands of A. F. Archer (1951), who bases his classification chiefly on the structure of the male genitalia. Although we consider, both from his published papers and from private correspondence, that Archer's conclusions are of importance and are likely to be adopted at any rate in part, they have still to be subjected to studied criticism. In the circumstances we feel that it is best for us to indicate where his observations concern our species, but to leave the nomenclature in its traditional form in the text. The genera removed from *Araneus* and affecting our species are :—

Gibbaranea, A. F. Archer, 1951 (3) includes our *Araneus bituberculatus* (Walck.) and *A. gibbosus* (Walck.). Group I.

Epeira, C. A. Walckenaer, 1805, includes our Group III.

Chinestela, R. V. Chamberlin, 1924, includes our *A. umbraticus* Cl. Group V.

Agalenatea, A. F. Archer, 1951 (3) includes our *A. redii* (Scop.). Group VI.

Neosconopsis, A. F. Archer, 1951 (3) includes our *A. adiantus* (Walck.). Group VII.

Atea, C. L. Koch, 1837, includes our Group VIII.

Araniella, R. V. Chamberlin and W. Ivie, 1942, includes our Group IX.

GROUP I.

Araneus bituberculatus (Walckenaer).

(Text-figs. 80, A ; 81, A ; 82, A)

Aranea bituberculata C. A. Walckenaer, 1802, p. 191. *Epeira dromedaria* C. L. Koch, 1845, XI, p. 90 ; C. Chyzer and L. Kulczynski, 1891–7, I, p. 129 ; O. P.-Cambridge, 1909, p. 111. *Araneus dromedarius* A. R. Jackson, 1909, p. 424. *Araneus bituberculatus* E. Simon, 1929, p. 699. *Aranea bituberculata* H. Wiehle, 1931 (1), p. 61.

DESCRIPTION. LENGTH : ♀ : about 5·5 mm. ♂ : about 5 mm. CARAPACE : Text-fig. 80, A. ♀ : sides and posterior region deep brown, middle region light brown. ♂ : similar, but darker throughout. ABDOMEN : Text-fig. 80, A. The humps prominent. ♀ : colouration brown, cream and black. ♂ : similar but darker parts approaching

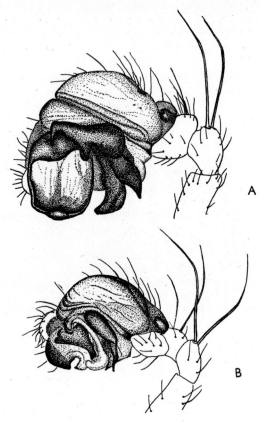

TEXT-FIG. 81.—Male palps: A, *Araneus bituberculatus;* B, *Araneus gibbosus.*

black and light parts in greater contrast. STERNUM: Deep brown, nearly black. LEGS: Light brown with darker annulations. EPIGYNE: Text-fig. 82, A. MALE PALP: Text-fig. 81, A.

OCCURRENCE: In one locality, on bushes at Burnham Beeches (Buckinghamshire). Adult in May.

Araneus gibbosus (Walckenaer).
(Text-figs. 80, B ; 81, B ; 82, B)

Aranea gibbosa C. A. Walckenaer, 1802, p. 190. *Epeira bicornis* id. 1806–7, fasc. II, tab. 2 ; C. L. Koch, 1845, XI, p. 92 ; J. Blackwall, 1861–4, p. 361 ; O. P.-Cambridge, 1879–81, p. 272. *Epeira gibbosa* C. Chyzer and L. Kulczynski, 1891–7, I, p. 129. *Araneus gibbosus* A. R. Jackson, 1909, p. 424, Pl. X, fig. 9 ; E. Simon, 1929, p. 698. *Aranea gibbosa* H. Wiehle (1), 1931, p. 67.

DESCRIPTION. LENGTH : ♀: 5·5–7 mm. ♂: 4·5–5 mm. CARAPACE : Text-fig. 80, B. ♀: dark brown, lighter towards centre. ♂: darker, otherwise similar. ABDOMEN : Text-fig. 80, B. The two humps are prominent. Colouration variable but usually dark brown or black, with light parts cream or white (with darker reticulations on them), occasionally much reduced or even absent. Some specimens have green patches on some of the dark regions. STERNUM : Brown, usually dark. LEGS : Light brown, annulated with deep brown or black.

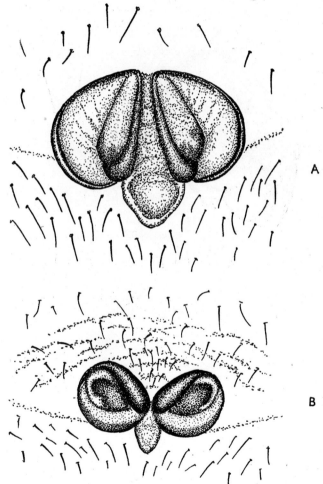

TEXT-FIG. 82.—Epigynes : A, *Araneus bituberculatus;* B, *Araneus gibbosus.*

(Some dark specimens have I and II almost uniformly dark.) Many of the spines are white, with brown bases, and sometimes appear striking in the living spiders, but the contrast in colour tends to disappear on preservation. EPIGYNE : Text-fig. 82, B. MALE PALP : Text-fig. 81, B.

OCCURRENCE : Frequently beaten from trees. Adult May, June and July. Widespread, but not found north of Cheshire and Lincolnshire.

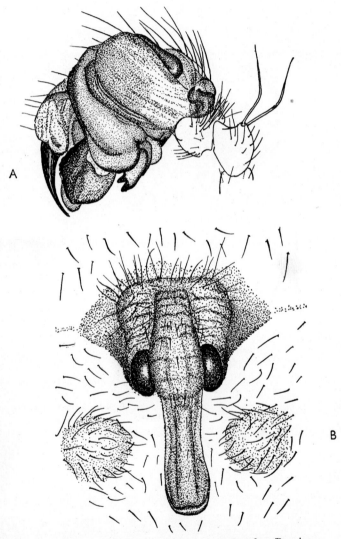

TEXT-FIG. 83.—*Araneus angulatus:* A, male palp ; B, epigyne.

Araneus angulatus Clerck.
(=*Aranea angulata* Linnaeus)
(Text-figs. 80, C ; 83)

Araneus angulatus C. Clerck, 1757, p. 22. *Aranea angulata* C. Linnaeus, 1758, p. 620. *Epeira angulata* C. L. Koch, 1845, XI, p. 77 ; J. Blackwall, 1861–4, p. 360 ; O. P.-Cambridge, 1879–81, p. 270, and 1891, p. 95 ; C. Chyzer and L. Kulczynski, 1891–7, I, p. 128. *Araneus angulatus* E. Simon, 1929, p. 677. *Aranea angulata* H. Wiehle, 1931 (1), p. 52.

DESCRIPTION. LENGTH : ♀ : about 14 mm. ♂ : 10–12 mm. CARA-PACE : ♀ : light reddish brown, with a darker border (Text-fig. 80, C). The whole covered with rather long white hairs, especially on the borders, head and thoracic juncture. ♂ : sometimes much darker, so that borders become indiscernible. ABDOMEN : Text-fig. 80, C. Light brown, but variable ; folium deeper brown. ♂ : much darker, so that folium is sometimes hardly visible. Sometimes a series of lozenges, each composed of white lines, runs from anterior border down the entire length (traces of these may be seen in some females). STERNUM : Dark brown, with a light yellow median mark, constricted in the middle. LEGS : ♀ : light brown, with wide deeper brown annulations, clearer on III and IV than on I and II. ♂ : Femora I and II dark, except at base ; other annulations darker than in ♀, and legs in consequence look dark with white annulations. EPIGYNE : Text-fig. 83, B. There are two brown mammillæ, one at each side of the scape. MALE PALP : Text-fig. 83, A.

OCCURRENCE : Rare, in woods. Devonshire, Dorsetshire, Hampshire, Isle of Wight, Sussex. Adult : June and July to September.

GROUP II.

Araneus diadematus Clerck.
(=*Aranea diadema* Linnaeus)
(Text-figs. 79, C ; 84, A ; 85, A ; 86, A ; 87, A)

Araneus diadematus C. Clerck, 1757, p. 25. *Aranea diadema* C. Linnaeus, 1758, p. 619. *Epeira diadema* J. Blackwall, 1861–4, p. 358. *E. diademata* O. P.-Cambridge, 1879–81, p. 266 ; C. Chyzer and L. Kulczynski, 1891–7, I, p. 129. *Araneus diadematus* E. Simon, 1929, p. 680. *Aranea diadema* H. Wiehle, 1931 (1), p. 70.

DESCRIPTION. LENGTH : ♀ : 10–12 mm. ♂ : 4·5–8 mm. (Sizes, particularly of males may vary outside these limits. Wiehle (1931(1), p. 71) states that sizes for the males tend to fall around two mean values.) CARAPACE : ♀ : light brown. Darker brown markings usually as in Text-fig. 84, A, but variable. ♂ : similar, but all markings less distinct, the median and lateral sometimes almost absent. ABDOMEN : Text-fig. 84, A. Although the species lacks the humps characteristic of Group I, the fore part is somewhat more angular than in the other species of Group II. Colour and markings extremely variable, but the general scheme almost always distinguishable. (The central cross is not always clear in fresh specimens, but usually so in spirit.) Colour very light brown (almost cream) to black. STERNUM : ♀ : colour variable ; light to dark brown. ♂ usually lighter. LEGS : ♀ : light yellowish brown, annulated with darker brown. ♂: annulations less distinct. Coxa II with a spur on the lower surface (Text-fig. 79, C). Epigyne: Text-fig. 85, A. Male palp: Text-figs. 86, A; 87, A. This needs to be distinguished from that of *A. marmoreus*. The median apophysis, m, is here larger, almost white, and more divergent, being always clearly visible, even with the naked eye.

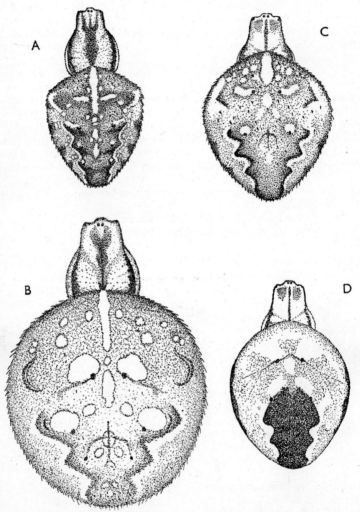

Text-fig. 84.—Carapace and abdomen: A, *Araneus diadematus*; B, *Araneus quadratus*; C, *Araneus marmoreus*; D, *Araneus marmoreus pyramidatus*.

OCCURRENCE : This is one of the most common and abundant species. Found all over the British Isles, on trees, low bushes, plants, window frames. Adult in August, September and October. Wiehle (1931 (1), p. 72) states that the young take two years to reach maturity, and they probably do so in this country as well as on the continent, though precise observation is lacking.

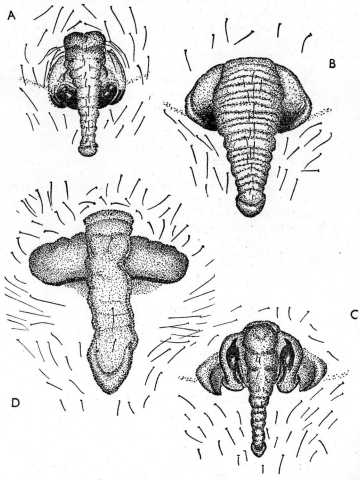

TEXT-FIG. 85.—Epigynes : A, *Araneus diadematus*; B, *Araneus quadratus*; C, *Araneus marmoreus*; D, *Araneus alsine*.

Araneus quadratus Clerck.
(=*Aranea reaumuri* Scopoli)
(Text-figs. 84, B ; 85, B ; 86, B)

Araneus quadratus C. Clerck, 1757, p. 27. *Aranea reaumuri* J. A. Scopoli, 1763, p. 393. *Epeira quadrata* J. Blackwall, 1861–4, p. 324 ; O. P.-Cambridge, 1879–81, p. 278 ; C. Chyzer and L. Kulczynski, 1891–7, I, p. 130. *Araneus quadratus* E. Simon, 1929, p. 683. *Aranea reaumuri* H. Wiehle, 1931 (1), p. 79.

DESCRIPTION. LENGTH : ♀ : 9–15 mm. ♂ : 6–8 mm. CARAPACE : ♀ : Light brown, with darker lateral bands, irregular on their inner edges ; a light region between these and the margin. Median band as in Text-fig. 84, B (wider than in *A. marmoreus*). The distinctness of these markings (colour red-brown to chocolate) is variable, but they can almost always be recognised easily, and are useful for distinguishing, with fair certainty, from *A. marmoreus* in the field. ♂ : median band reduced sometimes almost to a line. ABDOMEN : Pattern similar to, and sometimes not distinguishable from, that of *A.marmoreus* (Text-fig. 84, C). This becomes changed as ♀ becomes distended with eggs (Text-fig. 84, B). Colour very variable, e.g. rusty red, deep chocolate brown, olive green ; lighter regions cream. Edges of folium brown, of very varying depth. STERNUM : Usually uniform dark brown ; sometimes with a series of 2–3 yellow patches, nearly forming a median stripe. LEGS : ♀ : light brown, annulated with darker brown, sometimes distinctly, especially on I and II. ♂ : annulations often indistinct, especially on I and II. No spur on coxa I ; coxa II without a sharp projecting spur on the lower surface (cf. *A. marmoreus* and *A. diadematus*). EPIGYNE : Text-fig. 85, B. (The scape can appear more attenuated when viewed from somewhat in front, and care is needed in making comparisons.) MALE PALP : Text-fig. 86, B. The large bifid median apophysis is characteristic.

OCCURRENCE : Widespread and fairly common all over the British Isles. It is especially abundant in heather and gorse in northern England and Scotland. Adult in August and September.

Araneus marmoreus Clerck.
(=*Aranea raji* Scopoli)
(Text-figs. 79, D ; 84, C ; 85, C ; 86, C ; 87, B)

Araneus marmoreus C. Clerck, 1757, p. 29. *Aranea raji* J. A. Scopoli, 1763, p. 394. *Epeira marmorea* C. Chyzer and L. Kulczynski, 1891–7, I, p. 130. *Araneus marmoreus* E. Simon, 1929, p. 682. *Aranea raji* H. Wiehle, 1931 (1), p. 75. *Epeira raji* B. J. Kaston, 1948, p. 257.

DESCRIPTION. LENGTH : ♀ : 5–8 mm. ♂ : 5–6·5 mm. CARAPACE : ♀, Text-fig. 84, C. Light brown, with a single narrow, darker median line (cf. *A. quadratus*). Two dark patches usually occur anteriorly on either side of this line. Dark lateral bands are dentate on insides and rather variable ; there is a narrow clear region between these and margins. ♂ : median line reduced to, at most, a fine streak ; lateral bands sometimes much diminished. ABDOMEN : Text-fig. 84, C. Variable in colour, brown to greyish green, and often reticulated.

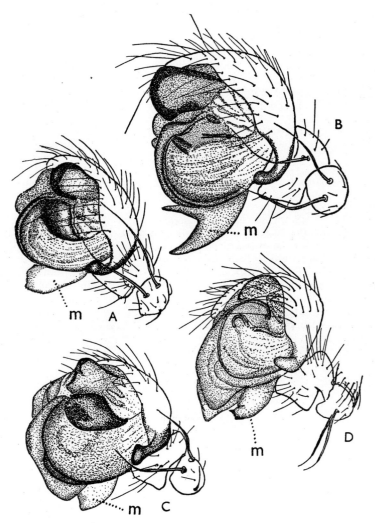

TEXT-FIG. 86.—Male palps: A, *Araneus diadematus;* B, *Araneus quadratus;* C, *Araneus marmoreus;* D, *Araneus alsine.*

Some specimens resemble *A. quadratus.* STERNUM: Uniform dark brown or black. LEGS: Distinctly annulated with orange to almost black. ♂: coxa II with a sharp spur on the lower surface (Text-fig. 79, D. cf. *A. quadratus*). EPIGYNE: Text-fig. 85, C. The scape is distinctly narrower than in *A. quadratus.* MALE PALP: Text-fig. 86, C. This needs to be distinguished from that of *A. diadematus.* The median apophysis, m, is darker in colour, not so large nor divergent. The difference is most clearly seen when the palp is viewed from below and a little from the inside (Text-fig. 87, A, B).

OCCURRENCE : It is a curious fact that, whereas this species has occurred very rarely, the variety *pyramidatus* Cl., though not common, is widespread over England, Scotland and Wales. *A. marmoreus* has been found near York and in some numbers on Skipwith Common (Yorkshire), on small birch trees. Adult in August and September.

Araneus marmoreus var. pyramidatus Clerck.
(=*Aranea raji betulæ* Sulzer)
(Text-fig. 84, D)

Araneus pyramidatus C. Clerck, 1757, p. 34. *Aranea betulæ* J. H. Sulzer, 1776, p. 254. *A. scalaris* G. W. Panzer, 1793, 4, t.4. *Epeira scalaris* J. Blackwall, 1861–4, p. 331 ; O. P.-Cambridge, 1879–81, p. 268. *E. pyramidata* C. Chyzer and L. Kulczynski, 1891–7, I, p. 130. *Araneus marmoreus pyramidatus* E. Simon, 1929, p. 682. *Aranea raji betulæ* H. Wiehle, 1931 (1), p. 76.

DESCRIPTION. LENGTH : ♀ : about 8 mm. ♂ : 5–7 mm. This variety differs from *A. marmoreus* in the abdominal pattern (Text-fig. 84, D). The folium is deep chocolate brown, the light areas cream or light yellow. Specimens intermediate between this and typical *A. marmoreus* have been taken from Skipwith Common (Yorkshire).

OCCURRENCE : Uncommon, but widespread in England, Scotland and Wales. It is usually beaten from trees, especially silver birch, but also occurs on bushes, brambles, etc. Adult in August and September.

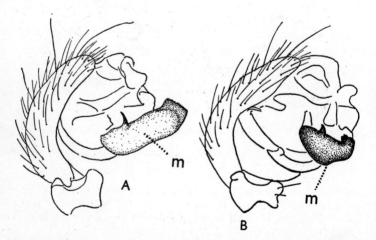

TEXT-FIG. 87.—Male palps (from below) : A, *Araneus diadematus;* B, *Araneus marmoreus.*

Araneus alsine (Walckenaer).
(Text-figs. 85, D ; 86, D)

Aranea alsine C. A. Walckenaer, 1802, p. 193. *Epeira lutea* C. L. Koch, 1837, I, p. 59 ; J. Blackwall, 1861–4, p. 345 ; O. P.-Cambridge, 1879–81, p. 530. *Araneus alsine* E. Simon, 1929, p. 684. *Aranea alsine* H. Wiehle, 1931 (1), p. 82.

DESCRIPTION. LENGTH : ♀ : about 8·5 mm. ♂ : about 6 mm. CARAPACE : Uniform orange (in preserved specimens). ABDOMEN : Reddish orange, uniformly speckled with white, with a glossy, glowing appearance, which is lost, with colour and markings, on preservation. It has also been described as having " a lovely violet hue " (O. P.-Cambridge 1902, p. 28). STERNUM : ♀ : Red brown. ♂ : Dark red-brown with a lighter patch adjacent to anterior border. LEGS : ♀ : Colour as carapace, with no annulations visible. ♂ : with faint annulations on middle of femora and extremities of other segments. No spurs on coxæ II. EPIGYNE : Text-fig. 85, D. MALE PALP : Text-fig. 86, D.

OCCURRENCE : Very rare, in woods or clearings. England (as far north as Lincolnshire) and Wales. Adult certainly in September and probably much earlier.

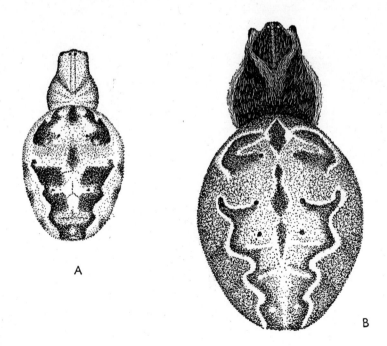

TEXT-FIG. 88.—Carapace and abdomen : A, *Araneus cornutus;* B, *Araneus sclopetarius.*

GROUP III.

Araneus cornutus Clerck.

(=*Aranea foliata* Fourcroy)

(Text-figs. 88, A ; 89, B ; 90, C)

Araneus cornutus C. Clerck, 1757, p. 39. *Aranea foliata* A. F. de Fourcroy, 1785, p. 533. *Epeira apoclisa* J. Blackwall, 1861–4, p. 325. *E. cornuta* O. P.-Cambridge, 1879–81, p. 275 ; C. Chyzer and L. Kulczynski, 1891–7, I, p. 133. *Araneus cornutus* E. Simon, 1929, p. 686. *Aranea foliata* H. Wiehle, 1931 (1), p. 86. *Epeira foliata* B. J. Kaston, 1948, p. 254.

DESCRIPTION. LENGTH : ♀ : 6–8·5 mm. ♂ : 5–8 mm. CARAPACE : ♀ : light brown with, usually, no very distinct markings beyond darker streaks radiating from fovea. Sometimes with a darker band at junction of head with thoracic region, and this band may be covered with white hairs. Two parallel lines run from fovea to posterior

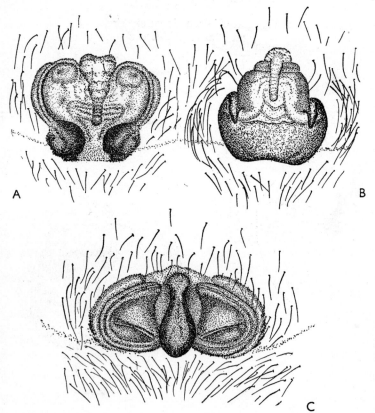

TEXT-FIG. 89.—Epigynes : A, *Araneus sclopetarius;* B, *Araneus cornutus;* C, *Araneus patagiatus.*

median eyes. ♂ : similar, but more variable in depth of colour.
ABDOMEN : ♀ : Text-fig. 88, A. Ground usually cream, with markings
brown or sepia, but there is great variation and some specimens have
the ground pink or reddish. ♂ : pattern darker and its edges much

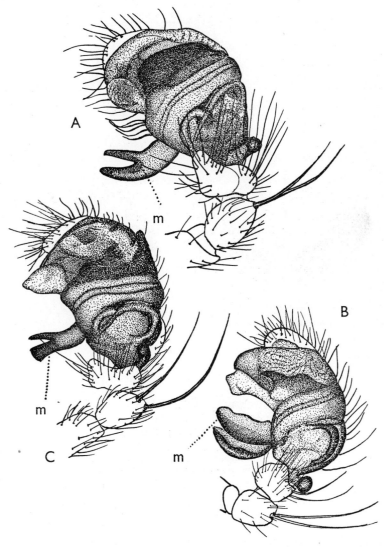

TEXT-FIG. 90.—Male palps : A, *Araneus sclopetarius;* B, *Araneus patagiatus;*
C, *Araneus cornutus.*

more clear cut. The light or clear region in the middle of the folium is replaced in most cases by a region as dark as the rest. STERNUM : Very dark brown. LEGS : Annulations sometimes distinct, sometimes quite absent. EPIGYNE : Text-fig. 89, B. (This was drawn from a fresh specimen. In others the scape seems often to be missing and the other parts may be contorted or apparently missing. The species cannot however be confused very well with any other). MALE PALP : Text-fig. 90, C.

OCCURRENCE : Widespread, all over the British Isles. Very abundant in some localities, especially near water, where it spins its web on reed heads, with a silken retreat amongst the florets of the plant. The male is often found in this retreat with the female. Adult probably at all seasons.

Araneus sclopetarius Clerck.
(=*Aranea undata* Olivier)
(Text-figs. 88, B ; 89, A ; 90, A)

Araneus sclopetarius C. Clerck, 1757, p. 43. *Aranea undata* A. G. Olivier, 1789, p. 206. *Epeira sericata* C. L. Koch (1), 1833, p. 120 and 1845, XI, p. 110 ; J. Blackwall, 1861–4, p. 328. *E. sclopetaria* O. P.-Cambridge, 1879–81, p. 277 ; C. Chyzer and L. Kulczynski, 1891–7, I, p. 132. *Araneus sericatus* E. Simon, 1929, p. 685. *Aranea undata* H. Wiehle, 1931 (1), p. 90. *Epeira undata* B. J. Kaston, 1948, p. 256.

DESCRIPTION. LENGTH : ♀ : 10–14 mm. ♂ : 8–8·5 mm. CARAPACE : Text-fig. 88, B. ♀ : black with white hairs forming a very characteristic " V " in front of the junction between cephalic and thoracic regions, and also a white border. ♂ : similar hairs, but ground colour lighter ; brown. ABDOMEN : ♀ : Text-fig. 88, B. Often very dark, with a light margin round folium. ♂ : very similar ; the abdomen being smaller, the markings often appear more distinct. STERNUM : Black. LEGS : ♀ : Annulated, but obscurely on dark specimens. Ground colour very variable, cream to deep brown. ♂ : annulated obscurely on I and II. EPIGYNE : Text-fig. 89, A. MALE PALP : Text-fig. 90, A.

OCCURRENCE : Uncommon in England (as far north as Westmorland and Lincolnshire). Found often near water, especially on bridges. Adult probably all the year round.

Araneus patagiatus Clerck.
(=*Aranea dumetorum* Fourcroy)
(Text-figs. 89, C ; 90, B)

Araneus patagiatus C. Clerck, 1757, p. 38. *A. ocellatus* idem. 1757, p. 36. *Aranea dumetorum* A. F. de Fourcroy, 1785, p. 331. *Epeira patagiata* J. Blackwall, 1861–4, p. 329 ; O. P.-Cambridge, 1879–81, p. 277 ; C. Chyzer and L. Kulczynski, 1891–7, I, p. 133. *Araneus ocellatus* E. Simon, 1929, p. 684. *Aranea dumetorum* H. Wiehle, 1931 (1), p. 88. *Epeira dumetorum* B. J. Kaston, 1948, p. 255.

DESCRIPTION. LENGTH : ♀ : about 6 mm. ♂ : about 5·5 mm. CARAPACE : ♀ : light to medium brown, with no special markings beyond those near the fovea and two parallel dark lines running thence to posterior median eyes (as in *A. cornutus*). ♂ : dark brown, with a darker stripe round sides of head enclosing lateral eyes but stopping short at anterior medians. ABDOMEN : ♀ : rather light with a sepia folium and very like the two foregoing species. ♂ : Markings more distinct ; white margins of folium usually striking. The clear region in the middle, present in females, here replaced by a region as dark as the rest of the folium (as in *A. cornutus*). STERNUM : ♀ : light brown. ♂ : black. LEGS : Usually clearly annulated in both sexes. EPIGYNE : Text-fig. 89, C. MALE PALP : Text-fig. 90, B. The form of

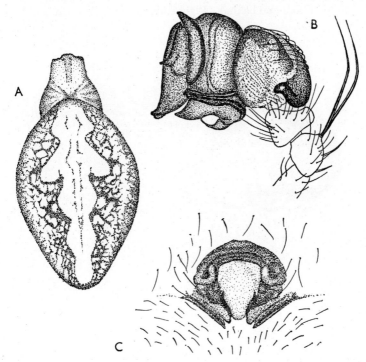

TEXT-FIG. 91.—*Araneus ceropegius:* A, Carapace and abdomen ; B, male palp ; C, epigyne (the scape is missing).

the median apophysis, cleft seemingly to the base, serves to distinguish the species from *A. cornutus*, which it resembles fairly closely.

OCCURRENCE : Rare. In England as far north as Northumberland ; Wales, Eire. It is usually beaten from trees and bushes or low plants. Adult males have been taken in May and September, and, as in the two foregoing species, the season may be extended throughout the year.

K

GROUP IV.

Araneus ceropegius (Walckenaer).

(Text-fig. 91)

Aranea ceropegia C. A. Walckenaer, 1802, p. 199. *Epeira ceropegia* J. Blackwall, 1861–4, p. 347 ; O. P.-Cambridge, 1879–81, p. 529 ; C. Chyzer and L. Kulczynski, 1891–7, I, p. 132. *Araneus ceropegia* E. Simon, 1929, p. 688. *Aranea ceropegia* H. Wiehle, 1931 (1), p. 100.

DESCRIPTION. LENGTH : ♀ : 11·5–14 mm. ♂ : about 6·5 mm. CARAPACE : ♀ : brownish yellow, with lighter margins (not visible from above). ♂ : much darker. ABDOMEN : ♀ : Text-fig. 91, A. Narrowed in front and behind. Light coffee colour with cream markings.

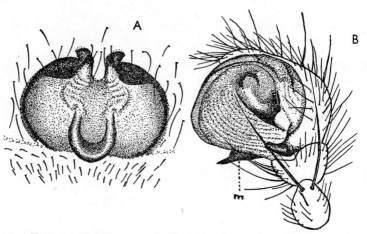

TEXT-FIG. 92.—*Araneus umbraticus:* A, epigyne ; B, male palp.

The pattern to some extent unsymmetrical. Ventrally : a light median stripe, on a dark ground, runs from the epigyne three-quarters of the way to the spinners (this is characteristic). ♂ : much darker, deep brown to black, with some cream markings. STERNUM : Deep brown or black. LEGS : Ground colour as carapace. Femora darkened dorsally, other segments annulated. EPIGYNE : Text-fig. 91, C. This is shown without the scape, which is frequently missing (no specimens were available with it present). The scape covers the region here shown and tapers to a point behind. MALE PALP : Text-fig. 91, B. (Drawings were made from foreign specimens).

OCCURRENCE : There is only one record : Piercefield, near Chepstow (Monmouthshire) in the autumn of 1853, when several specimens seem to have been taken.

GROUP V.
Araneus umbraticus Clerck.
(=*Aranea sexpunctata* Linnaeus)
(Text-fig. 92)

Araneus umbraticus C. Clerck, 1757, p. 31. *Aranea sexpunctata* C. Linnaeus, 1758, p. 622. *Epeira umbratica* J. Blackwall, 1861–4, p. 333 ; O. P.-Cambridge, 1879–81, p. 280 ; C. Chyzer and L. Kulczynski, 1891–7, I, p. 132. *Araneus umbraticus* E. Simon, 1929, p. 686. *Aranea sexpunctata* H. Wiehle, 1931 (1), p. 93.

DESCRIPTION. LENGTH : ♀ : 11–14 mm. ♂ : 8–9 mm. CARAPACE : ♀ : dark brown or black, with no special markings, except two parallel dark lines from fovea to posterior median eyes. ♂ : similar, generally lighter. ABDOMEN : ♀ : characteristically flattened, with a wide dark folium with white edges, which are often broken and sometimes form white patches instead of a continuous line. Four pairs of rusty brown depressions occur on the dorsal side, usually very clear. Sides (outside folium) mottled brown to black. ♂ : similar ; folium sometimes occupies whole dorsal surface. STERNUM : Black. LEGS : Usually dark ; annulated distinctly in lighter specimens, obscurely in dark ones, and less distinctly on I and II (especially males). EPIGYNE : Text-fig. 92, A. MALE PALP : Text-fig. 92, B. The curious flat appearance of the spider makes it easy to recognise.

OCCURRENCE : Found frequently all over the British Isles. It rarely appears in daylight, but remains hidden underneath loose bark of trees or posts until dusk.

GROUP VI.
Araneus redii (Scopoli).
(Text-fig. 93, A, B, C)

Aranea redii J. A. Scopoli, 1763, p. 394. *Epeira solers* C. A. Walckenaer, 1825, p. 60 ; J. Blackwall, 1861–4, p. 336. *E. sollers* N. Westring, 1861, p. 41 ; O. P.-Cambridge, 1879–81, p. 282. *E. redii* C. Chyzer and L. Kulczynski, 1891–7, I, p. 131. *Araneus redii* E. Simon, 1929, p. 688. *Aranea redii* H. Wiehle, 1931 (1), p. 97.

DESCRIPTION. LENGTH : ♀ : 5·5 – 7 mm. ♂ : 3·5 – 4·5 mm. CARAPACE : Text-fig. 93, A. Yellow brown with black markings ; variable, sometimes all, or nearly all, black. ABDOMEN : ♀ : Text-fig. 93, A. Characteristically broader than long or as broad as long. Colouration very variable ; brown to rusty red with black markings and cream outlines to folium, etc. Emphases on the different parts of the pattern vary very much. Covered with long hairs. ♂ : usually a little longer than broad. Pattern similar with equally wide variations. STERNUM : Dark brown to black, with a broken median yellow stripe (which may be reduced or absent in very dark specimens). LEGS : Brown, varying in depth, with annulations which are often broken, and almost absent in some males. EPIGYNE : Text-fig. 93, C. (This has been drawn from a little in front. It frequently appears much more foreshortened.) MALE PALP : Text-fig. 93, B.

OCCURRENCE : Local, but then considerable numbers may be found together, usually on heather, gorse, etc. Distributed all over the British Isles, but more frequent in the south. Adult in April and May.

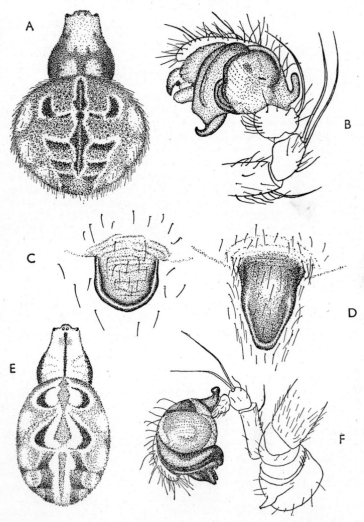

TEXT-FIG. 93.—*Araneus redii:* A, carapace and abdomen ; B, male palp ; C, epigyne.
Araneus adiantus: D, epigyne ; E, carapace and abdomen ; F, male palp.

VARIETIES : E. Simon (1874, p. 91) distinguished five varieties as occurring in France, but intermediates exist between these and the typical species. However the following two have been noted in this country.

Variety δ, has a pair of white patches on the anterior part of the abdomen. This occurs fairly frequently.

Variety ζ, has, on the posterior half of the abdomen, a very black, inverted triangle (as in *A. marmoreus pyramidatus* Cl.) bordered with white. This has been found near Haslemere (Surrey).

GROUP VII.

Araneus adiantus (Walckenaer).
(Text-fig. 93, D, E, F)

Aranea adianta C. A. Walckenaer, 1802, p. 199. *Epeira adianta* J. Blackwall, 1861–4, p. 348 ; O. P.-Cambridge, 1879–81, p. 261 ; C. Chyzer and L. Kulczynski, 1891–7, I, p. 133. *Araneus adianta* E. Simon, 1929, p. 693 ; *Aranea adianta* H. Wiehle, 1931 (1), p. 103.

DESCRIPTION. LENGTH : ♀ : 5–7 mm. ♂ : 4–4·5 mm. CARAPACE : ♀ : light brown, with narrow median and lateral black stripes and with a lighter border. ♂ : similar, the lateral stripes sometimes wide. ABDOMEN : Text-fig. 93, E. Shape and pattern characteristic. Colouration cream with light and dark brown and sometimes reddish brown. STERNUM : Black. LEGS : Rather thin. Light brown with dark annulations at joints (indistinct on I and II in males). EPIGYNE : Text-fig. 93, D. MALE PALP : Text-fig. 93, F.

OCCURRENCE : Uncommon ; usually on heather, sometimes in marshy places, in southern counties, especially along the south coast (not north of Cambridgeshire and Norfolk), also in Wales and Eire. Adult July to September.

GROUP VIII.

Araneus sturmi (Hahn).
(Text-figs. 94, A, B ; 95, A, B)

Epeira sturmi C. W. Hahn, 1831, p. 12 ; C. Chyzer and L. Kulczynski, 1891–7, I, p. 131 ; A. R. Jackson, 1909, p. 426. *Araneus sturmi* E. Simon, 1929, p. 697. *Aranea sturmi* H. Wiehle, 1931 (1), p. 113. (Until 1909 this species and *A. triguttatus* were confused in British records. Jackson (loc. cit.) thought that Blackwall (1861–4 p. 334) must have possessed both species and included them under the name *Epeira agelena*.)

DESCRIPTION. LENGTH : ♀ : 3–5 mm. ♂ : about 3·5 mm. CARAPACE : ♀ : light rusty brown, cephalic region sometimes lighter. ♂ : similar, but more variable in colour and often darker. ABDOMEN : Text-fig. 94, A. Generally more rounded than in *A. triguttatus*. Brown, with dark parts sepia or deep purple brown ; folium quite often well defined (as in the fig.) and the "shoulders" frequently quite dark. Both pattern and colour vary considerably (cf. A. R. Jackson, 1909, p. 426). STERNUM : ♀ : light brown. ♂ : dark brown. LEGS : ♀ : uniform reddish brown. ♂ : generally darker and annulated in dark

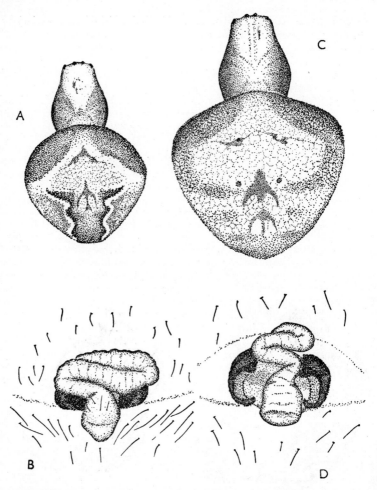

TEXT-FIG. 94.—*Araneus sturmi:* A, carapace and abdomen ; B, epigyne.
Araneus triguttatus: C, carapace and abdomen ; D, epigyne.

specimens. EPIGYNE : Text-fig. 94, B. This is distinguished from that
of *A. triguttatus* (a) by the S-shaped part reaching the full breadth of
the epigyne, (b) by the head of the scape being not twice as broad as
the S-shaped part leading to it. MALE PALP : Text-fig. 95, A, B. This
is very like that of *A. triguttatus*. There are several differences, but the
most convenient way to distinguish the species is to look at the palpal
organ from the tip of the tarsus. The form of the apophysis marked X in
Text-fig. 95, B is quite distinct.

Occurrence : Local, but then sometimes abundant, especially on evergreens ; in England, Wales and Scotland. Adult in April, May and possibly June.

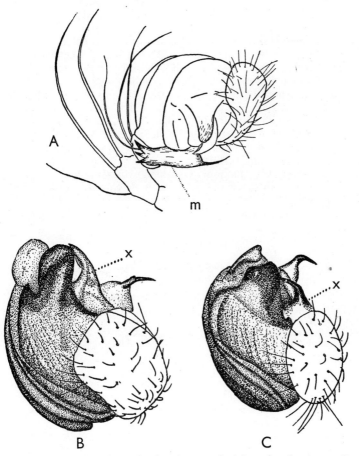

Text-fig. 95.—Male palps : A, *Araneus sturmi*, right palp, showing median apophysis, m ; B, left palp viewed from directly above tip of cymbium ; C, *Araneus triguttatus*, left palp from same position.

Araneus triguttatus (Fabricius).
(Text-figs. 94, C, D ; 95, C)

Aranea triguttata J. C. Fabricius, 1775, p. 436. *Epeira triguttata* C. Chyzer and L. Kulczynski, 1891–7, I, p. 131 ; A. R. Jackson, 1909, p. 426. *Araneus triguttatus* E. Simon, 1929, p. 697. *Aranea triguttata* H. Wiehle, 1931 (1), p. 115. *Conaranea triguttata* A. F. Archer, 1951 (2), pp. 30, 31, Figs. 18, 19, 31. (Until 1909 this species was confused with *A. sturmi* in British records.)

DESCRIPTION. This species resembles *A. sturmi*, from which it differs in the following respects. LENGTH : ♀ : 4·5–6 mm. ♂ : 3–4·5 mm. (It is bigger than *A. sturmi* as a general rule, but specimens may well be found, of either species, in which the measurements overlap.) ABDOMEN : Text-fig. 94, C. This is more angular and rarely has such a well developed folium as *A. sturmi*. The ground colour is often light brown with many small red streaks, giving a pink colouration to the living spider. EPIGYNE : Text-fig. 94, D. This is distinct from that of *A. sturmi* in that (a) the loops of the S-shaped part do not reach to the outside of the epigyne, (b) the head of the scape is about twice as broad as the S-shaped part leading to it. MALE PALP : Text-fig. 95, C. The part X provides the most convenient distinction from *A. sturmi*.

The species varies considerably. One female was taken at Box Hill (Surrey) in which the lighter region on the anterior part of the abdomen was a uniform cream-yellow. Another colour variety is recorded by O. P.-Cambridge (1909, p. 110).

OCCURRENCE : Not common. Obtained by beating trees and bushes. It is found more in deciduous trees than *A. sturmi*, which is usually found on evergreens. Found in England as far north as Lincolnshire ; recorded once from Scotland (Inverness-shire). Adult in April, May and June.

GROUP IX.

Araneus cucurbitinus Clerck.

(=*Aranea cucurbitina* Linnaeus)

(Text-figs. 96, A ; 97, B ; 98, A ; 99, A)

Araneus cucurbitinus C. Clerck, 1757, p. 44. *Aranea cucurbitina* C. Linnaeus, 1758, p. 620. *Epeira cucurbitina* J. Blackwall, 1861–4, p. 342 ; O. P.-Cambridge, 1879–81, p. 259 ; C. Chyzer and L. Kulczynski, 1891–7, I, p. 131 ; W. Bösenberg, 1901–3, p. 31. *Araneus cucurbitinus* E. Simon, 1929, p. 694 ; A. F. Millidge and G. H. Locket, 1952, p. 65. *Aranea cucurbitina* H. Wiehle, 1931 (1), p. 106.

DESCRIPTION. LENGTH : ♀ : 4–6 mm. ♂ : 3·5–4 mm. CARAPACE : ♀ : red- or yellow-brown. ♂ : similar (depth of colour variable) but with a pair of wide, almost black, marginal bands (these disappear on pre-servation). ABDOMEN : Bright green dorsally and laterally with, occasionally, lighter whitish areas, especially along the sides. Black spots on posterior half, variable in number, usually four–five pairs (Text-fig. 96, A). Ventrally : a median uniform area of rather deeper green with, sometimes, brown or yellow lateral lines on each side of it. Occasionally with four faint yellow patches (as in *A. alpicus*, but not so distinct). There is a red spot on the dorsal side of the spinners. STERNUM : Coloured as carapace with, sometimes, darker streaks running from between coxæ to centre. LEGS : ♀ : coloured as carapace. ♂ : darker and more reddish, annulated with black around the joints. EPIGYNE : Text-fig. 97, B. MALE PALP : Text-figs. 98, A ; 99, A. In order to distinguish this from the other species of the Group, the following characters should be noted : (a) the form of the knob of the paracymbium (Text-fig. 99, A), (b) the shape of the falciform median apophysis, which Kulczynski called the " retinaculum " (Text-fig. 98, A, " r "). In order to see this apophysis the palp must be viewed from below and from a little to the outside, using the position in which the spider normally holds it. The appearance of the parts changes very much with view-point and it is very important to have the specimens in similar positions when making comparisons.

OCCURRENCE : Common on trees and bushes all over the British Isles. Adult in May, June and July. The young often do not become green until nearly full grown.

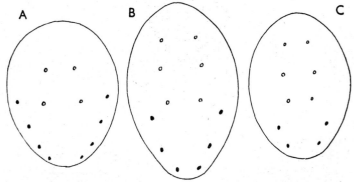

TEXT-FIG. 96.—Abdomen : A, *Araneus cucurbitinus;* B, *Araneus displicatus* var. *westringi;* C, *Araneus alpicus.*

Araneus cucurbitinus var. opistographus Kulczynski.
(Text-fig. 98, B)

Araneus cucurbitinus var. *opistographus* L. Kulczynski, 1905 (1), p. 231 ; R. de Lessert, 1910, p. 319 ; A. F. Millidge and G. H. Locket, 1952, p. 65.

DESCRIPTION. The MALE PALP differs from that of *A. cucurbitinus* Cl. in the shape of the retinaculum, Text-fig. 98, B, " r ". This is continuously curved without the inflexion present in *A. cucurbitinus* (cf. Text-fig. 98, A, " r "). The EPIGYNE is said by Kulczynski (1905) to have a longer scape, but in the opinion of the authors this character cannot be said to be completely reliable, and there appears to be no other distinguishing character. It may indeed be possible that we have to do here with a dimorphic male only.

OCCURRENCE : Recorded in England as far north as Yorkshire. Much less common than *A. cucurbitinus*, but it may well have been overlooked in the past.

Araneus inconspicuus (Simon).
(Text-figs. 97, A ; 98, C ; 99, D ; 100, B)

Epeira inconspicua E. Simon, 1874, p. 84 ; O. P.-Cambridge, 1906, p. 79 ; W. Bösenberg, 1901–3, p. 29. *E. westringii* O. P.-Cambridge, 1879–81, p. 260 (not *E. inconspicua* A. R. Jackson, 1924, p. 117). *Araneus inconspicuus* L. Kulczynski, 1905 (1), p. 239 ; E. Simon, 1929, p. 695 ; A. R. Jackson, 1933, p. 282 ; A. F. Millidge and G. H. Locket, 1952, p. 65. *Aranea inconspicua* H. Wiehle, 1931 (1), p. 112.

DESCRIPTION. LENGTH : ♀ : 5–5·5 mm. ♂ : 4–4·5 mm. CARAPACE : ♀ : uniform orange brown. ♂ : similar but sometimes with wide black borders (as in *A. cucurbitinus*), which may be present only in cephalic

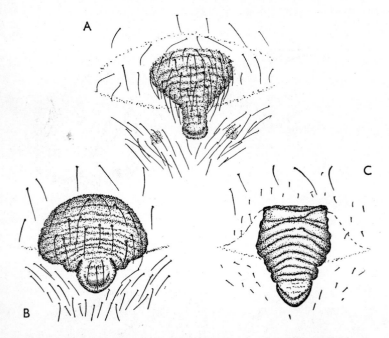

TEXT-FIG. 97.—Epigynes : A, *Araneus inconspicuus* and *A. alpicus;* B, *Araneus cucurbitinus;* C, *Araneus displicatus* var. *westringi.*

region. ABDOMEN : Light green dorsally in mature specimens. Usually without posterior lateral black spots (unlike other species of the Group). Ventrally : a darker more blue green (as in *A. cucurbitinus*). In specimens just adult two broad rose-coloured lateral bands sometimes extend from dorsal side of spinners to a little in front of the branchial opercula. If these occur they tend to become very indistinct as the abdomen gets distended on feeding. The central dark green region uniform, lacking, in all specimens examined so far, the four yellow patches present in *A. alpicus.* STERNUM : ♀ : coloured as carapace.

♂ : often with dark greenish streaks pointing inwards and forwards from the margins (these are variable and gradually disappear in spirit). LEGS : ♀ : uniform red-brown. ♂ : variable ; sometimes uniform red-brown, sometimes with patellæ and tips of tibiæ quite black (this dark colour fades in spirit). The small tubercle on the retrolateral margin of coxa I points outwards (Text-fig. 100, B, cf. *A. alpicus*). EPIGYNE : Text-fig. 97, A. This is probably indistinguishable with certainty from that of *A. alpicus*. MALE PALP : Text-figs. 98, C ; 99, D. This needs to be distinguished carefully from that of *A. alpicus*. The organs are here altogether smaller, and the branch of the retinaculum, r, is much reduced and in some specimens almost non-existent (even when present it is not visible in some positions).

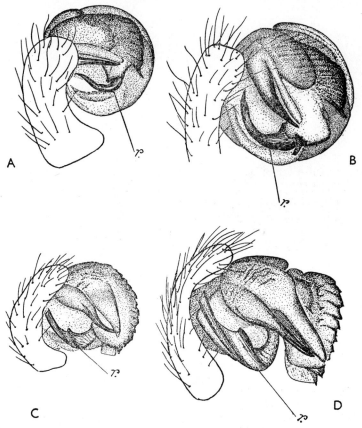

TEXT-FIG. 98.—Male left palps, seen from below and a little to the outside : A, *Araneus cucurbitinus;* B, *Araneus cucurbitinus* var *opistographus;* C, *Araneus inconspicuus;* D, *Araneus alpicus*.

This spider resembles *A. alpicus* closely; the differences are given in the description of that species.

OCCURRENCE: Hitherto rare, but it has probably been overlooked in the past owing to its resemblance to *A. cucurbitinus*. New Forest, Stockbridge (Hampshire), Surrey, Great Kimble (Buckinghamshire), Ruislip (Middlesex). It is beaten from trees (especially oak and ever-greens). Adult in April and May.

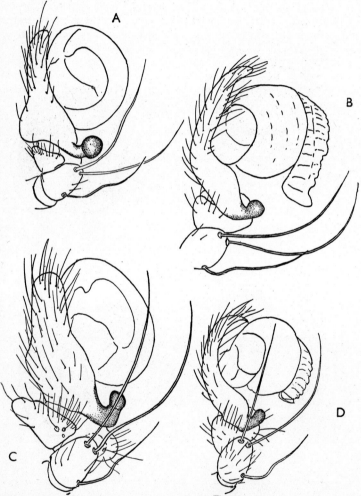

TEXT-FIG. 99.—Male right palp, seen from above: A, *Araneus cucurbitinus*; B, *Araneus alpicus*; C, *Araneus displicatus* var. *westringi*; D, *Araneus incon-spicuus*.

Araneus alpicus (L. Koch).
(Text-figs. 96, C ; 98, D ; 99, B ; 100, A)

Epeira alpica L. Koch, 1869, p. 173 ; C. Chyzer and L. Kulczynski, 1891–7, 1, p. 131 ; W. Bösenberg, 1901–3, p. 30. *Araneus alpicus* L. Kulczynski, 1905 (1), p. 238 ; R. de Lessert, 1910, p. 320 ; A. R. Jackson, 1932, p. 211 ; E. Simon, 1929, p. 695 ; A. F. Millidge and G. H. Locket, 1952, p. 65. *Aranea alpica* H. Wiehle, 1931 (1), p. 110.

DESCRIPTION. LENGTH : ♀ : about 6 mm. ♂ : about 4·5 mm. This species resembles *A. inconspicuus* closely. The distinguishing characters are as follows. FEMALES. EYES : The ratio of breadth of front to that of back of the median ocular trapezium is 0·95–1·09 (and 1·15–1·3 in *A. inconspicuus*), measurements being taken from the outside edges of the eyes. The distance between anterior medians is 0·13–0·17 mm. (0·185–0·19 mm. in *A. inconspicuus*). Kulczynski (1905, p. 248) considered that occasions may arise when the eye measurements are the only distinguishing feature. ABDOMEN : There are normally two pairs of lateral black spots on the posterior half (Text-fig. 96, C), but the number is variable. Ventrally : two light green bands enclose a dark green area on which are four rather large green-yellow patches set in a square (the front pair may sometimes be fused). These persist after long preservation and are very clearly visible in the field. EPIGYNE : Not distinguishable with certainty from that of *A. inconspicuus* (Text-fig. 97, A).

MALES. LEGS : The small tubercle on the retro-lateral apical margin of coxa I is bent back, whereas in *A. inconspicuus*, it points somewhat outwards, Text-fig. 100, A. MALE PALP : Text-figs. 98, D ; 99, B. The retinaculum, r, has a very distinct flat excrescence about half way along its length.

OCCURRENCE : Very rare. New Forest (Hampshire), Box Hill (Surrey), Great Kimble (Buckinghamshire).

Araneus displicatus var. westringi (Thorell).
(Text-figs. 96, B ; 97, C ; 99, C ; 100, C, E)

Epeira westringi T. Thorell, 1856, p. 106 ; 1870, p. 547 (not *E. westringi* O. P.-Cambridge, 1913, p. 123). *Aranea displicata* H. Wiehle, 1931 (1), p. 109. *Araneus displicatus* var. *westringi* A. F. Millidge and G. H. Locket, 1952, p. 63.

DESCRIPTION. LENGTH : ♀ : 5·5–6 mm. ♂ : about 4·5 mm. (Continental specimens seem to be larger, 8–11 mm.). CARAPACE : ♀ : uniform reddish brown. ♂ : reddish brown, sometimes with a pair of dark patches in thoracic region near the margin. ABDOMEN : ♀ : Text-fig. 96, B. Slightly pointed in front. The darker parts of the pattern vary in colour from a light brick red to orange. (The lateral part of the pattern which in the specimen figured is confined to the posterior half, in another specimen ran the whole length.) These median marks are surrounded by white borders and outside these is a green-yellow area. Along the outsides, usually not visible from above, and extending over some of the ventral side, is a wide, brick red band running right round the abdomen ; it passes just above the spinners

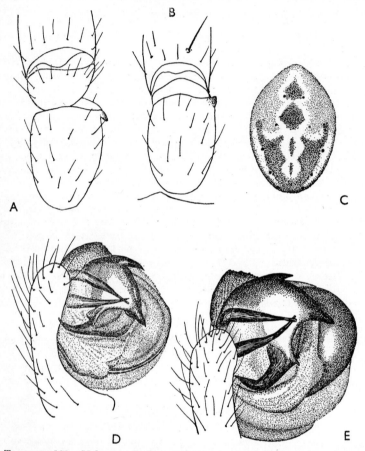

TEXT-FIG. 100.—Male coxa I (from below): A, *Araneus alpicus;* B, *Araneus inconspicuus.*
C, *Araneus displicatus* var *westringi:* abdomen, ♀.
Male left palps, seen from below and a little to the outside: D, *Araneus displicatus* Hentz; E, *Araneus displicatus* var. *westringi.*

and is only broken at the extreme anterior end. There are three lateral pairs of rather large black spots on the posterior half and a fourth, smaller, pair nearer the spinners (these may sometimes be absent). Ventrally: a carmine or brown quadrilateral lies between the epigastric fold and spinners; on this are two pairs of yellow-green blotches (as in *A. alpicus*), which may be fused forming a single yellow green area. The brown quadrilateral is flanked by a pair of longitudinal yellow green stripes, outside of which comes the brick coloured lateral band mentioned above. ♂: similar, but lacking the four light blotches ventrally; instead there is a single green band running transversely immediately behind the epigastric fold. STERNUM: ♀: uniform brown, as carapace. ♂: colour similar, with darker streaks coming from between coxæ towards centre. LEGS: ♀: Red brown, as carapace, with faint darkening at extremities of segments. ♂: coloured as carapace, with trochanters black; apical ends of femora slightly darker than basal; apical ends of other segments black. EPIGYNE: Text-fig. 97, C. This is quite distinct from those of the other species of the Group. MALE PALP: Text-figs. 99, C; 100, E. The paracymbium is similar to that of *A. inconspicuus* and *A. alpicus*, but disposed at a slightly different angle. The palp is most easily recognised when seen from below and a little to the outside (Text-fig. 100, E). It differs slightly but definitely from that of the American *A. displicatus* Hentz (Text-fig. 100, D).

In the few specimens available the colouration is variable, but the spiders are recognisable when alive by the red or orange markings, which are very beautiful on the green field and are quite different from those of the other species of the Group. (The young of *A. cucurbitinus* are sometimes coloured similarly, but they always become green on reaching maturity). All the abdominal colouration fades in spirit to a uniform dull brown.

OCCURRENCE: Harrow-on-the-Hill (Middlesex), a single male in April. South Croydon (Surrey) a male and three females, in May, found by beating pine trees.

3. Genus **ZILLA** C. L. Koch 1834.

CHARACTERS OF GENUS. The following characters separate the genus from *Araneus*. EYES: The anterior row (as seen from in front) is distinctly recurved. LEGS: ♂: there are no special stout spines on tibia II. MALE PALP: The patella bears only one large upright spine. There is one British species.

Zilla diodia (Walckenaer).
(Text-fig. 101)

Aranea diodia C. A. Walckenaer, 1802, p. 200. *Epeira albimacula* J. Blackwall, 1861–4, p. 355. *E. dioidia* O. P.-Cambridge, 1879–81, p. 263. *E. diodia* C. Chyzer and L. Kulczynski, 1891–7, I, p. 134. *Zilla diodia* E. Simon, 1929, p. 667. *Aranea diodia* H. Wiehle, 1931 (1), p. 117.

DESCRIPTION. LENGTH: ♀: about 3–4 mm. ♂: about 2–2·5 mm. CARAPACE: Light brown with a darker, sometimes reddish V, running from foveal region to posterior eyes. ABDOMEN: Text-fig. 101, A. Dark brown markings on silvery white. STERNUM: Light brown with a dark border. LEGS: Femora light brown or cream, obscurely annulated or blotched with sepia; other segments darker brown, similarly marked. EPIGYNE: Text-fig. 101, C. MALE PALP: Text-fig. 101, B. This little spider is easy enough to distinguish by the sexual organs. In the field it can be confused with small specimens of *Meta segmentata mengei* (Bl.), which comes to maturity at about the same time and whose abdominal pattern is somewhat similar (Text-fig. 75).

OCCURRENCE : Uncommon ; in southern counties (as far north as Worcestershire). Found on heather, bushes and trees ; adult from May to July.

4. Genus **SINGA** C. L. Koch 1836.

CHARACTERS OF GENUS. The spiders of this genus differ from those in the genus *Araneus* in having a shiny surface, with few hairs, to the abdomen, which is always oval (Text-fig. 102) and in having relatively shorter legs, which lack the ventral femoral spines almost always present in *Araneus*. The males have no protuberances on coxæ I and II. The male palpal organs are all rather similar.

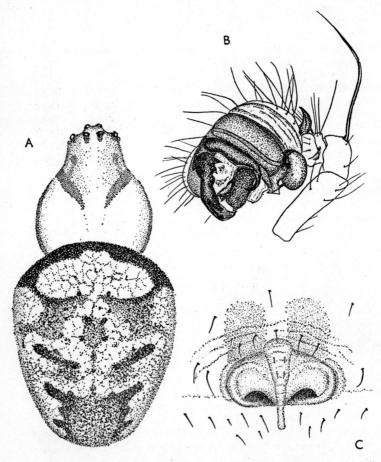

TEXT-FIG. 101.—*Zilla diodia:* A, carapace and abdomen ; B, male palp ; C, epigyne.

Five species occur in Britain : *Singa albovittata* (Westr.), *S. pygmœa* (Sund.), *S. sanguinea* C. L. K., *S. heri* (Hahn), *S. hamata* (Cl.). The first and last have distinct abdominal patterns (Text-fig. 102, A. B).

The others may have a pattern as in Text-fig. 102, C, the light stripes being white or light yellow. But these stripes are developed to a varying degree and in some specimens are quite absent, leaving the abdomen with no pattern.

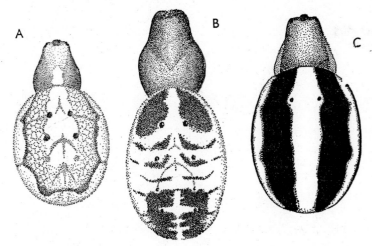

TEXT-FIG. 102.—Carapace and abdomen : A, *Singa albovittata;* B, *S. hamata;* C, *S. pygmaea.*

The chief distinguishing characters, other than the sexual organs, are as follows.

	Abdomen pattern	Dorsal spine on Metatarsi I and II	
S. albovittata	T.-fig. 102, A	None	Post. median eyes separated by *at least* one diameter.
S. pygmœa	T.-fig. 102, C or none	None	Ditto.
S. sanguinea	Ditto or none	None	Ditto.
S. heri	Ditto or none	Present	Post. median eyes separated by *less* than one diameter.
S. hamata	T.-fig. 102, B	Present	Ditto.

L

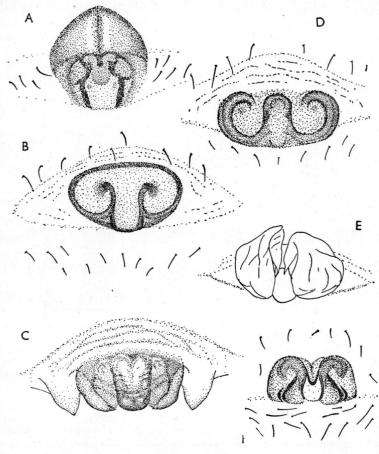

Text-fig. 103.—Epigynes : A, *Singa albovittata;* B, *S. pygmaea;* C, *S. hamata;* D, E, *S. sanguinea;* F, *S. heri.*

Singa albovittata (Westring).
(Text-figs. 102, A ; 103, A ; 104, A)

Epeira albovittata N. Westring, 1851, p. 36, and 1861, p. 59.   *Epeira calva* Blackwall, 1861–4, p. 365.   *Singa albovittata* O. P.-Cambridge, 1879–81, p. 252 C. Chyzer and L. Kulczynski, 1891–7, I, p. 135 ; H. Wiehle, 1931 (1), p. 46.   *Aranei albovittatus* E. Simon, 1929, pp. 703, 704.

DESCRIPTION.   LENGTH : ♀ : 2·5 – 3·5 mm.   ♂ : 2·25–3 mm.   CARA- PACE : ♀ : Thoracic region dark brown, cephalic region lighter.   There a characteristic and distinctive white median patch as in Text-fig. 102, A ♂ : cephalic region darker ;   white median patch may be reduced almost to a line.   ABDOMEN : ♀ : as in Text-fig. 102, A.   Reticulate region light brown, its marginal band deeper brown. Median patches and bands along sides white. (The extent of these and the reticulated areas varies considerably, but the anterior median white patch was present in all specimens examined.) ♂ : only anterior half of the white region present and clear cut ; lateral light bands as in ♀. Intermediate region a darker uniform brown without reticulations. STERNUM : Uniform dark brown. LEGS : ♀ : Pale brownish yellow. ♂ : Femora I and II sometimes darkened, except at base. EPIGYNE : Text-fig. 103, A. The membranous anterior covering is sometimes absent. MALE PALP : Text-fig. 104, A.

OCCURRENCE : Rare. On heather and low plants in England and Scotland. Adult in May and June.

Singa pygmæa (Sundevall).
(Text-figs. 102, C ; 103, B ; 104, B)

Theridion pygmæum C. J. Sundevall, 1831, p. 121 (in part). *Micryphantes anthracinus* (♂) C. L. Koch, 1837, I, p. 11. *Epeira anthracina* J. Blackwall, 1861–4, p. 357. *Singa pygmæa* O. P.-Cambridge, 1879–81, p. 249 ; C. Chyzer and L. Kulczynski, 1891–7, I, p. 135 ; H. Wiehle, 1931 (1), p. 47. *Araneus pygmæus* E. Simon, 1929, pp. 703, 707.

DESCRIPTION. LENGTH : ♀ : 3·5–4·5 mm. ♂ : 2·5–3 mm. CARAPACE : Dark brown to black. Thoracic region with lighter, yellowish brown margins of varying width (Text-fig. 102, C), usually absent in males. ABDOMEN : Text-fig. 102, C. Very dark brown to black with cream, or light yellow, dorsal stripes. There is much variation in these stripes which in some specimens are reduced to fine continuous, or broken, lines, or to dots ; occasionally they are quite absent. STERNUM : Black. LEGS : ♀ : uniform orange to yellow. ♂ : Femur I darkened apically. EPIGYNE : Text-fig. 103, B. There is some variation in the chitinisation of the different parts, but the general design is usually recognisable. MALE PALP : Text-fig. 104, B. This is quite distinct from the others, as long as comparisons are made with the palps in similar positions.

OCCURRENCE : This species is more frequently met with than the others of the genus, but is by no means common. Recorded in England as far north as Yorkshire, and from Eire ; adult in spring and early summer. Usually amongst low vegetation.

Singa sanguinea C. L. Koch.
(Text-figs. 103, D, E ; 104, C)

Singa sanguinea C. L. Koch, 1845, XI, p. 155. *Singa sanguinea* O. P.-Cambridge, 1879–81, p. 251 ; C. Chyzer and L. Kulczynski, 1891–7, I, p. 135 ; H. Wiehle, 1931 (1), p. 49. *Araneus rufulus* E. Simon, 1929, pp. 703, 705.

DESCRIPTION. LENGTH : ♀ : 3–3·75 mm. ♂ : about 3 mm. This species resembles *S. pygmæa* fairly closely and differs from it in the following respects. CARAPACE . ♀ : uniform reddish brown, lighter than in *S. pygmæa* and without the light lateral patches. ♂ : darker (but still lighter than *S. pygmæa*). LEGS : ♂ : femora I and II, and to a lesser extent III and IV, sometimes, but not always, darkened. EPIGYNE : Text-fig. 103, D. Specimens have been found (e.g. in the

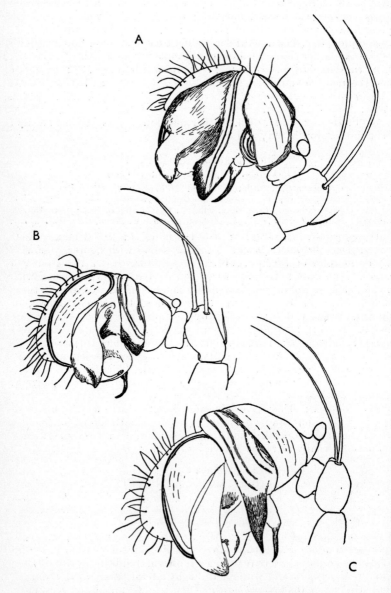

TEXT-FIG. 104.—Male palps : A, *Singa albovittata;* B, *S. pygmaea;* C, *S. sanguinea.*

Koch collection in the British Museum and in Mr. La Touche's collection) in which the epigyne is almost entirely covered with a dark but translucent membrane (Text-fig. 103, E), which must ordinarily become detached. MALE PALP : Text-fig. 104, C. The apophyses, although changing somewhat in appearance according to viewpoint, are quite distinctive and serve to identify the species without doubt.

OCCURRENCE : Very local, in southern counties (as far north as Staffordshire) and in Eire. Usually in heather. Adult in May and June.

Singa heri (Hahn).
(Text-figs. 103, F ; 105, A, B)

Epeira heri C. W. Hahn, 1831, p. 8. *Singa herii* C. Chyzer and L. Kulczynski, 1891–7, I, p. 135 ; O. P.-Cambridge, 1893, p. 160 ; A. R. Jackson, 1912, p. 315 ; H. Wiehle, 1931 (1), p. 48. *Araneus heri* E. Simon, 1929, pp. 703, 705. (It is not possible to establish the identity, in our view, of the *Epeira herii* of J. Blackwall, 1861–4, p. 366.)

DESCRIPTION. LENGTH : ♀ : about 4·25 mm. ♂ : about 2·25 mm. No fresh specimens were available and the description of the colouration is supplemented from O. P.-Cambridge's description (1893, p. 160). CARAPACE : ♀ : yellowish red with oblique dark lines showing junction of head and thoracic region. Head may be darker. ♂ : thoracic region light orange, head deep brown or black, the contrast being striking. ABDOMEN : As in *S. sanguinea* (the brown parts possibly lighter). LEGS : Yellow-brown. Metatarsi I and II with a single dorsal spine. EPIGYNE : Text-fig. 103, F. MALE PALP : Text-fig. 105, B.

OCCURRENCE : Very rare. Recorded from Berkshire and from Wicken Fen (Cambridgeshire). It should be sought by sweeping low plants near water. Probably adult in spring and early summer.

Singa hamata (Clerck).
(=*S. hamata* (Olivier))
(Text-figs. 102, B ; 103, C ; 105, C)

Araneus hamatus C. Clerck, 1757, p. 51. *Aranea tubulosa* C. A. Walckenaer, 1802, p. 200. *Epeira tubulosa* J. Blackwall, 1861–4, p. 364. *Singa hamata* O. P.-Cambridge, 1879–81, p. 248 ; C. Chyzer and L. Kulczynski, 1891–7, I, p. 134 ; H. Wiehle, 1931 (1), p. 42. *Araneus hamatus* E. Simon, 1929, p. 701.

DESCRIPTION. LENGTH : ♀ : 5–6 mm. ♂ : 3·5 mm. (one specimen). CARAPACE : Dark brown, head often darker than the rest. ABDOMEN : Text-fig. 102, B. There is some variation in the pattern, especially in males, but it is always easily recognisable. Colouration dark brown and yellowish white, the central part sometimes with a reddish tinge. STERNUM : Dark brown to black. LEGS : ♀ : yellow-brown, coloured more deeply sometimes at the joints. Metatarsi I and II with a dorsal spine. ♂ : I and II a little darker than III and IV. EPIGYNE : Text-fig. 103, C. MALE PALP : Text-fig. 105, C.

OCCURRENCE : Very rare. On heather, rushes and grass, in England and Scotland.

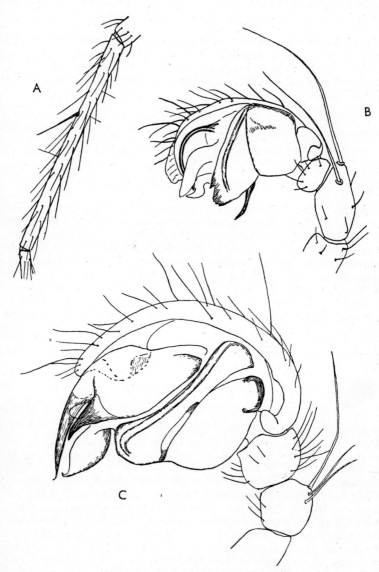

TEXT-FIG. 105.—*Singa heri:* A, metatarsus I ; B, male palp.
   Singa hamata: C, male palp.

5. Genus **CERCIDIA** T. Thorell 1870.

CHARACTERS OF GENUS. The spiders of this genus differ from those of *Araneus* in the following respects. CLYPEUS: Four to five times the diameter of an anterior median eye. ABDOMEN: Covered dorsally with hardened cuticle (a scutum) and provided anteriorly with a series of short, thick spines, almost like teeth, Text-fig. 106, B. LEGS: ♂: spines on tibia II are particularly thick (Text-fig. 106, E) considering the size of the spider. Femora are without ventral spines. There is one British species.

Cercidia prominens (Westring).
(Text-fig. 106)

Singa prominens N. Westring, 1851, p. 35, and 1861, p. 63. *Epeira bella* R. H. Meade, 1861, p. 20; J. Blackwall, 1861–4, p. 343. *Cercidia prominens* O. P.-Cambridge, 1879–81, p. 253; C. Chyzer and L. Kulczynski, 1891–7, I, p. 136; H. Wiehle, 1931 (1), p. 25; B. J. Kaston, 1948, p. 227. *Araneus prominens* E. Simon, 1929, p. 707.

DESCRIPTION. LENGTH: ♀: 3·5–5 mm. ♂: about 4 mm. CARAPACE: Brown, with darker markings as in Text-fig. 106, A. (These are variable in depth and sometimes absent.) ABDOMEN: Fore part pointed and greatly overhanging carapace. Pattern (Text-fig. 106, A) usually rusty-red colour on a lighter brown ground, variable in depth of colouring in its different parts. Lighter median region, in some specimens, constitutes a definite stripe, especially in males. STERNUM: Dark brown; surface punctate. LEGS: Coloured as carapace; annulations of deep rusty brown usually present. Femora I and II often darkened except towards base. EPIGYNE: Text-fig. 106, D. MALE PALP: 106, C.

OCCURRENCE: Uncommon, amongst low plants. England, Wales and Scotland (Berwickshire). Adult in early summer.

6. Genus **ZYGIELLA** F. O. Pickard-Cambridge 1902.

CHARACTERS OF GENUS. The spiders of this genus differ from those of *Araneus* in the following respects. EYES: Distance between posterior medians about equal to distance of these from adjacent laterals. ABDOMEN: Text-fig. 108, A. Shape and pattern are characteristic for the British species. LEGS: ♂: no special spinal armature on tibia II, nor protuberances nor spurs on coxæ I and II. MALE PALP: Paracymbium (a small chitinous piece) independent of the tarsus.

The three British species, *Zygiella x-notata* (Cl.), *Z. atrica* (C.L.K.), and *Z. stræmi* (Thor.) are similar in general appearance. Each builds a web with one segment missing, and a line in the middle of this region leads from the centre of the web to the spider's retreat. (Text-fig. 107).

Zygiella x-notata (Clerck).
(=*Z. litterata* (Olivier)).
(Text-figs. 108, A, C; 109, B)

Araneus x-notatus C. Clerck, 1757, p. 154. *Aranea litterata* A. G. Olivier, 1789, p. 206. *Epeira similis* J. Blackwall, 1861–4, p. 337. *Zilla x-notata* O. P.-Cambridge

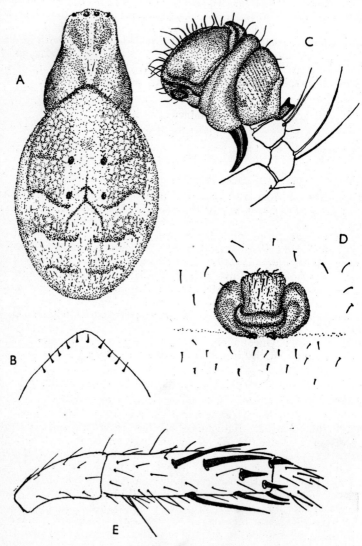

TEXT-FIG. 106.—*Cercidia prominens:* A, carapace and abdomen; B, spines on anterior margin of abdomen; C, male palp; D, epigyne; E, male tibia II, prolateral spines.

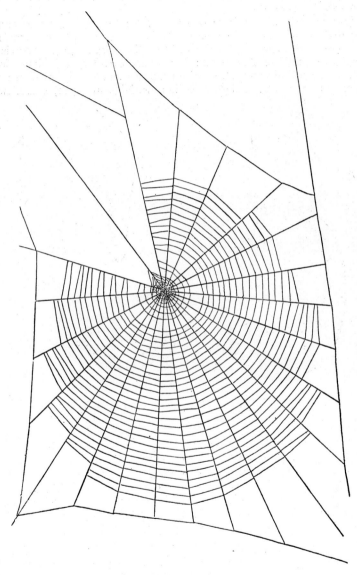

TEXT-FIG. 107.—Web of *Zygiella*.

1879–81, p. 255 ; C. Chyzer and L. Kulczynski, 1891–7, I, p. 137. *Zygiella x-notata* E. Simon, 1929, pp. 663, 665. *Z. litterata* B. J. Kaston, 1948, p. 243. *Zilla litterata* H. Wiehle, 1931 (1), p. 30.

DESCRIPTION. LENGTH : ♀ : 6–6·5 mm. ♂ : 3·5–5 mm. CARAPACE : Brown, depth of colour variable. Cephalic region darker than thoracic ; a darker marking usually in region of fovea (Text-fig. 108, A). There is a thin dark borderline. ABDOMEN : Text-fig. 108, A. General colouration dark brown to grey on a dull white or grey background, but depth of colour very variable. Edges of folium variable in shape, sometimes

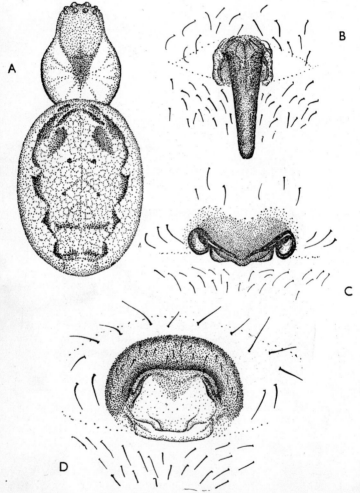

TEXT-FIG. 108.—A, *Zygiella x-notata* carapace and abdomen. Epigynes : B, *Zygiella strœmi*; C, *Z. x-notata*; D, *Z. atrica*.

rounded, sometimes as in Text-fig. 108, A. Dorsal surface sparsely covered with rather long silky hairs (not shown in Text-fig. 108, A). STERNUM : Sparsely covered with long silky hairs. Dark brown with a wide median light yellow mark, usually wedge-shaped, pointed behind. LEGS : Light to dark brown, with darker annuli. EPIGYNE : Text-fig. 108, C. MALE PALP : Text-fig. 109, B.

OCCURRENCE : Distributed all over the British Isles and common in most places. It is most noticeable in window frames of houses, under eaves of sheds etc. Adult from late July until September or later.

Zygiella atrica (C. L. Koch).
(Text-figs. 108, D ; 109, A)

Eucharia atrica C. L. Koch, 1845, XII, p. 201. *Epeira calophylla* J. Blackwall, 1861–4, p. 338. *Zilla atrica* O. P.-Cambridge, 1879–81, p. 257 ; C. Chyzer and L. Kulczynski, 1891–7, I, p. 137 ; H. Wiehle, 1931 (1), p. 33. *Zygiella atrica* E. Simon, 1929, pp. 661, 665 ; B. J. Kaston, 1948, p. 243.

DESCRIPTION. This species resembles *Z. x-notata* closely in size and general appearance. Colouration of the abdomen is quite as, if not more, variable, although there is frequently a rusty red tinge to the anterior dark patches and in the edges of the folium of living specimens. EPIGYNE : Text-fig. 108, D. MALE PALP : Text-fig. 109, A. The long tibia serves to distinguish this species from *Z. x-notata* immediately.

OCCURRENCE : Distributed all over the British Isles. Common in many places and abundant locally. Found on gorse and bushes and low plants generally, also amongst rocks by the sea close to high tide mark. It is not so partial to human habitations as the last species, but may be found there.

Zygiella strœmi (Thorell).
(Text-figs. 108, B ; 109, C)

Zilla strœmi T. Thorell, 1870, p. 235 ; C. Chyzer and L. Kulczynski, 1891–7, I, p. 137 ; A. R. Jackson, 1914, p. 125 ; H. Wiehle, 1931 (1), p. 36. *Zygiella strœmi* E. Simon, 1929, p. 664.

DESCRIPTION. LENGTH : ♀ : about 4 mm. ♂ : 3–3·5 mm. CARAPACE : Yellow, with a darker V-mark at junction of head and thoracic region. Sometimes with whole cephalic region darker than the thoracic. ABDOMEN : Design generally typical of genus. Dark edges of folium generally wide ; there is sometimes a dark median band. Colour of these darker parts black (as opposed to red or brown). STERNUM : Yellow, becoming brown towards edges, which are dark. LEGS : Yellow, with faint black annulations on femora (seen in fresh specimens). Tips of tibiæ and metatarsi darkened and tibiæ sometimes with black blotches or complete annulations. EPIGYNE : Text-fig. 108, B. This is quite different from those of the other species. MALE PALP : Text-fig. 109, C.

OCCURRENCE : The Black Wood of Rannoch (Perthshire), Wytham Woods (Berkshire). In rather small frail webs on the trunks of pine trees. Recorded as adult in June in Scotland and in August and September in Berkshire ; its season may well prove to be extended.

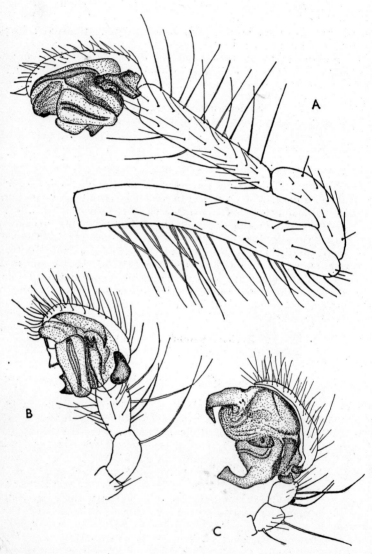

TEXT-FIG. 109.—Male palps: A, *Zygiella atrica;* B, *Z. x-notata;* C, *Z. strœmi.*

7. Genus **MANGORA** O. P.-Cambridge 1889.

CHARACTERS OF GENUS. CARAPACE : With a median cleft (best seen from a little in front). EYES : Medians closer to each other than to adjacent laterals. Median ocular trapezium longer than broad. ABDOMEN : Text-fig. 110, A. LEGS : ♀ : tibia III with a group of trichobothria which have a plumose structure (Text-fig. 110, D). ♂ : no special spines on tibia II. MALE PALP : Text-fig. 110, B. This has a single upright spine on the patella. Sexes very similar, but male smaller. There is one British species.

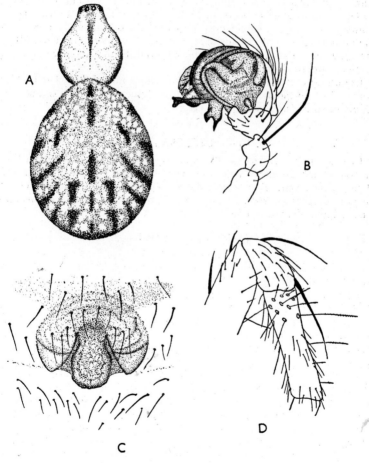

TEXT-FIG. 110.—*Mangora acalypha:* A, carapace and abdomen ; B, male palp ; C, epigyne ; D, trichobothria on tibia III (♀).

Mangora acalypha (Walckenaer).
(Text-fig. 110)

Aranea acalypha C. A. Walckenaer, 1802, p. 199. *Epeira acalypha* J. Blackwall, 1861–4, p. 341 ; O. P.-Cambridge, 1879–81, p. 264 ; C. Chyzer and L. Kulczynski, 1891–7, I, p. 133. *Mangora acalypha* E. Simon, 1929, p. 667 ; H. Wiehle, 1931 (1), p. 23.

DESCRIPTION. LENGTH : ♀ : about 4 mm. ♂ : about 2·5 mm. CARAPACE : Text-fig. 110, A. Light yellow-brown, with a dark margin. ABDOMEN : Text-fig. 110, A. Light parts made up of small white spots (as seen under the microscope) on a light grey or green-brown ground ; sometimes the white spots are confluent, to give cream coloured areas. Dark parts black. (A seemingly distinct colour variety is described by O. P.-Cambridge, 1879-81, p. 265). STERNUM : Dark brown. LEGS : Light yellow-brown, sometimes with dark blotches, rarely amounting to annulations except at ends of segments. EPIGYNE : Text-fig. 110, C. MALE PALP : Text-fig. 110, B. There is no difficulty about the identity of this species.

OCCURRENCE : Local, but then sometimes abundant. On heather, gorse, etc. In England (as far north as Lancashire), Wales and Eire. Adult in spring and summer.

8. Genus CYCLOSA A. Menge 1866.

CHARACTERS OF GENUS. The spiders of this genus differ from those of the genus *Araneus* in the following respects. EYES : Both rows strongly recurved. ABDOMEN : Extended posteriorly, Text-fig. 111, A. LEGS : Rather shorter. The web is provided with a *stabilimentum* (see below). There is one British species.

Cyclosa conica (Pallas).
(Text-fig. 111)

Aranea conica P. S. Pallas, 1772, p. 48. *Epeira conica* J. Blackwall, 1861–4, p. 362. *Cyclosa conica* O. P.-Cambridge, 1879–81, p. 246, and recent authors.

DESCRIPTION. LENGTH : ♀ : 4·5–7 mm. ♂ ; 3–4·5 mm. (measured to the end of the abdominal protuberance). CARAPACE : Black in living specimens, with white hairs. In preserved specimens, brown with a darker V at junction of head and thoracic region, with faint dark radiating striæ. ♀ : with a circular depression in foveal region ; ♂, with crossed longitudinal and transverse depressions. ABDOMEN : Shape characteristic, Text-fig. 111, A. (There is considerable variation in the extent of the posterior protuberance, especially in immature specimens : see Mary and B. J. Marples, 1937, p. 220.) Colouration extremely variable ; light parts cream to deep rusty red marbled with black, dark brown or greyish green. Ventrally : a pair of light yellow wedges point inwards on a dark ground. STERNUM : Black. LEGS : Short. Light yellow or cream, sometimes annulated clearly, sometimes scarcely at all. ♂ : some thick short spines on tibia II and a protuberance on coxa I (cf. *Araneus*). EPIGYNE : Text-fig. 111, D. MALE PALP :

Text-fig. 111, C. This spider is quite distinct and cannot be confused with any other British species. The web is provided with a *stabilimentum*, a thick band of silk extending along a radius above and below the hub. (See Bristowe, 1941, pp. 245, 249 and fig. 60.)

OCCURRENCE : Frequent in shrubberies and woods, often in dark places and on evergreens. Distributed all over the British Isles.

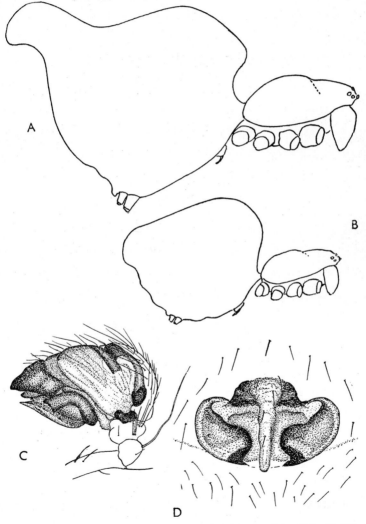

TEXT-FIG. 111.—*Cyclosa conica:* A, carapace and abdomen, ♀ (profile) ; B, ditto, smaller specimen ; C, male palp ; D, epigyne.

9. Genus **ARGIOPE** J. C. Savigny 1827.

CHARACTERS OF GENUS. CARAPACE : As in Text-fig. 112, A, notice-ably flat, with a transverse furrow in the foveal region (not easily seen). Head relatively small. EYES : Posterior row rather strongly procurved (Text-fig. 112, A) ; less marked in males. ABDOMEN : Shape as in Text-fig. 112, A, rather flat. LEGS : Metatarsus and tarsus I together longer than tibia with patella I. The males are much smaller than females. Webs are characterised by the presence of a *stabilimentum*, a zig-zag band of silk constructed between two adjacent radii and forming a diameter to the circle of the webs. There is one British species.

Argiope bruennichi (Scopoli).
(Text-fig. 112)

Aranea bruennichi J. A. Scopoli, 1772, p. 125. *Argiope bruennichi* C. Chyzer and L. Kulczynski, 1891–7, I. p. 117; E. Simon, 1929, p. 713; H. Wiehle, 1931 (1), p. 14; W. S. Bristowe, 1944, p. 829.

DESCRIPTION. LENGTH : ♀ : 11–14 mm. ♂ : about 4 mm. CARA-PACE : ♀ : Text-fig. 112, A. Black markings on a yellow-white ground ; the whole region covered with fine silky hairs, giving a silvery appearance in living spiders. Head relatively small. ♂ : Pattern essentially the same, but outlines blurred. Head more rounded. Clypeus, 1.5 to 2 times diameter of an anterior median eye. EYES : Posterior row strongly procurved in ♀, not strongly in ♂. ABDOMEN : ♀ : Text-fig. 112, A, flat and blunt behind. Colour : yellow-white, or cream, with black markings. Ventrally : a black oblong extends from epigastric fold to spinners and is flanked by a pair of light cream-brown bands. There are two light patches at each side of, and another posterior to, the spinners. ♂ : pattern absent, with only a few scattered light spots. STERNUM : Black, with conspicuous wide light median band. CHELI-CERÆ : ♀ : Light yellow-brown with dark reticulations, except apically on the inside. ♂ : Light brown all over, almost white. LEGS : ♀ : Light yellow-brown, clearly annulated with black. ♂ : similar, but annula-tions obscure or absent. EPIGYNE : Text-fig. 112, C. There is a certain amount of variation in the size and shape of the scape. MALE PALP : Text-fig. 112, B. The species is very distinct and cannot be mistaken for any other occurring at present in the British Isles.

OCCURRENCE : Locally frequent in Kent, Sussex, Hampshire, Dorsetshire. First recorded in 1922 from near Rye (Sussex).

10. Genus **THERIDIOSOMA** O. P.-Cambridge 1879.

CHARACTERS OF GENUS. CARAPACE : Clypeus wider than in most ARGIOPIDÆ (Text-fig. 113, A, B). EYES : Posterior row more or less procurved. Posterior medians larger than posterior laterals and further from them than from each other (Text-fig. 113, C). Median ocular trapezium longer than broad. Anterior medians darker than the rest. ABDOMEN : Text-fig. 113, A. CHELICERÆ : No lateral condyle. LABIUM : Much broader than long. PALPS : ♀, with no claw.

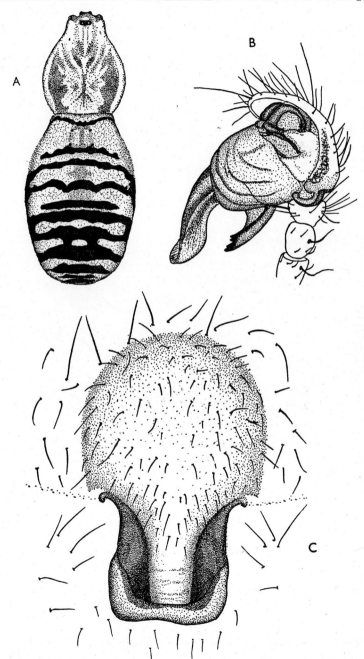

TEXT-FIG. 112.—*Argiope bruennichi:* A, carapace and abdomen; B, male palp;
C, epigyne.

The appearance of the single British species, *Theridiosoma gemmosum*
(L.K.) is very like that of a small member of the family THERIDIIDÆ,
but it differs from these in the absence of the comb of bristles on tarsus
IV, and is to be regarded as a diminutive Argiopid. It spins a small
orb web.

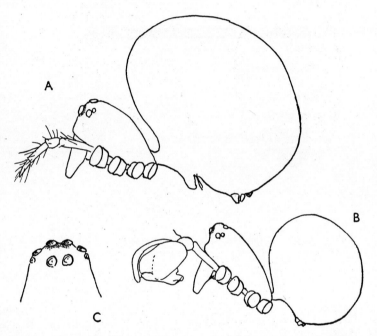

TEXT-FIG. 113.—*Theridiosoma gemmosum:* A, female carapace and abdomen;
B, male ditto ; C, eyes (from above).

Theridiosoma gemmosum (L. Koch).
(Text-figs. 113, 114)

Theridion gemmosum L. Koch, 1877, p. 181. *Theridiosoma argenteolum* O. P.
Cambridge, 1879, p. 194, and 1879–81, p. 428. *T. gemmosum* E. Simon, 1926, p. 319
H. Wiehle, 1931 (1), p. 131 ; B. J. Kaston, 1948, p. 262.

DESCRIPTION. LENGTH : ♀ : about 2 mm. ♂ : about 1·5 mm
CARAPACE : ♀ : light brown with faint dusky markings. Dark pigment
round anterior median eyes. ♂ : similar with more definite dusky
irregular reticulate lines on head and in thoracic area. ABDOMEN
♀ : very globose (Text-fig. 113, A) ; dorsal surface silvery with reticulations, usually having a darker wedge-shaped mark in posterior half

tapering in front. Sides often light brown, without the silver colour. ♂ : dark regions more emphasised, sometimes extending into fore part. STERNUM : Dark brown, yellow towards the middle. CHELICERÆ : Rather long and tapering, coloured as carapace. LEGS : Light uniform yellow. EPIGYNE : Text-fig. 114, A. MALE PALP : Text-figs. 114, B. This is large compared to body-size ; the tibia is hidden behind the tarsus when the palp is viewed from the side.

OCCURRENCE : Rare. Found in herbage and bushes in damp places. Recorded from Dorsetshire, Hampshire, Sussex, Surrey and Kent, and from Eire. Males found adult in May and August.

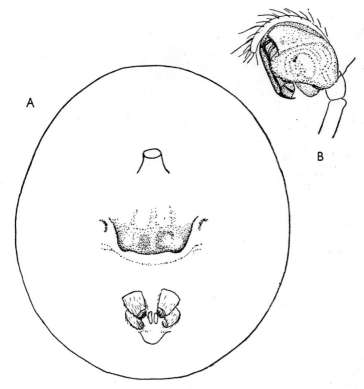

TEXT-FIG. 114.—*Theridiosoma gemmosum:* A, ventral side of female abdomen, showing epigyne ; B, male palp (tibia is hidden from the outside).

24. Family : LINYPHIIDÆ.

This large family, which contains more than 250 British species, is distinguished from the other families mainly by the *absence* of the positive characters delineating those families. The one positive distinction in the external morphology lies in the form and position of the paracymbium of the male palp, and in the palpal organs.

CHARACTERS OF FAMILY. CARAPACE : Of widely variable proportions. In the sub-family ERIGONINÆ (see below) the male head is often raised into a lobe (e.g. Text-fig. 130, B), or bears corniculers or other protuberances, or has sulci (grooves) running backwards from the posterior eyes (Text-fig. 163, H), or has holes in the sides. In the sub-family LINYPHIINÆ (see below) there are no such lobes, etc., but the head is occasionally raised anteriorly (e.g. *Floronia*, *Bolyphantes*). CLYPEUS : Of variable width, but generally wider than in ARGIOPIDÆ (exception : *Tapinopa*). EYES : In two rows, heterogeneous, with anterior medians slightly darker. ABDOMEN : Usually without pattern dorsally, but some Linyphiine species have well-defined patterns. Occasionally coriaceous or with a dorsal scutum (particularly in males) (Text-fig. 116, D). STERNUM : Heart-shaped, but may be relatively wide or narrow, pointed or truncated posteriorly. LABIUM : Rebordered. CHELICERÆ : Variable in dentition and development (for dentition, cf. J. E. Hull (1911 (1)). Outer sides have horizontal stridulating striæ visible in most species, but not all. LEGS : May be relatively short and stout, as in most Erigoninæ, *Centromerus*, *Meioneta*, etc., or relatively long and thin as in *Linyphia*, etc. They may be virtually spineless (as in *Lophocarenum*) or with numerous spines (as in *Linyphia*). Tarsi with three claws, which vary in dentition from large teeth to virtually none ; never with auxiliary claws (cf. ARGIOPIDÆ). Metatarsi with one dorsal trichobothrium (except only in *Mengea scopigera* where there are 3–4) ; fourth metatarsus sometimes without this trichobothrium. Tibiæ with two or more trichobothria dorsally. Tarsus of fourth leg without serrated ventral bristles characteristic of THERIDIIDÆ. ♀ PALP : With or without a claw. EPIGYNE : Very variable ; may be a simple plate covering the genital orifice, with the outlines of the spermathecæ, etc., showing through the integument, as in many Erigonine species ; or a more complex form in the Linyphiine species, many of which have a long or short tongue-like process ("scape", "languette") projecting backwards or downwards from the anterior or posterior border of the orifice. MALE PALP : Tibia with or without apophyses ; femur and patella occasionally have an apophysis. The tarsus (cymbium) may be drawn out above or posteriorly into a protuberance. The *palpal organs* vary from relatively simple to complex, but always have a chitinised paracymbium lying close to the apical face of the tibia and attached to the cymbium by an inconspicuous membraneous portion. The paracymbium varies from a simple crescentic or horse-shoe-shaped piece in most Erigonine species (*p*, Text-fig. 117, F) to a more complex development of this which may be equipped with teeth and accessory branches (*p*, Text-fig.

210, C). The position of the genital bulb, the form and position of the paracymbium and the form of the palpal organs are characteristic of the Family (Archer, 1951). For a discussion of the anatomy of the male palpal organs, see e.g. Comstock (1940), Blauvelt (1936), Zorsch (1937), Grassé (1949).

Some females of Linyphiidæ (particularly in Erigoninæ) do not differ notably in external morphology from the females of some genera of THERIDIIDÆ (e.g. *Robertus, Enoplognatha*, where the serrated bristles on tarsus IV are only weakly developed).

Biologically, the Family appears to be distinctive in the form of the web, a sheet which may or may not have lines above it ; the spider lives and runs on the underside of the sheet. The species, with few exceptions, are ground-living, and are found in moss, grass, vegetable detritus, under stones, etc. ; and occasionally on bushes and young trees.

The classification of the LINYPHIIDÆ has offered special difficulties, owing to the large number of species and their homogeneity, and to the few adequate characters apart from the sex organs. The family is split by most authorities into two divisions or sub-families, the LINY-PHIINÆ and ERIGONINÆ. Many authors have raised these groups to family status, calling them respectively Linyphiidæ and Micry-phantidæ (Bertkau, 1872), or Erigonidæ (Gerhardt, 1923). For our purpose we recognise two such sub-divisions, but regard them merely as having sub-family rank. On the one hand there is no distinct dividing line and, on the other, the differences between the most extreme forms seem to be not more than one can expect within a single family.

For the two sub-families, we follow those authors who use the names Linyphiinæ and Erigoninæ. Two good reasons seem to us to exclude the use of the name Micryphantidæ ; first, the genus *Micryphantes* is of doubtful validity and no longer recognised by us ; and second, if the genus *Micryphantes* were used in its most recently accepted form it would clearly fall within the sub-family Linyphiinæ, as does *Meioneta* to which its species have been transferred.

The division into Linyphiinæ and Erigoninæ is based broadly on the characters shown in the following table :

			Linyphiinæ	*Erigoninæ*
(a) Tibia IV	...		Two dorsal spines	One dorsal spine
(b) ♀ Palp	...	...	With claw	Without claw
(c) ♀ Epigyne	...		Relatively complex, often with scape	Relatively simple
(d) ♂ Palpal organs	...		Relatively complex	Relatively simple
(e) ♂ Palpal tibia	...		Without apophysis	With apophysis
(f) ♂ Paracymbium	...		Large, relatively complex	Small, simple
(g) ♂ Head	...	...	Not raised into lobe or with protuberances	Sometimes raised into lobe or with other protuberances
(h) Maxillæ	...	...	Practically parallel	Converging slightly in front of labium

Of these characters (c) and (d) merge into one another, and the remainder are not quite constant. In fact, no sharp division between the sub-families can be made, and there are some genera which are intermediate between the extremes.

For convenience, however, the Family is divided here into two groups (corresponding roughly to the two sub-families) depending essentially on the presence of one or two dorsal spines on the fourth tibia. The sub-families are split up into numerous genera, which particularly in the Erigoninæ, often appear at first sight to have rather ill-defined characters. With the males, the form of the palpal organs is most useful for grouping the species into genera, and numerous genera have been established based on male characters alone. With females, much more difficulty arises, and an unknown female could often be placed with certainty in a genus only when accompanied by its male. This lack of clear generic characters for many females has made the drawing up of a Key for Erigonine females particularly difficult. Keys to the Erigonine genera given by earlier authors (e.g. E. Simon, 1892 ; W. Falconer, 1910) were based to a considerable degree on the eye arrangements and the degree of curvature of the two rows of eyes. Such characters are frequently unsatisfactory ; the apparent curvature, in particular, differs so much depending on the angle of viewing. Furthermore, the male and female of a species are often so different that one key of this sort cannot apply to both sexes. Hull (1920) has proposed divisions based in part on the position and shape of the spiracular fold on the ventral side of the abdomen, a character which in practice seems to be of little value. In the present work, the generic keys (particularly for the Erigoninæ) are based to a large extent on the position of the metatarsal trichobothria, and the tibial spines (see J. Denis, 1948(3), 1949 ; Millidge, 1951). Because the two sexes of an Erigonine species often differ considerably one from the other, a separate key is provided for each sex ; this is not necessary with the Linyphiine species.

With the Erigonine species particularly, it has not been found possible to formulate " easy " keys, nor are they probably infallible. It may well be that the positions of the trichobothria and the lengths of the spines, for example, are not quite constant in the members of any one species, though the extent of any such variation remains to be dis-covered. It is hoped that the keys, which are applicable only to adults, will serve to guide the student through the maze of the genera.

The characters used have the disadvantage that if the legs are missing, or the trichobothria or spines are broken off, the keys may be valueless. The trichobothria are, however, very tenacious and even when broken off the circle at the base is frequently still visible.

Notes on Characters used in the Keys

TRICHOBOTHRIUM (Tm) : This is a long fine hair, rising practically vertically from the centre of a small circle on the leg, on its dorsal side. Several trichobothria are present on each leg, but the metatarsi (in the LINYPHIIDÆ) never bear more than one. The position of insertion of the trichobothrium on a metatarsus, while apparently fairly constant in any one species, may vary considerably from one genus to another. The method of expressing the position of the trichobothrium on the metatarsus is shown in Text-fig. 115, A, where the position is given by the expression : Tm I (i.e. on the metatarsus of leg I)=a/b (expressed as a decimal fraction).

TIBIAL SPINES : The tibiæ may have one or two dorsal spines (or none, in a few cases). In addition, there may be lateral and ventral spines. It is the dorsal spines which are mainly used in the keys. If only one dorsal spine is present, this is located in the basal half ; if a second spine is also present, this is in the apical half of the tibia. The spines are usually readily distinguishable from the hairs, being stouter,

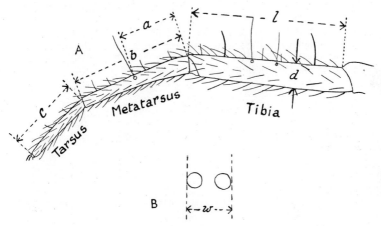

TEXT-FIG. 115.—A, leg of Erigonine spider ; B, eyes. (For explanation, see text.)

usually slightly curved (particularly in the Erigoninæ), and more upright (Text-fig. 115, A) ; they are usually longer than the hairs, but not invariably so. In the genera keyed as possessing two tibial spines, both spines should fulfil these conditions, and an erect hair (often present) towards the apex of the tibia should not be considered as a second spine. The *position* of a tibial spine is expressed in a similar manner to the position of a trichobothrium. The *length* of a tibial spine is expressed by the ratio : *length of spine/diameter of tibia* at point of insertion.

LEG SEGMENTS : The stoutness of the leg segments is expressed by the ratio : *length/diameter* (at the widest point, as seen from the side), i.e. by the ratio l/d in Text-fig. 115, A. The ratio of the length of the metatarsus to that of the tarsus is the ratio b/c (Text-fig. 115, A).

EYES : The term " width of anterior (or posterior) median eyes " signifies the total width (w in Text-fig. 115, B).

KEY TO SUB-FAMILIES.

Tibia IV with one dorsal spine, *and* all metatarsi spineless:

ERIGONINÆ.

Tibia IV with two dorsal spines, or if with one spine only, then with in addition one short spine on metatarsi I and II:

LINYPHIINÆ.

The genera included here under these two sub-families are as follows:

ERIGONINÆ.

1. Ceratinella	23. Peponocranium	45. Lophomma
2. Walckenaera	24. Pocadicnemis	46. Mioxena
3. Wideria	25. Hypselistes	47. Saloca
4. Trachynella	26. Œdothorax	48. Jacksonella
5. Prosopotheca	27. Trichopterna	49. Gongylidiellum
6. Tigellinus	28. Lophocarenum	50. Micrargus
7. Cornicularia	29. Silometopus	51. Notioscopus
8. Dicymbium	30. Mecopisthes	52. Glyphesis
9. Entelecara	31. Cnephalocotes	53. Erigonella
10. Mœbelia	32. Acartauchenius	54. Savignia
11. Erigonidium	33. Trichoncus	55. Diplocephalus
12. Gnathonarium	34. Styloctetor	56. Araeoncus
13. Tmeticus	35. Anacotyle	57. Panamomops
14. Gongylidium	36. Evansia	58. Lessertia
15. Dismodicus	37. Tiso	59. Asthenargus
16. Hypomma	38. Troxochrus	60. Caledonia
17. Metopobactrus	39. Minyriolus	61. Typhocrestus
18. Hybocoptus	40. Tapinocyba	62. Collinsia
19. Baryphyma	41. Aulacocyba	63. Scotargus
20. Gonatium	42. Perimones	64. Diplocentria
21. Minyrioloides	43. Thyreosthenius	65. Erigone
22. Maso	44. Monocephalus	66. Rhæbothorax
		67. Eboria

LINYPHIINÆ.

68. Donacochara	79. Agyneta	90. Drapetisca
69. Leptorhoptrum	80. Meioneta	91. Tapinopa
70. Drepanotylus	81. Microneta	92. Floronia
71. Phaulothrix	82. Maro	93. Taranucnus
72. Hilaira	83. Centromerus	94. Labulla
73. Halorates	84. Centromerita	95. Stemonyphantes
74. Ostearius	85. Sintula	96. Bolyphantes
75. Hillhousia	86. Oreonetides	97. Lepthyphantes
76. Porrhomma	87. Macrargus	98. Helophora
77. Syedrula	88. Bathyphantes	99. Linyphia
78. Syedra	89. Pœciloneta	100. Mengea

KEY TO ERIGONINE GENERA

The position of the trichobothrium in a species is probably not absolutely constant, and where the position of Tm I appears to be marginal between two groups in the key, the species should be followed into both parts of the key if necessary. In all cases the identity should be confirmed by the species description, and particularly by the sex organs.

Females

1. Metatarsus IV with a trichobothrium .... 2.
— Metatarsus IV without a trichobothrium .... 27.
2. Head elevated conically (Text-fig. 118, D); superior tarsal claws with numerous large teeth (Text-fig. 118, F) .... (2) *Walckenaera*.
— Head not elevated in this way .... 3.
3. Tibiæ and metatarsi I-II with two rows of very stout spines ventrally (Text-fig. 133, F) .... (22) *Maso*.
— Stout spines of this kind absent .... 4.
4. Tm. I ca. 0·4 .... 5.
— Tm. I 0·5 (or only very slightly less)–0·55 .... 6.
— Tm. I 0·6–0·65 .... 9.
— Tm. I 0·7–0·8 .... 14.
— Tm. I 0·85–0·95 .... 21.
5. Abdomen coriaceous, with four impressed dots dorsally, or with dorsal scutum. Sternum slightly broader than long .... (1) *Ceratinella*.
— Abdomen not coriaceous, without impressed dots. Sternum slightly longer than broad .... (3) *Wideria* (*fugax* only).
6. Superior tarsal claws with a few minute teeth or none (cf. Text-fig. 145, E) .... 7.
— Superior tarsal claws with large teeth (Text-fig. 118, F) 8.
7. Sternum dark and rugose; epigyne with median fissure (Text-figs. 129, E, F) .... (8) *Dicymbium*.
— Sternum not rugose; epigynes without median fissure (9) *Entelecara* (*acuminata, erythropus,* and *errata*).
8. Posterior median eyes less than 1 diam. apart .... (5) *Prosopotheca* (*incisa* only).
  (3) *Wideria* (*antica, cucullata, nodosa*).
  (7) *Cornicularia* (*cuspidata* only).
— Posterior median eyes 1 diam. or more apart .... (4) *Trachynella*.
  (7) *Cornicularia* (*vigilax* only).
9. Superior tarsal claws with large teeth (Text-fig. 118, F) 10.
— Superior tarsal claws with a few minute teeth or none 11.
10. Posterior median eyes less than 1 diam. apart .... (5) *Prosopotheca* (except *incisa*).
  (7) *Cornicularia* (*unicornis* only).
  (3) *Wideria* (*melanocephala* and *capito*).
  (6) *Tigellinus*.
— Posterior median eyes 1 diam. or more apart ....
11. Metatarsus I/tarsus I ca. 1·1 .... (10) *Mœbelia*.
— Metatarsus I/tarsus I greater than 1·1................... 12.
12. Epigynes of form shown in Text-fig. 145, A–F, with central area limited on either side by a black line ... (26) *Œdothorax*.

— Epigynes of different form ....   13.

13. Anterior median eyes practically 1 diam. apart.
     Width of clypeus equal to width of anterior median
     eyes. Abdomen without median whitish stripe ......   (11) *Erigonidium.*

— Anterior median eyes 0·5 diam. apart. Width of
     clypeus practically 1·5 times width of anterior
     median eyes. Abdomen with faint median whitish
     stripe ....   (12) *Gnathonarium.*

14. Superior tarsal claws with large teeth (as Text-fig.   (7) *Cornicularia*
     118, F) ....   (*kochi* only).

— Superior tarsal claws with only a few minute teeth or
     none ....   15.

15. Tibiæ I–II with two dorsal spines, tibiæ III–IV with
     one dorsal spine ....,..............   16.

— Tibiæ I–IV with one dorsal spine ....   18.

16. Tibial spines long (e.g. tibia IV spine ca. 2 diams. of
     tibia). Tibia I *l/d* ca. 7·5 ....   (14) *Gongylidium.*

— Tibial spines shorter (e.g. tibia IV spine ca. 1 diam. of
     tibia). Tibia I *l/d* ca. 5 ....   17.

17. Position of tibia I spine (basal) 0·3 or more ....   (21) *Minyrioloides.*
— Position of tibia I spine (basal) less than 0·3............   (13) *Tmeticus.*

18. Position of tibia I spine 0·3 or more ....   19.
— Position of tibia I spine not more than 0·2...............   20.

19. Clypeus width ca. 1·5 times width of anterior median
     eyes. Tibia I *l/d* ca. 4·5. Length of tibial spines
     1 diam. or more of tibia ....   (15) *Dismodicus.*

— Clypeus width ca. 1·0 times width of anterior median
     eyes. Tibia I *l/d* ca. 6. Length of tibial spines less   (16) *Hypomma*
     than 1 diam. of tibia ....   (except *cornuta*).

20. Spine on tibia IV ca. 0·35. Tibia I *l/d* ca. 4. Epigyne
     (Text-fig. 138, H) ....   (17) *Metopobactrus.*

— Spine on tibia IV ca. 0·23. Tibia I *l/d* ca. 6. Epigyne
     (Text-fig. 139, D)...   (18) *Hybocoptus.*

21. Length of tibia IV spine 1·5 diam. or more of tibia ...   22.
— Length of tibia IV spine less than 1·5 diam. of tibia   23.

22. Spine on tibia I ca. 0·24, on tibia IV ca. 0·35. Epigyne
     (Text-fig. 142, C) ....   (23) *Peponocranium.*

— Spine on tibia I ca. 0·14, on tibia IV ca. 0·23. Epigyne
     (Text-fig. 143, D)...   (24) *Pocadicnemis.*

23. Carapace with radiating rows of minute pits. (Ab-
     domen coriaceous, with four large reddish impressed
     dots) ....   (27) *Trichopterna*
                                                                                  (*mengei* only).

— Carapace without pits...   24.

24. Tibiæ I–II with two rows of stout bristles ventrally ...   25.
— Tibiæ I–II without such bristles ....   26.

25. Length of tibia IV spine more than 1 diam. of tibia...   (25) *Hypselistes.*
— Length of tibia IV spine less than 1 diam. of tibia...   (19) *Baryphyma.*

26. Tibia I *l/d* ca. 7 ; tibia I slightly curved, with gouty
     patella. Reddish spiders ....   (20) *Gonatium.*

— Tibia I *l/d* ca. 5 ; tibia I straight. Not noticeably   (27) *Trichopterna*
     reddish ....   (*thorelli* only).

27. Tibiæ I–IV with one spine or none dorsally ....   28.
— Tibiæ I–II with two spines, tibiæ III–IV with one spine   47.
— Tibiæ I–III with two spines, tibia IV with one spine   58.
28. Tm. I less than 0·5 ....   29.

— Tm. I 0·5–0·6 .... 33.

— Tm. I more than 0·6 .... 39.

29. Dark-coloured spider, with sternum dark and very rugose. Tm. I ca. 0·37. Epigyne (Text-fig. 155, A) ... (31) *Cnephalocotes.*

— Less dark, with sternum not rugose. Tm. I more than 0·37 .... 30.

30. Metatarsi and tarsi not very unequal in length (MT I/t I ca. 1·1, MT IV/t IV ca. 1·2) .... 31.

— Metatarsi and tarsi more unequal in length (MT I/t I ca. 1·25, MT IV/t IV ca. 1·5) .... 32.

31. Eyes large, with posteriors ca. 1 diam. or less apart. Tibia I spine ca. 0·1, tibia IV spine ca. 0·15 .... (41) *Aulacocyba.*

— Eyes small, with posteriors ca. 2–2·5 diam. apart. Tibia I spine ca. 0·2, tibia IV spine ca. 0·25–0·3. Spines slightly serrated .... (32) *Acartauchenius.*

32. Tibia I l/d 6–7, tibia IV l/d ca. 10. Epigyne (Text-fig. 156, D) .... (33) *Trichoncus.*

— Tibia I l/d 5, tibia IV l/d 6–7. Epigyne (Text-fig. 157, C) .... (34) *Styloctetor.*

33. Tibia IV spine 0·3 or more (or spine absent) .... 34.

— Tibia IV spine less than 0·3 .... 36.

34. Posterior median eyes 2 diam. apart. Spines and hairs slightly serrated. Abdomen without impressed dots dorsally .... (36) *Evansia.*

— Posterior median eyes less than 2 diam. apart. Spines and hairs not serrated. Abdomen with four reddish impressed dots dorsally .... 35.

35. Posterior row of eyes procurved .... (28) *Lophocarenum* (except *radicicola*).

— Posterior row of eyes practically straight .... (35) *Anacotyle.*

36. Eyes rather small, with posterior medians more than 1 diam. apart .... (37) *Tiso.*

— Eyes larger, with posterior medians 1 diam. or less apart .... 37.

37. Sternum rugose. Abdomen with four reddish impressed dots dorsally. Epigyne (Text-fig. 160, F) ... (38) *Troxochrus.*

— Sternum not rugose. Abdomen without such dots ... 38.

38. Dark coloured spider. Anterior median eyes ca. 1 diam. apart. Epigyne (Text-fig. 161, B) .... (39) *Minyriolus.*

— Pale coloured spiders. Anterior median eyes practically touching.. (40) *Tapinocyba.*

39. Abdomen with well-defined dorsal scutum (Text-fig. 152, H) .... (28) *Lophocarenum* (*radicicola* only).

— Abdomen without dorsal scutum .... 40.

40. Tibiæ I–II with two rows of seven–eight long spines ventrally. Epigyne (Text-fig. 164, D) .... (42) *Perimones.*

— Tibiæ I–II without such spines .... 41.

41. Tibia I spine short, ca. 0·5 times diam. of tibia, or scarcely more .... 42.

— Tibia I spine longer than 1 diam. of tibia .... 46.

42. Tibia I spine 0·2 or more. Larger spider (ca. 2·5 mm. in length). Epigyne (Text-fig. 138, D) .... (16) *Hypomma* (*cornuta* only).

— Tibia I spine less than 0·2. Smaller spiders (ca. 1·5–2 mm.) .... 43.

43. Tm. I 0·75–0·8 .... (29) *Silometopus* (except *interjectus*)

— Tm. I 0·6–0·7 .... 44.

44. Posterior eyes small, 1·5–2 diam. apart. Epigyne (Text-fig. 165, E) .... (43) *Thyreosthenius* (*biovatus* only).

— Posterior eyes rather larger, not more than 1·5 diam. apart .... 45.

45. Tibia IV spine ca. 0·44. Tm. I ca. 0·6 .... (30) *Mecopisthes*.
— Tibia IV spine ca. 0·25–0·3. Tm. I ca. 0·7 .... (29) *Silometopus* (*interjectus* only).

46. Posterior eyes slightly less than 1 diam. apart. Epigyne (Text-fig. 165, B, D) .... (43) *Thyreosthenius* (*parasiticus* only).

— Posterior eyes 1 diam. or more apart. Epigynes (Text-fig. 166, E, F) .... (44) *Monocephalus*.

47. Tm. I 0·4 or less .... 48.
— Tm. I 0·45–0·55 (*Panamomops* is only ca. 0·42) ..... 53.
— Tm. I 0·6. Epigyne (Text-fig. 172, C) .... (51) *Notioscopus*.

48. Sternum and carapace with numerous fairly large pits (Text-fig. 167, G). Tm. I ca. 0·36 .... (45) *Lophomma*.
— Sternum and carapace not punctate .... 49.

49. Very small, pale coloured spiders, ca. 1–1·2 mm. long. Tarsus I longer than, or scarcely shorter than, metatarsus I .... 50.
— Rather larger, usually darker spiders, ca. 1·5–2 mm. long. Tarsus I shorter than metatarsus I .... 51.

50. Tibia IV spine long (ca. 2 diam. of tibia). Tarsus I longer than metatarsus I. Epigyne (Text-fig. 169, C) (48) *Jacksonella*
— Tibia IV spine shorter (ca. 1 diam. of tibia). Tarsus I slightly shorter than metatarsus I. Epigyne (Text-fig. 168, B)... (47) *Saloca*.

51. Posterior median eyes ca. 1·5 diam. apart, and further from each other than from laterals .... (46) *Mioxena*.
— Posterior eyes practically equidistant, ca. 1 diam. apart .... 52.

52. Legs fairly stout, e.g. tibia I l/d ca. 4–4·5 .... (49) *Gongylidiellum*.
— Legs thinner, e.g. tibia I l/d ca. 6–7 .... (50) *Micrargus*.

53. Very small spider (ca. 1 mm.). Posterior median eyes 1·5–2 diam. apart. Epigyne (Text-fig. 173, C) ..... (52) *Glyphesis*.
— Larger spiders (1·3 mm. or more). Posterior median eyes not more than ca. 1·5 diam. apart .... 54.

54. Epigyne divided by a median longitudinal furrow or fissure .... 55.
— Epigyne not divided in this way .... 57.

55. Metatarsus IV/tarsus IV ca. 1·25–1·3. Sternum rather rugose .... (53) *Erigonella*.
— Metatarsus IV/tarsus IV ca. 1·5 or more. Sternum less rugose... 56.

56. Epigyne (Text-fig. 174, C) .... (54) *Savignia*.
— Epigynes as Text-figs. 174, D ; 179, D–H ; 181, A–D and (55) *Diplocephalus*. (56) *Araeoncus*.

57. Tm. I 0·42. Metatarsus IV/tarsus IV 1·25 .... (57) *Panamomops*.
— Tm. I practically 0·5. Metatarsus IV/tarsus IV 1·75 (9) *Entelecara* (*flavipes* and *omissa*).

58. Tm. I less than 0·4 .... 59.
— Tm. I 0·4–0·5 .... 60.
— Tm. I 0·55–0·6 .... 64.
— Tm. I 0·75–0·8. Epigyne (Text-fig. 192, A) .... (66) *Rhœbothorax*.

59. Tibia IV spine long (3 diam. or more of tibia). Epigyne (Text-fig. 182, B) .... (58) *Lessertia*.
— Tibia IV spine shorter. Epigyne (Text-fig. 182, E) ... (59) *Asthenargus*.

60. Carapace with usually some minute teeth around edges.
    Cheliceræ with small warts anteriorly and laterally.
    Epigynes (Text-figs. 189, A–M ; 190, C, D, E) ...... (65) *Erigone.*
— Carapace without minute teeth on edges. Cheliceræ
    devoid of small warts .... 61.
61. Eyes small, widely spaced ; anterior medians ca. 2
    diam. from anterior laterals, posterior medians 1·5–2
    diam. apart, and ca. 1·5 diam. from laterals.
    Epigyne (Text-fig. 183, C, D) .... (60) *Caledonia.*
— Eyes larger, more closely spaced .... 62.
62. Metatarsus I scarcely longer than tarsus I (MT I/t I ca.
    1–1·1). Epigyne (Text-fig. 184, D) .... (61) *Typhocrestus.*
— MT I/t I more than 1·2 .... 63.
63. Tibia IV spine ca. 0·3. Epigyne (Text-fig. 185, F) ... (62) *Collinsia*
                                                     (*distincta* only).
— Tibia IV spine ca. 0·23. Epigyne (Text-fig. 186, C) (63) *Scotargus.*
64. Posterior eyes close together (0·5 diam. or less apart).
    Epigyne (Text-fig. 186, D) .... (64) *Diplocentria.*
— Posterior eyes further apart (medians 1 diam. or
    more) 65
65. Anterior median eyes small, and more than 1 diam.
    from laterals. MT IV/t IV ca. 1·7. Epigyne (Text-
    fig. 185, E)... (62) *Collinsia*
                                                     (*holmgreni* only).
— Anterior median eyes larger, 0·5–1 diam. from
    laterals. MT IV/t IV 1·3–1·4. Epigyne (Text-fig.
    192, B, D) .... (67) *Eboria.*

Males

1. Metatarsus IV with a trichobothrium .... 2.
— Metatarsus IV without a trichobothrium .... 22.
2. (a) Carapace elevated into a long stalk, carrying the
    eyes (Text-fig. 118, C)..................................... (2) *Walckenaera.*
— (b) Carapace with posterior median eyes on a long
    horizontal lobe, bifid anteriorly (Text-fig. 125, C, D) (6) *Tigellinus.*
— (c) Ocular area with a cornicule or little cusp, but with
    otherwise no protuberance on carapace .... 3.
— (d) Carapace bears, in region of head, a well-defined
    lobe or elevation, either carrying posterior median
    eyes or immediately behind these (the lobe is rather
    shallow in *Pocadicnemis* (Text-fig. 143, C) and
    Entelecara errata) .... 4.
— (e) Carapace bears neither corniculus in ocular area,
    nor a well-defined lobe, though it may be elevated
    somewhat anteriorly .... 15.
3. Posterior median eyes less than 1 diam. apart, but
    ca. 2·5–3 diam. from posterior laterals. Cornicule
    with forward-directed barbed hairs (Text-fig. 124,
    F, G) .... (5) *Prosopotheca.*
— Posterior median eyes more than 1 diam. apart, and
    not more than 2 diam. from posterior laterals.
    Cornicule without barbed hairs (Text-fig. 126,
    D, H, I, J) .... (7) *Cornicularia*
                                             (except *vigilax*).
4. Abdomen with a well-defined scutum (Tm. I ca. 0·9) (27) *Trichopterna*
                                                  (*mengei* only).
— Abdomen without a scutum .... 5.
5. Tm. I 0·45–0·55 .... 6.
— Tm. I 0·6–0·65 .... 7.

— Tm. I 0·7–0·8 .... 8.

— Tm. I 0·85–0·95 .... 11.

6. Superior tarsal claws of legs I and II with large teeth
(cf. Text-fig. 118, F) .... (3) *Wideria*
(*antica, cucullata,
nodosa* and *polita*).

— Superior tarsal claws of legs I–II with only minute
teeth .... (9) *Entelecara*
(*acuminata,
erythropus* and *errata*)

7. Lobe behind eyes (Text-fig. 146, A, F) .... (26) *Œdothorax*
(*gibbosus* and *apicatus*)

— Lobe carrying posterior median eyes (Text-fig. 121, D) (3) *Wideria*
(*melanocephala* only).

8. Posterior median eyes on *top* of lobe, and a considerable
distance (ca. 4–7 diam. of one of them) from anterior
medians .... 9.

— Posterior median eyes on *front* of lobe, and only ca.
1·5 diam. from anterior medians .... 10.

9. Head from side (Text-fig. 139, C) .... (18) *Hybocoptus*.

— Head from side (Text-fig. 141, C) .... (21) *Minyrioloides*.

10. Clypeus projecting forwards over chelicerae (Text-fig.
136, H). Width of posterior median eyes scarcely
greater than width of anterior median eyes............ (15) *Dismodicus*.

— Clypeus not projecting in this way. Width of posterior
median eyes almost twice width of anterior median
eyes.. (16) *Hypomma*
(except *cornutum*).

11. Cephalic lobe shallow (Text-fig. 143, C) .... (24) *Pocadicnemis*.

— Cephalic lobe large .... 12.

12. Distance between posterior median eyes about five
times distance between anterior median eyes ...... 13.

— Distance between posterior median eyes about two–
three times distance between anterior median eyes 14.

13. Carapace from side (Text-fig. 142, D) .... (23) *Peponocranium*.

— Carapace with rather smaller lobe .... (25) *Hypselistes*
(*florens* only).

14. Carapace from side (Text-fig. 144, F). Width of lobe
(seen from above) ca. 1·6 times posterior median
eye width .... (25) *Hypselistes*
(*jacksoni* only).

— Carapace from side (Text-fig. 148, C). Width of lobe
(seen from above) ca. 2·5 times posterior median eye
width .... (27) *Trichopterna*
(*thorelli* only).

15. (a) Tibiae I–II with two rows of stout spines ventrally
(cf. Text-fig. 133, F) (Tm. I ca. 0·9)..................... (22) *Maso*.

— (b) Abdomen with scutum (Text-fig. 116, D) (Tm. I
ca. 0·4) .... (1) *Ceratinella*.

— (c) Description not covered by (a) or (b) .... 16.

16. Tm. I ca. 0·4 (Post-ocular sulci present) (Text-fig.
122, H) .... (3) *Wideria*.
(*fugax* only).

— Tm. I ca. 0·5 .... 17.

— Tm. I 0·6–0·65 .... 19.

— Tm. I 0·75–0·8 .... 20.

— Tm. I 0·85–0·95 .... 21.

17. Superior tarsal claws with only a few minute teeth ... (8) *Dicymbium*.

— Superior tarsal claws (at least of legs I–II) with large teeth (as Text-fig. 118, F) .... 18.

18. Ocular area narrow, total width of eyes being ca. 0·3 times width of carapace (at widest point, seen from above). Spiders ca. 3 mm. long .... (4) *Trachynella*.

— Ocular area wider, total width of eyes being ca. 0·4 times width of carapace. Spider ca. 2 mm. long ... (7) *Cornicularia* (*vigilax* only).

19. (a) Palpal tibia with bunch of bristles dorsally (Text-fig. 133, H) .... (10) *Mœbelia*.

— (b) Cheliceræ with large wart anteriorly (Text-fig. 134, G). Palpal organs with long embolus, curved roughly into semi-circle (Text-fig. 134, D) .... (12) *Gnathonarium*.

— (c) Palp with small patellar apophysis ventrally (Text-fig. 134, A)... (11) *Erigonidium*.

— (d) Not as (a)–(c). Palps (Text-fig. 147) .... (26) *Œdothorax* (except *gibbosus* and *tuberosus*).

20. (a) Tibia I with 2 dorsal spines. Palpal patella enlarged (Text-fig. 135, E) .... (14) *Gongylidium*.

— (b) Tibia I with one spine. Head raised somewhat conically anteriorly (Text-fig. 138, I) .... (17) *Metopobactrus*.

— (c) Tibia I spineless. Male palp (Text-fig. 135, A) ... (13) *Tmeticus*.

21. Head raised very slightly, with post-ocular sulci ...... (19) *Baryphyma*.

— Head not raised. Reddish spiders .... (20) *Gonatium*.

22. Abdomen with dorsal scutum .... (28) *Lophocarenum*.

— Abdomen without dorsal scutum .... 23.

23. Carapace and sternum with numerous pits (Text-fig. 167, G) .... (45) *Lophomma*.

— Carapace and sternum not strongly punctate........... 24.

24. (a) Carapace with deep transverse cleft (Text-fig. 172, G, H) .... (51) *Notioscopus*.

— (b) Carapace with two little horns, or clusters of bristles like horns, in ocular area .... 25.

— (c) Head drawn up anteriorly into a snout (Text-fig. 176, C) .... (54) *Savignia*.

— (d) Head drawn up anteriorly into a prominence, transversely bifid (as Text-fig. 176, D ; 177, H)...... (55) *Diplocephalus* (*cristatus, permixtus* and *adjacens*).

— (e) Carapace not as (a)–(d) .... 26.

25. Carapace (Text-fig. 181, E)................................... (57) *Panamomops*.

— Carapace (Text-fig. 168, D, E) .... (47) *Saloca*.

26. (a) No sharp elevation on head, and no post-ocular sulci 27.

— (b) Post-ocular sulci present (as Text-fig. 163, G–I), but head with no sharp elevation .... 43.

— (c) Head with elevation (which may be shallow), impressed at sides (except in *Acartauchenius*) and fairly sharply divided from thoracic area.............. 49.

27. (a) Tibiæ I–II spineless. (Abdomen with four reddish impressed dots) .... 28.

— (b) Tibiæ I–IV with one spine only .... 29.

— (c) Tibiæ I–II with two spines, tibiæ III–IV with one spine .... 33.

— (d) Tibiæ I–III with two spines, tibiæ IV with one spine .... 36.

28. Clypeus projecting slightly (Text-fig. 154, D). Tm. I 0·6 .... (30) *Mecopisthes*.

— Clypeus not projecting. Tm. I 0·75 .... (29) *Silometopus* (*curtus* only).

29. Tm. I 0·5 or slightly more .... 30.
— Tm. I less than 0·5 .... 31.
30. Spider dark coloured. Abdomen with four reddish
    impressed dots dorsally .... (35) *Anacotyle.*
— Spiders lighter coloured. Abdomen without four
    reddish impressed dots dorsally .... (37) *Tiso.*
31. Tibiæ I–II darkened. Tibia IV spine ca. 0·45 .... (33) *Trichoncus.*
— Tibiæ I–II not darkened. Tibia IV spine ca. 0·2 ...... 32.
32. Head smoothly elevated (Text-fig. 180, F, G) .... (56) *Araeoncus.*
— Head not elevated .... (34) *Styloctetor.*
33. Very small spider (ca. 1 mm. long). Tarsus I slightly
    longer than metatarsus I. (Chelicera with large
    tooth anteriorly) .... (48) *Jacksonella.*
— Larger spiders (1·3–2 mm.). Tarsus I shorter than
    metatarsus I .... 34.
34. Sternum punctate. Head smoothly elevated (Text-fig.
    175, G). Clypeus projecting anteriorly (Text-fig.
    175, D) .... (53) *Erigonella*
                                                (*ignobilis* only).
— Sternum not pitted. Head not elevated. Clypeus not
    projecting .... 35.
35. Chelicerae with small wart anteriorly. Palpal tibia
    with apophysis. Branchial opercula strongly striated (49) *Gongylidiellum.*
— Chelicerae without wart anteriorly. Palpal tibia
    without apophysis. Branchial opercula not striated (46) *Mioxena.*
36. (a) Tm. I less than 0·4 .... 37.
— (b) Tm. I 0·4–0·5 .... 38.
— (c) Tm. I 0·55–0·6 .... 42.
— (d) Tm. I 0·75–0·8. (Branchial opercula strongly
    rugose and striated (Text-fig. 192, C)) .... (66) *Rhæbothorax.*
37. Chelicera with large pointed tooth anteriorly .... (58) *Lessertia*
— Chelicera without tooth anteriorly .... (59) *Asthenargus.*
38. Palp with patellar apophysis ventrally (as Text-fig.
    187, A) .... (65) *Erigone.*
— Palp without patellar apophysis .... 39.
39. Eyes small, with posteriors ca. 2 diam. apart. Palp
    (Text-fig. 183, A) .... (60) *Caledonia.*
— Eyes larger, with posteriors ca. 1 diam. apart, or
    scarcely more .... 40.
40. Chelicera with warty tooth anteriorly .... (62) *Collinsia*
                                                  (*distincta* only).
— Chelicera with no wart anteriorly .... 41.
41. Branchial opercula very rugose .... (67) *Eboria*
                                                  (*caliginosa* only).
— Branchial opercula not rugose. Palp characteristic
    (Text-fig. 186, A) .... (63) *Scotargus.*
42. (a) Posterior median eyes less than 0·5 diam. apart.
    Palp (Text-fig. 186, E) .... (64) *Diplocentria.*
— (b) Posterior median eyes 0·5–1 diam. apart. Palp
    (Text-fig. 191, D) .... (67) *Eboria*
                                                  (*fausta* only).
— (c) Posterior median eyes more than 1 diam. apart.
    Palp (Text-fig. 185, C) .... (62) *Collinsia*
                                                  (*holmgreni* only).
43. (a) Tibiæ I–II spineless .... 44.
— (b) Tibiæ I–IV with one dorsal spine .... 45.
— (c) Tibiæ I–II with two dorsal spines, tibiæ III–IV
    with one spine .... 48.
44 Tm. I less than 0·5 .... (61) *Typhocrestus.*

— Tm. I more than 0·5	(29)	*Silometopus* (*interjectus* only).
45. Posterior median eyes 2–3 diam. apart	(36)	*Evansia.*
— Posterior median eyes ca. 1 diam. apart	46.	
46. Tm. I slightly less than 0·5	(41)	*Aulacocyba.*
— Tm. I 0·5 or more	47.	
47. Tm. I 0·5–0·55	(40)	*Tapinocyba.*
— Tm. I 0·65. Stout spines ventrally on tibiæ and metatarsi I–II	(42)	*Perimones.*
48. Very small spider (ca. 1 mm. long). Legs stout, e.g. metatarsus I *l/d* ca. 5. Head (Text-fig. 173, B) ...	(52)	*Glyphesis.*
— Larger spiders (1·5–2 mm.). Legs slimmer, e.g. metatarsus I *l/d* ca. 10	(50)	*Micrargus.*
49. (a) Head (Text-fig. 155, F)................................	(32)	*Acartauchenius.*
— (b) Posterior median eyes on protuberance which is bifid longitudinally	50.	
— (c) Head not as (a)–(b)	51.	
50. Posterior median eyes on top of lobe	(43)	*Thyreosthenius.*
— Posterior median eyes on front of lobe	(16)	*Hypomma* (*cornutum* only).
51. Tibiæ I–II spineless, or with very short spines (0·5 diam. of tibia or less)	52.	
— Tibiæ I–IV with one dorsal spine (ca. 1 diam. of tibia)	55.	
52. Tm. I ca. 0·45–0·5	53.	
— Tm. I ca. 0·65–0·7. Head (Text-figs. 167, A–D)	(44)	*Monocephalus.*
— Tm. I ca. 0·75	(29)	*Silometopus* (*elegans* only).
53. Anterior median eyes slightly greater than posterior median eyes	(9)	*Entelecara.* (*flavipes* and *omissa*).
— Anterior median eyes rather smaller than posterior median eyes	54.	
54. (a) Palpal tarsus dorsally with a row of little tubercles bearing bristles (Text-fig. 155, B)	(31)	*Cnephalocotes.*
— (b) Palpal tarsus (Text-fig. 175, A). Sternum rugose, with minute pits	(53)	*Erigonella* (*hiemalis* only).
— (c) Palps different from (a)–(b). Sternum not rugose	(55)	*Diplocephalus* (*picinus, latifrons, jacksoni* and *protuberans*).
55. Sternum distinctly rugose	(38)	*Troxochrus.*
— Sternum not rugose...	(39)	*Minyriolus.*

KEY TO LINYPHIINE GENERA

1. Tibia I (and often II) with one or more *lateral* spines (spines very weak in *Hilaira excisa* and *Drepanotylus*)	2.
— Tibiæ I and II without *lateral* spines*	22.
2. Legs long, with femora I and IV equal to or longer than carapace, or if shorter, with one or more ventral spines on tibiæ I and II. Legs usually fairly slender, with tibia I *l/d* (at *narrowest* point, from side) often 10 and seldom less. Metatarsus IV longer than, or scarcely shorter than, tibia IV. Abdomen often with dorsal pattern	3.
— Legs shorter, with femora I and IV shorter than carapace. Tibiæ I and II never with ventral spines. Legs relatively rather stouter, with tibia I *l/d* ca. 6–7. Metatarsus IV definitely shorter than tibia IV. Abdomen unicolorous dorsally (never with pattern)	16.

*Some *Centromerus* spp. have a prolateral spine on tibia I.

N

3. Outer cheliceral margin with 5–6 large but unequal
teeth (cf. Text-figs. 222, A, D) .... 4.
— Outer cheliceral margin with fewer and smaller teeth 6.
4. Cheliceræ with 3–4 conspicuous spines on prolateral
face (Text-fig. 222, A) .... (90) *Drapetisca.*
— Cheliceræ without such spines .... 5.
5. Clypeus narrow, equal to or less than one diameter of
anterior median eyes (Text-fig. 222, D) .... (91) *Tapinopa.*
— Clypeus wider (Text-fig. 223, C) .... (92) *Floronia.*
6. All metatarsi spineless .... (88) *Bathyphantes.*
— Some at least of metatarsi with a spine or spines
(ventrally, dorsally or laterally)........................... 7.
7. Posterior median eyes less than 0·5 diam. of one of
them from laterals (Text-fig. 224, C) .... (93) *Taranucnus.*
— Posterior median eyes at least 0·5 diam. from laterals 8.
8. Posterior median eyes appreciably more than 1 diam.
apart (except *L. marginata*, q.v.), and clearly more
than 1 diam. from the laterals (Text-fig. 237, F)... (99) *Linyphia.*
— Posterior median eyes not or scarcely more than one
diam. apart, and not or scarcely more than 1 diam.
from the laterals .... 9.
9. All eyes large and subequal, with width of anterior
median pair equal to or practically equal to width of
posterior median pair .... 10.
— Eyes rather more unequal in size, with anterior
medians usually smaller than posterior medians, and
width of anterior median eyes appreciably smaller
than width of posterior median eyes..................... 11.
10. Posterior median eyes less than 1 diam. from
laterals. Tibia I *l*/*d* ca. 10. Sex organs and ab-
dominal pattern characteristic .... (94) *Labulla.*
— Posterior median eyes 1 diam. or slightly more from
laterals. Tibia I *l*/*d* ca. 6. Sex organs and ab-
dominal pattern characteristic ....' (95) *Stemonyphantes.*
11. Metatarsi I–IV with a single spine (dorsally) (IV
sometimes spineless) .... (97) *Lepthyphantes*
(Groups II–V).

— Metatarsi with more than one spine (at least on III and
IV) .... 12.
12. Posterior median eyes less than 1 diam. from laterals
(Text-fig. 227, B) .... 13.
— Posterior median eyes 1 diam. or more from laterals
(Text-fig. 225, B) .... 14.
13. Metatarsi I and II spineless (or with one weak ventral
spine only). Abdomen with very faint pattern or
none .... (100) *Mengea*
(*warburtoni*).

— Metatarsi I and II with several spines. Abdomen with
pattern of black bars and markings dorsally .... (97) *Lepthyphantes*
(Group I).

14. Abdomen with dorsal pattern. Carapace with median
dark stripe. Both rows of eyes (seen from above)
strongly recurved (Text-fig. 225, B). Clypeus wide
and concave (particularly in ♂). Tm. I ca. 0·2
(difficult to see)... (96) *Bolyphantes.*
— Abdomen unicolorous dorsally. Carapace without
median dark stripe. Both rows of eyes (from above)
only slightly curved. Tm. I 0·4–0·8 (fairly easy to
see)... 15.

15. Metatarsi I and II with several stout spines. Tibial
spines long (ca. 2 diam. or more). Tm. I ca. 0·75.
Tm. IV present .... (98) *Helophora.*
— Metatarsi with one or two ventral spines only. Tibial
spines shorter (scarcely more than 1 diam.). Tm.
I ca. 0·8.. (100) *Mengea*
(*scopigera*).

— Metatarsi I-III with 1 fine dorsal spine. Tm. I ca.
0·4. No Tm. IV... (84) *Centromerita.*
16. Metatarsus IV with trichobothrium....................... 17.
— Metatarsus IV without trichobothrium...................... 19.
17. Tm. I ca. 0·55. Sex organs distinct .... (69) *Leptorhoptrum.*
— Tm. I 0·55–0·7 .... 18.
18. Eyes in compact group, with posterior eyes all less than
1 diam. apart. Basal spine on tibiæ rather short,
e.g. on tibia IV ca. 1·5 diams. Sex organs distinct (81) *Microneta.*
— Eyes in wider group, with posteriors more than 1
diam. apart. Basal spine on tibiæ rather long, e.g.
on tibia IV ca. 2 diams. or more. Sex organs
distinct .... (72) *Hilaira.*
19. Tm. I ca. 0·25. Only lateral spine on tibia I is retrolateral .... (80) *Meioneta*
(*mollis, saxatilis,
beata*).

— Tm. I ca. 0·3–0·4 .... 20.
— Tm. I slightly above 0·5. Only lateral spine on tibia I
is prolateral .... (70) *Drepanotylus.*
20. Tibia I (and often II) with a pro- and a retro-lateral
spine .... (76) *Porrhomma.*
— Tibia I with pro-lateral spine only .... 21.
21. ♀ Epigyne with large scape (Text-fig. 216, B, D, F).
♂ Palpal organs complex, with large paracymbium (86) *Oreonetides.*
— ♀ Epigyne small and inconspicuous (Text-fig. 198, B).
♂ Palpal organs simple (Text-fig. 198, A) .... (75) *Hillhousia.*
22. Femur I equal to or longer than carapace. Metatarsi
as long as or longer than tibiæ. Abdomen with
dorsal pattern .... (89) *Pœciloneta.*
— Femur I shorter than carapace. Metatarsi shorter
than tibiæ. Abdomen unicolorous dorsally (except
Donacochara and *Ostearius*) .... 23.
23. Metatarsus IV with a trichobothrium .... 24.
— Metatarsus IV without a trichobothrium .... 28.
24. Tm. I not greater than 0·7 .... 25.
— Tm. I greater than 0·7 .... 26.
25. Anterior median eyes ca. 0·5 diam. or less from
anterior laterals. Posterior laterals only ca. 0·5
diam. from medians. Basal spine on tibiæ not much
longer than 1 diam. ♂ Chelicera without tubercle
anteriorly .... (79) *Agyneta* (*conigera*).
— Anterior median eyes practically 1 diam. from
anterior laterals. Posterior laterals 1–1·25 diam.
from medians. Basal spine on tibiæ practically 2
diams. ♂ Chelicera with tubercle anteriorly .... (73) *Halorates.*
26. ♀ Palpal tarsus swollen (Text-fig. 204, B, F) (except
A. ramosa, q.v.). ♂ Palpal tibia without an
apophysis; palpal tarsus gibbous above (Text-figs.
204, A, E, G; 205, A, E) .... (79) *Agyneta*
(*subtilis, decora
cauta, ramosa*).

— ♀ Palpal tarsus not swollen. ♂ Palpal tibia with
   apophysis ; palpal tarsus not gibbous .... 27.
27. Pale coloured spider, with faint abdominal pattern
   (Text-fig. 193, C). Total width of ocular area (seen
   from in front) ca. four times width of clypeus. ♂
   No protuberance in ocular area .... (68) *Donacochara.*
— Dark coloured spider, with no abdominal pattern.
   Total width of ocular area ca. 2·5 times width of
   clypeus. ♂ With protuberance in ocular area ...... (71) *Phaulothrix.*
28. Metatarsi I-III with dorsal spine (at times small and
   slender : position ca. 0·4–0·6) .... 29.
— Metatarsi spineless .... 31.
29. Posterior eyes very large (Text-fig. 203, B, E) .... 30.
— Posterior eyes smaller .... (83) *Centromerus.*
30. Tarsi with one dorsal spine................................... (77) *Syedrula.*
— Tarsi spineless .... (78) *Syedra.*
31. Tm. I ca. 0·25 .... (80) *Meioneta*
                                                               (*rurestris, gulosa,
                                                               nigripes*).

— Tm. I 0·35–0·5 .... 32.
32. Very small spiders (less than 1·5 mm.), with metatarsi
   I scarcely if at all longer than tarsi I .... (82) *Maro.*
— Larger spiders (2–3·5 mm.), with metatarsi I longer
   than tarsi I .... 33.
33. Abdomen unicolorous. Tm. I ca. 0·4 .... (87) *Macrargus.*
— Abdomen reddish, black posteriorly. Tm. I 0·45–0·5 (74) *Ostearius.*

1. Genus **CERATINELLA** Emerton 1882.

CHARACTERS OF GENUS. CARAPACE : Broad and slightly punctate.
♂ Head without lobe. ABDOMEN : ♀ Rather globular, coriaceous or
with a scutum dorsally. ♂ With dorsal scutum (Text-fig. 116, D).
STERNUM : Broadly truncated posteriorly, with coxæ IV widely
separated. CHELICERÆ : Fang sinuous, with double curve, first
concave, then convex. LEGS : Metatarsus IV with a trichobothrium;
Tm I ca. 0·4–0·43. Short and robust, with metatarsi equal to or
scarcely longer than tarsi. Tibial spines very short and weak. MALE
PALP : With small tibial apophyses.
   The three species are separated mainly by the sex organs.

Ceratinella brevipes (Westring).
(Text-figs. 116, B, D ; 117, C, D)

Erigone brevipes N. Westring, 1851. *Walckenaera brevipes* O. P.-Cambridge, 1879–81,
p. 142. *Ceratinella brevipes* W. Bosenberg, 1901–3, p. 127 ; E. Simon, 1926, p. 333.

DESCRIPTION : LENGTH : ♀ : 1·7–1·8 mm. ♂ : about 1·5 mm.
CARAPACE : Dark chestnut-brown. ♂ Clypeus with some long upward-
pointing bristles (not present in *C. brevis* and *C. scabrosa*). ABDOMEN :
♀ Grey-black without a scutum ; ♂ chestnut-brown dorsal scutum.
STERNUM : Dark-brown, sometimes with black margins. LEGS :
Tm I 0·4–0·43. Orange-brown to dark brown, with numerous short,
fine hairs. EPIGYNE : Text-fig. 116, B. MALE PALP : Text-fig. 117,
C, D.

OCCURRENCE : In moss and vegetable detritus in woodland and open country. Frequent throughout the British Isles, but commoner in the Midlands and north. Adults at most seasons.

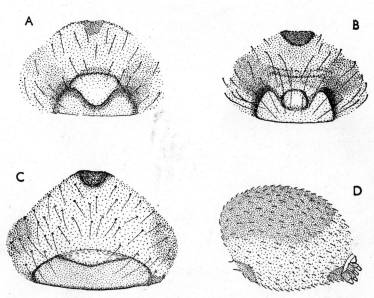

TEXT-FIG. 116.—Epigynes : A, *Ceratinella brevis;* B, *C. brevipes;* C, *C. scabrosa.* Abdominal scutum : D, *C. brevipes* ♂.

Ceratinella brevis (Wider).
(Text-figs. 116, A ; 117, A, B)

Theridion breve Wider, 1834, p. 242. *Walckenaera depressa* J. Blackwall, 1861–4, p. 306. *W. brevis* O. P.-Cambridge, 1879–81, p. 142. *Ceratinella brevis* C. Chyzer and L. Kulczynski, 1891–7, II, p. 137 ; W. Bosenberg, 1901–3, p. 128 ; E. Simon, 1926, p. 333.

DESCRIPTION. LENGTH : ♀♂ : about 2 mm. Colour as *C. brevipes.* ABDOMEN : ♀♂ With scutum. LEGS : Tm I 0·4–0·43. EPIGYNE : Text-fig. 116, A. MALE PALP : Text-fig. 117, A, B.

OCCURRENCE : In similar situations to the last species, and on mountains. Widespread throughout the British Isles, but less common. Adults in spring, autumn and winter.

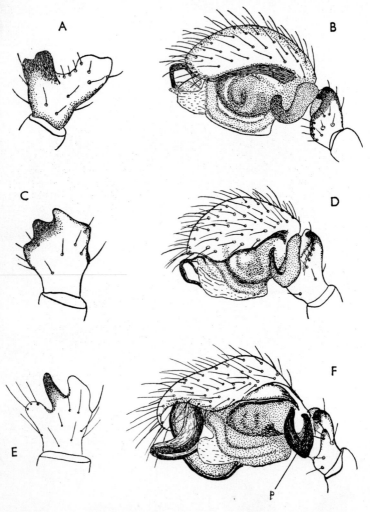

TEXT-FIG. 117.—Male palpal tibiæ (from above): A, *Ceratinella brevis;* C,
C. brevipes; E, *C. scabrosa.*
Male palps: B, *C. brevis;* D, *C. brevipes;* F, *C. scabrosa.*

Ceratinella scabrosa (O. P.-Cambridge).
(Text-figs. 116, C; 117, E, F)

Walckenaera scabrosa O. P.-Cambridge, 1871, p. 453. *Ceratinella scabrosa* C. Chyzer
and L. Kulczynski, 1891–7, II, p. 137; E. Simon, 1926, p. 334.

DESCRIPTION. LENGTH : ♀: about 2·2 mm. ♂: about 2 mm.
Colour as *C. brevipes.* ABDOMEN : ♀♂ With scutum. LEGS : Tm I

0·4–0·43. Epigyne : Text-fig. 116, C. Male palp : Text-fig. 117, E, F.

Occurrence : Rare, in the detritus of woods, marshes, etc. Recorded from a number of English counties and Eire. Adults in spring, autumn and probably winter.

Note on Genera **Walckenaera, Wideria, Trachynella, Prosopotheca, Cornicularia** *and* **Tigellinus.**

The species of these genera are all closely related, and in spite of the variations in the secondary sexual characters of the male and in the position of the trichobothria, it is possible that they should all be united into one genus. The sternum is longer than broad, the posterior end being pointed between coxæ IV. The tibial spines are very thin and weak. The superior tarsal claws have a number of large teeth (Text-fig. 118, F). The cheliceræ have clear transverse striæ on the lateral faces (Text-fig. 120, F), fewer in number and more pronounced than in the other Erigonine genera. The female palp has the tibia longer than the patella, and widened apically, while the tarsus is acuminate (Text-fig. 123, F). The head of the male has (with a few exceptions) a lobe or cornicule or horn, but in the female there is no elevation (except for *Walckenaera acuminata*). The male palpal organs are all of similar form. The position of the metatarsal trichobothria varies quite considerably from one species to another, even within the normally accepted genera.

The males in these genera are identified readily by the form of the head, and of the tibial apophyses. The female epigynes serve to identify the females, coupled with the position of the trichobothria and the relative position and size of the eyes.

2. Genus **WALCKENAERA** J. Blackwall 1833.

Characters of Genus. Carapace : The head elevation in ♂ is taken to an extreme form (Text-fig. 118, C), and even in ♀ the head is raised into small conical protuberance. Legs : Metatarsus IV with trichobothrium ; Tm I 0·7. Tibiæ I and II with two spines, tibiæ III and IV with one spine ; tibial spines very thin.

There is a single British species.

Walckenaera acuminata Blackwall.
(Text-fig. 118, A–F)

Walckenaera acuminata J. Blackwall, 1833, p. 106, and 1861–4, p. 289 ; O. P.-Cambridge, 1879–81, p. 171 ; C. Chyzer and L. Kulczynski, 1891–7, II, p. 142 ; E. Simon, 1926, p. 413 ; F. Miller, 1947, Tab. 7, fig. 3.

Description. Length : ♀ : 3–3·5 mm. ♂ : 3–3·25 mm. Carapace: Yellow-brown to orange-brown, with darker striæ. ♀ The head has a conical elevation, carrying the eyes in a compact group (Text-fig. 118, D). ♂ The head is drawn out into a slender, vertical turret (Text-fig. 118, C). Abdomen : Greyish-black. Sternum : Yellow-brown. Legs : Tm I

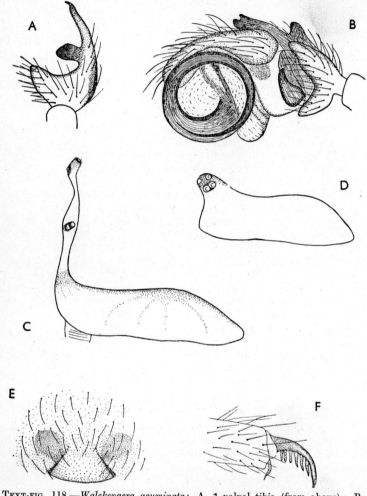

TEXT-FIG. 118.—*Walckenaera acuminata:* A, ♂ palpal tibia (from above); B, ♂ palp; C, ♂ carapace; D, ♀ carapace; E, epigyne; F, tarsal claws.

0·7. Orange-yellow, suffused with some brown. ♂ No obvious tibial spines. EPIGYNE: Text-fig. 118, E. MALE PALP: Text-fig. 118, A, B.

Occasionally the terminal segments of the legs and palps (♀) are suffused with black.

OCCURRENCE: In moss and detritus in woodland. Widespread throughout the British Isles, and not uncommon. Males adult in autumn, winter and spring, females all the year.

3. Genus **WIDERIA** E. Simon 1864.

CHARACTERS OF GENUS. CARAPACE : ♂ The head bears a lobe or lobes (except in *W. fugax*, where sulci are present behind posterior lateral eyes), and sometimes in addition a small horn. EYES : Posterior row noticeably procurved in *W. antica* and *W. cucullata*, but less so in other species. LEGS : Metatarsus IV with a trichobothrium ; Tm I shows a wide variation, 0·4–0·65. ♀ Tibiæ I and II with two spines, tibiæ III and IV with one spine, all rather thin. ♂ Tibial spines (particularly on legs I and II) reduced or absent.

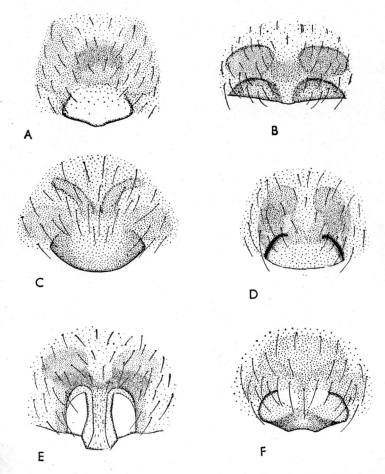

TEXT-FIG. 119.—Epigynes : A, *Wideria antica;* B, *W. cucullata;* C, *W. nodosa;* D, *W. melanocephala;* E, *W. fugax;* F, *W. capito.*

There are seven British species, which can be separated by the sex organs, and in the males also by the heads. *W. fugax* is somewhat anomalous, and a separate genus *Orthocara* has been proposed for it by Denis (1949).

Wideria antica (Wider).
(Text-figs. 119, A ; 120, A, B, C)

Theridion anticum Wider, 1834, p. 221. *Walckenaera antica* J. Blackwall, 1861–4, p. 310 ; O. P.-Cambridge, 1879–81, p. 153 ; C. Chyzer and L. Kulczynski, 1891–7, p. 143 ; W. Bosenberg, 1901–3, p. 141. *Wideria antica* E. Simon, 1926, pp. 406, 410 ; F. Miller, 1947, Tab. 6, fig. 14.

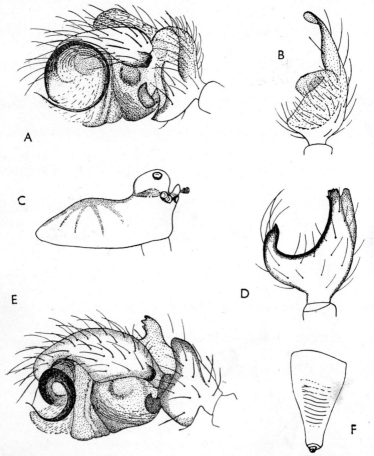

TEXT-FIG. 120.—*Wideria antica* ♂ : A, palp ; B, palpal tibia (from above) ; C, carapace.
   W. cucullata : D, ♂ palpal tibia (from above) ; E, ♂ palp ; F, ♀ chelicera (from side).

DESCRIPTION. LENGTH : ♀: 2–2·75 mm. ♂: 2–2·25 mm. CARAPACE : Brown to orange-brown, with blackish striæ and margins. ♂ Head elevated, and divided into two very unequal segments by a transverse cleft (Text-fig. 120, C). The posterior lobe carries the posterior median eyes ; just above the anterior median eyes, on the anterior lobe, is a bifid " horn ". EYES : ♀ Posterior row procurved, with medians large and slightly less than one diam. apart and from laterals. ABDOMEN : Grey to black. STERNUM : Brown or dark brown, with darkened margins ; shiny. LEGS : Tm I 0·5–0·55. Brown to orange brown, with tibiæ I and II darkened, sometimes practically black ; tibial spines very thin, particularly in ♂. EPIGYNE : Text-fig. 119, A. MALE PALP : Text-figs. 120, A, B.

OCCURRENCE : Frequent, in undergrowth, etc. Widespread throughout the British Isles. Adults in autumn, winter and spring.

Wideria cucullata (C. L. Koch).
(Text-figs. 119, B ; 120, D, E, F)

Micryphantes cucullatus C. L. Koch (I), 1836, p. 45. *Walckenaera cucullata* O. P.-Cambridge, 1879–81, p. 451 ; C. Chyzer and L. Kulczynski, 1891–7, II, p. 143 ; W. Bosenberg, 1901–3, p. 142. *Wideria cucullata* E. Simon, 1926, pp. 408, 412 ; F. Miller, 1947, Tab. 6, fig. 17.

DESCRIPTION. LENGTH : ♀♂: 2–2·25 mm. CARAPACE : Brown to dark brown, with slightly darker fovea and striæ. ♂ Head with bifid elevation as in *W. antica*, but without the " horn ". EYES : ♀ Large ; posterior row slightly procurved, with medians less than one diam. apart, and less than 0·5 diam. from laterals. ABDOMEN : Grey to black. STERNUM : Brown, with margins sometimes darkened ; shiny. LEGS : Tm I 0·5. Yellow-brown to orange-brown, with no darkening on anterior tibiæ (cf. *W. antica*). The tibial spines are very thin. EPIGYNE : Text-fig. 119, B. MALE PALP : Text-fig. 120, D, E.

OCCURRENCE : In moss and detritus (particularly pine-needles) in woods. Widespread throughout the British Isles, and common locally. Adult in spring, autumn and winter.

Wideria nodosa (O. P.-Cambridge).
(Text-figs. 119, C ; 121, A, B, C)

Walckenaera nodosa O. P.-Cambridge, 1873 (1), p. 550; and 1879–81, p. 509. *W. jucundissima*, idem, 1879–81, p. 449. *Wideria nodosa* E. Simon, 1926, pp. 409, 411.

DESCRIPTION. LENGTH : ♀♂: 1·5–1·8 mm. CARAPACE : Brown. ♂ Posterior median eyes on an elevated knob (Text-fig. 121, C). EYES : ♀ Posteriors practically straight, all less than one diam. apart. ABDOMEN : Grey. LEGS : Tm I 0·5. Yellow to yellow-brown. ♀ : Tibial spines very thin. ♂ Spines on tibiæ I and II minute, on tibiæ III and IV very small. STERNUM : Yellow-brown, with darker margins ; shiny. EPIGYNE : Text-fig. 119, C. MALE PALP : Text-figs. 121, A, B.

OCCURRENCE : In moss, in woods and marshes. Recorded from a few English counties (mainly northern), and Eire ; rare.

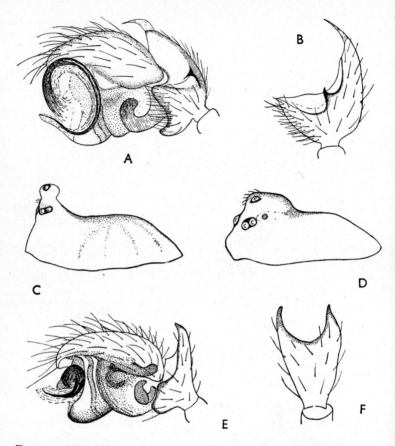

TEXT-FIG. 121.—*Wideria nodosa* ♂: A, palp; B, palpal tibia (from above); C, carapace.
W. melanocephala ♂: D, carapace; E, palp; F, palpal tibia (from above).

Wideria melanocephala (O. P.-Cambridge).
(Text-figs. 119, D; 121, D, E, F)

Walckenaera melanocephala O. P.-Cambridge, 1879–81, p. 596, and 1882, p. 8. C. Chyzer and L. Kulczynski, 1891–7, II, p. 144. *Wideria melanocephala* E. Simon, 1926, pp. 409, 410.

DESCRIPTION. LENGTH: ♀: 2·25 mm. ♂: 2 mm. CARAPACE: Orange, with fovea and head suffused with black. ♂ Head elevated and impressed at sides, with clypeus strongly convex (Text-fig. 121, D). EYES: ♀ Posterior row very slightly procurved, ca. one diam. apart. ABDOMEN: Grey to black. STERNUM: Yellow-brown to orange, sometimes suffused with black; shiny. LEGS: Tm I 0·6–0·64. Orange to yellow, with tibiæ I and II suffused with deep brown to

lack. Apical spine on tibiæ I and II very thin. EPIGYNE : Text-
ig. 119, D. MALE PALP : Text-fig. 121, E, F. The spider is somewhat
nt-like when running.

OCCURRENCE : Amongst grass and heather. Widespread but rare
not recorded from Scotland). Adults in spring and summer.

Wideria capito (Westring).
(Text-figs. 119, F ; 122, A, B, F)

Erigone capito N. Westring, 1861, p. 213. *Walckenaera capito* C. Chyzer and L.
Kulczynski, 1891–7, II, p. 143. *Wideria capito* O. P.-Cambridge, 1889, p. 119, and
1905, p. 53 ; E. Simon, 1926, pp. 408, 411.

DESCRIPTION. LENGTH : ♀ : 3–3·5 mm., ♂ : 2·75 mm. CARAPACE :
Brown to dark brown, slightly rugose posteriorly (particularly ♂).
♂ Head elevated strongly anteriorly, with posterior median eyes on
lobe (Text-fig. 122, F). EYES : ♀ Posterior row practically straight,
:a. one diam. apart. ABDOMEN : Grey to black. STERNUM : Yellow-
brown, with darker margins. LEGS : Tm I 0·6–0·64. Yellow to
orange-yellow. ♀ Tibial spines very thin. ♂ Tibial spines absent.
EPIGYNE : Text-fig. 119, F. MALE PALP : Text-figs. 122, A, B.

OCCURRENCE : Under stones, above 3,000 feet, in Snowdonia and the
Lake District ; frequent locally in these situations. Adult females
in May-August. Extremely rare otherwise, very few specimens having
been taken at low altitudes, in the south, where adult males have
occurred in September and October. No adult males have been captured
on the mountains.

Wideria fugax (O. P.-Cambridge).
(Text-figs. 119, E ; 122, G, H, I)

Neriene fugax O. P.-Cambridge, 1871, p. 445, and 1879–81, p. 121. *Walckenaera
fugax* C. Chyzer and L. Kulczynski, 1891–7, II, p. 146. *Wideria fugax* E. Simon,
1926, pp. 405, 410 ; F. Miller, 1947, Tab. 7, fig. 5.

DESCRIPTION. LENGTH : ♀ : 1·8–2 mm., ♂ : 1·75 mm. CARAPACE :
Orange-brown to brown, slightly rugose posteriorly. ♂ Head not raised,
but sulci run back from between posterior median and lateral eyes
(Text-fig. 122, H). EYES : ♀ Large ; posteriors very slightly procurved.
Posterior medians ca. 0·75 diam. apart, and ca. 0·5 diam. from laterals.
ABDOMEN : Grey. STERNUM : Orange-brown, with margins slightly
darker ; shiny. LEGS : Tm I ca. 0·4. Yellow to orange-brown ;
tibial spines very thin. EPIGYNE : Text-fig. 119, E. MALE PALP :
Text-figs. 122, G, I. The spider has a very slender appearance.

OCCURRENCE : Amongst pine needles and moss, in woods. Recorded
from a few English counties from the north to the south coast, but rare.
Adults in autumn, winter and spring.

Wideria polita (Simon).
(Text-fig. 122, C, D, E)

Erigone polita E. Simon, 1881, p. 251. *Wideria polita* idem, 1926, pp. 409.

DESCRIPTION. LENGTH : ♂ : 2·5 mm. CARAPACE : Pale brown
(probably recently moulted). Head suffused with some black, and

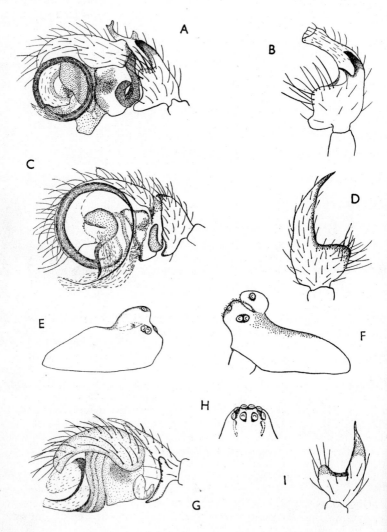

TEXT-FIG. 122.—*Wideria capito* ♂: A, palp; B, palpal tibia (from above); F, carapace.
 W. polita ♂: C, palp; D, palpal tibia (from above); E, carapace.
 W. fugax ♂: G, palp; H, head (from above); I, palpal tibia (from above).

elevated into lobe carrying posterior median eyes (Text-fig. 122, E), with hole in side ; clypeus strongly convex. ABDOMEN : Pale grey. LEGS : Tm I 0·52. Pale brown. Tibiæ I and II with two dorsal spines, tibiæ III and IV with one spine ; spines rather short and weak. MALE PALP : Text-figs. 122, C, D.

OCCURRENCE : A single male, in a wood, Ightham Common, Kent, autumn 1950 (taken by Mr. A. D. Blest, and recorded as British for the first time here).

4. Genus **TRACHYNELLA** J. Braendegaard 1932.

CHARACTERS OF GENUS. CARAPACE : ♂ Head not raised into lobe. LEGS : Metatarsus IV with a trichobothrium : Tm I 0·5 or very slightly less. Tibiæ I and II with two spines, tibiæ III and IV with one spine, all very thin.

There are two British species, which can be separated by the sex organs.

Trachynella nudipalpis (Westring).
(Text-fig. 123, A, B, E, F)

Erigone nudipalpis N. Westring, 1851. *Walckenaera nudipalpis* O. P.-Cambridge, 1879–81, p. 445 ; C. Chyzer and L. Kulczynski, 1891–7, II, p. 142 ; W. Bosenberg, 1901–3, p. 145. *Trachynotus nudipalpis* E. Simon, 1926, p. 413. *Trachynella nudipalpis* F. Miller, 1947, Tab. 7, fig. 1.

DESCRIPTION. LENGTH : ♀ : 2·75–3 mm., ♂ : 2·75 mm. CARAPACE : Brown to dark brown. ♂ Thoracic area rather rugose. EYES : ♀♂ Posterior medians ca. one diam. apart (occasionally rather less), somewhat less from laterals. ABDOMEN : Grey to black. STERNUM : Brown to orange-brown. LEGS : Tm I ca. 0·5. Orange-brown. Spines on tibiæ I and II short and very thin, scarcely stouter than hairs. EPIGYNE : Text-fig. 123, E. MALE PALP : Text-figs. 123, A, B.

OCCURRENCE : Frequent, in wet moss and detritus in woods, and in open country. Widespread throughout the British Isles. Adults in autumn, winter and spring.

Trachynella obtusa (Blackwall).
(Text-fig. 123, C, D, G)

Walckenaera obtusa J. Blackwall, 1836, p. 482, and 1861–4, p. 294 ; O. P.-Cambridge, 1879–81, p. 447 ; C. Chyzer and L. Kulczynski, 1891–7, II, p. 143 ; W. Bosenberg, 1901–3, p. 144. *Trachynotus obtusus* E. Simon, 1926, p. 413.

DESCRIPTION. LENGTH : ♀ : 3–3·3 mm., ♂ : 3 mm. CARAPACE : Deep chestnut-brown or orange-brown. ♂ Thoracic region rather rugose. EYES : ♀ Posterior medians slightly more than one diam. apart, and one diam. from laterals. ♂ Posterior medians 1·25–1·5 diam. apart, and ca. one diam. from laterals. ABDOMEN : Black. STERNUM : Deep orange-brown. LEGS : Tm I 0·47–0·49. Orange-brown. Tibial spines as *T. nudipalpis*. EPIGYNE : Text-fig. 123, G ; rather similar to *T. nudipalpis*. MALE PALP : Text-fig. 123, C, D.

OCCURRENCE : In moss or grass, usually in woods. Recorded from a few counties from the south coast to Scotland ; very rare. Adult in winter and spring.

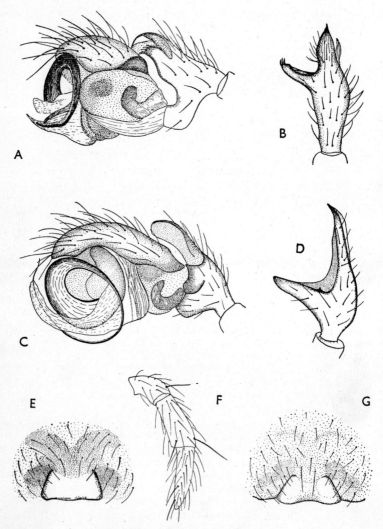

TEXT-FIG. 123.—*Trachynella nudipalpis:* A, ♂ palp ; B, ♂ palpal tibia (from above) ; E, epigyne ; F, ♀ palp (from side).
T. obtusa: C, ♂ palp ; D, ♂ palpal tibia (from above) ; G, epigyne.

5. Genus **PROSOPOTHECA** E. Simon 1884.

CHARACTERS OF GENUS. CARAPACE : ♂ Head with small horn in ocular area, bearing a crest of stout hairs. ♀ Much narrowed anteriorly, with eye width narrow. EYES : ♀ Large, and rather close together. ♂ Posterior medians close together and well-removed from remainder. LEGS : Metatarsus IV with a trichobothrium ; Tm I 0·47–0·65. Tibiæ I-II with two spines, tibiæ III-IV with one spine, all very thin.

There are three British species, which can be separated by the sex organs (both sexes) and by the head (♂).

Prosopotheca monoceros (Wider).
(Text-fig. 124, A, B, F, H, I)

Theridion monoceros Wider, 1834, p. 236. *Walckenaera monoceros* J. Blackwall, 1861–4, p. 291 ; O. P.-Cambridge, 1879–81, p. 148. *Cornicularia monoceros* W. Bösenberg, 1901–3, p. 185. *Prosopotheca monoceros* E. Simon, 1926, p. 416. *Wideria subita* O. P.-Cambridge, 1902, p. 36.

DESCRIPTION. LENGTH : ♀♂ : 2·25–2·5 mm. CARAPACE : Deep brown, with darker fovea and striæ. ♂ Head (Text-fig. 124, F). EYES : ♀ Posteriors ca. 0·6 diam. apart ; anteriors practically touching. ♂ Small, posterior medians ca. 0·75 diam. apart, and ca. 2·5–3 diam. from laterals. ABDOMEN : Black. STERNUM : Dark-brown. LEGS : Tm I 0·6–0·65. Orange-brown. Spines on tibiæ I-II not much stouter than hairs. EPIGYNE : Text-fig. 124, H, I. MALE PALP : Text-fig. 124, A, B ; the apical apophysis is bifid at the tip.

OCCURRENCE : Under stones, in detritus, on sandhills. Widely distributed, from the south coast to Scotland, but infrequent. Adult in autumn and winter.

Prosopotheca corniculans (O. P.-Cambridge).
(Text-fig. 124, C, D, E, G, J)

Erigone corniculans O. P.-Cambridge, 1875 (1), p. 199. *Cornicularia corniculans* W. Bösenberg, 1901–3, p. 186. *Prosopotheca corniculans* E. Simon, 1926, p. 416 ; F. Miller, 1947, Tab. 6, fig. 12.

DESCRIPTION. LENGTH : ♀ : 3 mm., ♂ : 2·5 mm. CARAPACE : Reddish orange to orange-brown. ♂ Head (Text-fig. 124, G). EYES : ♀ Large, with posteriors rather less than 1 diam. apart ; anteriors ca. 0·25 diam. apart. ♂ Posterior medians large, practically touching, and ca. 2 diams. from laterals. ABDOMEN : Black. STERNUM : Orange-brown. LEGS : Tm I 0·6–0·65. Orange-brown. ♂ Tibial spines very short. EPIGYNE : Text-fig. 124, J. MALE PALP : Text-fig. 124, C, D, E ; the apical apophysis is not bifid.

OCCURRENCE : Amongst beech leaves in a coppice at Great Kimble (Buckinghamshire), in autumn.

Prosopotheca incisa (O. P.-Cambridge).
(Text-fig. 125, E)

Neriene incisa O. P.-Cambridge, 1871, p. 447 ; and 1879–81, p. 489. *Prosopotheca incisa* E. Simon, 1926, p. 415. *Simocephalus incisa* J. Denis, 1949, p. 249.

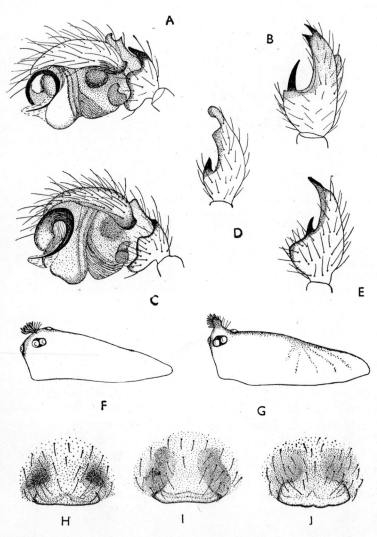

TEXT-FIG. 124.—*Prosopotheca monoceros:* A, ♂ palp; B, ♂ palpal tibia (from above); F, ♂ carapace; H and I, epigyne.
P. corniculans: C, ♂ palp; D, ♂ palpal tibia (from above and to inside); E, ditto (from above); G, ♂ carapace; J, epigyne.

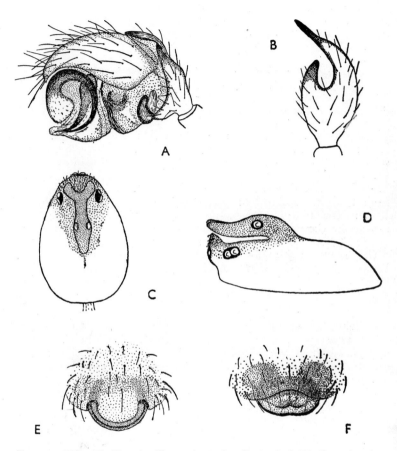

TEXT-FIG. 125.—*Tigellinus furcillatus:* A, ♂ palp ; B, ♂ palpal tibia (from above) ;
C, ♂ carapace (from above) ; D, ditto (from side) ; F, epigyne.
Prosopotheca incisa: E, epigyne.

DESCRIPTION. LENGTH : ♀ : 3·25 mm. CARAPACE : Orange-brown,
with darker fovea and striæ ; head elevated rather from the thorax.
EYES : Posteriors large, all ca. 0·5 diam. apart. ABDOMEN : Greyish-
black. STERNUM : Orange-yellow. LEGS : Tm I 0·47. Yellow-brown.
EPIGYNE : Text-fig. 125, E.

OCCURRENCE : Extremely rare, very few specimens having been
taken in Britain (in England and Wales), all of these being females.

6. Genus **TIGELLINUS** E. Simon 1884.

CHARACTERS OF GENUS. CARAPACE : ♂ Head raised into lobe which
is forked anteriorly (Text-fig. 125, C, D). LEGS : Metatarsus IV with a
trichobothrium ; Tm I 0·6. Tibiæ I–II with two spines, tibiæ III–IV
with one spine ; spines fairly long (particularly ♀), but thin.

Tigellinus furcillatus (Menge).
(Text-fig. 125, A, B, C, D, F)

Phalops furcillatus A. Menge, 1869, p. 220. *Walckenaera furcillatus* O. P.-Cambridge,
1879–81, p. 510. *Tigellinus furcillatus* E. Simon, 1926, p. 414 ; F. Miller, 1947, Tab. 7,
fig. 4.

DESCRIPTION. LENGTH : ♀ : 2·5–3 mm., ♂ : 2·25–2·4 mm. CARA-
PACE : ♀ Brown, with head suffused with black. ♂ Orange-brown, with
cephalic lobe black or blackish, carrying posterior median eyes (Text-
fig. 125, C, D) ; head with numerous short black hairs. EYES : ♀
Posterior medians practically 1·5 diam. apart, and ca. 1 diam.
from laterals. ABDOMEN : Black or grey. STERNUM : Blackish.
LEGS : Tm I 0·6. Orange-brown. EPIGYNE : Text-fig. 125, F ;
not unlike *Cornicularia cuspidata*, from which this species is distinguished by the eyes. MALE PALP : Text-fig. 125, A, B.

OCCURRENCE : Usually in heather, but also in moss and grass.
Widespread in England, but most records come from the southern half ;
rare. Adults April–July.

7. Genus **CORNICULARIA** A. Menge 1868.

CHARACTERS OF GENUS. CARAPACE : ♂ Head has small horn in
ocular area (except in *C. vigilax*). STERNUM : Pitted in *C. unicornis*
and *C. kochi*. LEGS : Metatarsus IV with trichobothrium ; Tm I
0·5–0·7. Tibiæ I–II with two spines, tibiæ III–IV with one spine,
all thin.

There are five British species, separated by the sex organs (♂♀)
and by the form of the horn (♂). *C. vigilax* has been placed in the
genus *Walckenaera* by some authors.

Cornicularia unicornis (O. P.-Cambridge).
(Text-figs. 126, A, E, H ; 128, A)

Walckenaria unicornis O. P.-Cambridge, 1861, p. 437, and 1879–81, p. 147 ; J.
Blackwall, 1861–4, p. 293. *Cornicularia unicornis* E. Simon, 1926, pp. 417.

DESCRIPTION. LENGTH : ♀ : 2–2·5 mm., ♂ : 2 mm. CARAPACE :
Very dark chestnut-brown, with faint black fovea and striæ ; a few
rows of minute pits radiate from the fovea. ♂ Horn bifid (Text-
fig. 126, H). ABDOMEN : Black. STERNUM : Deep brown, with
numerous minute pits ; shiny. LEGS : Tm I ca 0·65 (♀), 0·55 (♂).
Orange, with tarsi rather paler. ♂ Tibial spines on I–II very thin.
EPIGYNE : Text-fig. 128, A. MALE PALP : Text-fig. 126, A, E.

OCCURRENCE : Amongst moss and grass, often in marshy places.
Widespread throughout the British Isles, but not recorded from Scotland. Infrequent. Adult in spring, autumn and winter.

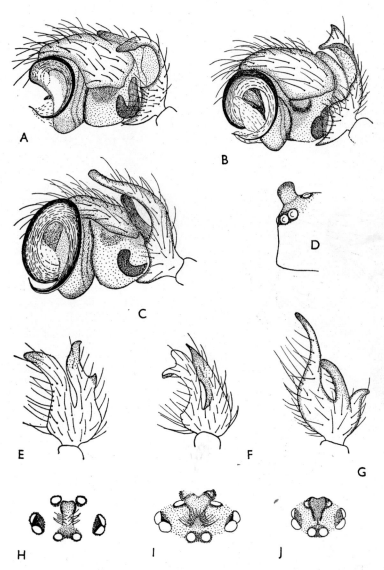

TEXT-FIG. 126.—*Cornicularia unicornis* ♂ : A, palp ; E, palpal tibia (from above) ; H, horn (from in front).
   C. kochi ♂ : B, palp ; F, palpal tibia (from above) ; I, horn (from in front).
   C. karpinskii ♂ : C, palp ; G, palpal tibia (from above) ; D, horn (from side) ; J, ditto (from in front).

Cornicularia kochi (O. P.-Cambridge).
(Text-figs. 126, B, F, I; 128, B)

Erigone kochi O. P.-Cambridge, 1872 (1), p. 759. *Walckenaera kochi* C. Chyzer and L. Kulczynski, 1891–7, II, p. 145. *Cornicularia valida* A. R. Jackson, 1909, p. 424; O. P.-Cambridge, 1909, p. 107. *C. kochi* W. Falconer, 1909, p. 295; E. Simon, 1926, p. 417.

DESCRIPTION. LENGTH: ♀♂: about 3 mm. CARAPACE: Colour as *C. unicornis*, but with thoracic area sometimes (particularly ♂) practically black; no pits present. ♂ Horn rather larger than in *C. unicornis* (Text-fig. 126, I). ABDOMEN: Black. STERNUM: Very dark chestnut-brown, with edges practically black. Shiny, with a few minute pits. LEGS: Tm I ca. 0·73 (♀), 0·69 (♂). Orange-brown.

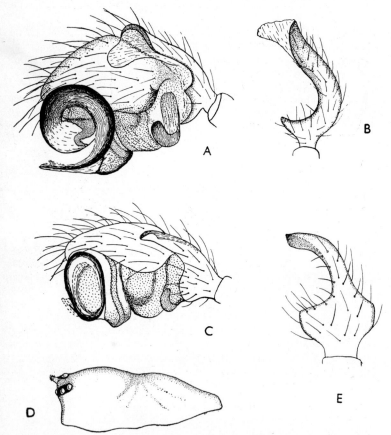

TEXT-FIG. 127.—*Cornicularia cuspidata* ♂: A, palp; B, palpal tibia (from above); D, carapace.
C. vigilax ♂: C, palp; E, palpal tibia (from above).

♀ Apical spine on tibiæ I–II very small. ♂ No spines (or extremely small) on tibiæ I and II. EPIGYNE : Text-fig. 128, B. MALE PALP : Text-fig. 126, B, F. This species is closely similar to the last, but can be distinguished by its larger size, by the slightly different form of the sex organs, by the form of the horn in ♂, and by the position of the trichobothrium. The sternum is less pitted than in *C. unicornis.*

OCCURRENCE : At the roots of grass, etc., on the banks of the River Gowy (Cheshire), and near the coast in Lincolnshire, Yorkshire, and Northumberland. Very local. Adults in autumn.

Cornicularia karpinskii (O. P.-Cambridge).
(Text-figs. 126, C, D, G, J ; 128, C)

Erigone karpinskii O. P.-Cambridge, 1873 (2), p. 447. *Neriene pavitans* idem, 1873 (2), p. 543. *Cornicularia karpinskii* idem, 1902, p. 27 ; J. Braendegaard, 1946, p. 35.

DESCRIPTION. LENGTH : ♀ : 2·5 mm., ♂ : 2·25–2·5 mm. CARAPACE : Brown to deep brown, with faint darker striæ ; not pitted. ♂ Horn rather similar to the preceding species (Text-fig. 126, D. J). ABDOMEN : Grey to black. STERNUM : Brown to orange, suffused with black at margins. LEGS : Tm I 0·5–0·53. Brown to orange-brown. ♀ Spines very thin on tibiæ I and II. ♂ Spines as *C. kochi.* EPIGYNE : Text-fig. 128, C, very distinct. MALE PALP : Text-fig. 126, C, G.

OCCURRENCE : In moss in swampy areas, above 3,000 feet, in Snowdonia, the Lake District, and the Scottish Highlands. Adults in late summer and autumn.

Cornicularia cuspidata (Blackwall).
(Text-figs. 127, A, B, D ; 128, E)

Walckenaera cuspidata J. Blackwall, 1833, p. 108, and 1861–4, p. 290 ; O. P.-Cambridge, 1879–81, p. 146 ; C. Chyzer and L. Kulczynski, 1891–7, II, p. 145 ; W. Bosenberg, 1901–3, p. 143. *Cornicularia cuspidata* E. Simon, 1926, p. 418.

DESCRIPTION. LENGTH : ♀♂ : 2·5–2·6 mm. CARAPACE : Orange-brown to dark brown, with faint darker striæ, not pitted, but slightly rugose particularly in ♂. ♂ Horn cusp-like, and distinct from preceding species (Text-fig. 127, D). EYES : ♀ : Posteriors large, all less than one diam. apart. ABDOMEN : Grey to black. STERNUM : Orange or yellow, shiny. LEGS : Tm I ca. 0·55. Orange-brown. Spines on tibiæ I–II very thin (♀), scarcely visible (♂). EPIGYNE : Text-fig. 128, E. MALE PALP : Text-fig. 127, A, B.

OCCURRENCE : In moss and detritus in woods, and in open country (including mountains). Widespread throughout the British Isles, but very local. Adults most of the year.

Cornicularia vigilax (Blackwall).
(Text-figs. 127, C, E ; 128, D)

Neriene vigilax J. Blackwall, 1853, p. 24, and 1861–4, p. 277 ; O. P.-Cambridge, 1879–81, p. 113. *Walckenaera vigilax* C. Chyzer and L. Kulczynski, 1891–7, II, p. 146 ; W. Bosenberg, 1901–3, p. 144 ; C. R. Crosby and S. C. Bishop, 1931, p. 378 ; B. J. Kaston, 1948, p. 206. *Cornicularia vigilax* E. Simon, 1926, p. 418.

DESCRIPTION. LENGTH : ♀♂ : 2–2·25 mm. CARAPACE : Yellow
or brown, suffused with black, with faint darker striæ. ♂ No horn
in ocular area. ABDOMEN : Black. STERNUM : Yellow or brown,
suffused with much black, with black margins. LEGS : Tm I ca. 0·5.
Yellow-brown to orange brown. Apical spines on tibiæ I–II very thin.
EPIGYNE : Text-fig. 128, D. MALE PALP : Text-fig. 127, C, E.

OCCURRENCE : In moss, grass, etc., in wet places. Widespread
throughout the British Isles, but rare. Adult probably at all seasons.

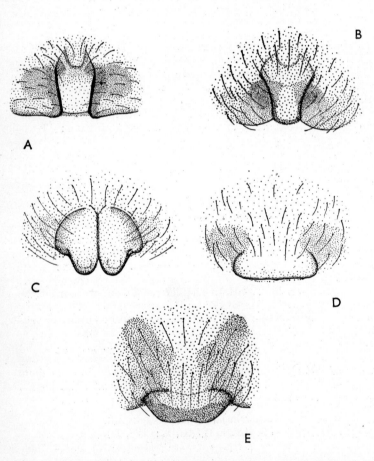

TEXT-FIG. 128.—Epigynes : A, *Cornicularia unicornis;* B, *C. kochi;* C, *C.
karpinskii;* D, *C. vigilax;* E, *C. cuspidata.*

8. Genus **DICYMBIUM** A. Menge 1867.

CHARACTERS OF GENUS. CARAPACE : ♂ Head smoothly raised, but no sharply defined lobe present. STERNUM : Rather rugose and pitted. LEGS : Metatarsus IV with trichobothrium ; Tm I ca. 0·5. ♀ Tibiæ I–II with two spines, tibiæ III–IV with one spine. ♂ Legs spineless. In *D. tibiale* tibiæ I are swollen (Text-fig. 129, C) in ♂. EPIGYNE : With central longitudinal fissure. MALE PALP : The patella and tibia are long.

There are two British species, with closely similar sex organs ; they are distinguished as shown under their descriptions.

Dicymbium nigrum (Blackwall).
(Text-fig. 129, A, B, D, E)

Neriene nigra J. Blackwall, 1834, p. 378, and 1861–4, p. 271 ; O. P.-Cambridge, 1879–81, p. 109. *Dicymbium nigrum* C. Chyzer and L. Kulczynski, 1891–7, II, p. 105 ; E. Simon, 1926, p. 402 ; F. Miller, 1947, Tab. 8, fig. 14.

DESCRIPTION. LENGTH : ♀♂ : 2–2·5 mm. CARAPACE : Dark brown to almost black, shiny. ♂ Head smoothly raised, with no sharply defined lobe. EYES : ♀ Anterior medians ca. 0·25 diam. apart, and slightly less than one diam. from laterals ; posterior medians usually slightly further from one another than from laterals. ♂ Posterior medians ca. two diam. apart. ABDOMEN : Grey-black. STERNUM : Dark brown, irregularly pitted and rugose. LEGS : Tm I ca. 0·5. Reddish-brown to yellow-brown, with numerous short, fine hairs. EPIGYNE : Text-fig. 129, E ; only with difficulty (and uncertainty) distinguishable from that of *D. tibiale* ; the central fissure is rather shorter than in *D. tibiale*. MALE PALP : Text-fig. 129, A, B, D ; a small black tooth projects from under the tibial apophysis. Palpal organs and tibia apparently indistinguishable from those of *D. tibiale*.

OCCURRENCE : In a variety of situations, e.g. heather, straw, undergrowth, etc., and a common aeronaut. Widespread throughout the British Isles, and common. Adult in spring, summer and autumn.

Dicymbium tibiale (Blackwall).
(Text-fig. 129, C, F)

Neriene tibialis J. Blackwall, 1836, p. 485, and 1861–4, p. 266 ; O. P.-Cambridge, 1879–81, p. 483. *Dicymbium tibiale* C. Chyzer and L. Kulczynski, 1891–7, II, p. 105 ; E. Simon, 1926, p. 402.

DESCRIPTION. LENGTH : ♀♂ : about 2·5 mm. Colour and form closely similar to *D. nigrum*. EYES : ♀ Anterior medians ca. 0·5 diam. apart, and slightly more than one diam. from laterals ; posterior medians slightly closer to one another than to corresponding lateral, or equidistant. ♂ Posterior medians ca. one diam. apart. STERNUM : Rather less rugose than in *D. nigrum*. LEGS : Tm I ca. 0·52. Tibiæ I enlarged and " gouty " (Text-fig. 129, C). EPIGYNE : Text-fig. 129, F ; see *D. nigrum*. MALE PALP : Not distinguishable from *D. nigrum*. This species is clearly distinguishable from *D. nigrum* in ♂, by the gouty tibiæ I. The females are distinguishable by the eyes, the sternum and the epigynes, but identification is not always reliable in the absence of the male.

OCCURRENCE: Under stones, and in detritus in swampy areas. Widespread, though with few records; much less common than *D. nigrum* though more frequent in northern England than in the south.

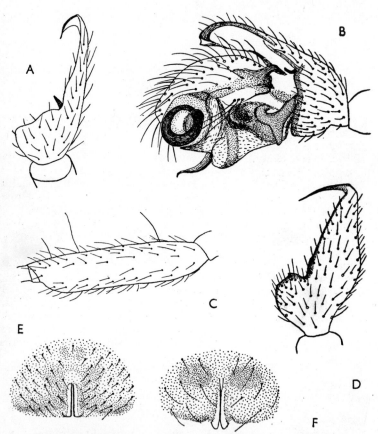

TEXT-FIG. 129.—*Dicymbium nigrum:* A, ♂ palpal tibia (from above and to outside); D, ditto (from above); B, ♂ palp; E, epigyne. *D. tibiale:* C, ♂ tibia I; F, epigyne.

9. Genus **ENTELECARA** E. Simon 1884.

CHARACTERS OF GENUS. CARAPACE: ♂ Head elevated and excavated at sides, into well-defined lobe. STERNUM: Smooth, not rugose. LEGS: Metatarsus IV with a trichobothrium, except in *E. flavipes* and *E. omissa* (which are otherwise quite typical of genus); Tm I 0·5–0·55.

♀ Tibiæ I–II with two spines, tibiæ III–IV with one spine. ♂ Spines much weaker, usually absent altogether from tibiæ I–II. EPIGYNES : All of similar form. MALE PALP : Tibia with two well-developed apophyses.

There are five British species. *E. flavipes* and *E. omissa* are separated from the remaining species by the lack of Tm IV. The males are separated by the form of the head, the tibial apophyses and the palpal organs. The females are distinguished by the epigynes and to some extent by the eyes. For a general description of the genus, see J. Denis (1945, p. 203).

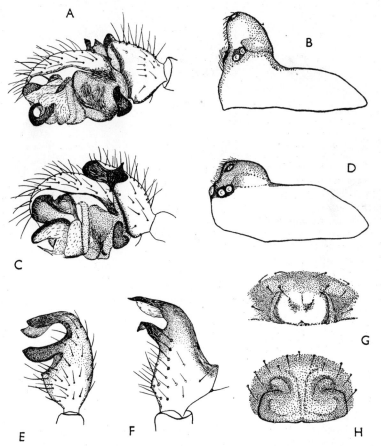

TEXT-FIG. 130.—*Entelecara acuminata*: A, ♂ palp ; B, ♂ carapace ; F, ♂ palpal tibia (from above) ; G, epigyne.
E. erythropus: C, ♂ palp ; D, ♂ carapace ; E, ♂ palpal tibia (from above) ; H, epigyne.

Entelecara acuminata (Wider).
(Text-fig. 130, A, B, F, G)

Theridion acuminatum Wider, 1834, p. 232. *Walckenaera altifrons* O. P.-Cambridge, 1879–81, p. 169. *Entelecara acuminata* C. Chyzer and L. Kulczynski, 1891–7, II, p. 113 ; F. P. Smith, 1908, p. 332 ; E. Simon, 1926, pp. 422, 426 ; F. Miller, 1947, Tab. 8, fig. 6.

DESCRIPTION. LENGTH : ♀ : 2·2 mm., ♂ : 1·8 mm. CARAPACE : Dark blackish-brown, with darker fovea and striæ. ♂ Head (Text-fig. 130, B). ABDOMEN : Black, fairly globular in ♀. STERNUM : Blackish, shiny ; broadly produced between coxæ IV. LEGS : Tm I slightly less than 0·5. Orange or orange-yellow. ♂ No spines on tibiæ I and II. EPIGYNE : Text-fig. 130, G. MALE PALP : Text-fig. 130, A, F.

OCCURRENCE : Obtained by beating low bushes and trees, in spring and early summer. The male occurs sometimes as an aeronaut. Not uncommon locally in the south, but rare in northern England ; not recorded from Scotland and Eire.

Entelecara erythropus (Westring).
(Text-fig. 130, C, D, E, H)

Erigone erythropus N. Westring, 1851. *Walckenaera erythropus* O. P.-Cambridge, 1879–81, p. 165. *Entelecara erythropus* C. Chyzer and L. Kulczynski, 1891–7, II, p. 113 ; F. P. Smith, 1908, p. 333 ; E. Simon, 1926, p. 425 ; J. Denis, 1942, p. 91 ; F. Miller, 1947, Tab. 8, fig. 8.

DESCRIPTION. LENGTH : ♀♂ : about 2 mm. CARAPACE : Blackish-brown, with darker striæ. ♂ Head elevation less than in *E. acuminata* (Text-fig. 130, D). EYES : ♀ Anterior medians rather smaller than posterior medians ; anteriors all ca. one diam. or less apart. Posteriors one diam. or slightly less apart, with medians slightly closer to each other than to laterals. ABDOMEN : Grey to black, fairly globular in ♀. STERNUM : Black, shiny but finely reticulated. LEGS : Tm I 0·5–0·55. Yellow, suffused with much brown or black. ♂ Spines on tibiæ I–III reduced to minute proportions. EPIGYNE : Text-fig. 130, H. MALE PALP : Text-fig. 130, C, E.

OCCURRENCE : Amongst moss and grass. Widespread throughout the British Isles, but uncommon. Adults in summer.

Entelecara flavipes (Blackwall).
(Text-fig. 131, A, B, C, D, E)

Walckenaera flavipes J. Blackwall, 1834, p. 322, and 1861–4, p. 298 ; O. P.-Cambridge, 1879–81, p. 159. *Entelecara flavipes* E. Simon, 1926, pp. 424, 426 ; J Denis, 1945, p. 214.

DESCRIPTION. LENGTH : ♀ : 1·6–1·7 mm. ♂ : 1·5 mm. CARAPACE : Yellowish black, with blackish fovea and striæ. ♂ Head (Text-fig. 131, D). EYES : ♀ Anterior medians only slightly smaller than posterior medians. Anterior medians ca. one diam. apart, and slightly more from laterals ; posteriors ca. 1·5 diam. apart. ♂ Anterior medians greater than posterior medians, and equal to anterior laterals ; posterior medians 2·5–3 diam. apart. ABDOMEN : Grey, fairly globular.

Sternum : Black or blackish. Legs : Tm I ca. 0·5 ; metatarsus IV *without* a trichobothrium. Pale yellow or whitish yellow. ♂ Tibiæ I–II spineless. Epigyne : Text-fig. 131, E ; fairly distinct from the remaining species. Male palp : Text-fig. 131, A, B, C.

Occurrence : Found by beating bushes and underwood, in woods. Recorded from a few English counties, from the south coast to Lanca-shire, and from Scotland ; very local. Adults in May-June.

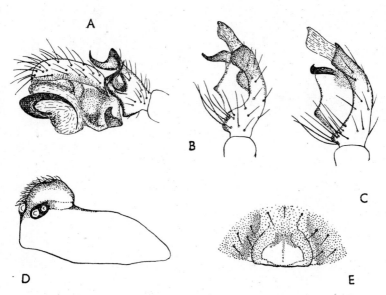

Text-fig. 131.—*Entelecara flavipes:* A, ♂ palp ; B, ♂ palpal tibia (from above) ; C, ditto (from above and outside) ; D, ♂ carapace ; E, epigyne.

Entelecara omissa O. P.-Cambridge.
(Text-fig. 132, A, B, E, F, G, H, I)

Entelecara omissa O. P.-Cambridge, 1902, p. 33.

Description. Length : ♀: 1·3–1·4 mm., ♂ : 1·25 mm. Carapace : Yellowish, suffused with black. ♂ Head with rather shallow lobe (Text-fig. 132, E), with holes in side ; ocular area with some fine hairs. Shape of lobe, from above (Text-fig. 132, I) differs a little from that of *E. errata.* Eyes : ♀ Anterior medians equal in size to posterior medians, and greater than anterior laterals. Anteriors 0·5 diam. or less apart ; posteriors ca. one diam. apart. ♂ Anterior medians slightly greater than posterior medians ; anterior medians ca. 0·5 diam. apart, and ca. one diam. from laterals ; posterior medians ca. 1·5 diam. apart and ca. 2–3 diam. from laterals. ABDOMEN : Greyish-black, fairly globular. STERNUM : Yellow, suffused with black. LEGS : Tm I ca. 0·45 ; metatarsus IV *without* a trichobothrium. Pale brown to yellow. ♂ Tibiæ I–II spineless. EPIGYNE : Text-fig. 132, F, G, H, very similar to *E. errata* and to *E. erythropus*. MALE PALP : Text-fig. 132, A, B ; closely similar to *E. erythropus* and not distinguishable with certainty from *E. errata*.

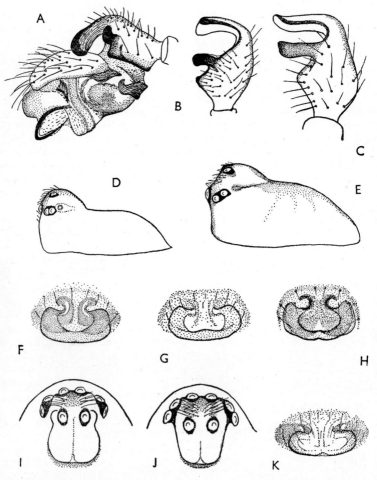

TEXT-FIG. 132.—*Entelecara omissa:* A, ♂ palp ; B, ♂ palpal tibia (from above) ; E, ♂ carapace ; I, ♂ head (from above) ; F, G, H, epigyne.
E. errata: C, ♂ palpal tibia (from above) D, ♂ carapace ; J, ♂ head (from above) ; K, epigyne.

This species can be distinguished from *E. errata* by the lack of a trichobothrium on metatarsus IV, by the epigyne (♀), by the shape of the cephalic lobe, seen from above (♂), and by the proportions of the eyes. Its smaller size and lighter colour distinguishes it from *E. erythropus*, from which it differs also by the position of Tm I and the absence of Tm IV.

OCCURRENCE : Wicken Fen (Cambridgeshire), where it is common amongst cut sedge, vegetable detritus, etc. Adults in May-June, and a few in autumn.

Entelecara errata O. P.-Cambridge.
(Text-fig. 132, C, D, J, K)

Entelecara errata O. P.-Cambridge, 1913, p. 134. *E. omissa*, idem, 1903, p. 167.

DESCRIPTION. LENGTH : ♀ : 1·5–1·7 mm., ♂ : about 1·5 mm. CARAPACE : Pale yellow, suffused with some grey. ♂ Cephalic lobe (Text-fig. 132, D) similar to *E. omissa*, but seen from above (Text-fig. 132, J) differs somewhat from that species. EYES : ♀ Anterior medians smaller than posterior medians, and smaller than anterior laterals. Anteriors 0·5–0·75 diam. apart ; posteriors slightly less than one diam. apart. ♂ Anterior medians slightly smaller than posterior medians, all ca. 0·5 diam. apart ; posterior medians ca. 1·5 diam. apart, and ca. 2 diams. from laterals. ABDOMEN : Grey, mottled with whitish-yellow. STERNUM : Yellow, suffused with black. LEGS : Tm I ca. 0·47; trichobothrium on metatarsus IV not always very clear. Yellow-brown. ♂ Tibial spines not clear in specimens available. EPIGYNE : Text-fig. 132, K. MALE PALP : Text-fig. 132, C. Not distinguishable with certainty from *E. omissa*. For differences from *E. omissa*, see that species.

OCCURRENCE : Under stones, on mountains (often above 3,000 feet), in Snowdonia, Lake District and Scottish Highlands ; rare. Adults in spring and summer, and possibly autumn.

10. Genus MŒBELIA F. Dahl 1886.

CHARACTERS OF GENUS. CARAPACE : ♂ Head not elevated into lobe. EYES : Rather large. LEGS : Metatarsus IV with a trichobothrium ; Tm I 0·6. Tibiæ I–II with two spines dorsally, tibiæ III–IV with one spine. Anterior femora and tibiæ with two rows of bristles ventrally (not very pronounced). Metatarsi only very slightly longer than tarsi. MALE PALP : Tibia with tuft of black bristles dorso-laterally.

There is one British species.

Mœbelia penicillata (Westring).
(Text-fig. 133, G, H, I)

Erigone penicillata N. Westring, 1851. *Neriene penicillata* O. P.-Cambridge, 1879–81, p. 130. *Styloctetor penicillatus* E. Simon, 1926, p. 356. *Mœbelia penicillata* C. Chyzer and L. Kulczynski, 1891–7, II, p. 97 ; F. Miller, 1947, Tab. 7, fig. 8.

DESCRIPTION. LENGTH : ♀ : 1·6–1·8 mm., ♂ : 1·4–1·5 mm. CARAPACE : Dark brown with blackish fovea and striæ. EYES : Posteriors

slightly less than one diam. apart. ABDOMEN: Black. STERNUM:
Yellow, but suffused with much black. LEGS: Tm I 0·6. Yellow-
brown to orange-brown. Femora and tibiæ I–II with two rows of
bristles ventrally. MT I/t I ca. 1·1. EPIGYNE: Text-fig. 133, G.
MALE PALP: Text-fig. 133, H, I.

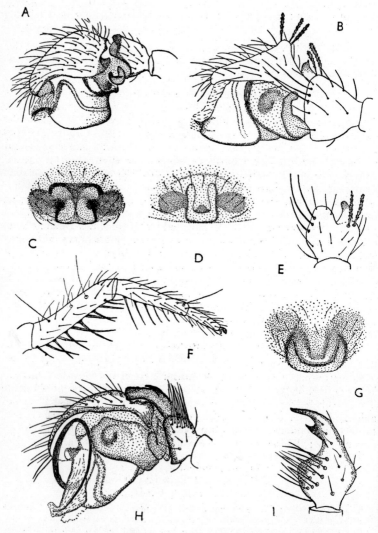

TEXT-FIG. 133.—*Maso sundevalli*: A, ♂ palp; C, epigyne; F, leg I (♀).
M. gallica: B, ♂ palp; D, epigyne; E, ♂ palpal tibia (from above).
Mœbelia penicillata: G, epigyne; H, ♂ palp; I, ♂ palpal tibia (from above).

OCCURRENCE : On the bark of trees, in crevices and amongst lichen on tree trunks. Widespread throughout the British Isles, and fairly common. Adults in spring and summer.

11. Genus **ERIGONIDIUM** F. P. Smith 1904.

CHARACTERS OF GENUS. CARAPACE : ♂ Head not elevated into lobe. EYES : Rather small. CHELICERÆ : ♂ With strong boss anteriorly. LEGS : Metatarsus IV with a trichobothrium ; Tm I 0·6. Tibiæ I–II with two dorsal spines, tibiæ III–IV with one spine. MALE PALP : Patella has small ventral apophysis, similar to *Erigone*.
There is one British species.

Erigonidium graminicola (Sundevall).
(Text-fig. 134, A, B, C)

Linyphia graminicola C. J. Sundevall, 1829, p. 213. *Neriene graminicola* J. Blackwall, 1861–4, p. 272 ; O. P.-Cambridge, 1879–81, p. 108. *Tmeticus graminicola* E. Simon, 1926, p. 450.

DESCRIPTION. LENGTH : ♀ 2·5–3·2 mm., ♂ : about 2·5 mm. CARAPACE : Yellow-brown or brown, with blackish fovea and striæ ; head suffused with some black, particularly in ocular area. EYES : Posteriors ca. one diam. apart. ABDOMEN : Grey to black, with sometimes (particularly in ♀) an ill-defined central pale band. STERNUM : Dark-brown, suffused with black. CHELICERÆ : ♂ With a strong boss on front, pointing inwards, and a row of small warts anterio-laterally. LEGS : Tm I 0·6. Yellow-brown, with femora orange-brown. Text-fig. 134, C. MALE PALP : Text-fig. 134, A, B.
OCCURRENCE : Obtained by beating bushes (e.g. furze, box) and low trees. Widespread throughout the British Isles, but local. Adult in early summer.

12. Genus **GNATHONARIUM** F. Karsch 1881.

CHARACTERS OF GENUS. CARAPACE : ♂ Gibbous behind the eyes (but with no lobe). EYES : Fairly large and closely grouped. CHELICERÆ : ♂ With a pointed boss anteriorly. LEGS : Metatarsus IV with a trichobothrium ; Tm I about 0·6. Tibiæ I–II with two spines, tibiæ III–IV with one spine. MALE PALP : Palpal organs with long curved embolus.
There is one British species.

Gnathonarium dentatum (Wider).
(Text-fig. 134, D, E, F, G)

Theridion dentatum Wider, 1834, p. 223. *Neriene dentatum* J. Blackwall, 1861–4, p. 258 ; O. P.-Cambridge, 1879–81, p. 115. *Trachygnatha dentatum* C. Chyzer and L. Kulczynski, 1891–7, II, p. 91. *Gnathonarium dentatum* E. Simon, 1926, p. 476 ; S. C. Bishop and C. R. Crosby, 1935, p. 222.

DESCRIPTION. LENGTH : ♀ : 2·5–3 mm., ♂ : 2·25–2·5 mm. CARAPACE : Brown to dark brown, with dark fovea. ♂ Rather gibbous behind the eyes, with head projecting somewhat over clypeus ; head

P

with a number of long, forward-directed, pale-coloured silky hairs ; ocular area blackish. EYES : ♀ Posterior medians ca. one diam. apart, and less from the laterals. ♂ Posterior medians 1·5–2 diam. apart, and ca. one diam. from laterals. ABDOMEN : Grey to black, with an indistinct whitish median band ; very faint white chevrons sometimes

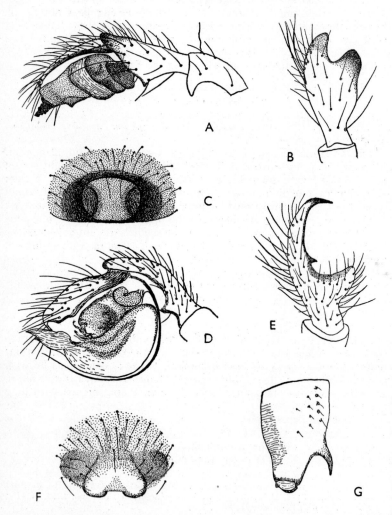

TEXT-FIG. 134.—*Erigonidium graminicola :* A, ♂ palp ; B, ♂ palpal tibia (from above) ; C, epigyne.
   Gnathonarium dentatum : D, ♂ palp ; E, ♂ palpal tibia (from above) ; F, epigyne ; G, ♂ chelicera (right, from side).

visible in ♂. STERNUM : Orange-brown, faintly reticulated, sometimes suffused with black. CHELICERÆ : ♂ With pronounced pointed boss in front (Text-fig. 134, G), and a number of small warts basally, on front and to side. MAXILLÆ : ♂ With some minute warts, bearing long black bristles. LEGS : Tm I ca. 0·6. Yellow-brown to orange-brown. EPIGYNE : Text-fig. 134, F. MALE PXLP : Text-fig. 134, D, E.

OCCURRENCE : In wet marshy situations by the side of streams, etc. Widespread throughout the British Isles, and common. Adult in spring, summer and autumn.

13. Genus **TMETICUS** A. Menge 1866.

CHARACTERS OF GENUS. CARAPACE : ♂ No cephalic lobe present. CHELICERÆ : ♂ With large warty tooth anteriorly. LEGS : Metatarsus IV with a trichobothrium ; Tm I 0·74. ♀ Tibiæ I–II with two spines, tibiæ III–IV with one spine ; spines rather short (e.g. spine on tibia IV is about one diam. of tibia). ♂ Tibiæ I–II spineless, tibiæ III–IV with one very weak spine. MALE PALP : Tarsus and palpal organs small.

There is one British species, closely resembling *Donacochara speciosa* (q.v.) in the sex organs.

Tmeticus affinis (Blackwall).
(Text-fig. 135, A, B, D)

Neriene affinis J. Blackwall, 1861–4, p. 259 ; O. P.-Cambridge, 1879–81, p. 114 ; *Tmeticus affinis* S. C. Bishop and C. R. Crosby, 1935, p. 226. *Anglia hancocki* F. P. Smith, 1905, p. 247.

DESCRIPTION. LENGTH : ♀ : 3 mm., ♂ : 2·5–2·7 mm. CARAPACE : Reddish brown, rather darker in ♂. EYES : ♀♂ Posterior medians ca. 1·5 diam. apart, and ca. one diam. from laterals. ABDOMEN : Black, with four impressed dots dorsally. STERNUM : Orange-yellow, with numerous hairs. CHELICERÆ : ♀ Outer teeth fairly large, but smaller than in *Donacochara*. ♂ With large warty tooth anteriorly, and several small warts on front and to side. LEGS : Tm I ca. 0·74. Orange-brown. Ventrally with longitudinal rows of long, rather stout hairs. EPIGYNE : Text-fig. 135, B ; the outlines of the spermathecæ are not always so clear as shown, leaving the epigyne with a similar appearance to *Œdothorax*. MALE PALP : Text-fig. 135, A, D ; there is a small bifid tooth on the outer dorsal margin of the tibia.

OCCURRENCE : Amongst moss and grass, usually in wet or swampy localities. Recorded from a few English counties from the south coast to Yorkshire ; rare. Adults at most seasons.

14. Genus **GONGYLIDIUM** A. Menge 1868.

CHARACTERS OF GENUS. CARAPACE : ♂ No cephalic lobe present. CHELICERÆ : ♂ With small wart anteriorly. LEGS : Metatarsus IV with a trichobothrium ; Tm I about 0·75. Tibiæ I–II with two spines, tibiæ III–IV with one spine. MALE PALP : Patella enlarged and "gouty."

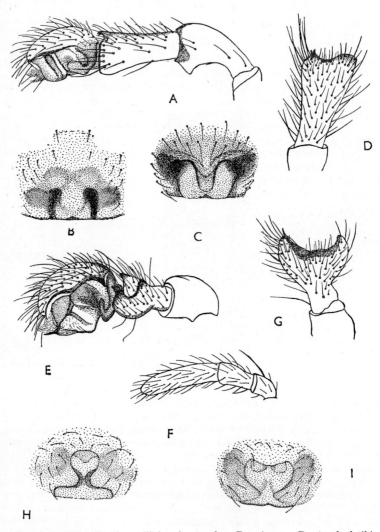

TEXT-FIG. 135.—*Tmeticus affinis:* A, ♂ palp ; B, epigyne ; D, ♂ palpal tibia (from above).
  Gongylidium rufipes: C, epigyne ; E, ♂ palp ; G. ♂ palpal tibia (from above).
  Dismodicus bifrons: F, ♀ palp ; H, epigyne.
  D. elevatus: I, epigyne.

Gongylidium rufipes (Sundevall).
(Text-fig. 135, C, E, G)

Linyphia rufipes C. J. Sundevall, 1829, p. 216, and 1832, p. 259. *Neriene munda* J. Blackwall, 1861–4, p. 265. *N. rufipes* O. P.-Cambridge, 1879–81, p. 110. *Gongylidium rufipes* C. Chyzer and L. Kulczynski, 1891–7, II, p. 92 ; E. Simon, 1926, p. 451.

DESCRIPTION. LENGTH : ♀ : 3–3·5 mm., ♂ : 2·75–3 mm. CARA-PACE : Orange-brown, with darker striæ. ♂ Head suffused with black. EYES : ♀♂ Posterior medians slightly more than one diam. apart, and one diam. from laterals. ABDOMEN : Grey to black. STERNUM : Orange, suffused with some black in ♂. CHELICERÆ : ♂ With small wart anteriorly. LEGS : Tm I 0·74–0·78. Bright orange or reddish orange. EPIGYNE : Text-fig. 135, C. MALE PALP : Text-fig. 135, E, G. The general colouration of this spider is orange and black.

OCCURRENCE : On bushes and low trees, and in undergrowth. Widespread throughout the British Isles, and fairly common. Adults in spring and autumn.

15. Genus DISMODICUS E. Simon 1884.

CHARACTERS OF GENUS. ♂ Head elevated into large lobe, bifid longitudinally, with posterior median eyes on front of lobe. Clypeus relatively wider than in *Hypomma* (♀) (see Key to Genera) ; clypeus projecting in ♂. LEGS : Metatarsus IV with a trichobothrium ; Tm I 0·75–0·8. ♀ Tibiæ I–IV with one spine, one diam. or slightly more in length ; position of spine on tibia I is 0·3 or more. ♂ Tibial spines absent. Legs rather stouter than in *Hypomma*, with e.g. tibia I *l/d* ca. 4·5. FEMALE PALP : Blunt-ended (Text-fig. 135, F). MALE PALP : Tibia with small apophysis only.

There are two British species, distinguished by the sex organs (♀ ♂), and by the cephalic lobe (♂).

Dismodicus bifrons (Blackwall).
(Text-figs. 135, F, H ; 136, A, B, E)

Walckenaera bifrons J. Blackwall, 1841, p. 634, and 1861–4, p. 302 ; O. P.-Cambridge, 1879–81, p. 149. *Dismodicus bifrons* C. Chyzer and L. Kulczynski, 1891–7, II, p. 101 ; E. Simon, 1926, p. 437 ; A. F. Millidge and G. H. Locket, 1947, p. 114.

DESCRIPTION. LENGTH : ♀ : 2–2·25 mm. ♂ : 1·75–2 mm. CARA-PACE : Dark blackish-brown. ♀ With a few forward-directed spines in ocular area. ♂ Cephalic lobe (Text-fig. 136, E) ; the clypeus projects anteriorly. EYES : ♀ Posterior medians large, slightly more than one diam. apart. ABDOMEN : Black, with 4 faint impressed reddish dots. STERNUM : Brown, suffused with black. LEGS : Tm I 0·78–0·8. Yellow-brown to brown. ♂ Tibial spines absent. EPIGYNE : Text-fig. 135, H. MALE PALP : Text-fig. 136, A, B.

Differs from *D. elevatus* (♀) in the epigyne, which in the latter species has the central fovea rather in the shape of a wine-glass. In the ♂, the form of the cephalic lobe and the tibial apophysis give a clear distinction.

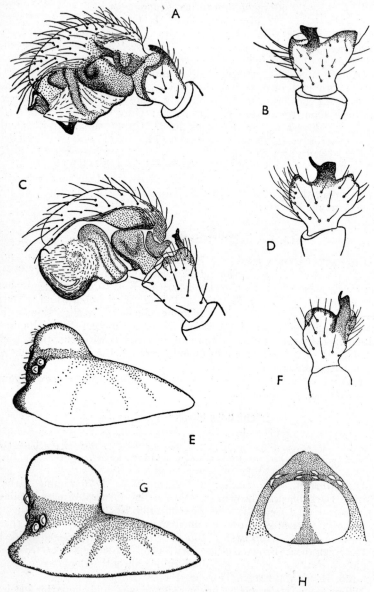

Text-fig. 136.—*Dismodicus bifrons:* ♂ A, palp ; B, palpal tibia (from above) ;
E, carapace.
D. elevatus ♂ : C, palp ; D, palpal tibia (from above) ; F, ditto (from above
and outside) ; G, carapace ; H, head and clypeus (from above).

OCCURRENCE : On low bushes and underwood, and amongst moss and undergrowth, usually in or near wooded areas, or in swampy localities. Widely distributed throughout England, Wales and Eire ; recorded once from Scotland. Frequent locally. Adults in spring and summer.

Dismodicus elevatus (C. L. Koch).
(Text-figs. 135, I ; 136, C, D, F, G, H)

Micryphantes elevatus C. L. Koch, 1838, p. 133. *Dismodicus elevatus* C. Chyzer and L. Kulczynski, 1891–7, II, p. 101 ; A. R. Jackson, 1915, p. 187 ; E. Simon, 1926, p. 436 ; A. F. Millidge and G. H. Locket, 1947, p. 113.

DESCRIPTION. LENGTH : ♀ : 2·3 mm. ♂ : 1·8 mm. CARAPACE : ♀ Dark brown, with darker fovea and striæ. ♂ Dark brownish black, with head raised into very large lobe, wider and longer than in *D. bifrons* (Text-fig. 136, G, H) ; clypeus projects anteriorly. EYES : Posterior medians slightly more than one diam. apart, and ca. 1·5 diam. from laterals. ABDOMEN : Black, with four impressed reddish dots. LEGS : Tm I 0·75. Orange-brown. ♂ Tibial spines absent. EPIGYNE : Text-fig. 135, I. MALE PALP : Text-fig. 136, C, D, F. For distinctions from *D. bifrons*, see that species.

OCCURRENCE : Scotland, on low pine boughs or juniper : Abernethy Forest and Loch Garten. Adults in summer.

16. Genus HYPOMMA F. Dahl 1886.

CHARACTERS OF GENUS. CARAPACE : ♂ Head elevated into large lobe, bifid longitudinally, with posterior median eyes on front of lobe. Clypeus relatively narrower than in *Dismodicus* (♀) (see Key to Genera) ; clypeus not projecting in ♂. LEGS : Metatarsus IV with a trichobothrium in *H. bituberculatum* and *H. fulvum*, but without a trichobothrium in *H. cornutum*. Tm I 0·66–0·8. ♀ Tibiæ I–IV with one dorsal spine, short (less than one diam.) and thin ; position of spine on tibia I is 0·25–0·33. ♂ Tibial spines absent. Legs rather thinner than in *Dismodicus*, with e.g. tibia I *l/d* ca. 6. FEMALE PALP : Blunt-ended as in *Dismodicus*. MALE PALP : Tibia with two apophyses, one short and small, one long.

There are three British species, readily distinguished by the sex organs, and the trichobothria.

Hypomma bituberculatum (Wider).
(Text-figs. 137, A, B, F, G ; 138, C)

Theridion bituberculatum Wider, 1834, p. 222. *Neriene bituberculata* J. Blackwall, 1861–4, p. 268 ; O. P.-Cambridge, 1879–81, p. 119. *Hypomma bituberculatum* C. Chyzer and L. Kulczynski, 1891–7, II, p. 100 ; E. Simon, 1926, p. 435 ; F. Miller, 1947, Tab. 7, fig. 6. *Enidia bituberculata* F. P. Smith, 1904, p. 115.

DESCRIPTION. LENGTH : ♀ : 2·5–3 mm. ♂ : 2·25–2·5 mm. CARAPACE : Bright reddish-brown. ♀ Head with a median line of short hairs, and a few hairs behind each posterior lateral eye. ♂ Head (Text-fig. 137, F, G) ; ocular area suffused with black. EYES : ♀

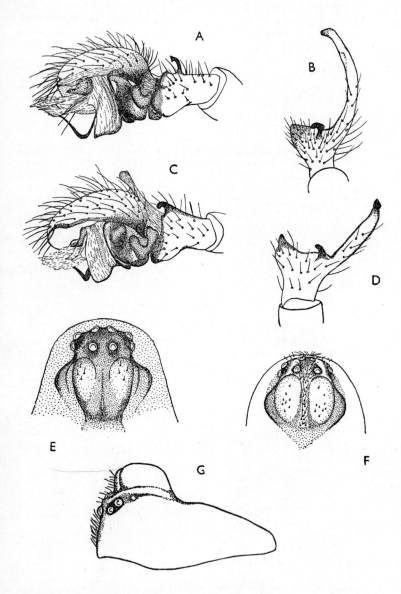

TEXT-FIG. 137.—*Hypomma bituberculatum* ♂: A, palp; B, palpal tibia (from
above); F, head (from above); G, carapace.
H. cornutum ♂: C, palp; D, palpal tibia (from above); E, head (from above).

Posterior medians slightly more than one diam. apart, and ca. one diam. from laterals. ABDOMEN : Black with four reddish impressed dots. STERNUM : Orange ; broad between coxæ IV. LEGS : Tm I ca. 0·8. Orange. ♀ Tibial spines very short (ca. two-thirds diam. of leg). ♂ Tibiæ spineless. EPIGYNE : Text-fig. 138, C. MALE PALP : Text-fig. 137, A, B ; there is a small hook-like apophysis on the tibia, in addition to a long apophysis.

OCCURRENCE : In wet swampy areas, by the sides of streams or ponds. Widespread throughout the British Isles ; common, and locally abundant. Adults in spring, summer and autumn.

Hypomma fulvum Bösenberg.
(Text-figs. 138, A, B, E ; 254, I)

Hypomma fulvum W. Bösenberg, 1902, p. 162. *H. mallezi* J. Denis, 1943 (2), p. 106.

DESCRIPTION. LENGTH : ♀♂ : about 2·5 mm. Colour and form as *H. bituberculata*. LEGS : Tm I 0·75–0·8. ♀ Tibial spines very short and thin. ♂ Tibiæ spineless. EPIGYNE : Text-figs. 138, E ; 254, I ; quite distinct from *H. bituberculata*. MALE PALP : Text-fig. 138, A, B ; the tibia has a barbed hook, and the patella is enlarged.

OCCURRENCE : Three females only have been taken in Britain, all in fen country (Norfolk, and Wicken Fen (Cambridgeshire)). The figures of the male were drawn from a European specimen in the British Museum (Natural History).

Hypomma cornutum (Blackwall).
(Text-figs. 137, C, D, E ; 138, D)

Neriene cornuta J. Blackwall, 1833, p. 190, and 1861–4 p. 267 ; O. P.-Cambridge, 1879–81, p. 118. *Dicyphus cornutus* C. Chyzer and L. Kulczynski, 1891–7, II, p. 100. *Falconeria cornuta* F. P. Smith, 1904, p. 116. *Hypomma cornutum* E. Simon, 1926, p. 436 ; F. Miller, 1947, Tab. 7, fig. 7.

DESCRIPTION. LENGTH : ♀ : 2·5–2·8 mm. ♂ : about 2·25 mm. CARAPACE : Brown, with darker fovea and striæ ; head with black margins, and with median line of short hairs. ♂ Head (Text-fig. 137, E) ; lobes smaller than in *H. bituberculatum*. EYES : ♀ : Posterior medians slightly less than one diam. apart, and one diam. from laterals. ABDOMEN : Black, with four reddish impressed dots. STERNUM : Dark brown, broad between coxæ IV. LEGS : Tm I 0·66 ; metatarsus IV *without* trichobothrium. Orange-brown. ♀ Tibial spines very short (ca. 0·5 diam. of tibia), but stout. ♂ Legs spineless. EPIGYNE : Text-fig. 138, D. MALE PALP : Text-fig. 137, C, D.

OCCURRENCE : On bushes and underwood. Widespread, but not recorded from Scotland. Frequent, and abundant locally. Adult in spring and early summer.

17. Genus **METOPOBACTRUS** E. Simon 1884.

CHARACTERS OF GENUS. CARAPACE : ♂ Head raised conically anteriorly (Text-fig. 138, I) ; less so in ♀. EYES : Fairly large, and closely grouped. LEGS : Metatarsus IV with a trichobothrium ;

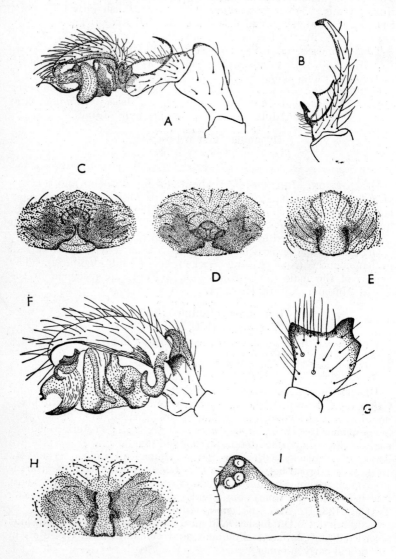

Text-fig. 138.—*Hypomma fulvum:* A, ♂ palp ; B, ♂ palpal tibia (from above) ;
E, epigyne.
Hypomma bituberculatum: C, epigyne.
H. cornutum: D, epigyne.
Metopobactrus prominulus: F, ♂ palp ; G, ♂ palpal tibia (from above) ; H,
epigyne ; I, ♂ carapace.

Tm I ca. 0·75. Tibiæ I–IV with one dorsal spine, close to base on tibia I (position 0·18 in ♀, 0·12 in ♂). Metatarsi appreciably longer than tarsi, with MT I/t I ca. 1·4, MT IV/t IV ca. 1·9. Legs fairly stout, with e.g. tibia I *l/d* ca. 4.

There is one British species.

Metopobactrus prominulus (O. P.-Cambridge).
(Text-fig. 138, F, G, H, I)

Erigone prominula O. P.-Cambridge, 1872 (1), p. 750. *Walckenaera prominula* idem, 1879–81, p. 448. *Microneta territa* O. P.-Cambridge, 1906, p. 88. *Metopobactrus prominulus* E. Simon, 1926, pp. 358, 359 ; F. Miller, 1947, Tab. 6, fig. 11.

DESCRIPTION. LENGTH : ♀ : 1·5–1·75 mm. ♂ : 1·4–1·5 mm. CARAPACE : Dark brown, with blackish striæ, and ocular area suffused with black. ♂ Head elevated conically (Text-fig. 138, I). EYES : ♀ Anteriors ca. 0·5 diam. apart ; posterior medians ca. one diam. apart, and 0·5 diam. from laterals. ♂ Anteriors ca. one diam. apart ; posterior medians slightly more than one diam., apart and one diam. laterals. ABDOMEN : Grey, often pinkish when alive. CHELICERÆ : Very short. LEGS : Tm I ca. 0·75. Brown. Tibiæ I and metatarsi I have dorsally a number of erect hairs. EPIGYNE : Text-fig. 138, H. MALE PALP : Text-fig. 138, F, G.

OCCURRENCE : In moss, undergrowth, straw, etc. Widespread in the British Isles ; uncommon, but frequent locally. Adults in spring, summer and autumn.

18. Genus HYBOCOPTUS E. Simon 1884.

CHARACTERS OF GENUS. CARAPACE : ♂ Head raised into large lobe. STERNUM : Wide and truncated between coxæ IV. LEGS : Metatarsus IV with a trichobothrium ; Tm I about 0·7. Tibiæ I–IV with one spine ; position of spine on tibia I ca. 0·2. Metatarsi moderately longer than tarsi, with MT I/t I 1·35 ; MT IV/t IV 1·6. Tibia I *l/d* ca. 6.

There is one British species.

Hybocoptus decollatus (Simon).
(Text-fig. 139, A, B, C, D)

Erigone decollata E. Simon, 1881, p. 237. *Hybocoptus decollatus* idem, 1926, p. 386.

DESCRIPTION. LENGTH : ♀ : 1·75 mm. ♂ : 1·5 mm. CARAPACE : Brown, with blackish striæ and margins, and head suffused with black. ♂ Head raised into large lobe (Text-fig. 139, C), impressed at sides and in front, with some short hairs anteriorly. EYES : ♀ Posterior medians one diam. apart, and 1·5 diam. from laterals. ABDOMEN : Grey or yellowish grey, rather globular in ♀. STERNUM : Yellow-brown suffused with black on margins. LEGS : Tm I ca. 0·7. Yellow-brown. EPIGYNE : Text-fig. 139, D ; not very distinctive. MALE PALP : Text-fig. 139, A, B ; palpal organs somewhat similar to *Entelecara*.

OCCURRENCE : On bushes (e.g. furze) near the coast in the Isle of Wight (the only British locality) ; frequent locally. Adult in summer.

19. Genus **BARYPHYMA** E. Simon 1884.

CHARACTERS OF GENUS. CARAPACE : ♂ Head raised into shallow, flat lobe, compressed at sides, with sulci behind lateral eyes. ABDOMEN : With four reddish impressed dots dorsally. LEGS : Metatarsus IV with a trichobothrium ; Tm I 0·9–0·95. ♀♂ Tibiæ I–II with two short spines, tibiæ III–IV with one short spine (all less than one diam. in length (♀), or less than 0·5 diam. in length (♂)). Tibiæ I–II with 9–10 pairs of stout bristles ventrally ; less well-developed in ♂. Metatarsi much longer than tarsi, with MT I/t I 1·75 ; MT IV/t IV 2·3.

There is one British species.

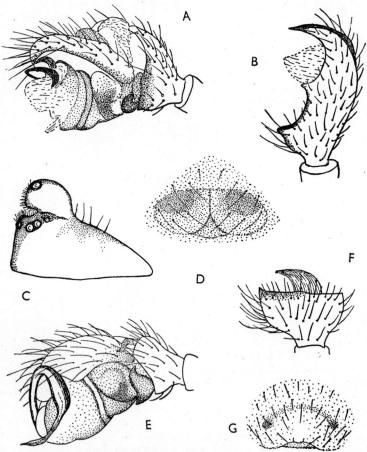

TEXT-FIG. 139.—*Hybocoptus decollatus*: A, ♂ palp ; B, ♂ palpal tibia (from above) ; C, ♂ carapace ; D, epigyne.
Baryphyma pratensis: E, ♂ palp ; F, ♂ palpal tibia (from above) ; G, epigyne.

Baryphyma pratensis (Blackwall).
(Text-fig. 139, E, F, G)

Walckenaera pratensis J. Blackwall, 1861, p. 445, and 1861–4, p. 306 ; O. P.-Cambridge, 1879–81, p. 502. *Baryphyma pratensis* E. Simon, 1926, p. 374.

DESCRIPTION. LENGTH : ♀ : 2·75–3 mm. ♂ : 2·25–2·5 mm. CARAPACE : Brown, with blackish striæ and margins. ♂ Head with shallow lobe, and sulci behind lateral eyes. EYES : ♀ Anterior medians ca. one diam. apart, and ca. 2 diam. from laterals ; posterior medians ca. one diam. apart, and slightly more than one diam. from laterals. ♂ Posterior medians 1·5 diam. apart, and ca. 2 diams. from laterals. ABDOMEN : Black or grey, with four impressed reddish dots dorsally ; rather globular. STERNUM : Brown, suffused with black, particularly on margins. LEGS : Tm I ca. 0·93 ; trichobothrium bent. Yellow to brown. Spines short (see generic description). EPIGYNE : Text-fig. 139, G. MALE PALP : Text-fig. 139, E, F ; the tibia has a semi-transparent process apically.

OCCURRENCE : Amongst grass and herbage in damp meadows, usually near streams or rivers. Recorded from a number of English counties from the south coast to the Scottish border ; rare. Adult in April-May.

20. Genus GONATIUM A. Menge 1866.

CHARACTERS OF GENUS. CARAPACE : ♂ Head without cephalic lobe. ABDOMEN : With four reddish impressed dots dorsally. LEGS : Metatarsus IV with a trichobothrium ; Tm I ca. 0·9. ♀ Tibiæ I–IV with one short spine ; position of tibia I spine ca. 0·25. ♂ Tibiæ I–II spineless, tibiæ III–IV with one very small spine. ♂ Tibia I slightly curved, with patella swollen (Text-fig. 140, E). Metatarsi much longer than tarsi, with MT I/t I ca. 1·65; MT IV/t IV ca. 1·85–1·9. MALE PALP : Patella greatly enlarged ; tibia with prominent apophyses.

There are two British species, each with a distinct reddish tinge. They are readily separated by their sex organs.

Gonatium rubens (Blackwall).
(Text-fig. 140, A, B, E, F)

Neriene rubens J. Blackwall, 1833, p. 189, and 1861–4, p. 270 ; O. P.-Cambridge, 1879–81, p. 111. *Gonatium rubens* C. Chyzer and L. Kulczynski, 1891–7, II, p. 99 ; W. Bosenberg, 1901–3, p. 160 ; E. Simon, 1926, pp. 430, 434 ; S. C. Bishop and C. R. Crosby, 1935, p. 255 ; B. J. Kaston, 1948, p. 172.

DESCRIPTION. LENGTH : ♀ : 3 mm. ♂ : 2·5 mm. CARAPACE : Reddish-yellow or reddish-brown. ♂ Head narrowed anteriorly, and raised a little, but with no lobe. EYES : In compact group, each sharply ringed with black. ABDOMEN : Reddish grey to black, with four impressed reddish brown dots. STERNUM : Orange-brown. LEGS : Tm I 0·88. Orange-brown. ♂ Tibia I curved, with patella swollen (Text-fig. 140, E). ♂ Femur I with rows of short, stout, curved spines ventrally ; tibiæ I–II spineless, tibiæ III–IV with very small spines. EPIGYNE : Text-fig. 140, F. MALE PALP : Text-fig. 140, A, B ;

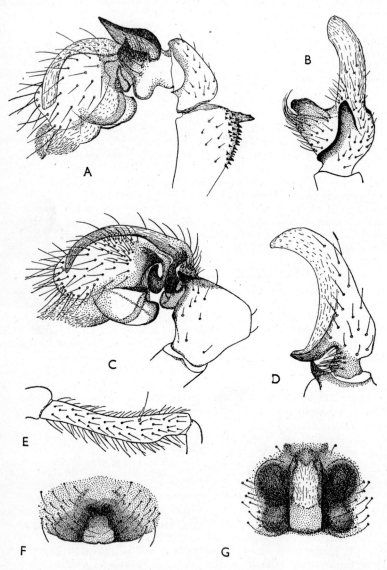

TEXT-FIG. 140.—*Gonatium rubens*: A, ♂ palp; B, ♂ palpal tibia (from above); E, tibia I (♂); F, epigyne.
G. rubellum: C, ♂ palp; D, ♂ palpal tibia (from above); G, epigyne.

the femur has a prominent pointed apophysis dorsally, and numerous black granulations.

OCCURRENCE : In a variety of situations, e.g. in undergrowth, on bushes, in gardens, etc. Widespread throughout the British Isles, and common. Adults most of the year.

Gonatium rubellum (Blackwall).
(Text-fig. 140, C, D, G)

Neriene rubella J. Blackwall, 1841, p. 648, and 1861–4, p. 281. *N. isabellina* O. P.-Cambridge, 1879–81, p. 112. *Gonatium isabellinum* C. Chyzer and L. Kulczynski, 1891–7, II, p. 99. *Gonatium rubellum* E. Simon, 1926, pp. 431, 433.

DESCRIPTION. LENGTH : ♀ : 3 mm. ♂ : 2·5 mm. CARAPACE : Reddish-brown, with a more pronounced fovea than in *G. rubens*. ♂ Head elevated less sharply than in *G. rubens*. EYES : As *G. rubens*. ABDOMEN : Grey, suffused with pink, with four impressed reddish-brown dots. STERNUM : Orange-brown. LEGS : Tm I 0·88. Pale orange-brown. ♂ Tibia I curved, with long fine hairs ventrally ; femur I as *G. rubens* (but less pronounced). ♂ Metatarsus I with short, stout, curved spines ventrally. EPIGYNE : Text-fig. 140, G. MALE PALP : Text-fig. 140, C, D ; the patella is greatly enlarged.

OCCURRENCE : In moss, undergrowth, etc., usually in woods. Widespread throughout the British Isles, but less common than *G. rubens*. Adults are found most of the year.

21. Genus MINYRIOLOIDES E. Schenkel 1929.

CHARACTERS OF GENUS. CARAPACE : ♂ : Head raised into large lobe. ABDOMEN : With four reddish impressed dots dorsally. LEGS : Metatarsus IV with a trichobothrium ; Tm I about 0·8. ♀ : Tibiæ I–II with two spines, tibæ III–IV with one spine. ♂ : Tibiæ I–II spineless, tibiæ III–IV with one spine. Metatarsi much longer than tarsi, with MT I/t I 1·5, MT IV/t IV 2·0. MALE PALP : Palpal organs with long embolus.

There is one British species.

Minyrioloides trifrons (O. P.-Cambridge).
(Text-fig. 141, A, B, C, D)

Walckenaera trifrons O. P.-Cambridge, 1863, p. 8589, and 1879–81, p. 166. *Entelecara trifrons* F. P. Smith, 1908, p. 333 ; E. Simon, 1926, pp. 424, 425. *Porrhothrix trifrons* J. Denis, 1945, fig. 7. *Minyrioloides trifrons* A. Holm, 1945, p. 31. *Minyriolus aquatilis* C. R. Crosby and S. C. Bishop, 1933, p. 135.

DESCRIPTION. LENGTH : ♀ : 1·9–2·1 mm. ♂ : 1·75 mm. CARAPACE : Brown to dark brown, with ocular area sometimes suffused with black. ♂ : Head raised into large lobe (Text-fig. 141, C), carrying posterior median eyes, and with numerous fine hairs anteriorly. EYES : ♀ : Posterior medians ca. one diam. apart, and very slightly more from laterals. ABDOMEN : Black, with four reddish impressed dots. STERNUM : Brown, suffused with black. LEGS : Tm I ca. 0·8. Orange-yellow to brown. EPIGYNE : Text-fig. 141, D. MALE PALP : Text-figs. 141, A, B.

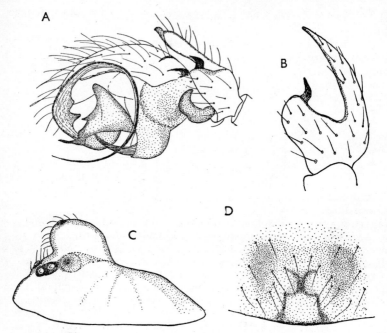

TEXT-FIG. 141.—*Minyrioloides trifrons:* A, ♂ palp; B, ♂ palpal tibia (from above); C, ♂ carapace; D, epigyne.

OCCURRENCE: In marshy localities. Widespread in Britain, but not recorded from Wales; rare usually, but common in Wicken Fen. Adult in spring and early summer.

22. Genus **MASO** E. Simon 1884.

CHARACTERS OF GENUS. CARAPACE: ♂: Head not elevated into lobe. LEGS: Metatarsus IV with a trichobothrium; Tm I 0·9 or more. Tibiæ I–IV with one dorsal spine. Tibiæ and metatarsi I–II with two longitudinal rows of stout spines ventrally (Text-fig. 133, F). (Similar but less developed spines are present in *Perimones* (q.v.)). Metatarsi about twice as long as tarsi.

There are two British species, which are readily separated by their sex organs.

Maso sundevalli (Westring).
(Text-fig. 133, A, C, F)

Erigone sundevalli N. Westring, 1851. *Neriene sundevalli* O. P.-Cambridge, 1879–81, p. 125. *Maso sundevalli* C. Chyzer and L. Kulczynski, 1891–7, II, p. 133; E. Simon, 1926, p. 330; S. C. Bishop and C. R. Crosby, 1935, p. 233; F. Miller, 1947, Tab. 6, fig. 5; B. J. Kaston, 1948, p. 145.

DESCRIPTION. LENGTH: ♀: 1·4–1·6 mm. ♂: about 1·3 mm. CARAPACE: Yellow-brown, with black fovea and striæ; head or ocular area suffused with black. 2–3 long forward-directed spines present in median line. EYES: Posteriors one diam. or slightly less apart. ABDOMEN: Grey to black. STERNUM: Yellow-brown, suffused black. LEGS: Tm I 0·9 or more. Yellow-brown. Ventral spines less strongly developed in ♂, but still clear. EPIGYNE: Text-fig. 133, C. MALE PALP: Text-fig. 133, A; tibia with no apophysis.

OCCURRENCE: In moss, grass, detritus, etc., in woods and open land. Widespread throughout the British Isles; fairly common. Males adult in spring and early summer, females all the year.

Maso gallica Simon.
(Text-fig. 133, B, D, E)

Maso gallica E. Simon, 1894, p. 641 (footnote); W. Falconer, 1912, p. 320; O. P.-Cambridge, 1913, p. 132; E. Simon, 1926, p. 330.

DESCRIPTION. LENGTH: ♀: 1·5 mm. ♂: 1·3 mm. Closely similar to *M. sundevalli*, from which it differs in the genitalia. EPIGYNE:

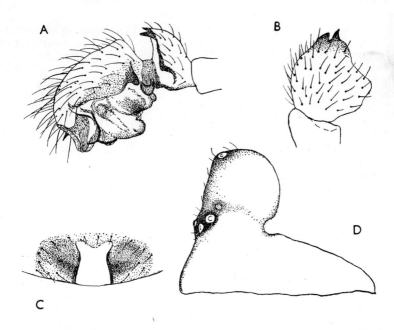

TEXT-FIG. 142.—*Peponocranium ludicrum:* A, ♂ palp; B, ♂ palpal tibia (from above); C, epigyne; D, ♂ carapace.

R

Text-fig. 133, D ; has a central tongue-like process, absent in *M. sunde-valli*. MALE PALP : Text-figs. 133, B, E ; the tibia has a short black-tipped apophysis, at the base of which there are 2–3 clavate spines. The tarsus is raised conically at the base, bearing 3 clavate spines.

OCCURRENCE : Wicken Fen (Cambridgeshire), where it is fairly common amongst cut sedge, etc. Adult in spring and early summer.

23. Genus **PEPONOCRANIUM** E. Simon 1884.

CHARACTERS OF GENUS. CARAPACE : ♂ : Head raised into large lobe. LEGS : Metatarsus IV with a trichobothrium ; Tm I $0 \cdot 85$–$0 \cdot 9$. ♀ : Tibiæ I–IV with one dorsal spine ; position of tibia I spine ca. $0 \cdot 24$, of tibia IV spine ca. $0 \cdot 35$; tibia IV spine ca. $1 \cdot 5$ diam. in length. ♂ : Tibiæ I–II spineless, tibiæ III–IV with one spine. Metatarsi much longer than tarsi, with MT I/t I $1 \cdot 5$, MT IV/t IV $2 \cdot 0$. MALE PALP : Tibia without apophysis.

There is one British species.

Peponocranium ludicrum (O. P.-Cambridge).
(Text-fig. 142, A, B, C, D)

Walckenaera ludicra O. P.-Cambridge, 1861, p. 438, and 1879–81, p. 168 ; J. Blackwall, 1861–4, p. 226. *Peponocranium ludicrum* E. Simon, 1926, p. 332 ; F. Miller, 1947, Tab. 4, figs. 7, 8.

DESCRIPTION. LENGTH : ♀ : $1 \cdot 8$–$2 \cdot 2$ mm. ♂ : $1 \cdot 8$ mm. CARAPACE : Pale yellow to yellow-brown, with darker fovea and striæ. Ocular area suffused with some black. ♂ : Head (Text-fig. 142, D) darker brown, suffused with black particularly around the eyes. EYES : Ringed with black. ♀ : Posteriors ca. one diam. apart. ABDOMEN : Pale greyish yellow, sometimes suffused with black ; sometimes four small reddish impressed dots are visible. STERNUM : Pale yellow, suffused with black. LEGS : Tm I $0 \cdot 85$–$0 \cdot 9$. Yellow-brown ; tibiæ sometimes suffused with black, particularly in ♂. ♂ : Tibiæ I–II spineless. EPIGYNE : Text-fig. 142, C. MALE PALP : Text-fig. 142, A, B ; tibia and tarsus sometimes black.

OCCURRENCE : On bushes, in heather, grass, moss and undergrowth. Widespread throughout the British Isles, and common at times. Adult males in spring and early summer, females most of the year.

24. Genus **POCADICNEMIS** E. Simon 1884.

CHARACTERS OF GENUS. CARAPACE : ♂ : Head raised into shallow lobe. LEGS : Metatarsus IV with a trichobothrium ; Tm I $0 \cdot 85$–$0 \cdot 9$. ♀ : Tibiæ I–IV with one spine. Position of tibia I spine ca. $0 \cdot 14$, of tibia IV spine ca. $0 \cdot 23$. Tibial spines long, e.g. tibia IV spine ca. 2 diam. in length. ♂ : Tibiæ I–IV with one spine (very weak on tibia I). Metatarsi much longer than tarsi, with MT I/t I $1 \cdot 6$, MT IV/t IV $2 \cdot 1$. MALE PALP : The embolus is long and free.

There is one British species.

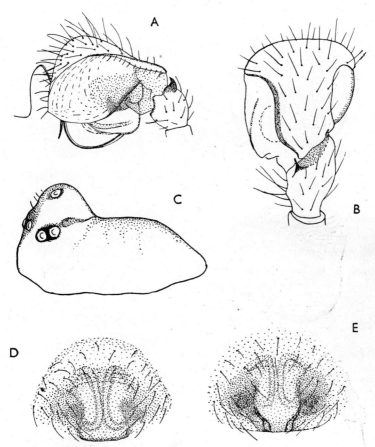

TEXT-FIG. 143.—*Pocadicnemis pumila:* A, ♂ palp; B, ditto (from above); C, ♂ carapace; D, epigyne; E, ditto, var. *juncea.*

Pocadicnemis pumila (Blackwall).
(Text-fig. 143, A, B, C, D, E)

Walckenaera pumila J. Blackwall, 1841, p. 639, and 1861–4, p. 312; O. P.-Cambridge, 1879–81, p. 157. *Pocadicnemis pumila* C. Chyzer and L. Kulczynski, 1891–7, II, p. 122; E. Simon, 1926, p. 361; C. R. Crosby and S. C. Bishop, 1933, p. 140; F. Miller, 1947, Tab. 6, fig. 8; B. J. Kaston, 1948, p. 180.

DESCRIPTION. LENGTH: ♀: 1·7–2 mm. ♂: about 1·7 mm. CARA-PACE: Yellow-brown, with blackish fovea and striæ, and blackish margins. ♂: Head (Text-fig. 143, C). EYES: ♀: Posteriors all slightly less than one diam. apart. ABDOMEN: Grey to black. STERNUM: Yellow, suffused and reticulated with black, particularly at margins. LEGS: Tm I 0·85–0·9. Yellow-brown. EPIGYNE: Text-fig. 143, D;

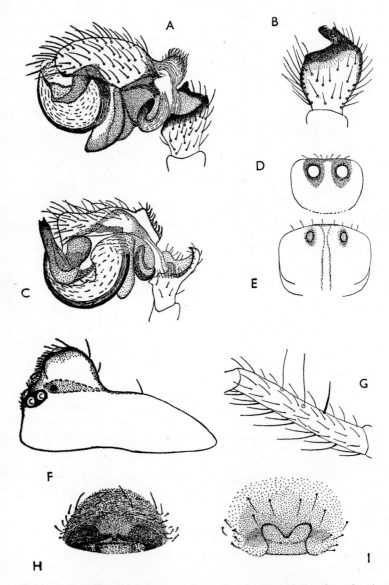

TEXT-FIG. 144.—*Hypselistes jacksoni:* A, ♂ palp ; B, ♂ palpal tibia (from above) ;
D, ♂ cephalic lobe (from above) ; F, ♂ carapace ; G, tibia I (♀) ; H, epigyne.
H. florens: C, ♂ palp ; E, ♂ cephalic lobe (from above) ; I, epigyne.

the appearance is somewhat variable, but the x-shape of spermathecal tubes is characteristic. A variety which we now call *juncea* (a name suggested by A. R. Jackson), has the epigyne as Text-fig. 143, E ; no corresponding variation in the male palp could be found. MALE PALP : Text-fig. 143, A, B ; the embolus is long and whip-like.

OCCURRENCE : Common in a variety of situations ; in undergrowth, heather, woods, marshes, etc. Widespread throughout the British Isles. Males adult in spring, summer and autumn ; females all the year.

25. Genus **HYPSELISTES** E. Simon, 1894.

CHARACTERS OF GENUS. CARAPACE : ♂ : Head raised into large lobe. ABDOMEN : Coriaceous, with metallic sheen, with four reddish impressed dots dorsally. LEGS : Metatarsus IV with a trichobothrium ; Tm I 0·88–0·95. ♀ : Tibiæ I–IV with one short spine ; position of tibia I spine 0·27–0·3. ♂ : Tibial spines absent. Tibia I and metatarsus I with two rows of stout bristles ventrally (Text-fig. 144, G), much reduced on legs II–IV. Metatarsi much longer than tarsi, with MT I/t I 1·5–2·0, MT IV/t IV 1·65–2.2.

There are two British species, readily distinguished by the sex organs and the cephalic lobes (♂).

Hypselistes jacksoni (O. P.-Cambridge).
(Text-fig. 144, A, B, D, F, G, H)

Entelecara jacksoni O. P.-Cambridge, 1902, p. 32.

DESCRIPTION. LENGTH : ♀ : 2 mm. ♂ : 1·8 mm. CARAPACE : Orange-brown. ♂ : Head (Text-fig. 144, F) ; lobe (from above) (Text-fig. 144, D) rather smaller than in *H. florens*, blackish. EYES : ♀ : Posteriors one diam. or slightly more apart. ♂ : Posterior medians larger and closer together than in *H. florens* (Text-fig. 144, D). ABDOMEN : Black, shiny, rather coriaceous, with four small impressed dots. STERNUM : Orange, with darker margins ; broad between coxæ IV. LEGS : Tm I ca. 0·88. Orange, suffused with black, particularly on patellæ, tibiæ and tarsi of ♂. EPIGYNE : Text-fig. 144, H. MALE PALP : Text-fig. 144, A, B ; tarsus suffused with brownish black, and raised into conical hairy protuberance near base.

OCCURRENCE : In moss, etc., in marshy areas. Recorded from a few localities from the south coast almost to the Scottish border ; rare. Adults in spring, autumn and winter.

Hypselistes florens (O. P.-Cambridge).
(Text-fig. 144, C, E, I)

Erigone florens O. P.-Cambridge, 1875 (3), p. 403. *Hypselistes florens* J. E. Hull, 1910, p. 588 ; O. P.-Cambridge, 1910, p. 54 ; C. R. Crosby and S. C. Bishop, 1933, p. 133 ; B. J. Kaston, 1948, p. 182.

DESCRIPTION. LENGTH : ♀ : 2·25 mm. ♂ : 2–2·2 mm. CARAPACE : Orange-brown. ♂ : Head with lobe (seen from above) (Text-fig. 144, E) wider than in *H. jacksoni*. EYES : ♀ : As *H. jacksoni*. ♂ : Posterior

medians smaller and further apart than in *H. jacksoni* (Text-fig. 144, E).
ABDOMEN : Black, with metallic sheen, coriaceous ; with four impressed
dots dorsally. STERNUM : Orange-yellow ; broad between coxæ IV.
LEGS : Tm I 0·9–0·95. Yellow-brown, suffused with black. EPIGYNE :
Text-fig. 144, I. MALE PALP : Text-fig. 144, C.

OCCURRENCE : Yorkshire (Eston Nab), in a wet, marshy spot.

26. Genus **ŒDOTHORAX** P. Bertkau 1883.

CHARACTERS OF GENUS. CARAPACE : ♂ : Elevated considerably, or
only to a slight extent, behind the eyes. EYES : Fairly large. CHELI-
CERÆ : ♂ : With a boss anteriorly in *Œ. gibbosus* and *Œ. tuberosus.*

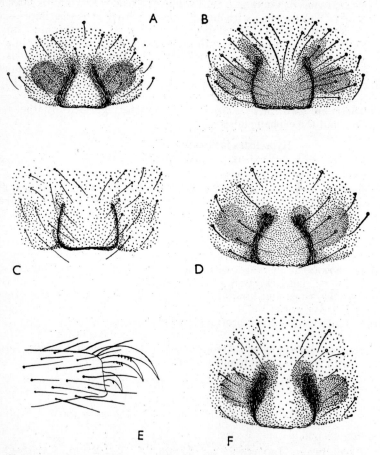

TEXT-FIG. 145.—Epigynes : A, *Oedothorax gibbosus* and *tuberosus;* B, *Oe. fuscus;*
C, *Oe. agrestis;* D, *Oe. retusus;* F, *Oe. apicatus.*
Tarsal claws : E, *Oe. retusus.*

LEGS : Metatarsus IV with a trichobothrium ; Tm I $0 \cdot 6$–$0 \cdot 66$. ♀ : Tibiæ I–II with two spines, tibiæ III–IV with one spine. ♂ : Spines reduced in size. Metatarsi moderately longer than tarsi, with MT I/t I $1 \cdot 25$–$1 \cdot 4$, MT IV/t IV $1 \cdot 5$–$1 \cdot 7$. EPIGYNES : All of closely similar form. MALE PALP : Palpal organs all closely similar, but the tibial apophyses differ.

There are six British species, which fall into three pairs :—

Œ. tuberosus	*Œ. fuscus*	*Œ. apicatus*
Œ. gibbosus	*Œ. agrestis*	*Œ. retusus*

The females of each pair cannot be distinguished readily, if at all. The males are readily separated by the form of the head and the tibial apophyses.

For a general description of the genus, see Denis, 1947(1).

Œdothorax gibbosus (Blackwall).
(Text-figs. 145, A ; 146, A, G, H)

Neriene gibbosa J. Blackwall, 1841, p. 653, and 1861–4, p. 278 ; O. P.-Cambridge, 1879–81, p. 117. *Œdothorax gibbosus* W. Bosenberg, 1901–3, p. 213 ; E. Simon, 1926, pp. 451, 454 ; S. C. Bishop and C. R. Crosby, 1935, p. 264 ; J. Denis, 1947 (1), pp. 138, 149.

DESCRIPTION. LENGTH : ♀ : $2 \cdot 5$ mm. ♂ : 2–$2 \cdot 25$ mm. CARAPACE : Brown, with fairly clear blackish striæ. ♂ : With large protuberance, bearing black hairs anteriorly, behind eyes (Text-fig. 146, A). EYES : ♀ : Posteriors ca. one diam. apart. ABDOMEN : Grey to blackish. STERNUM : Yellow-brown, mottled with black. CHELICERÆ : ♂ With large tooth on front and to inside. LEGS : Tm I $0 \cdot 63$–$0 \cdot 66$. Yellow-brown. ♂ : Tibiæ I–II spineless, tibiæ III–IV with very small spines ; legs with numerous short fine hairs. EPIGYNE : Text-fig. 145, A. MALE PALP : Text-fig. 146, G, H.

OCCURRENCE : Amongst moss, grass, etc., in wet and swampy places. Widespread in Britain, and fairly common. Adults in spring and summer.

Œdothorax tuberosus (Blackwall).
(Text-figs. 145, A ; 146, B, G, H)

Neriene tuberosa J. Blackwall, 1841, p. 654, and 1861–4, p. 279 ; O. P.-Cambridge, 1879–81, p. 117. *Œdothorax tuberosus* E. Simon, 1926, pp. 452, 454 ; J. Denis, 1947 (1), pp. 138, 149.

DESCRIPTION. This spider is possibly a dimorphic male of *O. gibbosus*, and the corresponding female (if it exists) cannot be distinguished from *Œ. gibbosus*. LENGTH : ♂ : 2–$2 \cdot 25$ mm. CARAPACE : ♂ : Brown, with blackish striæ, raised behind eyes (Text-fig. 146, B). LEGS : ♂ : Tm I ca. $0 \cdot 65$. Spines on tibiæ I–II short, but fairly long on tibiæ III–IV ; legs lack the short fine hairs present in *Œ. gibbosus*. CHELICERÆ : ♂ : Tooth on front and to inside. MALE PALP : Text-figs. 146, G, H. Not distinguishable from *Œ. gibbosus*, either in palpal organs or in tibial apophysis.

OCCURRENCE : Mixed with *Œ. gibbosus* ; equally common. Widespread in Britain ; adults in spring, summer and autumn.

Œdothorax fuscus (Blackwall).
(Text-figs. 145, B ; 146, C ; 147, A, B)

Neriene fusca J. Blackwall, 1834, p. 382, and 1861–4, p. 275. *N. agrestis* O. P.-Cambridge, 1879–81, p. 115. *N. fusca* C. Chyzer and L. Kulczynski, 1891–7, II, p. 94. *Œdothorax fuscus* E. Simon, 1926, pp. 453, 454 ; J. Denis, 1947 (1), pp. 140, 143.

DESCRIPTION. LENGTH : ♀ : 2·5 mm. ♂ : 2 mm. CARAPACE : ♀ : Yellow to orange-brown, with slightly darker fovea and striæ. ♂ : Rather darker, slightly elevated behind eyes (Text-fig. 146, C) ; ocular area

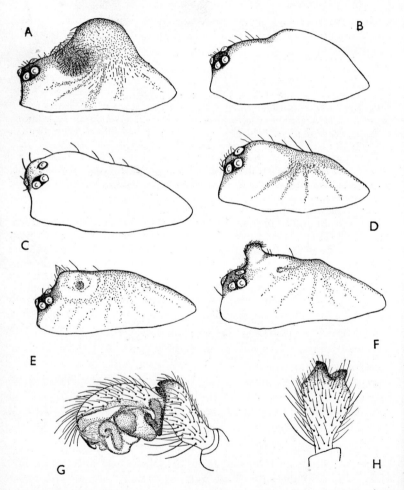

TEXT-FIG. 146.—Male carapace : A, *Oedothorax gibbosus;* B, *Oe. tuberosus;* C, *Oe. fuscus;* D, *Oe. agrestis;* E, *Oe. retusus;* F, *Oe. apicatus.*
Oe. gibbosus-tuberosus ♂ : G, palp ; H, palpal tibia (from above).

slightly more prominent than in *Œ. agrestis*. EYES : ♀ : Large ; posteriors less than one diam. apart. ABDOMEN : Grey to black, with usually a median white stripe, more visible in alcohol than in living spider (cf. *Œ. agrestis*). STERNUM : Yellow to orange-brown. LEGS : Tm I 0·66. Yellow-brown. ♂ : Spines on tibiæ I–II finer than in ♀. EPIGYNE : Text-fig. 145, B, very similar to *Œ. agrestis*, and not always distinguishable from it with certainty. MALE PALP : Text-fig. 147, A, B.

OCCURRENCE : In a variety of situations ; in grass, undergrowth, etc. Widespread throughout the British Isles ; common. Adults at most seasons.

Œdothorax agrestis (Blackwall).
(Text-figs. 145, C ; 146, D ; 147, C, D)

Neriene agrestis J. Blackwall, 1853, p. 23, and 1861–4, p. 276 ; O. P.-Cambridge, 1879–81, pp. 486, 574 ; C. Chyzer and L. Kulczynski, 1891–7, II, p. 94. *Œdothorax agrestis* E. Simon, 1926, pp. 453, 454 ; J. Denis, 1947 (1), pp. 140, 143.

DESCRIPTION. LENGTH : ♀ : 2·5 mm. ♂ : 2·25 mm. Very similar to *Œ. fuscus*, from which it differs in the following respects. CARAPACE : ♂ : Ocular area rather less prominent (Text-fig. 146, D). ABDOMEN : Without the median white stripe. EPIGYNE : Text-fig. 145, C ; not always distinguishable with certainty. MALE PALP : Text-figs. 147, C, D ; tibial apophyses distinct.

OCCURRENCE : In damp places, amongst grass, etc. Widespread throughout the British Isles, but much less common than *Œ. fuscus*.

Œdothorax retusus (Westring).
(Text-figs. 145, D, E ; 146, E ; 147, E, F)

Erigone retusa N. Westring, 1851. *Neriene retusa* O. P.-Cambridge, 1879–81, p. 116 ; C. Chyzer and L. Kulczynski, 1891–7, II, p. 94. *Œdothorax retusus* E. Simon, 1926, pp. 452, 454 ; J. Denis, 1947 (1), p. 145.

DESCRIPTION. LENGTH : ♀ : 2·5–3 mm. ♂ : 2 mm. Colour as *Œ. fuscus*. CARAPACE : ♂ : Fairly sharply elevated behind eyes (Text-fig. 146, E), with a hole on each side ; suffused sometimes with much black. EYES : As *Œ. fuscus*. LEGS : Tm I 0·6–0·65. ♂ : Spines on tibiæ I–II thinner and shorter than in ♀. ♀ : Length of tibia IV spine usually 2 diam. or more of tibia (cf. *Œ. apicatus*). EPIGYNE : Text-Text-fig. 145, D ; usually not distinguishable with certainty from *Œ. apicatus*. MALE PALP : Text-fig. 147, E, F.

OCCURRENCE : In similar localities to *Œ. fuscus*. Widespread throughout the British Isles ; fairly common, particularly in northern England. Adults most of year.

Œdothorax apicatus (Blackwall).
(Text-figs. 145, F ; 146, F ; 147, G, H)

Neriene apicata J. Blackwall, 1850, p. 339, and 1861–4, p. 269 ; O. P.-Cambridge, 1879–81, p. 116 ; C. Chyzer and L. Kulczynski, 1891–7, II, p. 93. *Œdothorax apicatus* E. Simon, 1926, pp. 452, 454 ; J. Denis, 1947 (1), p. 145.

DESCRIPTION. LENGTH : ♀ : 2·5 mm. ♂ : 2·25 mm. Colour similar to *Œ. fuscus*. CARAPACE : ♂ : Behind eyes, carapace rises into a knob,

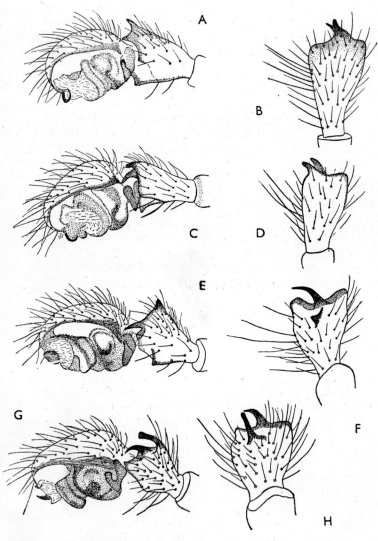

TEXT-FIG. 147.—Male palps : A, *Oedothorax fuscus;* C, *Oe. agrestis;* E, *Oe.
retusus;* G, *Oe. apicatus.*
   Male palpal tibiæ (from above) : B, *Oe. fuscus;* D, *Oe. agrestis* F, *Oe. retusus;*
H, *Oe. apicatus.*

carrying some bristles ; behind knob, on either side, is a hole (Text-fig. 146, F). Eyes : Large ; posterior medians slightly less than one diam. apart, and ca. 0·5 diam. from laterals. Legs : Tm I 0·6–0·64. ♂ : Spines on tibiæ I–II short. ♀ : Length of tibia IV spine usually less than 1·75 diam. of tibia (cf. *Œ. retusus*). Epigyne : Text-fig. 145, F ; not always distinguishable with certainty from *Œ. retusus*. Male palp : Text-fig. 147, G, H.

Occurrence : In grass and undergrowth. Widespread throughout the British Isles, but generally rare. Adults in summer.

27. Genus **TRICHOPTERNA** L. Kulczynski 1894.

Characters of Genus. Carapace : ♂ : Head elevated into large lobe. Abdomen : With four reddish impressed dots dorsally ; a scutum is present in *T. mengei* (♂). Legs : Metatarsus IV with a

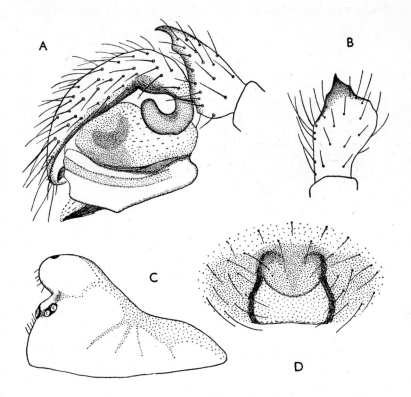

Text-fig. 148.—*Trichopterna thorelli*: A, ♂ palp ; B, ♂ palpal tibia (from above) ; C, ♂ carapace ; D, epigyne.

trichobothrium ; Tm I 0·85–0·9. ♀: Tibiæ I–IV with one short spine ; position of tibia I spine 0·17–0·22. ♂: Tibiæ spineless. Metatarsi much longer than tarsi, with MT I/t I 1·5–1·8, MT IV/t IV 1·9–2·1.

There are two British species, readily distinguished by the sex organs, and by the cephalic lobes (♂).

Trichopterna thorelli (Westring).
(Text-fig. 148, A, B, C, D)

Erigone thorelli N. Westring, 1861, p. 228. *Walckenaera fastigata* J. Blackwall, 1861–4, p. 314. *W. thorelli* O. P.-Cambridge, 1879–81, p. 508. *Entelecara thorelli* W. Falconer, 1911, p. 285 ; E. Simon, 1926, pp. 422, 425.

DESCRIPTION. LENGTH : ♀♂ : 2–2·25 mm. CARAPACE : Brown to dark brown with narrow black margin, and faint blackish striæ. ♂ : Head raised into wide, forward-projecting lobe, deeply impressed at sides (Text-fig. 148, C), carrying posterior median eyes ; lobe suffused with black, and clypeus rather prominent. EYES : ♀ : Posterior medians ca. one diam. apart, and 1·5–2 diam. from laterals. ABDOMEN : Black, with four indistinct reddish-brown impressed dots. STERNUM :

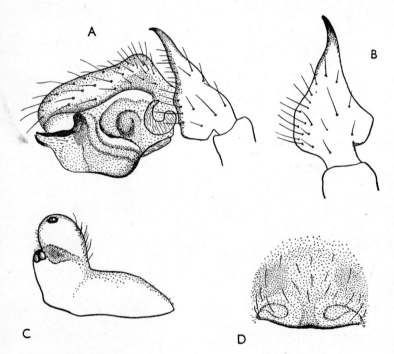

TEXT-FIG. 149.—*Trichopterna mengei:* A, ♂ palp ; B, ♂ palpal tibia (from above) ; C, ♂ carapace ; D, epigyne.

Blackish. LEGS: Tm I ca. 0·9. Orange-brown. ♂: Tibial spines absent. ♀: Tibiæ I and II with two rows of stout bristles ventrally. EPIGYNE: Text-fig. 148, D. MALE PALP: Text-figs. 148, A, B; tibial apophysis short.

OCCURRENCE: In moss and grass. Widespread in Britain, but very local. Adults in May-July.

Trichopterna mengei (Simon).
(Text-fig. 149, A, B, C, D)

Lophocarenum mengei E. Simon, 1884, p. 676 (♂); F. O. P.-Cambridge, 1892, p 387 (♀♂); E. Simon, 1926, p. 336. *Pelecopsis excavatum* C. R. Crosby and S. C. Bishop, 1931, p. 383; B. J. Kaston, 1948, p. 161. *Trichopterna mengei* Å. Holm, 1945, p. 37.

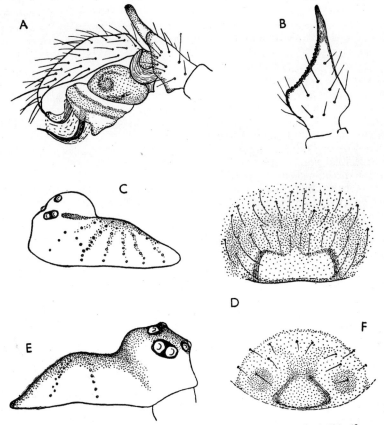

TEXT-FIG. 150.—*Lophocarenum parallelum:* A, ♂ palp; B, ♂ palpal tibia (from above); C, ♂ carapace; D, epigyne.
L. elongatum: E, ♀ carapace; F, epigyne.

DESCRIPTION. LENGTH : ♀♂ : 1·8–2 mm. CARAPACE : ♀ : Dark brown, with radiating lines of minute pits ; head elevated behind eyes. ♂ : Dark-brown ; head raised into large lobe (Text-fig. 149, C). EYES : ♀ : Posteriors strongly procurved, 1–1·5 diam. apart. ABDOMEN : ♀ : Dark-brown to black, coriaceous, with numerous short hairs each arising from a minute reddish-brown pit ; dorsally with four large impressed reddish-brown dots, close together. ♂ : With chestnut-brown scutum ; impressed with a large number of small pits. STERNUM : Brown to dark brown, with black margins, and with a few small pits. LEGS : Tm I ca. 0·85. Yellow-brown. ♂ : Tibial spines absent. ♀ : Tibial spines very small. EPIGYNE : Text-fig. 149, D. MALE PALP : Text-fig. 149, A, B ; tibial apophysis long.

OCCURRENCE : In moss and grass, in damp places. Recorded from a few northern English counties, Scotland and Eire. Fairly common locally. Females adult all the year, males in spring and early summer.

28. Genus **LOPHOCARENUM** A. Menge 1868.

CHARACTERS OF GENUS. CARAPACE : With some small pits (in some species). ♂ : Head with lobe, usually large, carrying posterior median eyes. EYES : ♀ : Posteriors strongly procurved. ABDOMEN : ♀ : Coriaceous, with four reddish-brown dots dorsally ; dorsal scutum present only in *L. radicicola*. ♂ : With dorsal scutum. STERNUM : Fairly broad, widely truncated posteriorly between coxæ IV ; pitted in some species. LEGS : Metatarsus IV without a trichobothrium ; Tm I 0·6–0·7. ♀ : Tibiæ I–IV with one spine, sometimes very weak. ♂ : Tibial spines absent. EPIGYNES : Closely similar in form, and often distinguished only with difficulty.

There are five British species. Except for *L. nemorale* and *L. stramineum*, they are distinguished from each other fairly readily (see descriptions).

Lophocarenum parallelum (Wider).
(Text-fig. 150, A, B, C, D)

Theridion parallelum Wider, 1834, p. 228. *Walckenaera parallela* J. Blackwall, 1861–4, p. 296 ; O. P.-Cambridge, 1879–81, p. 156. *Brachycentrum parallelum* C. Chyzer and L. Kulczynski, 1891–7, II, p. 116. *Lophocarenum parallelum* W. Bosenberg, 1901–3, p. 199 ; E. Simon, 1926, pp. 336, 340 ; F. Miller, 1947, Tab. 5, fig. 3.

DESCRIPTION. LENGTH : ♀ : 1·5–1·75 mm. ♂ : 1·25–1·3 mm. CARAPACE : Brown (or somewhat darker in ♂), with blackish striæ, and with radiating lines of small pits, and small pits around margins. ♀ : Head smoothly elevated. ♂ : Head with small lobe (Text-fig. 150, C). EYES : ♀ : Posterior medians ca. 1·5 diam. apart, and ca. one diam. from laterals. ABDOMEN : ♀ : Grey or greyish-black, fairly globular, with four strongly impressed dots. ♂ : With brown or dark-brown scutum dorsally, very punctate. STERNUM : Brown, with small pits (fewer in ♂), each with a fine hair. LEGS : Tm I 0·57–0·6. Yellow to yellow-brown. ♂ : Tibial spines absent. EPIGYNE : Text-fig. 150, D. MALE PALP : Text-fig. 150, A, B.

OCCURRENCE : Amongst moss and detritus in woods, under turfs and stones, etc. Widespread throughout the British Isles ; local. Adult from May to July and in autumn.

Lophocarenum nemorale (Blackwall).
(Text-fig. 151, A, B, C, D, E, F, I)

Walckenaera nemoralis J. Blackwall, 1841, p. 641, and 1861–4, p. 315; O. P.-Cambridge, 1879–81, p. 167. *Brachycentrum nemorale* C. Chyzer and L. Kulczynski, 1891–7, II, p. 116. *Lophocarenum stramineum* O. P.-Cambridge, 1907, p. 32. *L nemorale* E. Simon, 1926, pp. 339, 341.

DESCRIPTION. LENGTH : ♀ : 1·5–1·75 mm. ♂ : 1·5 mm. CARAPACE : ♀ : Brown to dark brown, with darker radiating striæ, and a few very small pits (much smaller than in *L. parallelum*) ; head smoothly elevated. ♂ : Colour as ♀, with few, if any, pits ; head raised into large globular lobe (Text-fig. 151, C, D). EYES : ♀ : Posteriors ca. one diam. apart. ABDOMEN : ♀ : Greyish black, with four impressed dots ; more coriaceous than in *L. parallelum*, with surface pitted. ♂ : With dorsal scutum. STERNUM : Brown, with few, if any, minute pits. LEGS : Tm I 0·6. Yellow to yellow-brown. Tibial spines absent in ♂, virtually absent in ♀. EPIGYNE : Text-fig. 151, E, F. MALE PALP : Text-fig. 150, A, B, I.

OCCURRENCE : In pine needles, grass, etc., and on sandhills. Widespread throughout the British Isles, but uncommon.

Lophocarenum stramineum Menge.
(Text-fig. 151, G, H, J)

Lophocarenum stramineum A. Menge, 1868, p. 199. *Lophocarenum stramineum* A. R. Jackson, 1924, p. 112.

DESCRIPTION. LENGTH : ♀ : 1·6 mm. ♂ : 1·5 mm. Colour as *L. nemorale*. CARAPACE : ♂ : Lobe wider, with posterior median eyes more widely spaced (Text-fig. 151, G). LEGS : Tm I 0·6. ♀♂ : Tibial spines absent or very weak. EPIGYNE : Text-fig. 151, H ; scarcely distinguishable from *L. nemorale*. MALE PALP : Text-fig. 151, J ; scarcely distinguishable from *L. nemorale*.

This species is very close to *L. nemorale* ; insufficient material was available for study to be certain whether the minor differences between the two species are constant.

OCCURRENCE : Cornwall, Sussex. Very rare.

Lophocarenum elongatum (Wider).
(Text-fig. 150, E, F)

Theridion elongatum Wider, 1834, p. 233. *Brachycentrum elongatum* C. Chyzer and L. Kulczynski, 1891–7, II, p. 116. *Lophocarenum elongatum* W. Bosenberg, 1901–3, p. 198 ; E. Simon, 1926, pp. 335, 340 ; A. R. Jackson, 1924, p. 112 ; F. Miller, 1947, Tab. 5, fig. 2.

DESCRIPTION. Only the ♀ was available for study. LENGTH : ♀ : 1·5 mm. CARAPACE : Dark brown, with some darker radiating striæ, and radiating lines of very small pits ; with a fairly deep depression

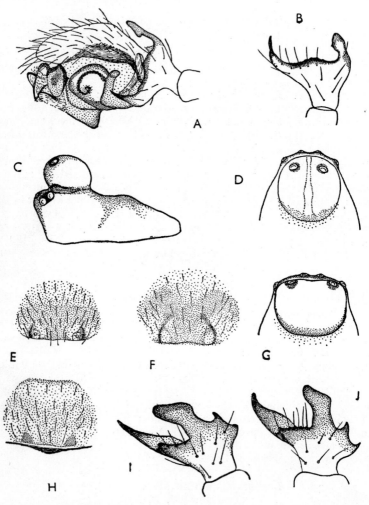

TEXT-FIG. 151.—*Lophocarenum nemorale:* A, ♂ palp ; B, ♂ palpal tibia (from
   above and outside) ; I, ditto (from above) ; C, ♂ carapace ; D, ♂ head (from
   above) ; E, F, epigyne.
   L. stramineum: G, ♂ head (from above) ; H, epigyne ; J, ♂ palpal tibia (from
   above).

between head and thorax (Text-fig. 150, E). EYES : Posteriors about one diam. apart. ABDOMEN : As *L. parallelum.* STERNUM : Dark brown, smooth, with few, if any, little pits. LEGS : Tm I 0·6. Yellow-brown. EPIGYNE : Text-fig. 150, F.

OCCURRENCE : Rothiemurchus Forest, Scotland, June 1914.

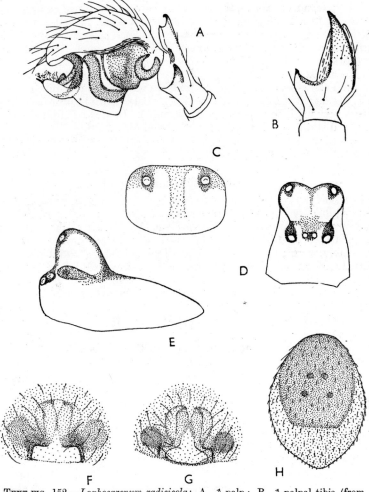

TEXT-FIG. 152.—*Lophocarenum radicicola:* A, ♂ palp ; B, ♂ palpal tibia (from above) ; C, ♂ head (from above) ; D, ditto (from in front) ; E, ♂ carapace ; F, G, epigyne ; H, abdomen (♀) (from above).

S

Lophocarenum radicicola (L. Koch).
(Text-fig. 152, A, B, C, D, E, F, G, H)

Erigone radicicola L. Koch, 1875, p. 259. *Brachycentrum thoracatum* C. Chyzer and L. Kulczynski, 1891–7, II, p. 116. *Lophocarenum radicicola* E. Simon, 1926, pp. 334, 340 ; A. F. Millidge and G. H. Locket, 1952, p. 70.

DESCRIPTION. LENGTH : ♀ : 1·5 mm. ♂ : 1·3 mm. CARAPACE : ♀ : Brown, suffused with black at margins, with blackish fovea and striæ, along which are some small pits. ♂ : Head raised into large lobe, suffused with black, compressed and hollowed at the sides (Text-fig. 152, E) ; seen from above, the lobe is almost twice as broad as long and is divided by a median longitudinal furrow (Text-fig. 152, C), very clear when viewed from in front (Text-fig. 152, D). EYES : ♀ : Posterior medians more than one diam. apart, and ca. one diam. from laterals. ABDOMEN : ♀ : Grey, with brown scutum dorsally on anterior two-thirds (Text-fig. 152, H). ♂ : Brown scutum covers whole dorsal area. STERNUM : Yellow-brown, with black margins ; a few minute pits present in ♀. LEGS : Tm I ca. 0·7 (♀), 0·65 (♂). Pale brown to brown. Tibial spines very weak and short (♀), or absent (♂). EPIGYNE : Text-fig. 152, F, G ; distinctive. MALE PALP : Text-fig. 152, A, B.

OCCURRENCE : Both sexes, near Heyshott (Sussex) ; June 1949, September 1951 and June 1952.

29. Genus SILOMETOPUS E. Simon 1926.

CHARACTERS OF GENUS. CARAPACE : ♂ : Head with or without a shallow lobe, or with post-ocular sulci. ABDOMEN : With four reddish impressed dots dorsally. LEGS: Metatarsus IV without a trichobothrium; Tm I 0·7–0·8. ♀ : Tibiæ I–IV with one dorsal spine, sometimes extremely weak ; position of tibial spine ca. 0·1. ♂ : Tibial spines absent. Metatarsi not much longer than tarsi, with MT I/t I 1·1–1·2, MT IV/t IV ca. 1·35. MALE PALP : Embolus long and fine.

There are five British species. They can be distinguished by consideration of the position of the trichobothria, by the epigynes, the palpal tibial apophyses, the head (♂), and the eyes.

Silometopus elegans (O. P.-Cambridge).
(Text-fig. 153, B, E, F)

Erigone elegans O. P.-Cambridge, 1872 (1), p. 766 (♂). *Cnephalocotes elegans*, idem, 1905, p. 52 (♀). *Silometopus elegans* E. Simon, 1926, p. 355.

DESCRIPTION. LENGTH : ♀ : 1·5 mm. ♂ : 1–1·2 mm. CARAPACE : Brown to dark brown, with black fovea and striæ. ♂ : Head elevated slightly, impressed at sides, carrying posterior median eyes (Text-fig. 153, E). EYES : ♀ : Posteriors 1·25–1·5. diam. apart. ABDOMEN : Grey to blackish, with four impressed dots, not very clear in ♂. STERNUM : ♀ : Dark brown, shiny. ♂ : as ♀, but with very few minute pits near edges. LEGS : Tm I 0·80. Yellow to brown. EPIGYNE : Text-fig. 153, F ; rather similar to *Diplocephalus cristatus*. MALE PALP : The palpal organs are closely similar to *S. incurvatus* (Text-fig. 154, A) ; the tibial apophysis (Text-fig. 153, B) is relatively long and fine.

OCCURRENCE : In moss and grass, generally in wet or marshy areas. Recorded from Scotland, the northern half of England, Wales and Eire. Rare ; adult in spring and summer.

Silometopus curtus (Simon).
(Text-fig. 153, A, H)

Erigone curta E. Simon, 1881, p. 253. *Cnephalocotes curtus* O. P.-Cambridge, 1894, p. 112. *Silometopus curtus* E. Simon, 1926, p. 353.

DESCRIPTION. LENGTH : ♀ : 1·5 mm. ♂ : 1·3–1·4 mm. CARAPACE : Yellow to dark brown, with black fovea and striæ. ♂ : Head not elevated into lobe ; ocular area black. EYES : ♀♂ : Posterior medians ca. one diam. apart ; anterior medians less than one diam. apart, and ca. 1–1·2 diam. from laterals. ABDOMEN : Greyish black to black, with 4 reddish impressed dots. STERNUM : Yellow to brown, mottled with black particularly on margins ; darker in ♂. Shiny. LEGS : Tm I 0·75–0·8. Brown. ♀ : Tibial spines very weak (less than one diam.). ♂ : No tibial spines. EPIGYNE : Text-fig. 153, H ; not distinguishable with any certainty from *S. ambiguus*. MALE PALP : The palpal organs are similar to those of *S. incurvatus* ; the tibial apophysis (Text-fig. 153, A) is short and fine (cf. *S. ambiguus*).

OCCURRENCE : On salt-marshes, tidal estuaries, sandhills by the sea. Probably fairly frequent in these localities. Widespread, but with few records ; adults in late summer to winter.

Silometopus ambiguus (O. P.-Cambridge).
(Text-fig. 153, D, I)

Cnephalocotes ambiguus O. P.-Cambridge, 1905, p. 67.

DESCRIPTION. LENGTH : ♀ : 1·5 mm. ♂ : 1·3–1·4 mm. Colour and form as *S. curtus*, except for the following : CARAPACE : ♂ : Clypeus and ocular area with numerous minute granulosities, bearing short fine hairs. EYES : ♀ : Posterior medians ca. 1·5 diam. apart. ♂ : Anterior medians practically one diam. apart, and ca. 1·5 diam. from laterals. EPIGYNE : Text-fig. 153, I ; cannot be distinguished with certainty from *S. curtus*. MALE PALP : Text-fig. 153, D ; the tibial apophysis seems to be rather longer and more curved than in *S. curtus*, and along the anterior margin of tibia are 2–3 very small warts, each bearing a short hair.

This species may be only a variety of *S. curtus*. It has not been possible to examine a wide enough range of specimens to discover whether the differences given are constant.

OCCURRENCE : On the sea coast, in Yorkshire, Northumberland, Buteshire and Morayshire.

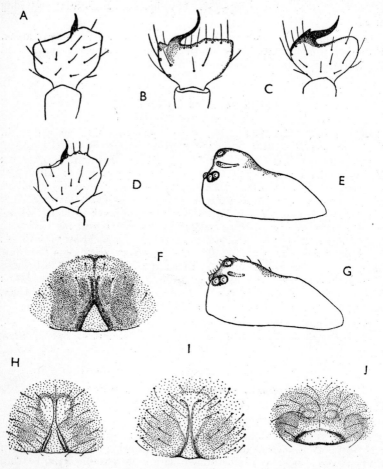

TEXT-FIG. 153.—Male palpal tibiæ (from above): A, *Silometopus curtus;* B, *S. elegans;* C, *S. interjectus;* D, *S. ambiguus.*
Male carapace: E, *S. elegans:* G, *S. interjectus.*
Epigynes: F, *S. elegans;* H, *S. curtus;* I, *S. ambiguus;* J, *S. interjectus.*

Silometopus interjectus (O. P.-Cambridge).
(Text-fig. 153, C, G, J)

Walckenaera interjecta O. P.-Cambridge, 1888, p. 18 (♂).   *Cnephalocotes interjectus* idem, 1905, p. 52 (♀); C. Chyzer and L. Kulczynski, 1891–7, II, p. 118.   ? *Silometopus reussi* E. Simon, 1926, p. 354.   ? *S. læsus* J. Denis, 1943 (1), p. 123.

DESCRIPTION. LENGTH: ♀: 1·5–1·6 mm.   ♂: ca. 1·3 mm. CARA-PACE: ♀: Dark brown, with black striæ and fovea.   ♂: as ♀, with a few minute impressions along the stiræ; head not elevated into lobe, but with sulci running backwards from between posterior median and lateral eyes (Text-fig. 153, G). Eyes : ♀ : Posterior medians ca. one diam. apart, and slightly more from laterals. Abdomen : Grey to black, with four reddish impressed dots. Sternum : Dark brown, shiny, with a few minute pits carrying minute hairs. Legs : Tm I 0·7. Orange-yellow. ♂ : No tibial spines, save for a minute one on tibia IV. ♀ : Tibial spines very weak. Epigyne : Text-fig. 153, J ; somewhat similar to *Mecopisthes*. Male palp : Palpal organs similar to *S. incurvatus* ; tibial apophysis (Text-fig. 153, C) relatively long and stout, with a small tooth on its anterior side near to the base.

Occurrence : In straw, and undergrowth. Widespread, but recorded localities rather few. Adults in spring, autumn and winter.

Silometopus incurvatus (O. P.-Cambridge).
(Text-fig. 154, A, C)

Walckenaera incurvata O. P.-Cambridge, 1873 (1), p. 551, and 1879–81, p. 503. *Cnephalocotes incurvatus* J. E. Hull, 1909, p. 283, and 1911 (2), p. 57 (?♀).

Description. Length : ♂ : 1·5 mm. It was not possible to find a ♀ referable to this species. Carapace : Brown, with black striæ and fovea ; head suffused with black, and not elevated into lobe. Abdomen: Grey to yellow-grey, with four faint impressed dots. Sternum : Brown, suffused with black. Legs : Tm I 0·78. Yellow-brown. No tibial spines. Male palp : Text-fig. 154, A, C ; tibial apophysis (seen from side) with an incurved hook apically.

Occurrence : On the sea coast, Northumberland, Aberdeenshire and Morayshire.

30. Genus MECOPISTHES E. Simon 1926.

Characters of Genus. Carapace : ♂ : Head with no lobe or sulci, but with clypeus projecting anteriorly. Abdomen : With four reddish impressed dots dorsally. Legs : Metatarsus IV without a trichobothrium : Tm I 0·6. ♀ : Tibiæ I–IV with one minute spine ; position of tibia IV spine about 0·44. ♂ : Tibial spines absent. Metatarsi only slightly longer than tarsi, with MT I/t I 1·15. Male palp : Palpal organs very similar to *Silometopus*.

There is one British species.

Mecopisthes pusillus (Menge).
(Text-fig. 154, B, D, E, F, G)

Microneta pusilla A. Menge, 1868–79, III, p. 232. *Erigone sila* O. P.-Cambridge, 1872 (1), p. 753. *Cnephalocotes silus* G. H. Carpenter, 1900, p. 201 (♂ only). *C. pusillus* C. Chyzer and L. Kulczynski, 1891–7, II, p. 119 ; O. P.-Cambridge, 1900, pp. 19, 23 ; A. R. Jackson, 1908, p. 64. *Mecopisthes silus* E. Simon, 1926, p. 351.

Description. Length : ♀ : 1·4–1·5 mm. ♂ : 1·3–1·4 mm. Carapace : Brown, with blackish fovea and striæ, and black margins. ♂ : Clypeus projecting (Text-fig. 154, B, D). Eyes : ♀♂ : Posteriors rather more than one diam. apart. Abdomen : Black, with four reddish impressed dots ; rather coriaceous in ♂. STERNUM : Blackish-brown. LEGS : Tm I ca. 0·6. Brown to orange-brown ; tarsus I fusiform. EPIGYNE : Text-fig. 154, F ; rather similar to that of *Silometopus interjectus*. MALE PALP : Text-fig. 154, E, G.

OCCURRENCE : At the roots of coarse grass on sand dunes on the Lancashire coast ; and on heather, New Forest. Very rare.

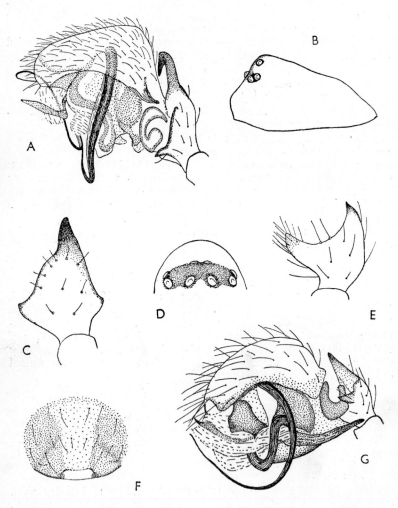

TEXT-FIG. 154.—*Silometopus incurvatus* ♂ : A, palp ; C, palpal tibia (from above). *Mecopisthes pusillus:* B, ♂ carapace ; D, ♂ head (from above) ; E, ♂ palpal tibia (from above) ; F, epigyne ; G, ♂ palp.

31. Genus **CNEPHALOCOTES** E. Simon 1884.

CHARACTERS OF GENUS. CARAPACE : Very rugose. ♂ : Head with shallow lobe. ABDOMEN : With four reddish impressed dots dorsally. STERNUM : Very rugose. LEGS : Metatarsus IV without a trichobothrium ; Tm I about 0·37. Tibiæ I–IV with one short spine (very weak in ♂) ; position of tibia I spine 0·16, of tibia IV spine 0·3. Metatarsi moderately longer than tarsi, with MT I/t I 1·2–1·25, MT IV/t IV 1·5.

There is one British species.

Cnephalocotes obscurus (Blackwall).
(Text-fig. 155, A, B, C)

Walckenaera obscura J. Blackwall, 1834, p. 321, and 1861–4, p. 297 ; O. P.-Cambridge, 1879–81, p. 158. *Nematogmus obscurus* C. Chyzer and L. Kulczynski, 1891–7, II, p. 123 ; W. Bosenberg, 1901–3, p. 210. *Cnephalocotes obscurus* E. Simon, 1926, p. 362 ; J. Denis, 1946, p. 11.

DESCRIPTION. LENGTH : ♀ : 1·7 mm. ♂ : 1·5 mm. CARAPACE : Dark chestnut brown, often almost black posteriorly ; very rugose. ♂ : Head slightly elevated and impressed at sides. EYES : ♀ : Posteriors 1·5 diam. (or slightly more) apart. ABDOMEN : Grey to black, with four reddish impressed dots (sometimes not very clear). STERNUM : Dark brown to almost black, very rugose. LEGS : Tm I ca. 0·37. Brown. EPIGYNE : Text-fig. 155, A ; rather indistinct, as the result of heavy pigmentation. MALE PALP : Text-fig. 155, B, C ; very distinct, the tarsus having a longitudinal ridge bearing numerous warts each carrying a bristle.

OCCURRENCE : Amongst moss and detritus. Widespread throughout the British Isles, and frequent locally ; perhaps commoner in the north than in the south. Adults at all seasons.

32. Genus **ACARTAUCHENIUS** E. Simon 1884.

CHARACTERS OF GENUS. CARAPACE : ♂ : Head elevated into lobe, but not impressed at sides. EYES : Small, widely spaced. LEGS : Metatarsus IV without a trichobothrium ; Tm I 0·43. Tibiæ I–IV with one spine (very short in ♂) ; position of tibia I spine 0·2 (♀), of tibia IV spine 0·3 (♀). Metatarsi only slightly longer than tarsi, with MT I/t I 1·1, MT IV/t IV 1·2. Hairs and spines on legs slightly serrated.

Acartauchenius scurrilis (O. P.-Cambridge).
(Text-fig. 155, D, E, F, G)

Erigone scurrilis O. P.-Cambridge, 1872 (1), p. 760. *Acartauchenius scurrilis* C. Chyzer and L. Kulczynski, 1891–7, II, p. 121 ; E. Simon, 1926, p. 392 ; F. Miller, 1947, Tab. 8, figs. 9–12. *Araeoncus æquus* O. P.-Cambridge, 1910, p. 69.

DESCRIPTION. LENGTH : ♀♂ : 1·75–1·9 mm. CARAPACE : Pale brown, with 3–4 fairly strong forward-projecting spines in median line. ♂ : Head (Text-fig. 155, F) bears numerous strong spines. EYES : ♀ : Posterior medians ca. 2·5 diams. apart and ca. 2 diams. from laterals. ABDOMEN : Whitish grey. STERNUM : Pale yellow-

brown, clothed with fairly long hairs. LEGS: Tm I ca. 0·43. Pale
yellow-brown. ♀: Tibial spines fairly strong. ♂: Tibial spines weaker.
Hairs and spines slightly serrated. EPIGYNE: Text-fig. 155, E. MALE
PALP: Text-fig. 155, D, G.

OCCURRENCE: In the nest of the ant *Tetramorium cæspitum*;
Lundy Island, Cornwall and Hampshire. Very rare.

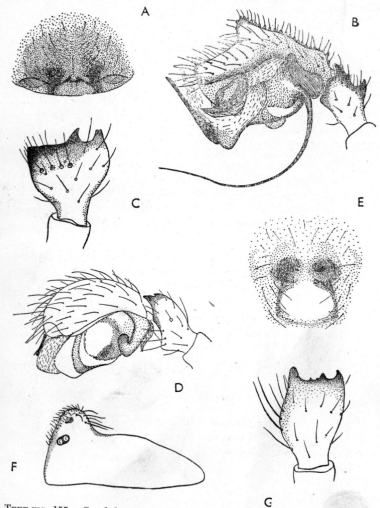

TEXT-FIG. 155.—*Cnephalocotes obscurus:* A, epigyne; B, ♂ palp; C, ♂ palpal
tibia (from above).
Acartauchenius scurrilis: D, ♂ palp; E, epigyne; F, ♂ carapace; G, ♂
palpal tibia (from above).

33. Genus **TRICHONCUS** E. Simon 1884.

CHARACTERS OF GENUS. CARAPACE : ♂ : Head not elevated into lobe. STERNUM : Slightly longer than broad. LEGS : Metatarsus IV without a trichobothrium ; Tm I ca. 0·4. Tibiæ I–IV with one spine (weaker in ♂) ; position of tibia I spine 0·3–0·35, of tibia IV spine 0·35–0·45 (♀). Metatarsi moderately longer than tarsi, with MT I/t I 1·15–1·25, MT IV/t IV 1·5. MALE PALP : Tibial apophyses long.

There are two British species, separated by the sex organs.

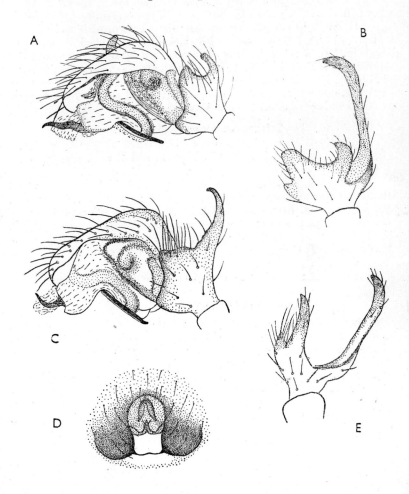

TEXT-FIG. 156.—*Trichoncus saxicola:* A, ♂ palp ; B, ♂ palpal tibia (from above) ; D, epigyne.
T. affinis: C, ♂ palp ; E, ♂ palpal tibia (from above).

Trichoncus saxicola (O. P.-Cambridge).
(Text-fig. 156, A, B, D)

Walckenaera saxicola O. P.-Cambridge, 1861, p. 440 ; J. Blackwall, 1861–4, p. 301.
Trichoncus saxicola C. Chyzer and L. Kulczynski, 1891–7, II, p. 105 ; W. Bosenberg,
1901–3, p. 188 ; E. Simon, 1926, p. 460 ; F. Miller, 1947, Tab. 8, fig. 2.

DESCRIPTION. LENGTH : ♀ : 1·75 mm. ♂ : 1·6–1·7 mm. CARA-
PACE : Orange-brown to dark-brown, with darker striæ and black
margins. EYES : ♀ : Posteriors ca. 1·5 diam. apart. ♂ : Posterior
medians ca. 1·25 diam. apart, and ca. 1·5 diam. from laterals. ABDO-
MEN : Black. STERNUM : Yellow to dark brown, suffused with black.
LEGS : Tm I 0·4–0·42. Brown to yellow-brown, with tibiæ (parti-
cularly of I and II) suffused with dark brown or black. EPIGYNE :
Text-fig. 156, D ; the detail is often obscured by heavy pigmentation.
MALE PALP : Text-fig. 156, A, B ; the palpal organs are very similar to
T. affinis, but the tibial apophysis is quite distinct.
OCCURRENCE : In moss and grass. Recorded from a few southern
counties only ; rare. Adults in May-July.

Trichoncus affinis Kulczynski.
(Text-fig. 156, C, E)

Trichoncus affinis C. Chyzer and L. Kulczynski, 1891–7, II, p. 103 ; E. Simon,
1926, p. 460 ; F. Miller, 1947, Tab. 8, fig. 5.

DESCRIPTION. The male only has been found in this country, and
no female was available for study. LENGTH : ♂ : 2 mm. CARAPACE :
Brown, with slightly darker striæ. EYES : Posterior medians ca.
one diam. apart, and 1·5 diam. from laterals. ABDOMEN : Black.
STERNUM : Brown, suffused with black. LEGS : Tm I 0·4. Brown.
MALE PALP : Text-fig. 156, C, E ; tibial apophysis quite distinct from
T. saxicola.
OCCURRENCE : A single male at Dungeness (Kent).

34. Genus STYLOCTETOR E. Simon 1884.

CHARACTERS OF GENUS. CARAPACE : ♂ : Head not elevated into lobe.
ABDOMEN : With four reddish impressed dots dorsally. LEGS :
Metatarsus IV without a trichobothrium ; Tm I 0·4. Tibiæ I–IV
with one spine (weaker in ♂) ; position of tibia IV spine ca. 0·3 (♀).
Metatarsi moderately longer than tarsi, with MT I/t I 1·3, MT IV/t
IV 1·5. Femora and tibiæ (particularly of I and II) with two rows of
long fine bristles ventrally.
This genus is rather close to *Anacotyle*. There is one British species.

Styloctetor romanus (O. P.-Cambridge).
(Text-fig. 157, A, B, C)

Neriene romana O. P.-Cambridge, 1872 (1), p. 752. *Styloctetor romanus* C. Chyzer
and L. Kulczynski, 1891–7, II, p. 96 ; E. Simon, 1926, p. 357 ; F. Miller, 1947, Tab. 5,
figs. 19–23.

DESCRIPTION. LENGTH : ♀ : 1·75 mm. ♂ : 1·5 mm. CARAPACE :
Brown to reddish-brown, with blackish margins, and blackish fovea

and striæ. ♂ : Some forward-directed spines present. EYES : ♀♂ :
Posterior medians one diam. apart, and slightly more from laterals.
ABDOMEN : Grey to black, with four small reddish impressed dots
dorsally. STERNUM : Brown, with blackish margins. LEGS : Tm I 0·4.
Orange to brown. EPIGYNE : Text-fig. 157, C. MALE PALP : Text-
fig. 157, A, B.

OCCURRENCE : On sandhills on the coast ; there are not many
records, mainly from the west coast of England and Wales. Rare.
Adults in May-June and in autumn.

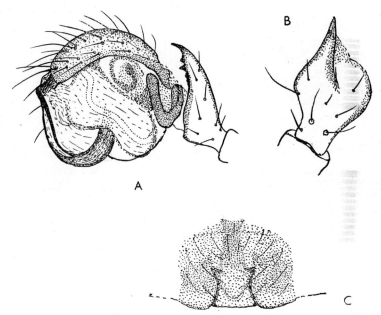

TEXT-FIG. 157.—*Styloctetor romanus:* A, ♂ palp ; B, ♂ palpal tibia (from above) .
  C, epigyne.

35. Genus **ANACOTYLE** E. Simon 1926.

CHARACTERS OF GENUS. CARAPACE : ♂ : Head not elevated. ABDO-
MEN : With four reddish impressed dots dorsally. LEGS : Metatarsus
IV without a trichobothrium ; Tm I 0·55. Tibiæ I–IV with one spine ;
position of tibia I spine ca. 0·25, of tibia IV spine 0·34 (♀). Metatarsi
moderately longer than tarsi, with MT I/t I 1·3, MT IV/t IV 1·6.
There is one British species.

Anacotyle stativa (Simon).
(Text-fig. 158, A, B, C)

Erigone stativa E. Simon, 1881, p. 256. *Lophomma stativa* O. P.-Cambridge, 1905, p. 64. *Anacotyle stativa* E. Simon, 1926, p. 360 ; F. Miller, 1947, Tab. 6, figs. 15–16.

DESCRIPTION. LENGTH : ♀ : 2–2·5 mm. ♂ : 2 mm. CARAPACE : Brown to dark brown, slightly rugose, with fovea, striæ and margins blackish. ♂ : With a few forward-directed spines. EYES : ♀♂ : Posterior medians 1·5 diam. apart, and slightly more than one diam. from laterals. ABDOMEN : Grey to black, with four reddish impressed dots. STERNUM : Brown to dark brown, slightly reticulated ; margins suffused with black. Broadly truncated posteriorly. LEGS : Tm I 0·55. Brown to orange-brown. Femora and tibiæ (particularly of I and II) with two rows of bristles ventrally (not very clear). EPIGYNE : Text-fig. 158, C. MALE PALP : Text-fig. 158, A, B.

OCCURRENCE : Amongst grass and sphagnum. Recorded from a few English counties (as far north as Cheshire) and Eire ; very rare. Adult in summer.

36, Genus EVANSIA O. P.-Cambridge 1900.

CHARACTERS OF GENUS. CARAPACE : ♂ : Head very slightly elevated, with post-ocular sulci. EYES : Small, fairly widely spaced. LEGS : Metatarsus IV without a trichobothrium ; Tm I 0·55. Tibiæ I–IV with one spine ; position of tibia I spine ca. 0·33 (♀). Metatarsi moderately longer than tarsi, with MT I/t I 1·3, MT IV/t IV 1·4. Spines and hairs on legs slightly serrated. MALE PALP : Palpal organs with long stylus, coiled into a circle.

There is one British species, which is myrmecophilous.

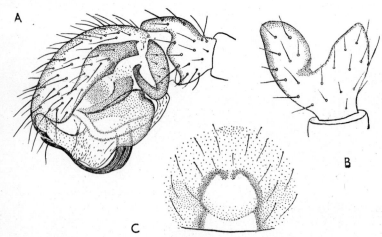

TEXT-FIG. 158.—*Anacotyle stativa:* A, ♂ palp ; B, ♂ palpal tibia (from above) ; C, epigyne.

Evansia merens O. P.-Cambridge.
(Text-fig. 159, A, B, C)

Evansia merens O. P.-Cambridge, 1900, p. 38 (♂); 1902, p. 27 (♀); E. Simon, 1926, p. 396.

DESCRIPTION.   LENGTH : ♀ :   2·5–2·75 mm.   ♂ :   2–2·25 mm.
CARAPACE : Brown to yellow-brown. ♂ : Head raised slightly, with small sulci behind posterior lateral eyes.   EYES : ♀ :   Posterior medians ca. 2 diam. apart, and ca. 1·5 diam. from laterals.   ♂ : Posterior medians almost 3 diam. apart, and ca. 1·5 diam. from laterals.   ABDOMEN : Grey to blackish.   STERNUM : Yellow-brown, suffused with some black.   LEGS : Tm I 0·55–0·58 (♀), 0·52 (♂).   Yellow-brown to brown. Tibial spines short (equal to one diam. of tibia or less) and stout ; spines and hairs slightly serrated.   EPIGYNE : Text-fig. 159, C.   MALE PALP : Text-fig. 159, A, B.

OCCURRENCE : In the nests of ants (*Lasius niger* and *Formica fusca*) usually under stones ; occasionally running near ants' nests.   Recorded from Scotland, Wales, Eire and the more northern English counties. Adults all the year, but most frequent in autumn.

37. Genus **TISO** E. Simon 1884.

CHARACTERS OF GENUS. ♂ : Head not elevated into lobe.   EYES : Fairly small.   LEGS : Metatarsus IV without a trichobothrium ; Tm I 0·5–0·57.   Tibiæ I–IV with one spine (weaker in ♂) ; position of tibia I spine 0·1–0·15, of tibia IV spine 0·2 (♀).   Metatarsi slightly longer than tarsi, with MT I/t I 1·15–1·2, MT IV/t IV 1·3–1·45.

There are two British species, one of which is found only at high altitudes.   They are readily separated by the sex organs.

Tiso vagans (Blackwall).
(Text-figs. 159, D, E ; 160, A)

Neriene vagans J. Blackwall, 1834, p. 374, and 1861–4, p. 257.   *N. longimana* O. P.-Cambridge, 1879–81, p. 110.   *Tiso longimana* W. Bosenberg, 1901–3, p. 164.   *T. vagans* E. Simon, 1926, p. 371.

DESCRIPTION. LENGTH : ♀ : 2–2·2 mm.   ♂ : 1·5–2 mm.   CARAPACE : Brown, somewhat reticulated.   EYES : ♀ : Posterior medians slightly more than one diam. apart, and one diam. or slightly less from laterals. ♂ : Posteriors ca. 1·5 diam. apart.   ABDOMEN : Grey to black.   STERNUM : Brown, shiny, but slightly reticulated.   LEGS : Tm I 0·57.   Yellow-brown to brown.   EPIGYNE : Text-fig. 160, A.   MALE PALP : Text-fig. 159, D, E ;   the tibia has some fairly stout bristles, and the femur and patella are both elongated.

OCCURRENCE : In moss, grass and detritus ; a common aeronaut. Widespread throughout the British Isles ; common.   Adult in spring to autumn.

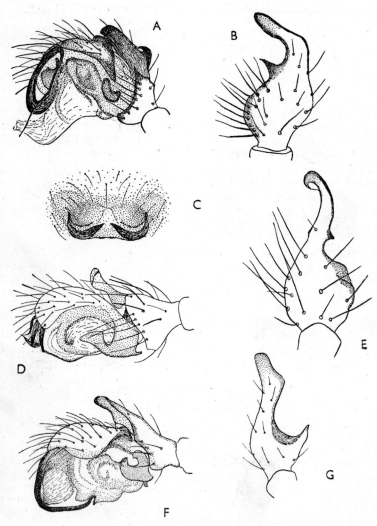

TEXT-FIG. 159.—*Evansia merens:* A, ♂ palp ; B, ♂ palpal tibia (from above) ;
C, epigyne.
Tiso vagans ♂ : D, palp ; E, palpal tibia (from above).
T. œstivus ♂ : F, palp ; G, palpal tibia (from above).

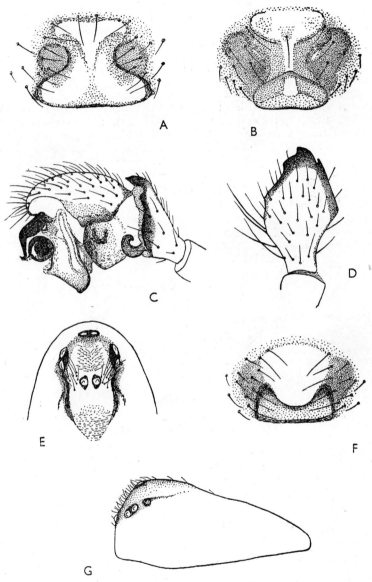

TEXT-FIG. 160.—*Tiso vagans:* A, epigyne.
T. æstivus: B, epigyne.
Troxochrus scabriculus: C, ♂ palp; D, ♂ palpal tibia (from above); F, epigyne; G, ♂ carapace.
T. cirrifrons: E, ♂ head (from above).

Tiso aestivus (L. Koch).
(Text-figs. 159, F, G ; 160, B)

Erigone æstiva L. Koch, 1872, p. 271. *Tiso æstivus* C. Chyzer and L. Kulczynski, 1891–7, II, p. 127 ; A. R. Jackson, 1914, p. 127 ; O. P.-Cambridge, 1914, p. 132 ; J. Braendegaard, 1946, p. 51.

DESCRIPTION.   LENGTH : ♀ : 1·75–1·9 mm.   ♂ : 1·5–1·6 mm. CARAPACE : Brown, slightly reticulated. EYES : ♀♂ : Posteriors slightly more than one diam. apart. ABDOMEN : Grey to black. STERNUM : Brown, with darker borders ; slightly reticulated. LEGS : Tm I 0·5. Brown. EPIGYNE : Text-fig. 160, B. MALE PALP : Text-fig. 159, F, G.

OCCURRENCE : At high altitudes (3,000 feet or more) in Snowdonia, the Lake District and the Scottish Highlands. Infrequent in these localities. Adult in spring and summer.

38. Genus TROXOCHRUS E. Simon 1884.

CHARACTERS OF GENUS.   CARAPACE : Rugose. ♂ : Head elevated slightly. ABDOMEN : With four impressed dots dorsally. STERNUM : Rugose. LEGS : Metatarsus IV without a trichobothrium ; Tm I 0·5–0·54. Tibiæ I–IV with one spine (weaker in ♂) ; position of tibia I spine 0·15 (♀). Metatarsi only slightly longer than tarsi, with MT I/t I 1–1·1, MT IV/t IV 1·25.

There are two British species, but *T. cirrifrons* may be only a variety of *T. scabriculus*.

Troxochrus scabriculus (Westring).
(Text-fig. 160, C, D, F, G)

Erigone scabricula N. Westring, 1851. *Walckenaera aggeris* J. Blackwall, 1861–4, p. 301. *W. scabricula* O. P.-Cambridge, 1879–81, p. 156. *Troxochrus scabriculus* C. Chyzer and L. Kulczynski, 1891–7, II, p. 124 ; E. Simon, 1926, p. 369 ; J. Denis, 1948 (1), p. 21.

DESCRIPTION. LENGTH : ♀♂ : 1·8–2 mm. CARAPACE : Dark brown, with darker striæ ; rugose. ♂ : Head elevated slightly, and compressed at sides (Text-fig. 160, G). EYES : ♀ : Posterior medians ca. one diam. apart, and ca. 1·5 diam. from laterals. ♂ : In four widely separated pairs ; anterior medians ca. 0·5 diam. apart, and ca. 3 diam. from laterals ; posterior medians ca. one diam. apart, and ca. 3 diam. from laterals. ABDOMEN : Grey to black, with 4 impressed dots dorsally. STERNUM : Dark brown, very rugose. LEGS : Tm. I 0·5–0·54.   Orange-brown. EPIGYNE : Text-fig. 160, F ; usually obscured by heavy pigmentation. MALE PALP : Text-fig. 160, C, D ; dark in colour.

OCCURRENCE : On sandhills, and in dry places. Widespread throughout the British Isles, and common locally. Adults at most seasons.

Troxochrus cirrifrons (O. P.-Cambridge).
(Text-fig. 160, E)

Walckenaera cirrifrons O. P.-Cambridge, 1871, p. 458, and 1879–81, p. 508. *Troxochrus cirrifrons* E. Simon, 1926. p. 369.

DESCRIPTION. Only the ♂ is known, and the ♀, if it exists, cannot be distinguished from *T. scabriculus*; the ♂ is probably only a dimorphic form of *T. scabriculus*. LENGTH : ♂ : 1·7–2 mm. Colour and form as *T. scabriculus*, and the ♂ differs from this only in the presence of long bristles in the ocular area (Text-fig. 160, E). MALE PALP : Appears to be identical with that of *T. scabriculus*.

OCCURRENCE : As *T. scabriculus*, but less common.

39. Genus **MINYRIOLUS** E. Simon 1884.

CHARACTERS OF GENUS. CARAPACE : ♂ : Head raised into shallow lobe. LEGS : Metatarsus IV without a trichobothrium ; Tm I 0·5. Tibiæ I–IV with one spine (rather weaker in ♂) ; position of tibia I spine 0·1–0·15 (♀). Metatarsi slightly longer than tarsi, with MT I/t I 1·15, MT IV/t IV 1·3–1·4.

There is one British species.

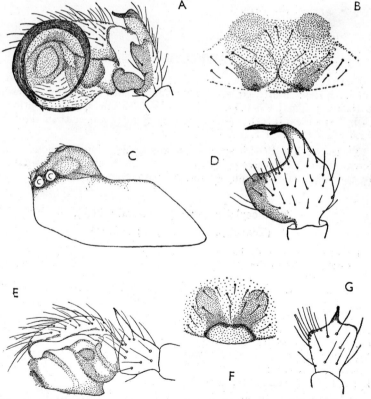

TEXT-FIG. 161.—*Minyriolus pusillus:* A, ♂ palp ; B, epigyne ; C, ♂ carapace ; D, ♂ palpal tibia (from above).
Tapinocyba praecox: E, ♂ palp ; F, epigyne ; G, ♂ palpal tibia (from above).

Minyriolus pusillus (Wider).
(Text-fig. 161, A, B, C, D)

Theridion pusillum Wider, 1834, p. 243. *Walckenaera pusilla* O. P.-Cambridge, 1879–81, p. 164. *Minyriolus pusillus* C. Chyzer and L. Kulczynski, 1891–7, II, p. 113 ; E. Simon, 1926, p. 353 ; F. Miller, 1947, Tab. 6, fig. 7.

DESCRIPTION. LENGTH : ♀: 1·2–1·35 mm. ♂: 1·1–1·25 mm. CARAPACE : Yellow-brown, with blackish fovea and striæ, and blackish markings on head. ♂ : Head raised and compressed at sides (Text-fig. 161, C), with some short hairs in ocular area. EYES : ♀: Posteriors 0·75–1 diam. apart. ABDOMEN : Mottled greyish-black, rather globular. STERNUM : Yellowish black, broad between coxæ IV. LEGS : Tm I ca. 0·5. Yellow to orange-brown. EPIGYNE : Text-fig. 161, B. MALE PALP : Text-fig. 161, A, D.

OCCURRENCE : In moss and grass, undergrowth, and on low bushes. Widely distributed throughout the British Isles, and not uncommon. Adults most of the year.

40. Genus **TAPINOCYBA** E. Simon 1884.

CHARACTERS OF GENUS. CARAPACE : ♂ : Head with post-ocular sulci. EYES : Fairly large. LEGS : Metatarsus IV without a trichobothrium ; Tm I 0.5–0.55. Tibiæ I–IV with one spine ; position of tibia I spine ca. 0.1(♀). Metatarsi only slightly longer than the tarsi, with MT I/t I 1.0–1.1, MT IV/t IV 1.2.

There are five British species, all small pale-coloured spiders. The females have distinctive epigynes, and the males are readily separated by the palpal tibial apophyses and the palpal organs.

Tapinocyba praecox (O. P.-Cambridge).
(Text-figs. 161, E, F, G ; 163, H)

Walckenaera praecox O. P.-Cambridge, 1873 (1), p. 549, and 1879–81, p. 143. *Tapinocyba praecox* A. R. Jackson, 1905, p. 253 ; E. Simon, 1926, p. 398 ; J. Denis, 1948 (1), p. 24.

DESCRIPTION. LENGTH : ♀♂: about 1.25 mm. CARAPACE : Yellow-brown. ♂ : With some long forward-directed spines in median line ; head scarcely elevated, but with hole and long sulci behind posterior lateral eyes (Text-fig. 163, H). EYES : ♀: Posterior medians ca. one diam. apart, and ca. 0.7 diam. from laterals. ABDOMEN : Pale grey to black. STERNUM : Yellow ; sometimes mottled with brown (♂). LEGS : Tm I 0.5. Pale yellow-brown. EPIGYNE : Text-fig. 161, F. MALE PALP : Text-fig. 161, E. G.

OCCURRENCE : In moss, grass. Widespread throughout England and Eire, but not recorded from Scotland ; frequent locally. Adults most of the year.

Tapinocyba pallens (O. P.-Cambridge).
(Text-figs. 162, A, B ; 163, C, I)

Erigone pallens O. P.-Cambridge, 1872 (1), p. 753. *Colobocyba pallens* E. Simon, 1926, p. 399. *Tapinocyba pallens* C. Chyzer and L. Kulczynski, 1891–7, II, p. 130 ; A. R. Jackson, 1905, p. 256 ; J. Denis, 1948 (1), p. 25.

DESCRIPTION. LENGTH : ♀♂ : about 1.5 mm. CARAPACE : Orange-brown. ♂ : Long sulci run backwards from posterior lateral eyes (Text-fig. 163, I) ; there are a few long forward-directed spines on carapace, and some fine hairs in ocular area. EYES : ♀ : Posteriors

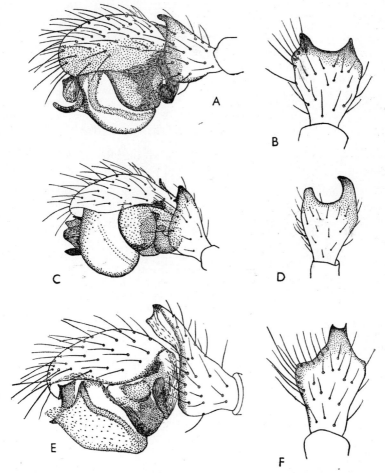

TEXT-FIG. 162.—*Tapinocyba pallens* ♂ : A, palp ; B, palpal tibia (from above).
T. insecta ♂ : C, palp ; D, palpal tibia (from above).
T. mitis ♂ : E, palp ; F, palpal tibia (from above).

ca. one diam. apart. ABDOMEN : Grey to pale grey. STERNUM :
Yellow to yellow-brown. LEGS : Tm I 0.5–0.55. Pale yellow-brown
or slightly darker. EPIGYNE : Text-fig. 163, C. MALE PALP : Text-
fig. 162, A, B.

OCCURRENCE : Amongst pine needles and dead leaves in woods.
Recorded from Scotland, the North of England and North Wales ;
common locally (e.g. in Delamere Forest, Cheshire), in these areas.
Adults in spring, autumn and winter.

Tapinocyba insecta (L. Koch).
(Text-figs. 162, C, D ; 163, D)

Erigone insecta L. Koch, 1869, p. 187. *Colobocyba insecta* E. Simon, 1926, p. 400 ;
F. Miller, 1947, Tab. 8, fig. 13 ; J. Denis, 1948 (1), p. 25. *Tapinocyba insecta* C. Chyzer
and L. Kulczynski, 1891–7, II, p. 130 ; A. R. Jackson, 1905, p. 257.

DESCRIPTION. LENGTH : ♀♂ : 1.5–1.6 mm. CARAPACE : ♀ :
Yellow-brown. ♂ : As ♀, with darker striæ and with head outlined
with a dark line ; post-ocular sulci shorter than in *T. pallens*, spines
and hairs as in *T. pallens*. EYES : ♀ : Posterior medians ca. one diam.
apart, and slightly less from laterals. ABDOMEN : Grey to pale grey.
STERNUM : Yellow, flecked with black, bearing a few long hairs.
LEGS : Tm I 0.54. Yellow-brown. EPIGYNE : Text-fig. 163, D.
MALE PALP : Text-fig. 162, C, D.

OCCURRENCE : In moss and detritus in woods. Recorded in England
from the south coast to Northumberland ; and from Eire. Very local.
Adults in spring and autumn.

Tapinocyba mitis (O. P.-Cambridge).
(Text-figs. 162, E, F ; 163, F)

Walckenaera mitis O. P.-Cambridge, 1882, p. 8, and 1893, p. 159. *Tapinocyba
mitis* A. R. Jackson, 1905, p. 258.

DESCRIPTION. LENGTH : ♀♂ : about 1.5 mm. CARAPACE : ♀ :
Yellow-brown with several forward-directed spines. ♂ : Orange-
brown, with sulci shorter than in *T. pallens*, and head without black
marginal line of *T. insecta* ; spines and hairs as in *T. pallens*. EYES :
♀ : Posterior medians ca. 1.5 diam. apart, and ca. one diam. from
laterals. ABDOMEN : Grey to pale grey. STERNUM : Yellow. LEGS :
Tm I 0·5. Yellow-brown. EPIGYNE : Text-fig. 163, F. MALE PALP :
Text-fig. 162, E, F.

OCCURRENCE : In pine needles, under stones in sandy banks,
amongst heather and leaves in damp places ; once in the nest of the
ant *D. fuliginosus*. Recorded from a few counties in southern England
only ; very rare. Adults in autumn, winter and spring.

Tapinocyba antepenultima (O. P.-Cambridge).
(Text-fig. 254, A, B, C, D, E, F, G, H)

Walckenaera antepenultima O. P.-Cambridge, 1882, p. 259 (♂). *Diplocephalus
antepenultimus* L. Kulczynski, 1898, p. 64. *Tapinocyba pygmaea* Muller and E.
Schenkel, 1895, p. 740. *T. antepenultima* R. de Lessert, 1904, p. 320.

DESCRIPTION. LENGTH : ♀ : 1·1–1·2 mm. ♂ : 1·2–1·35 mm.
CARAPACE : Yellow to pale yellow-brown, occasionally suffused with

some black, particularly at the fovea and along the striae. Moderately convex behind the eyes (Text-fig. 254, C). ♂ Short sulci run backwards from a hole on either side between the posterior median and lateral eyes (Text-fig. 254, B, C). ♂ Clypeus and ocular area with some fine hairs. EYES: With black margins. ♀ Anterior medians ca. 0·5 diam apart, and 0·5 diam. from laterals ; posteriors all ca. one diam. apart. ♂ Anterior medians ca. 0·5 diam. apart, and 1–1·5 diam. from laterals ;

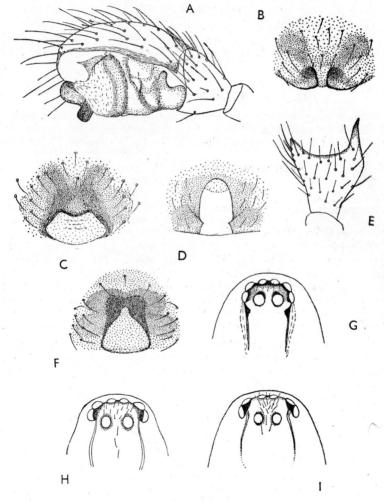

TEXT-FIG. 163.—*Aulacocyba subitanea* ♂ : A, palp ; E, palpal tibia (from above). Epigynes : B, *A. subitanea;* C, *Tapinocyba pallens;* D, *T. insecta;* F, *T. mitis.* Male heads (from above) : G, *A. subitanea;* H, *T. praecox;* I, *T. pallens.*

posteriors all 1·25–1·5 diam. apart. ♀♂ Anterior medians appreciably smaller than the remainder. ABDOMEN : Pale grey, with numerous fine hairs. STERNUM : Yellow to yellow-brown, sometimes mottled with a little black ; some fine hairs present. LEGS : Tm I 0·45–0·47 ; metatarsus IV without a trichobothrium. Pale yellow to yellow brown. EPIGYNE : Text-fig. 254, G, H ; similar in general outline to the other members of the genus. MALE PALP : Text-fig. 254, A, D, E, F ; readily distinguished from the other members of the genus. The tibia has some minute granulations on the two short apophyses.

OCCURRENCE : Both sexes occurred fairly freely amongst grass roots on the South Downs near Heyshott (Sussex), in September, 1951 ; taken by Mr. A. D. Blest, and recorded as British for the first time here.

41. Genus **AULACOCYBA** E. Simon 1926.

CHARACTERS OF GENUS. Very similar to *Tapinocyba*, from which it differs by having Tm I 0·45–0·48, rather larger eyes, and in the structure of the sex organs. There is one British species.

Aulacocyba subitanea (O. P.-Cambridge).
(Text-fig. 163, A, B, E, G)

Erigone subitanea O. P.-Cambridge, 1875 (2), p. 249, and 1879–81, p. 144. *Tapinocyba subitanea* A. R. Jackson, 1905, p. 254. *T. parisiensis* O. P.-Cambridge, 1902, p. 25. *Aulacocyba subitanea* E. Simon, 1926, p. 441 ; C. R. Crosby and S. C. Bishop, 1933, p. 131 ; J. Denis, 1948 (1), p. 29 ; B. J. Kaston, 1948, p. 175.

DESCRIPTION. LENGTH : ♀ : 1·3–1·5 mm. ♂ : 1·2 mm. CARAPACE : ♀ : Yellow-brown, with darker striæ. ♂ : Orange-brown, with long sulci slightly indented behind posterior eyes (Text-fig. 163, G). EYES : ♀ : Posteriors ca. one diam. apart. ABDOMEN : Grey. STERNUM : Yellow-brown, mottled with darker brown ; broadly truncated between coxæ IV. LEGS : Tm I 0·45–0·48. Orange-brown. EPIGYNE : Text-fig. 163, B. MALE PALP : Text-fig. 163, A, E.

OCCURRENCE : In straw ricks, and debris from straw ricks ; amongst hay and straw in outhouses, etc. Widespread throughout England, but few records for Scotland or Wales. Infrequent. Adult in spring, autumn and winter.

42. Genus **PERIMONES** A. R. Jackson 1932.

CHARACTERS OF GENUS. CARAPACE : ♂ : Head slightly elevated and impressed at sides. LEGS : Metatarsus IV without a trichobothrium ; Tm I 0·65. ♀ : Tibiæ I–IV with one spine ; position of tibia I spine 0·23. ♂ : Tibiæ I–II spineless ; tibiæ III–IV with one small spine. Metatarsi moderately longer than tarsi, with MT I/t I 1·4, MT IV/t IV 1·85. Tibiæ and metatarsi I–II with two longitudinal rows of strong spines ventrally (less strong than in *Maso*).

There is one British species.

Perimones britteni (Jackson).
(Text-fig. 164, A, B, C, D)

Maso britteni A. R. Jackson, 1913, p. 27 ; O. P.-Cambridge, 1914, p. 131. *Perimones britteni* A. R. Jackson, 1932, p. 210.

DESCRIPTION. LENGTH : ♀ : 1·8–2 mm.   ♂ : 1·6–1·8 mm. CARA-PACE : Deep orange-brown, with darker fovea and striæ.   ♂ : Head slightly elevated, with a hole on either side (Text-fig. 164, C) ; clypeus with numerous short stout bristles. EYES : ♀♂ : Posteriors ca. 1.25 diams. apart. ABDOMEN : Brown to black. STERNUM : Dark red-brown, often suffused with black ; shiny. LEGS : Tm I 0·65. Yellow, with coxæ and trochanters suffused with brown. Tibiæ and metatarsi I–II with two longitudinal rows of strong spines (8–10, and 6–7 spines respectively in each row) ventrally, which are reduced on legs III–IV to strong hairs.   ♂ : Ventral spines as ♀, but femora I–II also have short stout spines ventrally. EPIGYNE : Text-fig. 164, D. MALE PALP : Text-fig. 164, A, B.

OCCURRENCE : In swampy localities. Very few records, from the New Forest to Scotland ; very rare, though once common in one spot in Delamere Forest (Cheshire). Adult in spring.

43. Genus THYREOSTHENIUS E. Simon 1884.

CHARACTERS OF GENUS. CARAPACE :   ♂ : Head raised into lobe (very large in *T. biovatus*), bifid longitudinally. LEGS : Metatarsus IV without a trichobothrium ; Tm I ca. 0·65.   ♀ : Tibiæ I–IV with one spine ; position of tibia I spine 0·1–0·15, of tibia IV spine 0·25–0·32.   ♂ : Tibial spines much reduced, sometimes absent. Metatarsi moderately longer than tarsi, with MT I/t I 1·25, MT IV/t IV 1·35–1·45.

There are two British species. The males are distinguished at once by the cephalic lobes, and the females are separated by the eyes and the epigynes.

Thyreosthenius parasiticus (Westring).
(Text-figs. 164, E, F ; 165, A, B, D, F)

Erigone parasitica N. Westring, 1851, p. 45. *Walckenaera becki* O. P.-Cambridge, 1871, p. 460, and 1879–81, p. 162. *Tapinocyba becki* C. Chyzer and L. Kulczynski, 1891–7, II, p. 130. *Thyreosthenius becki* E. Simon, 1926, p. 393. *T. parasiticus* A. Holm, 1945, p. 20.

DESCRIPTION. LENGTH : ♀♂ : 1·5–1·6 mm. CARAPACE : Yellow to brown.   ♂ : Head raised into small lobe, with a median longitudinal groove, impressed at sides and with a small hole just behind posterior lateral eyes (Text-fig. 165, A, F). EYES : ♀ : Large ; anterior medians 0·75 diam. apart, ca. 0·5 diam. from laterals ; posterior medians rather less than one diam. apart, and ca. one diam. from laterals.   ♂ : Small ; posterior medians rather less than one diam. apart. ABDOMEN : Grey. STERNUM : Yellow to brown, reticulated with black. LEGS : Tm I 0·66. Yellow to brown.   ♂ : Tibiæ I–II spineless, tibiæ III-IV with

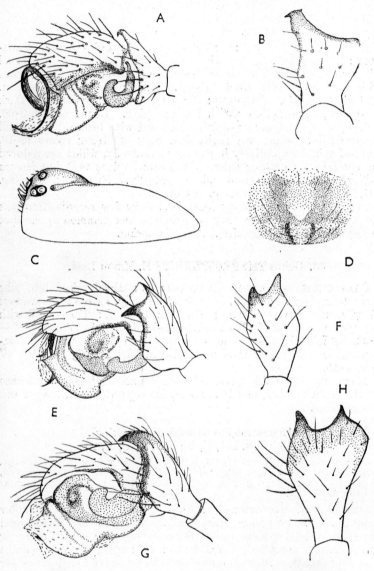

TEXT-FIG. 164.—*Perimones britteni:* A, ♂ palp ; B, ♂ palpal tibia (from above) ;
C, ♂ carapace ; D, epigyne.
Thyreosthenius parasiticus ♂ : E, palp ; F, palpal tibia (from above).
T. biovatus ♂ : G, palp ; H, palpal tibia (from above).

very small spine. EPIGYNE: Text-fig. 165, B, D. MALE PALP: Text-fig. 164, E, F.

OCCURRENCE: In subterranean places (e.g. disused sewers, inspection pits, cellars, mines), outhouses, birds' nests. Widespread throughout the British Isles ; infrequent. Adults at most seasons.

Thyreosthenius biovatus (O. P.-Cambridge).
(Text-figs. 164, G, H ; 165, C, E, G)

Erigone biovata O. P.-Cambridge, 1875 (1), p. 215. *Thyreosthenius biovatus* E. Simon, 1926, p. 393.

DESCRIPTION. LENGTH : ♀: 1·8–2·1 mm. ♂: 1·6–1·7 mm. CARAPACE : Brown. ♂: Head raised into very large lobe, divided into two by a longitudinal groove (Text-fig. 165, C, G). EYES : ♀: Anterior medians ca. 0.5 diam. apart, and ca. 1·5 diam. from laterals ; posterior medians 1·5' diam. apart, and ca. 2 diams. from laterals. ♂: Eyes very small. ABDOMEN : Grey to black. STERNUM : Yellow-brown, with fairly long hairs. LEGS : Tm I 0·64. Orange-brown. ♀: Tibial spines short, but fairly stout. ♂: Tibial spines very short. EPIGYNE : Text-fig. 165, E ; similar to *T. parasiticus*. MALE PALP : Text-fig. 164, G, H.

OCCURRENCE : In the nests of ants (*Formica rufa*, *F. pratensis*, *F. fusca*) ; recorded occasionally away from ants. Widespread throughout the British Isles, and probably common in ants' nests.

44. Genus **MONOCEPHALUS** F. P. Smith 1906.

CHARACTERS OF GENUS. CARAPACE : ♂: Head elevated, and excavated at sides. LEGS : Metatarsus IV without a trichobothrium ; Tm I 0·65–0·7. ♀: Tibiæ I–IV with one spine ; position of tibia I spine ca. 0·15, of tibia IV spine ca. 0·28. ♂: Tibiæ I–II spineless, tibiæ III–IV with one fine spine. Metatarsi moderately longer than tarsi, with MT I/t I 1·25, MT IV/t IV 1·45.

There are two British species. They are distinguished by the epigynes (♀), and by the heads and tibial apophyses (♂).

Monocephalus fuscipes (Blackwall).
(Text-figs. 166, A, B, E ; 167, A. C)

Walckenaera fuscipes J. Blackwall, 1836, p. 481, and 1861–4, p. 295 ; O. P.-Cambridge, 1879–81, p. 154. *Monocephalus fuscipes* F. P. Smith, 1906, p. 300. *Plaesiocraerus fuscipes* E. Simon, 1926, pp. 379, 382.

DESCRIPTION. LENGTH : ♀♂: 1·75–2 mm. CARAPACE : Brown, with slightly darker fovea and striæ. ♂: Head elevated, and deeply impressed at sides (Text-fig. 167, A) ; lobe, from above (Text-fig. 167, C), narrower than in *M. castaneipes*. EYES : ♀: Posterior medians ca. one diam. apart, and 1.5 diam. from laterals. ♂: Posterior medians one diam. or slightly more apart. ABDOMEN : Grey to black. STERNUM : Orange-brown, darker at margins ; reticulated. LEGS : Tm I 0·65–0·68. Brown to orange-brown. EPIGYNE : Text-fig.

166, E. MALE PALP : Text-fig. 166, A, B ; the tibia is broader apically than in *M. castaneipes*.

OCCURRENCE : In detritus of woods, particularly of coniferous woods. Widespread throughout the British Isles ; common. Adults at all seasons.

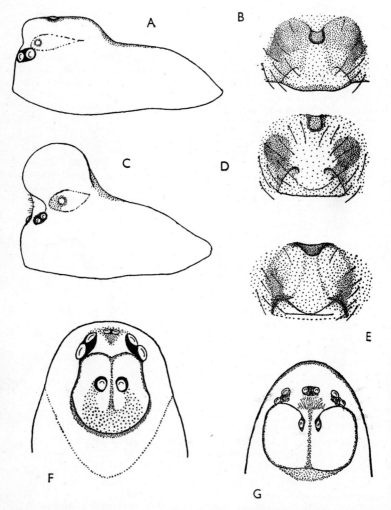

TEXT-FIG. 165.—*Thyreosthenius parasiticus:* A, ♂ carapace ; B, D, epigyne ; F, ♂ head (from above).
    T. biovatus: C, ♂ carapace ; E, epigyne ; G, ♂ head (from above).

Monocephalus castaneipes (Simon).
(Text-figs. 166, C, D, F ; 167, B, D)

Plaesiocraerus castaneipes E. Simon, 1884, p. 768 ; O. P.-Cambridge. 1906, p. 91.

DESCRIPTION. LENGTH : ♀♂ : 1·75–1·9 mm. Colour and form as *M.fuscipes*. CARAPACE : ♂ : Head (Text-fig. 167, B) ; lobe, from above (Text-fig. 167, D), broader than in *M. fuscipes*. EYES : ♀ : Posteriors ca. one diam. apart. ♂ : Posterior medians slightly less

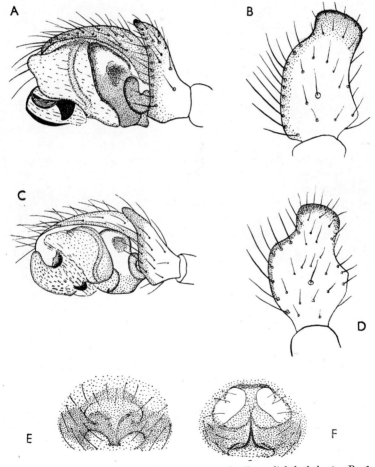

TEXT-FIG. 166.—*Monocephalus fuscipes:* A, ♂ palp (from slightly below) ; B, ♂ palpal tibia (from above) ; E, epigyne.
   M. castaneipes: C, ♂ palp (from slightly below) ; D, ♂ palpal tibia (from above) ; F, epigyne.

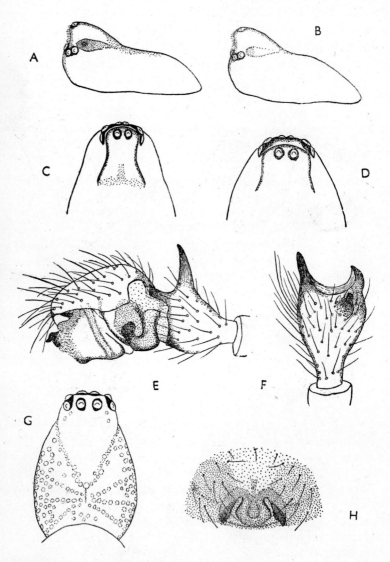

TEXT-FIG. 167.—*Monocephalus fuscipes* ♂ : A, carapace ; C, head (from above).
M. castaneipes ♂ : B, carapace ; D, head (from above).
Lophomma punctatum: E, ♂ palp ; F, ♂ palpal tibia (from above) ; G,
carapace (from above) ; H, epigyne.

than one diam. apart. LEGS : Tm I 0·66–0·69. EPIGYNE : Text-fig. 166, F. MALE PALP : Text-fig. 166, C, D ; the tibia is narrower apically than in *M. fuscipes*.

OCCURRENCE : On high ground (above about 1,000 feet) in North Wales, Northern England, Scotland and Eire, under stones, etc. ; frequent in these localities. Has been recorded at sea level from the south of England.

45. Genus **LOPHOMMA** A. Menge 1867.

CHARACTERS OF GENUS. CARAPACE : With numerous large pits (Text-fig. 167, G). ♂ : Head slightly elevated, with post-ocular sulci. ABDOMEN : With four impressed dots dorsally. STERNUM : With numerous large pits, like carapace. LEGS : Metatarsus IV without a trichobothrium ; Tm I 0·36. Tibiæ I–II with two fine spines, tibiæ III–IV with one spine ; position of tibia IV spine ca. 0·3 (♀). Metatarsi moderately longer than tarsi, with MT I/t I 1·25, MT IV/t IV ca. 1·45.

There is one British species, which is readily recognisable in both sexes by the heavily pitted carapace and sternum.

Lophomma punctatum (Blackwall).
(Text-fig. 167, E, F, G, H)

Walckenaera punctata J. Blackwall, 1841, p. 629, and 1861–4, p. 295 ; O. P.-Cambridge, 1879–81, p. 148. *Lophomma punctatum* C. Chyzer and L. Kulczynski, 1891–7, II, p. 127 ; E. Simon, 1926, p. 440.

DESCRIPTION. LENGTH : ♀♂ : 2·25–2·5 mm. CARAPACE : Dark chestnut-brown to black ; punctured with numerous large pits, radiating from fovea, and round margins (including clypeus) (Text-fig. 167, G). ♂ : Head somewhat elevated, with sulci behind posterior lateral eyes. EYES : ♀♂ : Posteriors ca. one diam. apart. ABDOMEN : Grey to black, with four small reddish impressed dots dorsally. STERNUM : Dark chestnut-brown, heavily pitted ; broad between coxæ IV. LEGS : Tm I 0·35–0·38. Yellow-brown to dark-brown. Tibial spines very thin. EPIGYNE : Text-fig. 167, H ; heavily pigmented. MALE PALP : Text-fig. 167, E, F.

OCCURRENCE : In wet, swampy areas, amongst moss, grass, etc. Widespread throughout the British Isles, but infrequent. Adults all the year.

46. Genus **MIOXENA** E. Simon 1926.

CHARACTERS OF GENUS. CARAPACE : ♂ : Head not elevated. EYES : Posterior medians closer to laterals than to each other. LEGS : Metatarsus IV without a trichobothrium ; Tm I 0·33. ♀♂ : Tibiæ I–II with two fine spines, tibiæ III–IV with one spine ; position of tibia I spine ca. 0·1, of tibia IV spine ca. 0·23 (♀). Metatarsi moderately longer than tarsi, with MT I/t I 1·3, MT IV/t IV 1·5. MALE PALP : Tibia with no apophysis.

There is one British species.

Mioxena blanda (Simon).
(Text-fig. 168, F, G, H)

Gongylidiellum blandum E. Simon, 1884, p. 604 ; A. R. Jackson, 1911 (1), p. 388 ; O. P.-Cambridge, 1911, p. 53. *Mioxena blanda* E. Simon, 1926, p. 401 ; J. E. Hull, 1931, p. 7, and 1932, p. 108 ; J. Denis, 1947 (2), p. 81.

DESCRIPTION. LENGTH : ♀ : 1·6 mm. ♂ : 1·5 mm. CARAPACE : Pale yellow-brown, slightly reticulated. There are some forward-

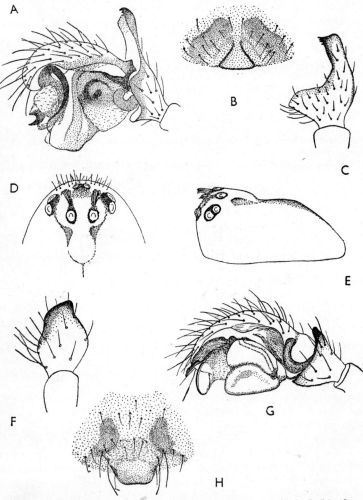

TEXT-FIG. 168.—*Saloca diceros:* A, ♂ palp ; B, epigyne ; C, ♂ palpal tibia (from above) ; D, ♂ head (from above) ; E, ♂ carapace.
Mioxena blanda: F, ♂ palpal tibia (from above) ; G, ♂ palp ; H, epigyne.

directed spines along median line, and in ocular area, stouter in ♂ than ♀. EYES : ♀ : Posterior medians 1·25–1·5 diam. apart. and ca. 0·75 diam. from laterals. ♂ : Posterior medians ca. 1·5 diam. apart, and 0·5 diam. from laterals. ABDOMEN : Pale grey, clothed with long hairs. STERNUM : Whitish yellow. LEGS : Tm I ca. 0·33. Pale yellow-brown. Tibial spines long but fine. EPIGYNE : Text-fig. 168, H. MALE PALP : Text-fig. 168, F, G ; the tibia is chitinised dorsally at the tip.

OCCURRENCE : Under stones embedded in mud-flats, River Dee (Cheshire) and River Tyne (Northumberland) ; amongst marram grass on sandhills, Formby (Lancashire). Adults in autumn.

47. Genus **SALOCA** E. Simon 1926.

CHARACTERS OF GENUS. CARAPACE : ♂ : Head with slight elevation, and two little " horns " composed of bristles in the ocular area. EYES : ♀ Fairly large, with posterior medians closer to laterals than to each other. LEGS : Metatarsus IV without a trichobothrium ; Tm I about 0·4. ♀♂ : Tibiæ I–II with two fine spines, tibiæ III–IV with one spine ; position of tibia IV spine about 0·18 (♀). Metatarsi only very slightly longer than tarsi, with MT I/t I 1·05, MT IV/t IV 1·2.

There is one British species, a minute, pale coloured spider.

Saloca diceros (O. P.-Cambridge).
(Text-fig. 168, A, B, C, D, E)

Walckenaera diceros O. P.-Cambridge, 1871, p. 454 ; and 1879–81, p. 145. non *Panamomops diceros* C. Chyzer and L. Kulczynski, 1891–7, II, p. 132. *Saloca diceros* E. Simon, 1926, p. 397.

DESCRIPTION. LENGTH : ♀♂ : 1·0–1·2 mm. CARAPACE : ♀ : Yellow-brown, with faintly darker striæ and fovea. ♂ : Orange-brown, with head raised slightly and compressed at sides (Text-fig. 168, E) ; a row of stout, forward-directed, hooked bristles runs from each posterior median eye to the corresponding anterior median eye (Text-fig. 168, D), giving the appearance of two little horns. Clypeus with a number of short, fairly stout hairs. EYES : ♀ : Rather large, with anterior medians only slightly smaller than the remaining eyes. Posterior medians slightly more than one diam. apart, and rather less than one diam. from laterals. ABDOMEN : Pale whitish yellow, covered with short fine hairs. STERNUM : Very pale yellow to yellow-brown, with darker edges. LEGS : Tm I 0·4 or slightly less. ♀ : Whitish yellow ♂ : Yellow, with dusky markings particularly on femora I–II ; tibial spines rather weaker than in ♀. EPIGYNE : Text-fig. 168, B. MALE PALP : Text-fig. 168, A, C.

OCCURRENCE : In moss in woods and damp places. Extremely rare ; recorded only from Dorset and Staffordshire. Adult probably in early spring.

48. Genus **JACKSONELLA** A. F. Millidge 1951.

CHARACTERS OF GENUS. CARAPACE : ♂ : Head not elevated into lobe. EYES : Fairly large, with posterior medians closer to laterals than to each other. CHELICERÆ : ♂ : With boss anteriorly. LEGS : Metatarsus IV without a trichobothrium ; Tm I about 0·37. ♀♂ : Tibiæ I–II with two short spines, tibiæ III–IV with one spine. Legs short, with metatarsi shorter than, or only slightly longer than, tarsi : MT I/t I 0·9–0·95, MT IV/t IV 1·15. MALE PALP : Tibia with no apophysis, but slightly produced and chitinised on its anterior dorsal margin.

There is one species, a very small, pale coloured spider.

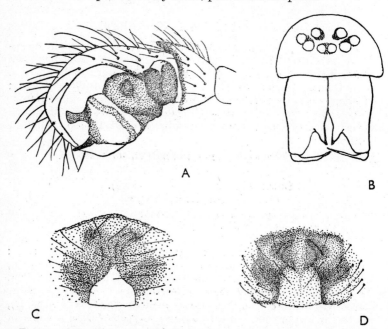

A

B

C

D

TEXT-FIG. 169.—*Jacksonella falconeri:* A, ♂ palp ; B, ♂ cheliceræ (from in front) ; C, epigyne ; D, ditto (another specimen).

Jacksonella falconeri (Jackson).
(Text-fig. 169, A, B, C, D)

Maro falconeri A. R. Jackson, 1908, p. 61 ; O. P.-Cambridge, 1908, p. 174 ; and 1912, p. 76 ; W. Falconer, 1919, fig. 8.

DESCRIPTION. LENGTH : ♀ : 1·1–1·2 mm. ♂ : about 1 mm. CARAPACE : Pale yellow-brown, with a few forward-directed spines in median line. EYES : ♀♂ : Posterior medians rather more than one diam. apart, and rather less than one diam. from laterals. ABDOMEN : Whitish grey, with short hairs. STERNUM : Whitish yellow.

CHELICERÆ : ♂ : With a fairly large warty tooth anteriorly (Text-fig. 169, B). LEGS : Tm I ca. 0·37. Pale yellow to yellow-brown. EPIGYNE : Text-fig. 169, C, D (somewhat variable). MALE PALP : Text-fig. 169, A ; there is no tibial apophysis.

OCCURRENCE : In pine needles, and under stones. Recorded from southern England to the north of Scotland, but records are few ; rare. Adult in spring and autumn.

49. Genus **GONGYLIDIELLUM** E. Simon 1884.

CHARACTERS OF GENUS. CARAPACE : ♂ : Head not elevated. ABDOMEN : ♂ : Branchial opercula rugose, there being a corresponding stridulating point on coxæ IV. LEGS : Metatarsus IV without a trichobothrium ; Tm I 0·33–0·38. ♀♂ : Tibiæ I–II with two spines, tibiæ III–IV with one spine. Metatarsi only slightly longer than tarsi, with MT I/t I 1·1–1·3, MT IV/t IV 1·25–1·35. CHELICERÆ : ♂ : With a boss anteriorly.

There are three British species, distinguished by the sex organs.

Gongylidiellum vivum (O. P.-Cambridge).
(Text-figs. 170, A, C ; 171, A)

Erigone viva O. P.-Cambridge, 1875 (1), p. 330. *Neriene viva* idem, 1879–81, p. 435. *Gongylidiellum vivum* E. Simon, 1926, p. 457.

DESCRIPTION. LENGTH : ♀ : 1·5 mm. ♂ : 1·2–1·4 mm. CARAPACE : Yellow-brown with darker fovea, with some forward-directed spines along median line. EYES : ♀♂ : Posteriors rather less than one diam. apart. ABDOMEN : Mottled grey. STERNUM : Yellow, reticulated. CHELICERÆ : ♂ : Small warty tooth anteriorly. LEGS : Tm I 0·33. Orange-brown. EPIGYNE : Text-fig. 171, A. MALE PALP : Text-fig. 170, A, C ; viewed from the side, very similar to the rare *G. murcidum*, but the tibial apophysis seen from above readily distinguishes it.

OCCURRENCE : In moss, grass, etc., in damp places. Widespread throughout the British Isles ; frequent. Adults in spring, early summer and autumn.

Gongylidiellum latebricola (O. P.-Cambridge).
(Text-figs. 170, E, F ; 171, C)

Neriene latebricola O. P.-Cambridge, 1871, p. 444, and 1879–81, p. 120. *Micrargus latebricola* W. Bösenberg, 1901–3, p. 177. *Gongylidiellum latebricola* E. Simon, 1926, p. 456.

DESCRIPTION. LENGTH : ♀♂ : about 1·5 mm. Similar to *G.vivum* in colour and form. STERNUM : Yellow, mottled with blackish ; reticulated. LEGS : Tm I 0·34–0·38. EPIGYNE : Text-fig. 171, C. MALE PALP : Text-fig, 170, E, F ; the long tibial apophysis distinguishes it readily from the remaining species.

OCCURRENCE : In moss, dead leaves, grass, etc., in woods. Widespread throughout the British Isles, but few records ; rare. Adult in spring and autumn.

U

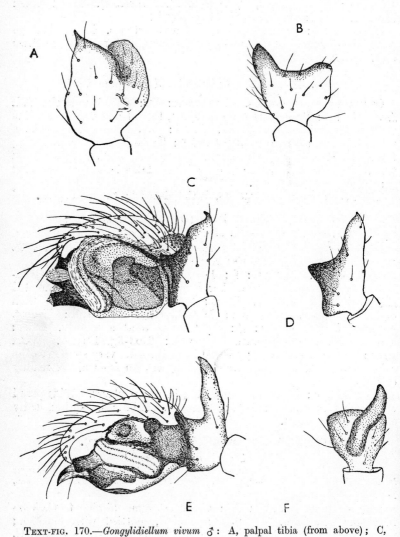

TEXT-FIG. 170.—*Gongylidiellum vivum* ♂ : A, palpal tibia (from above) ; C, palp.
 G. murcidum ♂ : B, palpal tibia (right, from above) ; D, palpal tibia (from side).
 G. latebricola ♂ : E, palp ; F, palpal tibia (from above).

Gongylidiellum murcidum Simon.
(Text-figs. 170, B, D ; 171, B)

Gongylidiellum murcidum E. Simon, 1884, p. 608 ; C. Chyzer and L. Kulczynski, 1891–7, II, p. 128 ; O. P.-Cambridge, 1895, p. 105 ; E. Simon, 1926, p. 457.

DESCRIPTION. LENGTH : ♀♂ : about 1·5 mm. Colour and form as *G. vivum*. STERNUM : Yellow, mottled with black. LEGS : Tm I 0·35. EPIGYNE : Text-fig. 171, B. MALE PALP : Text-fig. 170, B, D ; similar to *G. vivum*, but distinguishable by the tibial apophysis seen from above.

OCCURRENCE : Wicken Fen, in detritus, where it is common in May-June. New Forest, in a damp area.

50. Genus **MICRARGUS** F. Dahl 1886.

CHARACTERS OF GENUS. CARAPACE : ♂ : Head elevated slightly, with post-ocular sulci. LEGS : Metatarsus IV without a trichobothrium ; Tm I 0·35–0·40. ♀♂ : Tibiæ I–II with two spines (reduced in *M. subaequalis* ♂ to hairs), tibiæ III–IV with one spine. Metatarsi only slightly longer than tarsi, with MT I/t I 1·1–1·2, MT IV/t IV 1·25–1·35.

There are three British species, distinguished by the sex organs.

Micrargus herbigradus (Blackwall).
(Text-figs. 171, D, E ; 172, A)

Neriene herbigrada J. Blackwall, 1854, p. 179, and 1861–4, p. 285 ; O. P.-Cambridge, 1879–81, p. 113. *Lophomma herbigrada* C. Chyzer and L. Kulczynski, 1891–7, II, p. 127. *Blaniargus herbigradus* E. Simon, 1926, p. 439. *Micrargus herbigradus* J. Denis, 1950, p. 89.

DESCRIPTION. LENGTH : ♀♂ : 2 mm. CARAPACE : Brown to dark-brown, rather rugose. ♂ : Very slightly elevated behind eyes, with holes and sulci behind posterior lateral eyes. EYES : ♀ : Posteriors ca. one diam. apart. ABDOMEN : Grey to black. STERNUM : Brown, suffused with a variable amount of black ; rather rugose. CHELICERÆ : ♂ : Somewhat enlarged and divergent. LEGS : Tm I 0·35–0·40. Brown to orange-brown. Spines on tibiæ I–II short and rather thin. EPIGYNE : Text-fig. 172, A. MALE PALP : Text-fig. 171, D. E ; the embolus is long and whip-like. There is a distinct tibial apophysis.

OCCURRENCE : In moss, detritus, etc., usually in woods. Widespread throughout the British Isles ; common. Adults at all seasons.

Micrargus subaequalis (Westring).
(Text-figs. 171, G ; 172, B)

Erigone subœqualis N. Westring, 1851. *Walckenaera subœqualis* O.P.-Cambridge, 1879–81, p. 501. *Lophomma subœquale* F. P. Smith, 1908, p. 331. *Nothocyba subœqualis* E. Simon, 1926, p. 440 ; F. Miller, 1947, Tab. 7, figs. 12–14. *Micrargus subœqualis* J. Denis, 1950, p. 89.

DESCRIPTION. LENGTH : ♀♂ : 1·75–2 mm. CARAPACE : Yellow to brown, with faint black fovea and striæ. ♂ : Head raised slightly behind eyes with a sulcus on either side just behind eyes. EYES :

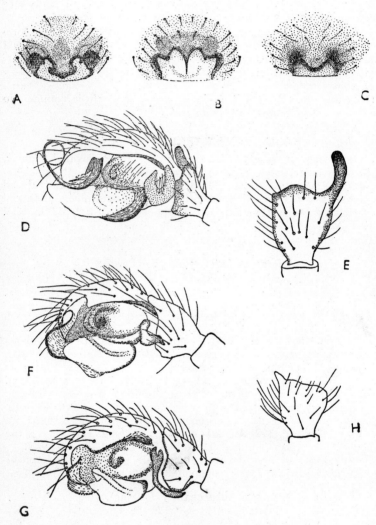

TEXT-FIG. 171.—Epigynes: A, *Gongylidiellum vivum;* B, *G. murcidum;* C, *G. latebricolum.*
    Micrargus herbigradus ♂ : D, palp ; E, palpal tibia (from above).
    M. laudatus ♂ : F, palp ; H, palpal tibia (from above).
    M. subœqualis ♂ : G, palp.

♀ : Posteriors ca. one diam. apart. ♂ : Posteriors ca. 1·5 diam. apart. ABDOMEN : Grey. STERNUM : Blackish yellow to brown, reticulated with black ; not very rugose. LEGS : Tm I 0·37. Yellow-brown to brown. ♂ : Spines on tibiæ I–II reduced to hairs ; spines on tibiæ III–IV very short and weak. EPIGYNE : Text-fig. 172, B. MALE PALP : Text-fig. 171, G ; there is no tibial apophysis. The para-cymbium is produced basally into a long " tail."

OCCURRENCE : Amongst grass, low plants, etc. Widely distributed throughout the British Isles, but uncommon. Adults at most seasons.

Micrargus laudatus (O. P.-Cambridge).
(Text-figs. 171, F, H ; 172, D)

Walckenaera laudata O. P.-Cambridge, 1879–81 (1881), p. 594. *Lophomma laudatum* O. P.-Cambridge, 1905, p. 50 ; F. P. Smith, 1908, p. 331.

DESCRIPTION. LENGTH : ♀♂ : 1·6–1·8 mm. CARAPACE : Brown to dark-brown, faintly reticulated, with faint black fovea and striæ. ♂ : With post-ocular sulci. EYES : ♀♂ : Posterior medians ca. one diam. apart, and ca. 1·5 diams. from laterals. ABDOMEN : Grey to black. STERNUM : Blackish yellow to brown, reticulated with much black ; rather rugose. LEGS : Tm I 0·4. Yellow-brown to brown. EPIGYNE : Text-fig. 172, D. MALE PALP : Text-fig. 171, F, H ; there is a short tibial apophysis.

OCCURRENCE : Under stones, and in heather. Recorded from the more southern counties of England, and in Wales ; rare. Adults in spring and summer.

51. Genus NOTIOSCOPUS E. Simon 1884.

CHARACTERS OF GENUS. CARAPACE : ♂ : Head raised behind eyes, with deep transverse cleft. LEGS : Metatarsus IV without a tricho-bothrium ; Tm I 0·6. ♀ : Tibiæ I–II with two spines, tibiæ III–IV with one spine ; position of tibia IV spine 0·28. ♂ : Tibiæ I–IV with one short spine. Metatarsi moderately longer than tarsi, with MT I/t I 1·25, MT IV/t IV 1·5.

There is one British species.

Notioscopus sarcinatus (O. P.-Cambridge).
(Text-fig. 172, C, E, F, G, H)

Erigone sarcinata O. P.-Cambridge, 1872 (1), p. 757. *Oedothorax sarcinatus* W. Bosenberg, 1901–3, p. 213. *Notioscopus sarcinatus* J. E. Hull, 1910, p. 587 ; E. Simon, 1926, p. 372. *Coryphaeolanus lapponicus* E. Schenkel, 1939, p. 98.

DESCRIPTION. LENGTH : ♀♂ : about 2 mm. CARAPACE : Brown to orange-brown, with darker striæ. ♂ : There are a few short hairs behind eyes ; a deep cleft behind eyes and in front of fovea cuts out a wedge-shaped area (Text-fig. 172, G, H), which is paler in colour. EYES : ♀ : Posteriors ca. one diam. apart. ABDOMEN : Brownish-grey. STERNUM : Yellow-brown. LEGS : Tm I ca. 0·6. Orange-brown. EPIGYNE : Text-fig. 172, C. MALE PALP : Text-fig. 172, E, F.

OCCURRENCE : In wet, swampy areas. There are few records, in England only, from Hampshire to Yorkshire ; rare.

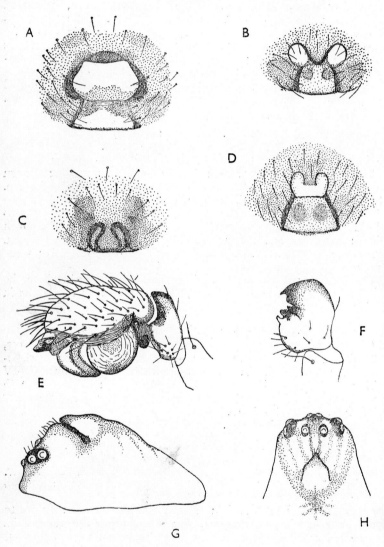

TEXT-FIG. 172.—Epigynes: A, *Micrargus herbigradus;* B, *M. subæqualis;* D, *M. laudatus.*
  Notioscopus sarcinatus: C, epigyne; E, ♂ palp; F, ♂ palpal tibia (from above); G, ♂ carapace; H, ditto (from above).

52. Genus **GLYPHESIS** E. Simon 1926.

CHARACTERS OF GENUS. The following species (*cottonae* La Touche) is placed in this genus, though its characters may not be entirely typical of the genus. CARAPACE : ♂ : Head elevated slightly, with post-ocular sulci. EYES : Small, fairly widely spaced. STERNUM : Broad, widely truncated posteriorly. LEGS : Metatarsus IV without a tricho-bothrium ; Tm I̔ ca. 0·45. ♀♂ : Tibiæ I–II with two short, thin spines, tibiæ III–IV with one spine. Metatarsi practically equal in length to tarsi.

There is one British species.

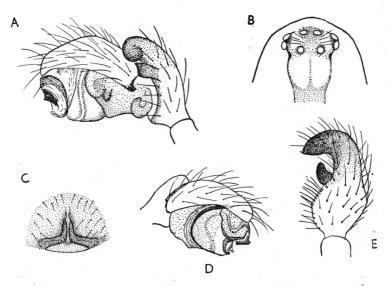

TEXT-FIG. 173.—*Glyphesis cottonae:* A, ♂ palp (from side) ; D, ditto (from inside) ; B, ♂ head (from above) ; C, epigyne ; E, ♂ palpal tibia (from above).

Glyphesis cottonae (La Touche).
(Text-fig. 173, A, B, C, D, E)

Diplocephalus cottoni A. La Touche, 1945, p. 282.

DESCRIPTION. LENGTH : ♀♂ : 1 mm. CARAPACE : Yellow-brown, with blackish striæ and fovea. ♂ : Head edged with black, and elevated somewhat and rounded behind the eyes ; there is a hole, with a short sulcus, behind each posterior lateral eye (Text-fig. 173, B). ♂ : Clypeus somewhat prominent ; there are several short whisker-like hairs in ocular area. EYES : Small. ♀ : Posterior medians 1·5–2 diams. apart. ♂ : Posteriors ca. 2·5 diams. apart. ABDOMEN : Black, somewhat mottled, clothed with short hairs. STERNUM : Yellow or greenish-yellow, suffused or mottled with black ; broadly heart-shaped, with coxæ IV widely separated. LEGS : Tm I 0·44–0·46. Yellow-brown. Tibial spines very short and thin, not much different from hairs. EPIGYNE : Text-fig. 173, C. MALE PALP : Text-fig. 173, A, D, E.

OCCURRENCE : In a swamp near Beaulieu Road Station (Hampshire). Adults in spring, autumn and winter.

53. Genus **ERIGONELLA** F. Dahl 1901.

CHARACTERS OF GENUS. CARAPACE : ♂ : Head elevated, but not into a definite lobe in *E. ignobilis*. STERNUM : Rather rugose, or with small pits. LEGS : Metatarsus IV without a trichobothrium ; Tm I 0·45–0·5. ♀♂ : Tibiæ I–II with two spines (weaker in ♂), tibiæ III–IV with one spine ; position of tibia IV spine ca. 0·28 (♀). Metatarsi only slightly longer than tarsi, with MT I/t I 1·1, MT IV/t IV 1·25–1·3.

There are two British species, readily distinguished by their size, sex organs and male head.

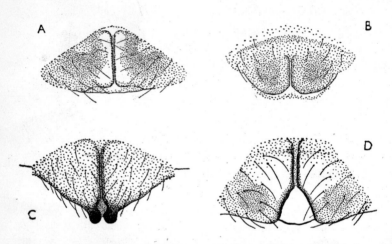

TEXT-FIG. 174.—Epigynes : A, *Erigonella hiemalis;* B, *E. ignobilis;* C, *Savignia frontata;* D, *Diplocephalus cristatus.*

Erigonella hiemalis (Blackwall).
(Text-figs. 174, A ; 175, A, B, F)

Walckenaera hiemalis J. Blackwall, 1841, p. 632, and 1861–4, p. 302 ; O. P.-Cambridge, 1879–81, p. 160. *Troxochrus hiemalis* E. Simon, 1926, p. 370 ; F. Miller, 1947, Tab. 7, fig. 10. *Erigonella hiemalis* J. Denis, 1948, p. 23.

DESCRIPTION. LENGTH : ♀ : 1·65–1·75 mm. ♂ : 1·5 mm. CARAPACE : Brown to dark-brown, with blackish fovea and striæ. ♂ : Head elevated slightly and impressed at sides (Text-fig. 175, F). EYES : ♀ : Anterior medians large (almost as great as remainder), ca. 0·5 diam. apart, and less than one diam. from laterals ; posteriors ca. one diam.

apart. ABDOMEN : Grey to black. STERNUM : Dark-brown to almost black, with large number of small pits. LEGS : Tm I 0·5. Yellow to dark-brown. EPIGYNE : Text-fig. 174, A. MALE PALP : Text-fig. 175, A, B.

OCCURRENCE : Amongst moss and grass, usually in wooded areas. Widespread throughout the British Isles ; fairly frequent. Adults in spring, autumn and winter.

Erigonella ignobilis (O. P.-Cambridge).
(Text-figs. 174, B ; 175, C, D, E, G)

Walckenaera ignobilis O. P.-Cambridge, 1871, p. 457, and 1879–81, p. 155. *Troxochrus ignobilis* E. Simon, 1926, p. 370.

DESCRIPTION. LENGTH : ♀♂ : 1·3–1·4 mm. CARAPACE : Dark reddish-brown to very dark brown, with blackish striæ. ♂ : Head slightly prominent behind eyes, with clypeus produced anteriorly (Text-fig. 175, D, G). Ocular area with numerous short fine hairs. EYES : ♀ : Posteriors slightly more than one diam. apart. ♂ : Posteriors 1·5–1·75 diam. apart. ABDOMEN : Grey to black. STERNUM : Dark-brown, almost black at margins ; with numerous small pits. LEGS : Tm I 0·45. Brown to dark reddish-brown. EPIGYNE : Text-fig. 174, B. MALE PALP : Text-fig. 175, C, E.

OCCURRENCE : In damp, marshy areas. Recorded from the Isle of Wight to the north of England, and from Wales and Eire ; rare. Adults in spring and early summer.

54. Genus SAVIGNIA J. Blackwall 1833.

CHARACTERS OF GENUS. CARAPACE : ♂ : Raised into snout anteriorly. LEGS : Metatarsus IV without a trichobothrium ; Tm I 0·5. Tibiæ I–II with two spines (very minute in ♂), tibiæ III–IV with one spine ; position of tibia IV spine 0·28 (♀). Metatarsi moderately longer than tarsi, with MT I/t I 1·2, MT IV/t IV 1·5.

There is one British species, which is very close to *Diplocephalus* in general structure and in the form of the sex organs.

Savignia frontata Blackwall.
(Text-figs. 174, C ; 176, A, B, C)

Savignia frontata J. Blackwall, 1833, p. 105. *Walckenaera frontata* idem, 1861–4, p. 317 ; O. P.-Cambridge, 1879–81, p. 170. *Savignia frontata* idem, 1894, p. 112, and 1896, p. 60 ; E. Simon, 1926, p. 403.

DESCRIPTION. LENGTH : ♀♂ : 1·5–1·9 mm. CARAPACE : Brown, with darker fovea and striæ. ♂ : Carapace long, raised anteriorly into a snout bearing a tuft of hairs (Text-fig. 176, C). EYES : ♀ : Posteriors ca. one diam. apart. ABDOMEN : Grey to black. STERNUM : Brown, suffused with black at margins. LEGS : Tm I 0·5. Brown. EPIGYNE : Text-fig. 174, C. MALE PALP : Text-fig. 176, A, B.

OCCURRENCE : In a variety of situations, in grass, straw, undergrowth, etc. : a frequent aeronaut. Widespread throughout the British Isles : common. Adults all the year.

55. Genus **DIPLOCEPHALUS** P. Bertkau 1883.

CHARACTERS OF GENUS. CARAPACE: ♂: Head elevated, in a variety of forms. LEGS: Metatarsus IV without a trichobothrium; Tm I 0·46–0·54. ♀: Tibiæ I–II with two spines, tibiæ III–IV with one spine. ♂: Tibial spines reduced and sometimes absent. Metatarsi moderately longer than tarsi, with MT I/t I 1·2–1·3, MT IV/t IV 1·5–1·6. EPIGYNE: All similar in form, with median longitudinal fissure.

There are seven British species. The males are readily separated by the cephalic lobes, the palpal tibiæ and palpal organs. The females are separated by the epigynes, but only with difficulty in some species.

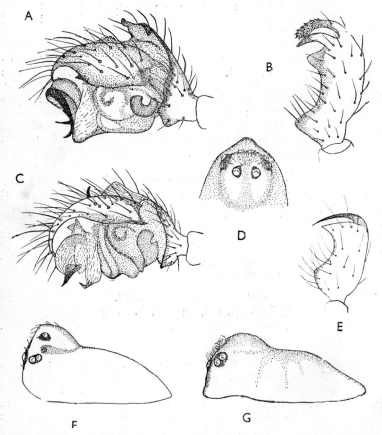

TEXT-FIG. 175.—*Erigonella hiemalis* ♂: A, palp; B, palpal tibia (from above); F, carapace.
E. ignobilis ♂: C, palp; D, head (from above); E, palpal tibia (from above); G, carapace.

Diplocephalus cristatus (Blackwall).
(Text-figs. 174, D ; 176, D, E, F)

Walckenaera cristata J. Blackwall, 1833, p. 107, and 1861–4, p. 309 ; O. P.-Cambridge, 1879–81, p. 152. *Diplocephalus cristatus* C. Chyzer and L. Kulczynski, 1891–7, II, p. 109 ; E. Simon, 1926, p. 376 ; S. C. Bishop and C. R. Crosby, 1935, p. 239 ; B. J. Kaston, 1948, p. 170.

DESCRIPTION. LENGTH : ♀ : 2 mm. ♂ : 1·75 mm. CARAPACE : Brown to dark-brown, with faint blackish striæ. ♂ : Head elevated anteriorly, and divided by a transverse groove (Text-fig. 176, D). EYES : ♀ : Large ; posterior medians ca. 0·7 diam. apart, and 0·5 diam. from laterals. ♂ : Small ; posterior medians rather less than

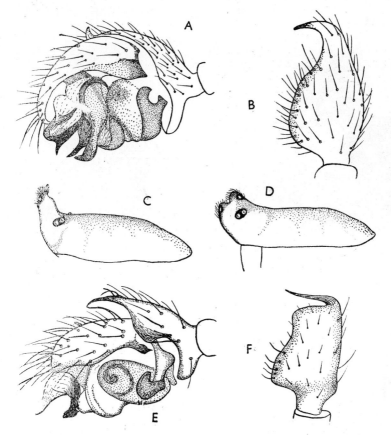

TEXT-FIG. 176.—*Savignia frontata* ♂ : A, palp ; B, palpal tibia (from above) ; C, carapace.
Diplocephalus cristatus ♂ : D, carapace ; E, palp ; F, palpal tibia (from above).

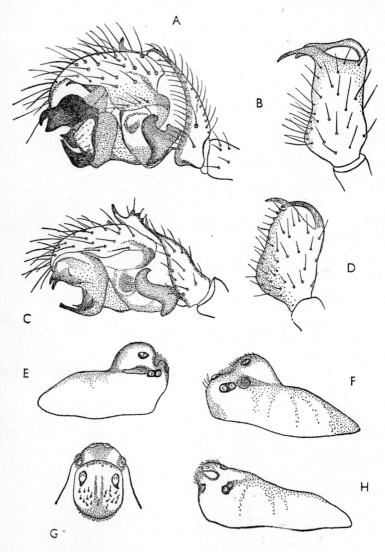

TEXT-FIG. 177.—*Diplocephalus latifrons* ♂ : A, palp ; B, palpal tibia (from above) ; E, carapace ; G, head (from above).
D. adjacens ♂ : C, palp ; D, palpal tibia (from above) ; H, carapace.
D. jacksoni ♂ : F, carapace.

one diam. apart, and 2–3 diams. from laterals. ABDOMEN : Grey to black. STERNUM : Brown to dark-brown, shiny. LEGS : Tm I 0·5–0·54. Orange-brown to brown. ♀ : Tibial spines shorter and weaker than in ♀. EPIGYNE : Text-fig. 174, D ; the plates on either side of the central opening are somewhat variable in shape. The epigyne could be confused with that of *Araeoncus humilis* (p. 298), but the size and the eyes distinguish this. MALE PALP : Text-fig. 176, E, F.

OCCURRENCE : In grass, straw, moss, etc. Has been found in or near ants' nests. Widespread throughout the British Isles ; frequent. Adults throughout the year.

Diplocephalus permixtus (O. P.-Cambridge).
(Text-figs. 178, A, B, C ; 179, H)

Walckenaera permixta O. P.-Cambridge, 1871, p. 455, and 1879–81, p. 153. *Streptosphœnus permixtus* E. Simon, 1926, p. 385.

DESCRIPTION. LENGTH : ♀♂ : 1·5–1·6 mm. CARAPACE : Brown to dark-brown, with faint blackish fovea and striæ. ♂ : Carapace long, and elevated anteriorly, projecting considerably over cheliceræ, with elevation divided by a transverse groove (Text-fig. 178, C) ; a number of short, stiff hairs are present on head and in ocular area. EYES : ♀ : Posterior medians rather less than one diam. apart, and ca. 0·5 diam. from laterals. ♂ : Posterior medians 2·5 diams. apart. ABDOMEN : Grey to black. STERNUM : Yellow-brown to brown, suffused with some black ; shiny. LEGS : Tm I 0·48–0·5. Brown to yellow-brown. ♂ : Tibia I spineless, tibiæ II–IV with one small spine ; patellæ, tibiæ and metatarsi I–II bear large numbers of fine, rather hooked hairs. EPIGYNE : Text-fig. 179, H. MALE PALP : Text-fig. 178, A, B ; the tibial apophysis has at its apex three short, very stout spines, and a number of short stout spines on its outer margin.

OCCURRENCE : In moss, grass, etc., in damp places. Widespread throughout the British Isles ; frequent. Adults most of the year.

Diplocephalus latifrons (O. P.-Cambridge).
(Text-figs. 177, A, B, E, G ; 179, E)

Walckenaera latifrons O. P.-Cambridge, 1863, p. 8694, and 1879–81, p. 161. *Diplocephalus latifrons* C. Chyzer and L. Kulczynski, 1891–7, II, p. 111. *Plœsiocrœrus latifrons* E. Simon, 1926, pp. 380, 381.

DESCRIPTION. LENGTH : ♀♂ : 1·5–1·75 mm. CARAPACE : Brown to reddish brown, with darker fovea and striæ. ♂ : Head raised into large lobe (Text-fig. 177, E, G), deeply impressed at sides ; ocular area with some fine hairs. EYES: ♀ : Posteriors all one diam. or rather less apart. ABDOMEN : Grey to black. STERNUM : Brown, suffused with black on margins ; shiny but slightly reticulated. LEGS : Tm I 0·46–0·48. Brown to orange-brown. ♂ : Tibiæ I–II spineless, tibiæ III–IV with one small spine ; hairs rather like *D. permixtus*. EPIGYNE : Text-fig. 179, E. MALE PALP : Text-fig. 177, A, B.

OCCURRENCE : In undergrowth, grass, straw, garden refuse, etc. Widespread throughout the British Isles ; frequent. Adults throughout the year.

Diplocephalus adjacens O. P.-Cambridge.
(Text-figs. 177, C, D, H ; 179, F)

Diplocephalus adjacens O. P.-Cambridge, 1903, p. 165.

DESCRIPTION. LENGTH : ♀♂ : 1·75–1·9 mm. CARAPACE : Brown, with darker margins. ♂ : Head elevated rather like *D. cristatus*, but with transverse cleft much deeper (Text-fig. 177, H). EYES : ♀ :

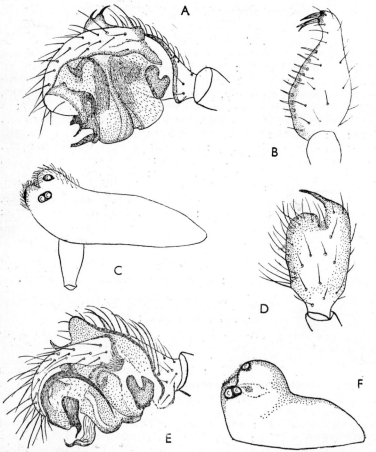

TEXT-FIG. 178.—*Diplocephalus permixtus* ♂ : A, palp ; B, palpal tibia (from above) ; C, carapace.
D. protuberans ♂ : D, palpal tibia (from above) ; E, palp ; F, carapace.

Posterior medians rather less than one diam. apart, and rather more than one diam. from laterals. ABDOMEN : Grey to black. STERNUM : Dark-brown or brown, slightly reticulated. LEGS : Tm I 0·47–0·5. Yellow to brown. ♂ : Tibiæ I–II spineless, tibiæ III–IV with one small spine ; hairs like *D. permixtus*. EPIGYNE : Text-fig. 179, F ; rather similar to *D. latifrons*, the specimens available not being in good enough condition to show any clear distinction between these two species. MALE PALP : Text-fig. 177, C, D ; similar in form to, but quite distinct from, *D. latifrons*.

OCCURRENCE : On the banks of the River Tyne, at Hexham (Northumberland).

Diplocephalus jacksoni O. P.-Cambridge.
(Text-fig. 177, F)

Diplocephalus jacksoni O. P.-Cambridge, 1903, p. 166.

DESCRIPTION. Colour and size as *D. adjacens*. The male palpal organs and tibial apophyses appear to be identical with those of *D. adjacens;* the female corresponding to the male is not distinguishable from *D. adjacens*. The male may be a dimorphic form of *D. adjacens*. CARAPACE : ♂ : Head elevated into fairly large lobe (Text-fig. 177, F), quite different from *D. adjacens*.

OCCURRENCE : In the same place as *D. adjacens*.

Diplocephalus picinus (Blackwall).
(Text-fig. 179, A, B, C, D)

Walckenaera picina J. Blackwall, 1841, p. 640, and 1861–4, p. 313 ; O. P.-Cambridge, 1879–81, p. 163. *Diplocephalus picinus* C. Chyzer and L. Kulczynski, 1891–7, II, p. 112. *Plæsiocrærus picinus* E. Simon, 1926, pp. 380, 382 ; F. Miller, 1947, Tab. 7, fig. 11.

DESCRIPTION. LENGTH : ♀ : 1·5–1·6 mm. ♂ : 1·3–1·5 mm. CARAPACE : Brown to very dark brown, with blackish striæ. ♂ : Head raised and impressed at sides (Text-fig. 179, C) ; ocular area with a few hairs. EYES : ♀ Posterior medians one diam. apart, and rather less than one diam. from laterals. ABDOMEN : Grey to black. STERNUM : Brown to black, shiny. LEGS : Tm I 0·46–0·48. Yellow-brown to brown. ♂ : Tibial spines very minute. EPIGYNE : Text-fig. 179, D. MALE PALP : Text-fig. 179, A, B.

OCCURRENCE : In undergrowth, moss, etc. Widespread throughout the British Isles, but rather local. Adults in spring, autumn and winter.

Diplocephalus protuberans (O. P.-Cambridge).
(Text-figs. 178, D, E, F ; 179, G)

Erigone protuberans O. P.-Cambridge, 1875 (1), p. 218. *Diplocephalus protuberans* idem, 1907, p. 144 ; A. R. Jackson, 1907, p. 3 ; W. Falconer, 1911, p. 284. *Plæsiocrærus protuberans* E. Simon, 1926, pp. 381, 384 ; J. Denis, 1942 (2), p. 82.

DESCRIPTION. LENGTH : ♀ : 2–2·5 mm. ♂ : 2–2·25 mm. Colour as *D. latifrons* and *D. adjacens*. CARAPACE : ♂ : Cephalic lobe (Text-fig. 178, F) similar to *D. latifrons*. EYES : ♀ : Posteriors less than one diam. apart, with medians larger than laterals. LEGS: Spines etc, like *D. adjacens*. EPIGYNE: Text-fig. 179, G; the variability of this could not be assessed because too few specimens were available. MALE PALP: Text-fig. 178, D, E; very characteristic.

OCCURRENCE: A few specimens only have been taken. Amongst moss, near Gibside (Co. Durham); near Slaithwaite (Yorkshire).

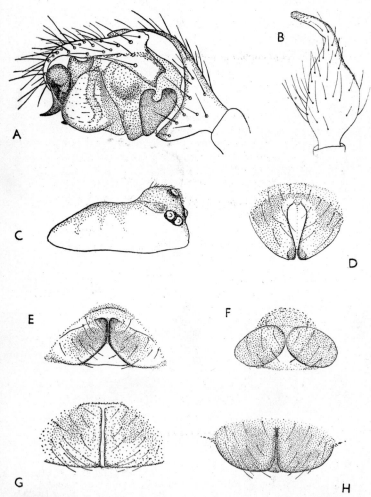

TEXT-FIG. 179.—*Diplocephalus picinus:* A, ♂ palp; B, ♂ palpal tibia (from above); C, ♂ carapace; D, epigyne.
Epigynes: E, *D. latifrons;* F, *D. adjacens;* G, *D. protuberans;* H, *D. permixtus.*

56. Genus **ARAEONCUS** E. Simon 1884.

CHARACTERS OF GENUS. CARAPACE : ♂ : Elevated smoothly anteriorly, but without definite lobe. LEGS : Metatarsus IV without a trichobothrium ; Tm I 0·45–0·48. ♀ : Tibiæ I–II with two spines, tibiæ III–IV with one spine. ♂ : Tibial spines very small or absent, Metatarsi only slightly longer than tarsi, with MT I/t I 1·1–1·25, MT IV/t IV 1·4.

There are two British species, which are separated fairly readily by the sex organs (♀♂) and the form of the head (♂).

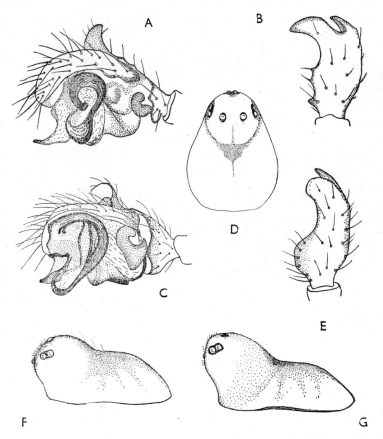

TEXT-FIG. 180.—*Araeoncus humilis* ♂ : A, palp ; B, palpal tibia (from above); D, carapace (from above) ; F, ditto (from side).
A. crassiceps ♂ : C, palp ; E, palpal tibia (from above) ; G, carapace.

X

Araeoncus humilis (Blackwall).

(Text-figs. 180, A, B, D, F ; 181, A, B, C)

Walckenaera humilis J. Blackwall, 1841, p. 636, and 1861–4, p. 307 ; O. P.-Cambridg 1879–81, p. 150. *Diplocephalus humilis* C. Chyzer and L. Kulczynski, 1891–7, I p. 111. *Araeoncus humilis* E. Simon, 1926, p. 367 ; F. Miller, 1947, Tab. 6, fig. 6 J. Denis, 1948, p. 19.

DESCRIPTION. LENGTH : ♀♂: 1·5–1·6 mm. CARAPACE : Browr with blackish fovea and striæ. ♂ : Whole head rather raised (Text-fig 180, D, F). EYES : ♀ : Posteriors all ca. one diam. or more apart anterior medians only slightly smaller than posterior median ABDOMEN : Grey to blackish. STERNUM : Brown, suffused wit some black. LEGS : Tm I 0·45. Yellow-brown to brown. ♂ : Tibi I–IV with one spine, spines on I and II often small and inconspicuous tibia I with numerous short, stout, hooked bristles. EPIGYNE : Tex fig. 181, A, B, C, rather variable, and similar to *Diplocephalı cristatus*. MALE PALP : Text-fig. 180, A, B.

OCCURRENCE : In moss, grass, straw, undergrowth, etc. ; a frequer aeronaut. Widespread throughout the British Isles ; fairly commor Adults at most seasons.

Araeoncus crassiceps (Westring).

(Text-figs. 180, C, E, G ; 181, D)

Erigone crassiceps N. Westring, 1861, p. 231. *Walckenaera crassiceps* O. P.-Can bridge, 1879–81, p. 151. *Arœoncus crassiceps* W. Falconer, 1911, p. 284 ; E. Simo 1926, p. 368.

DESCRIPTION. LENGTH : ♀♂: 1·8–2 mm. CARAPACE : Brown t dark brown, with blackish striæ and fovea. ♂ : Whole head raisec very protuberant anteriorly (Text-fig. 180, G). EYES : ♀ : Posterior 1·5–1·75 diams. apart. ABDOMEN : Grey to black. STERNUM : Dar brown suffused with black ; shiny. LEGS : Tm I 0·46–0·48. Yellow brown to brown. ♂ : Tibial spines absent ; hairs short and rathe hooked. EPIGYNE : Text-fig. 181, D. MALE PALP : Text-fig. 18(C, E.

OCCURRENCE : In moss and grass, in swampy areas. Widesprea throughout the British Isles ; rare.

57. Genus PANAMOMOPS E. Simon 1884.

CHARACTERS OF GENUS. CARAPACE : ♂ : Truncated anteriorl with a little horn on each fore-corner. EYES : Rather small. LEGS Metatarsus IV without a trichobothrium ; Tm I 0·42. ♀♂: Tibi I–II with two spines, tibiæ III–IV with one spine ; position of tib: IV spine 0·28 (♀). Metatarsi only slightly longer than tarsi, wit MT I/t I 1·1, MT IV/t IV ca. 1·2.

There is one British species.

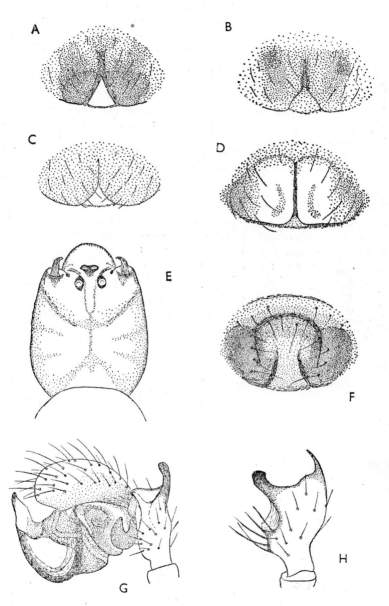

TEXT-FIG. 181.—Epigynes : A, B, C, *Araeoncus humilis;* D, *A. crassiceps.*
Panamomops sulcifrons: E, ♂ carapace (from above) ; F, epigyne ; G, ♂ palp ;
H, ♂ palpal tibia (from above).

Panamomops sulcifrons (Wider).
(Text-fig. 181, E, F, G, H)

Theridion sulcifrons Wider, 1834, p. 231. *Neriene bicuspis* O. P.-Cambridge, 1879–81, p. 139. *Panamomops bicuspis* W. Bosenberg, 1901–3, p. 179. *P. sulcifrons* E. Simon, 1926, p. 349.

DESCRIPTION. LENGTH : ♀ : 1·4–1·5 mm. ♂ : 1·2–1·3 mm. CARAPACE : Brown, with faint black fovea and striæ. ♂ : Head (Text-fig. 181, E) ; clypeus projecting anteriorly. EYES : Rather small. ♀ : Posterior medians rather more than one diam. apart, and ca. 1·5 diam. from laterals. ABDOMEN : Greyish brown to black. STERNUM : Yellow to brown, suffused with a variable amount of black. LEGS : Tm I 0·42. Yellow-brown to brown. EPIGYNE : Text-fig. 181, F. MALE PALP : Text-fig. 181, G, H.

OCCURRENCE : In straw, undergrowth, grass ; occasionally in gardens. Recorded in England from the south coast to Northumberland ; very local. Adults in autumn and spring, males mainly in spring.

58. Genus LESSERTIA F. P. Smith 1908.

CHARACTERS OF GENUS. CARAPACE : ♂ : Head not elevated into lobe. CHELICERÆ : ♂ : With strong tooth anteriorly. LEGS : Metatarsus IV without a trichobothrium ; Tm I 0·36. ♀♂ : Tibiæ I–III with two spines, tibia IV with one spine ; tibia IV spine long (ca. three diams. of segment), position ca. 0·25. Metatarsi much longer than tarsi, with MT I/t I 1·6, MT IV/t IV 1·9.

There is one British species.

Lessertia dentichelis (Simon).
(Text-fig. 182, A, B, C)

Tmeticus dentichelis E. Simon, 1884, p. 390. *T. simplex* F. O. P.-Cambridge, 1892, p. 384. *Lessertia dentichelis* E. Simon, 1926, p. 473.

DESCRIPTION. LENGTH : ♀♂ : 2·75–3·5 mm. CARAPACE : Brown to orange-brown. EYES : Posteriors one diam. or slightly more apart. ABDOMEN : Grey to whitish-grey, with fairly long hairs. STERNUM : Yellow-brown, pointed posteriorly, with coxæ IV not widely separated. CHELICERÆ : ♂ : With a large pointed tooth anteriorly, towards apex ; a number of small warts, each bearing a hair, are also present. MAXILLÆ : ♂ : With 4–5 little warts, each bearing a black hair. LEGS : Tm I 0·36. Brown to yellow-brown. EPIGYNE : Text-fig. 182, B. MALE PALP : Text-fig. 182, A, C.

OCCURRENCE : In caves, mines, sewers, etc. ; also amongst marram grass on sandhills. Widespread throughout the British Isles, but probably more frequent in the south ; rather local.

59. Genus ASTHENARGUS E. Simon and L. Fage 1922.

CHARACTERS OF GENUS. CARAPACE : ♂ : Head not elevated into lobe. EYES : Rather large, and fairly close together. LEGS : Metatarsus IV without a trichobothrium ; Tm I 0·35. ♀♂ : Tibiæ

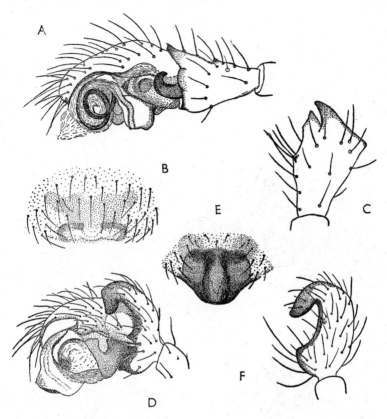

TEXT-FIG. 182.—*Lessertia dentichelis:* A, ♂ palp; B, epigyne; C, ♂ palpal tibia (from above).
Asthenargus paganus: D, ♂ palp; E, epigyne; F, ♂ palpal tibia (from above).

I–III with two spines, tibia IV with one spine; position of tibia IV spine 0·22. Metatarsi not much longer than tarsi, with MT I/t I 1·0–1·2, MT IV/t IV 1·1–1·3.

There is one British species.

Asthenargus paganus (Simon).
(Text-fig. 182, D, E, F)

Gongylidiellum paganum E. Simon, 1884, p. 602; O. P.-Cambridge, 1903, p. 165, and 1908, p. 175; A. R. Jackson, 1908, p. 62. *Asthenargus paganus* E. Simon, 1926, p. 459.

DESCRIPTION. LENGTH: ♀♂: 1·25–1·5 mm. CARAPACE: Pale yellow-brown, with slightly darker striæ; there are a few forward-directed spines in median line. EYES: ♀♂: Posteriors ca. one diam.

apart, or slightly less. ABDOMEN : Pale whitish grey to grey, clothed with fairly long hairs. STERNUM : Pale yellow, reticulated with black. LEGS : Tm I 0·35. Pale yellow to yellow-brown. EPIGYNE : Text-fig. 182, E. MALE PALP : Text-fig. 182, D, F.

OCCURRENCE : In moss and grass, usually in woods. Recorded from a few English counties from Warwickshire to Yorkshire, and from North Wales and Eire ; very local. Adults in autumn, winter and spring.

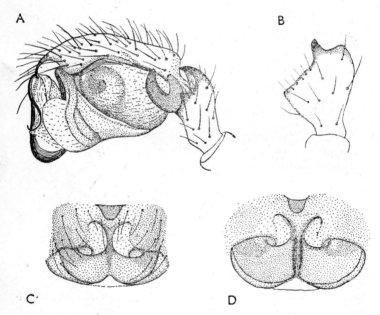

TEXT-FIG. 183.—*Caledonia evansi:* A, ♂ palp ; B, ♂ palpal tibia (from above) ; C, D, epigyne.

60. Genus **CALEDONIA** O. P.-Cambridge 1894.

CHARACTERS OF GENUS. CARAPACE : ♂ : Head elevated smoothly, but without a definite lobe. EYES : Small, and widely spaced. LEGS : Metatarsus IV without a trichobothrium ; Tm I ca. 0·5. ♀♂ : Tibiæ I–III with two spines, tibia IV with one spine ; position of tibia IV spine ca. 0·33. Metatarsi moderately longer than tarsi, with MT I/ t I 1·2, MT IV/t IV 1·5.

There is one British species.

Caledonia evansi O. P.-Cambridge.
(Text-figs. 183, A, B, C, D ; 184, E)

Caledonia evansi O. P.-Cambridge, 1894 (2), p. 18, and 1894 (1), p. 111 ; J. Braende-gaard, 1946, p. 43.

DESCRIPTION. LENGTH : ♀ : 1·8–2 mm. ♂ : 1·75–1·8 mm. CARAPACE : Yellow to brown. ♂ : Head elevated roundly, with anterior median eyes on front (Text-fig. 184, E) ; ocular area with some fine hairs. EYES : ♀ : Posterior medians 1·5–2 diam. apart, and ca. 1·5 diam. from laterals. ♂ : Rather more widely spaced. ABDOMEN : Grey. STERNUM : Brown, suffused with black. LEGS : Tm I 0·5. Brown to yellow. EPIGYNE : Text-fig. 183, C, D. MALE PALP : Text-fig. 183, A, B.

OCCURRENCE : In grass and heather, and under stones. In Scottish and northern English counties ; frequent locally.

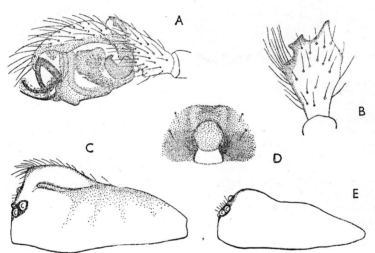

TEXT-FIG. 184.—*Typhocrestus digitatus:* A, ♂ palp ; B, ♂ palpal tibia (from above) ; C, ♂ carapace ; D, epigyne.
Caledonia evansi ♂ : E, carapace.

61. Genus TYPHOCRESTUS E. Simon 1884.

CHARACTERS OF GENUS. CARAPACE : ♂ : Head with shallow lobe. EYES : Rather small. LEGS : Metatarsus IV without a trichobothrium ; Tm I 0·42 (♂), 0·47 (♀). ♀ : Tibiæ I–III with two spines, tibia IV with one spine ; position of tibia IV spine ca. 0·3. ♂ : Tibiæ I–II spineless, tibiæ III–IV with one small spine. Metatarsi scarcely longer than tarsi, with MT I/t I 1·0–1·1.

There is one British species.

Typhocrestus digitatus (O. P.-Cambridge).
(Text-fig. 184, A, B, C, D)

Erigone digitata O. P.-Cambridge, 1872 (1), p. 758. *Typhocrestus digitatus* A. R. Jackson, 1908, p. 64 ; O. P.-Cambridge, 1908, p. 177 ; E. Simon, 1926, p. 396 ; Å. Holm, 1943, Fig. 6a–d ; F. Miller, 1947, Tab. 6, fig. 9.

DESCRIPTION. LENGTH : ♀♂ : 1·3–1·5 mm. CARAPACE : Yellow-brown, with blackish striæ and fovea ; rather long, broad anteriorly. ♂ : Head elevated fairly sharply behind posterior median eyes, and compressed at sides (Text-fig. 184, C). EYES : Posteriors rather more

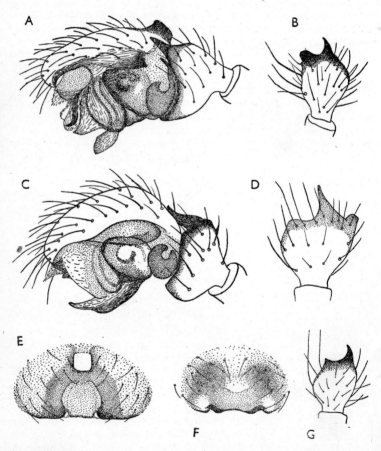

TEXT-FIG. 185.—*Collinsia distincta:* A, ♂ palp ; B, ♂ palpal tibia (from above and outside) ; G, ditto (from above) ; F, epigyne.
C. holmgreni: C, ♂ palp ; D, ♂ palpal tibia (from above) ; E, epigyne.

than one diam. apart. ABDOMEN : Grey. STERNUM : Blackish yellow, finely reticulated. LEGS : Tm I 0·47 (♀), 0·42 (♂). Yellow-brown. EPIGYNE : Text-fig. 184, D. MALE PALP : Text-fig. 184, A, B.

OCCURRENCE : Sandhills, sandy places, and moorland : occasionally in woods. Widespread throughout the British Isles ; common locally. Adults in autumn and winter.

62. Genus **COLLINSIA** O. P.-Cambridge 1913.

CHARACTERS OF GENUS. CARAPACE : ♂ : Head not elevated into lobe. LEGS : Metatarsus IV without a trichobothrium ; Tm I 0·4–0·56. ♀♂ : Tibiæ I–III with two spines, tibia IV with one spine ; position of tibia IV spine 0·28–0·31. Metatarsi moderately longer than tarsi, with MT I/t I 1·3, MT IV/t IV 1·5–1·6.

There are two British species (*C. holmgreni* is confined to the highlands and northern parts of Scotland), which are readily distinguished by the sex organs.

Collinsia distincta (Simon).
(Text-fig. 185, A, B, F, G)

Gongylidium distinctum E. Simon, 1884, p. 497 ; O. P.-Cambridge. 1903, p. 164. *Coryphæolanus distinctus* E. Simon, 1926, p. 475. *Collinsia notabilis* O. P.-Cambridge, 1913, p. 136. *C. distincta* Å. Holm, 1950, p. 138.

DESCRIPTION. LENGTH : ♀♂ : About 2 mm. CARAPACE : Yellow-brown, with faint striæ ; there are a few hairs in ocular area. EYES : ♀♂ : Posteriors ca. one diam. apart, or rather less. ABDOMEN : Mottled greyish black. STERNUM : Mottled yellow-brown. CHELICERÆ : ♂ : With small wart anteriorly, bearing a bristle. LEGS : Tm I 0·41–0·44. Yellow-brown. EPIGYNE : Text-fig. 185. F. MALE PALP : Text-fig. 185, A, B, G.

OCCURRENCE : In damp places. Widespread in England ; rare.

Collinsia holmgreni (Thorell).
(Text-fig. 185, C, D, E)

Erigone holmgreni T. Thorell, 1871 (2), p. 691. *Coryphæus mendicus* A. R. Jackson, 1914, p. 127 ; O. P.-Cambridge, 1914, p. 132. *Coryphæolana holmgreni* J. Braendegaard, 1940, p. 14, and 1946, p. 44.

DESCRIPTION. LENGTH : ♀ : 2·25–2·5 mm. ♂ : About 2 mm. CARAPACE : Yellow-brown to brown, with slightly darker striæ. EYES : ♀♂ : Posteriors all rather more than one diam. apart. ABDOMEN : Grey to black. STERNUM : Yellow, suffused and reticulated with much black. LEGS : Tm I 0·56. Brown. EPIGYNE : Text-fig. 185, E. MALE PALP : Text-fig. 185, C. D.

OCCURRENCE : At high altitudes in the Scottish Highlands and in Skye. Adults in autumn and early summer.

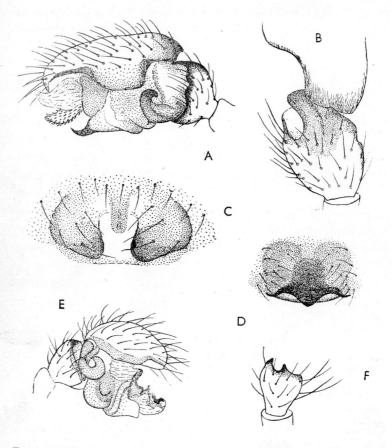

Text-fig. 186.—*Scotargus inerrans:* A, ♂ palp ; B, ♂ palpal tibia (from above) ; C, epigyne.
Diplocentria bidentata: D, epigyne ; E, ♂ palp (right) ; F, ♂ palpal tibia (right, from above).

63. Genus **SCOTARGUS** E. Simon 1913.

Characters of Genus. Carapace : ♂ : Head not elevated into lobe. Cheliceræ : ♂ : With small wart anteriorly. Legs : Metatarsus IV without a trichobothrium ; Tm I 0·4. ♀♂ : Tibiæ I–III with two spines, tibia IV with one spine ; position of tibia IV spine ca. 0·25. Metatarsi moderately longer than tarsi, with MT I/t I 1·25, MT IV/t IV 1·45.

There is one British species.

Scotargus inerrans (O. P.-Cambridge).
(Text-fig. 186, A, B, C)

Neriene inerrans O. P.-Cambridge, 1884, p. 11. *Tmeticus fortunatus* idem, 1895, p. 123, and 1907, p. 142. *Scotargus inerrans* E. Simon, 1926, p. 471.

DESCRIPTION. LENGTH : ♀: 2–2·5 mm. ♂ : 2 mm. CARAPACE : Brown, with darker fovea and striæ, and rather darker on head. EYES : ♀♂ : Posteriors ca. one diam. apart. ABDOMEN : Black. STERNUM : Brown, suffused with much black. CHELICERÆ : ♂ : With small wart anteriorly. LEGS : Tm I ca. 0·4. Brown to yellow-brown, sometimes suffused with black. EPIGYNE : Text-fig. 186, C ; has a central scape-like process. MALE PALP : Text-fig. 186, A, B.

OCCURRENCE : In wet meadows ; on sandhills amongst marram grass. Recorded only from the southern counties of England, and (?) Scotland ; rare. Adult in May-July.

64. Genus **DIPLOCENTRIA** J. E. Hull 1911.

CHARACTERS OF GENUS. CARAPACE : ♂ : Head not elevated into lobe. EYES : Large, all scarcely more than 0·5 diam. apart. LEGS : Metatarsus IV without a trichobothrium ; Tm I 0·56. ♀♂ : Tibiæ I–III with two spines, tibia IV with one spine ; position of tibia IV spine ca. 0·26. Metatarsi moderately longer than tarsi, with MT I/ t I 1·2, MT IV/t IV 1·7.
There is one British species.

Diplocentria bidentata (Emerton).
(Text-fig. 186, D, E, F)

Tmeticus bidentatus E. Emerton, 1882, p. 56. *Tmeticus rivalis* O. P.-Cambridge, 1905, p. 61. *Diplocentria rivalis* J. E. Hull, 1911 (1), p. 581. *D. torrentum* E. Simon, 1929, p. 642. *D. bidentata* Å. Holm, 1945, p. 19 ; J. Denis, 1947 (2), p. 80. *Scotoussa bidentata* C. R. Crosby and S. C. Bishop, 1938, p. 87 ; B. J. Kaston, 1948, p. 212.

DESCRIPTION. LENGTH : ♀: 2–2·2 mm. ♂ : 1·8 mm. CARAPACE : Yellow-brown. EYES : ♀♂ : Anteriors all ca. 0·5 diam. apart ; posteriors all rather less than 0·5 diam. apart. ABDOMEN : Grey. STERNUM : Yellow, suffused with some black. LEGS : Tm I 0·56. Yellow-brown to brown. EPIGYNE : Text-fig. 186, D. MALE PALP : Text-fig. 186, E, F.

OCCURRENCE : In moss, grass, under stones, often in woods ; sometimes on mountains. Recorded from a few northern English counties, Scotland and Eire ; very local. Adults in autumn and winter.

65. Genus **ERIGONE** V. Audouin 1826.

CHARACTERS OF GENUS. CARAPACE : Margins toothed, particularly in ♂. ♂ : Head somewhat raised, but with no definite lobe. CHELI-CERÆ : Robust, with warts and teeth anteriorly, particularly in ♂. MAXILLÆ : ♂ : With warts. LEGS : Metatarsus IV without a tricho-bothrium : Tm I 0·42–0·5. ♀♂ : Tibiæ I–III with two spines, tibia IV with one spine ; position of tibia IV spine 0·26–0·3. Metatarsi

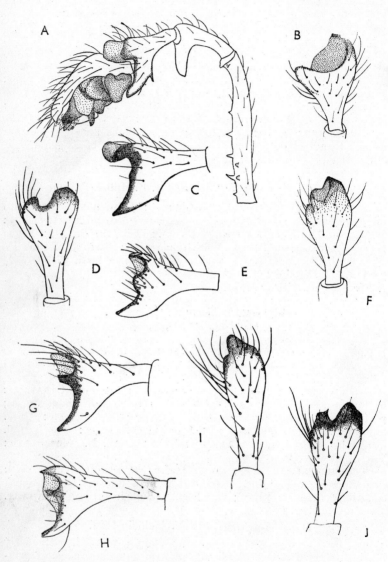

TEXT-FIG. 187.—A, *Erigone dentipalpis* ♂ : Palp.
Male palpal tibiæ (from above) : B, *E. dentipalpis*; D, *E. atra*; F, *E. promiscua*;
I, *E. longipalpis*; J, *E. arctica*.
Male palpal tibiæ (from side) : C, *E. promiscua*; E, *E. atra*; G, *E. arctica*;
H, *E. longipalpis*.

moderately longer than tarsi, with MT I/t I 1·3–1·4, MT IV/t IV ca. 1·6. EPIGYNES : Of closely similar form (but *E. vagans* is somewhat anomalous). MALE PALP : With well-defined ventral patellar apophysis apically. Femora with warty teeth ventrally. Palpal organs all of similar type.

There are nine British species, which can be separated by consideration of the epigynes (♀), and the palpal tibia and patella (♂). For general discussions of this genus, see Kulczynski (1902), Jackson (1910, 1930), Crosby and Bishop (1928) and Braendegaard (1940).

Erigone dentipalpis (Wider).
(Text-figs. 187, A, B ; 189, A, C, D)

Theridion dentipalpis Wider, 1834, p. 248. *Neriene dentipalpis* O. P.-Cambridge, 1879–81, p. 108. *Erigone dentipalpis* C. Chyzer and L. Kulczynski, 1891–7, II, p. 91 ; L. Kulczynski, 1902, p. 539 ; A. R. Jackson, 1910, p. 143 ; E. Simon, 1926, pp. 445, 446 ; F. Miller, 1947, Tab. 8, fig. 1.

DESCRIPTION. LENGTH : ♀♂ : 1·8–2·5 mm. CARAPACE : ♀ : Yellow-brown to brown, with darker striæ and fovea ; very minute wart-like teeth on lateral margins. ♂ : Dark chestnut-brown, with black striæ and blackish margins ; head somewhat raised, and suffused with black ; lateral borders with distinct teeth. EYES : ♀ : Fairly large ; anterior medians scarcely smaller than posterior medians. Posterior medians ca. one diam. apart, and ca. 1·5 diam. from laterals. ♂ : Posterior medians rather more than one diam. apart. ABDOMEN : Grey to black. LEGS : Tm I 0·42–0·45. Yellow-brown to brown. STERNUM : Blackish-brown, slightly reticulated. CHELICERÆ : ♀ : With small warts anteriorly, bearing short fine hairs. ♂ : With more pronounced warts. MAXILLÆ : ♂ : With a few warts. EPIGYNE : Text-fig. 189, A, C, D ; readily distinguished from *E. atra* when viewed from in front or from behind. MALE PALP : Text-fig. 187, A, B ; the femur has some small knobs or teeth extending from base to one-half or two-thirds of length. Tibia usually with pronounced tooth beneath.

OCCURRENCE : Universally distributed, and one of our commonest spiders ; a common aeronaut. Adults the whole year.

Erigone atra (Blackwall).
(Text-figs. 187, D, E ; 189, B, E, H)

Neriene atra J. Blackwall, 1841, p. 195 ; O. P.-Cambridge, 1879–81, p. 106. *Neriene longipalpis* (in part) J. Blackwall, 1861–4, p. 274. *Erigone atra* C. Chyzer and L. Kulczynski, 1891–7, II, p. 90 ; L. Kulczynski, 1902, p. 539 ; A. R. Jackson, 1910, p. 143 ; E. Simon, 1926, pp. 444, 445 ; C. R. Crosby and S. C. Bishop, 1928, p. 15 ; F. Miller, 1947, Tab. 7, fig. 9 ; B. J. Kaston, 1948, p. 189.

DESCRIPTION. LENGTH : ♀♂ : 2–2·5 mm. Colour as *E. dentipalpis*, from which it differs only as follows : CARAPACE : ♀ : Usually with no teeth on lateral borders. CHELICERÆ : ♀ : No small warts present. MAXILLÆ : ♂ : With only a few very minute warts. LEGS : Tm I 0·4–0·45. EPIGYNE : Text-fig. 189, B, E, H ; readily distinguished from *E. dentipalpis* when viewed from behind or in front. MALE

PALP : Text-fig. 187, D, E ; the femur has teeth extending to about two-thirds of its length. The tibia usually has no tooth beneath, but occasionally a vestigial one is present.

OCCURRENCE : Universally distributed, and as common as *E. dentipalpis;* a common aeronaut. Adults the whole year.

Erigone promiscua (O. P.-Cambridge).
(Text-figs. 187, C, F ; 189, F)

Neriene promiscua O. P.-Cambridge, 1872 (2), p. 449, and 1879–81, p. 482. *Erigone promiscua* L. Kulczynski, 1902, p. 539 ; O. P.-Cambridge, 1905, p. 50 ; A. R. Jackson, 1910, p. 143 ; E. Simon, 1926, p. 445.

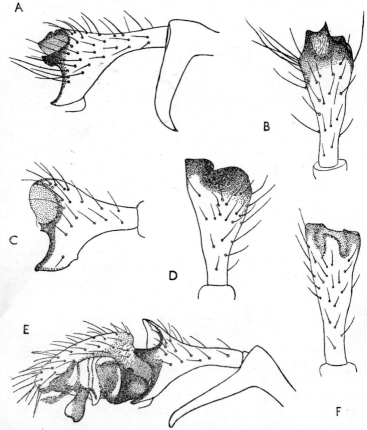

Text-fig. 188.—Male palp (or tibia) (from side) : A, *Erigone tirolensis;* C, *E. capra;* E, *E. welchi.*
  Male palpal tibia (from above) : B, *E. tirolensis;* D, *E. capra* (right) ; F, *E. welchi.*

DESCRIPTION. LENGTH : ♀♂ : About 2–2·2 mm. Colour and form as *E. dentipalpis*, from which it differs as follows : CARAPACE : ♂ : Large teeth on margins. EPIGYNE : Females caught in company with males of this species have the epigyne shown in Text-fig. 189, F ; seen squarely from below, this appears identical with *E. dentipalpis*, but when seen from behind slight differences appear. Whether these differences are constant is not certain. MALE PALP : Text-fig. 187, C, F ; clearly distinct from *E. dentipalpis* in the form of the tibia, and there are slight differences in the palpal organs. The tibia has usually (but not invariably) a small tooth ventrally ; the femur has fewer teeth ventrally than in *E. dentipalpis*.

OCCURRENCE : In similar situations to *E. dentipalpis* and *E. atra*, but much less common. Widespread throughout the British Isles, but there seem to be more records from the northern part of the country. Adults in summer.

Erigone arctica (White).
(Text-figs. 187, G, J ; 189, G, J)

Micryphantes arcticus A. White, 1852, fig. 11–12. *Erigone arctica* L. Kulczynski, 1902, p. 542 ; O. P.-Cambridge, 1905, p. 49 ; A. R. Jackson, 1910, p. 143, and 1934, fig. 13–14 ; C. R. Crosby and S. C. Bishop, 1928, p. 12 ; J. Braendegaard, 1940, p. 28.

DESCRIPTION. LENGTH : ♀ : 2·3–2·75 mm. ♂ : About 2·5 mm. Colour and form as *E. dentipalpis*, from which it differs as follows : CHELICERÆ : ♀ : Three or four small warts basally, on outside. ♂ : With pronounced warts. LEGS : Tm I 0·5. EPIGYNE : Text-fig. 189, G, J. MALE PALP : Text-fig. 187, G, J ; this shows the variety *maritima* Kulczynski (1902, p. 539) which differs from the type only in the absence of a very small tooth beneath the tibia, and in having the tibia somewhat shorter (this is very probably a case of allometric growth).

OCCURRENCE : It is usually the var. *maritima* which is found in Britain, though the typical form has occurred occasionally. On the sides of tidal estuaries, and on the seashore, amongst stones and seaweed. Widespread throughout the British Isles, and common locally. Adult in spring, summer and autumn.

Erigone longipalpis (Sundevall).
(Text-figs. 187, H, I ; 189, I, L)

Linyphia longipalpis C. J. Sundevall, 1830 (1829), p. 213, and 1832 (1831), p. 259. *Neriene longipalpis* O. P.-Cambridge, 1879–81, p. 107. *Erigone longipalpis* L. Kulczynski, 1902, p. 541 ; A. R. Jackson, 1910, p. 143 ; E. Simon, 1926, p. 446.

DESCRIPTION. LENGTH : ♀♂ : 2·5–3·5 mm. As *E. dentipalpis* except for the following : EYES : ♀ : Posterior medians ca. 1·5 diam. apart, and 1·5–2 diam. from laterals. CHELICERÆ : ♀ : A row of warts extends along practically the whole length, anterio-laterally. ♂ : With numerous small warts anteriorly. LEGS : Tm I 0·5. Trochanter and femur I with a few small teeth. EPIGYNE : Text-fig. 189, I, L. MALE PALP : Text-fig. 187, H, I ; femur with teeth and

warts extending to practically the whole length, and with a fairly
large tooth apically. No tooth beneath tibia.

OCCURRENCE : In wet places, and on tidal estuaries, occasionally
mixed with *E. arctica*. Widespread throughout the British Isles, but
uncommon. Adults in spring and autumn.

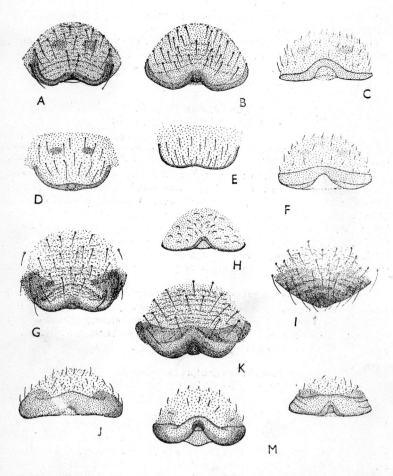

Text-fig. 189.—Epigynes : A, *Erigone dentipalpis;* C, ditto (from behind) ; D,
ditto (from in front) ; B, *E. atra;* E, ditto (from in front) ; H, ditto (from behind) ;
F, *E. promiscua* (from behind) ; G, *E. arctica;* J, ditto (from behind) ; I, *E.
longipalpis;* L, ditto (from behind) ; K, *E. tirolensis;* M, ditto (from behind).

Erigone tirolensis L. Koch.
(Text-figs. 188, A, B ; 189, K, M)

Erigone tirolensis L. Koch, 1872, p. 277 ; C. Chyzer and L. Kulczynski, 1891–7, II, p. 90 ; L. Kulczynski, 1902, p. 550 ; A. R. Jackson, 1914, p. 126, and 1934, fig. 15 ; E. Simon, 1926, pp. 443, 447 ; J. Braendegaard, 1940, pp. 20, 27.

DESCRIPTION. LENGTH : ♀♂ ; about 2·5 mm. As *E. dentipalpis*, except for the following :—CHELICERÆ : ♂ : With 6–7 fairly large warty teeth anteriorly. LEGS : Tm I 0·42. Yellow-brown, suffused with some black. EPIGYNE : Text-fig. 189, K, M. MALE PALP : Text-fig. 188, A, B ; femur with warty teeth extending to practically whole length. No tooth beneath tibia.

OCCURRENCE : In the Scottish Highlands, around 4,000 feet altitude. Adults in summer and autumn.

Erigone capra Simon.
(Text-figs. 188, C, D ; 190, D)

Erigone capra E. Simon, 1884, p. 5 29 ; L. Kulczynski, 1902, p. 541 ; A. R. Jackson, 1910, p. 142 ; E. Simon, 1926, p. 444.

DESCRIPTION. LENGTH : ♀♂ : 2.25–2.5 mm. Similar to the above species. CARAPACE : Brown to orange-brown. LEGS : Tm I 0.43–0.46. EPIGYNE : Text-fig. 190, D. MALE PALP : Text-fig. 188, C, D ; femur with warty teeth extending to about halfway from base.

OCCURRENCE : Found on one occasion only (October 1909), on the banks of the Ulster Canal, near Monaghan, Eire.

Erigone welchi Jackson.
(Text-figs. 188, E, F ; 190, E)

Erigone welchi A. R. Jackson, 1911 (2), p. 28 ; O. P.-Cambridge, 1911, p. 41 ; Å. Holm, 1951, p. 141.

DESCRIPTION. LENGTH : ♀♂ : 2·5 mm. CARAPACE : Orange-brown, with fairly large teeth on borders. CHELICERÆ : With a longitudinal row of seven warty teeth anteriorly. LEGS : Tm I ca. 0·4 : Yellow-brown. ♂ : Femur I with several teeth ventrally. MALE PALP : Text-fig. 188, E, F ; femur with long warty teeth, extending to only about one-third of its length. EPIGYNE : Text-fig. 190, E.

OCCURRENCE : Found on one occasion only (September 1908), not far from the sea coast, near Bunbeg, County Donegal, Eire.

Erigone vagans Audouin.
(Text-fig. 190, A, B, C)

Erigone vagans V. Audouin, 1827, Tab. 1, fig. 9. *Neriene spinosa* O. P.-Cambridge, 1872 (1), p. 292. *Erigone spinosa* idem, 1908, p. 175, and 1909, p. 106. *E. vagans* L. Kulczynski, 1902, p. 539 ; E. Simon, 1926, pp. 442, 446 ; J. Denis, 1948 (2), p. 588 ; and 1950, p. 96.

DESCRIPTION. LENGTH : ♀♂ : 2·25–2·5 mm. Colour similar to the other species of the genus. CARAPACE : ♀ : Margins practically toothless. ♂ : Margins strongly dentate. EYES : ♀♂ : Posteriors all ca. 1–1·25 diam. apart. Anterior medians as large as posterior

Y

medians. CHELICERÆ: ♀: With small warts anteriorly. ♂: Wit▶
very large pointed warts, and some smaller ones, anteriorly. MAXIL▶
LÆ: ♂: With numerous warts. LEGS: Tm I ca. 0·45. ♂: Femor▶
(and sometimes coxæ and trochanters) I–II with a few pointed warty
teeth ventrally. EPIGYNE: Text-fig. 190, C; quite distinct in appear
ance from the other species of the genus. MALE PALP: Text-fig. 190
A, B; the tarsus and palpal organs are smaller than in the othe▶
speeies. The patellar apophysis is long, curved and tapering. Th▶
length of the patella and tibia varies, and in the true *vagans* for▶
(Denis, 1948) they are somewhat shorter than in Text-fig. 190, A, whil▶
in the var. *spinosa* Cambridge they are somewhat longer. Howeve▶
amongst numerous specimens taken at Finchley (London) there wer▶
intermediates between the two extreme forms, and it seems likely tha▶

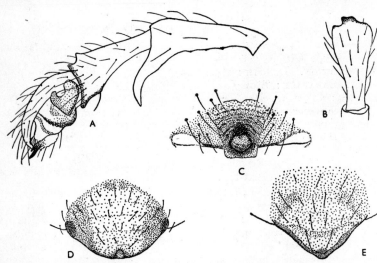

Text-fig. 190.—*Erigone vagans* ♂: A, Palp; B, Palpal tibia (from above.) *Epigynes*
C, *E. vagans*; D, *E. capra*; E, *E. welchi*.

the male of *E. vagans* exhibits allometric growth (according to ▶
suggestion made by Mr. A. D. Blest). The *spinosa* form has more an▶
larger warts than the true *vagans*.

OCCURRENCE: Near Hull (Yorkshire) on salt flats; Staffordshire
and in Finchley (London), where it has been found swarming in sewa▶
filter beds. Adult in autumn and spring.

66. Genus **RHAEBOTHORAX** E. Simon 1926.

CHARACTERS OF GENUS. CARAPACE: ♂: Head not elevated in▶
lobe. ABDOMEN: ♂: Branchial opercula very rugose, with strid▶
lating ridges, coxæ IV having corresponding stridulating point. LEGS▶
Metatarsus IV without a trichobothrium; Tm I 0·7–0·77. ♀▶

Tibiæ I–III with two spines (rather weaker in ♂), tibia IV with one spine ; position of tibia IV spine ca. 0·33. Metatarsi not much longer than tarsi, with MT I/t I ca. 1·1, MT IV/t IV ca. 1·5.

There is one British species.

Rhaebothorax morulus (O. P.-Cambridge).
(Text-figs. 191, A, B ; 192, A, C)

Neriene morula O. P.-Cambridge, 1873 (1), p. 545, and 1879–81, p. 494. *Styloctetor uncinus* idem, 1905, p. 51. *S. morula* idem, 1912, p. 77. *Rhæbothorax morulus* Å. Holm, 1943, p. 14 ; J. Braendegaard, 1946, p. 42.

DESCRIPTION. LENGTH : ♀♂ : 1·6–1·7 mm. CARAPACE : Yellow with darker fovea and striæ. ♂ : Ocular area with a number of short curved hairs. EYES : ♀♂ : Posterior medians rather more than one

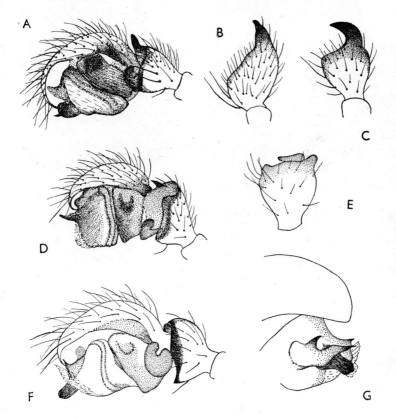

Text-fig. 191.—*Rhaebothorax morulus* ♂ : A, palp ; B, palpal tibia (from above). *Eboria fausta* ♂ : C, palpal tibia (from above) ; D, palp. *E. caliginosa* ♂ : E, palpal tibia (from above) ; F, palp ; G, palpal organs (from inside, at tip).

diam. apart, and rather less than one diam. from laterals. ABDOMEN :
Greyish black. Branchial opercula of ♂ with pronounced stridulating
ridges (Text-fig. 192, C), much less developed in ♀. STERNUM : Blackish
yellow. LEGS : Tm I 0·7–0·77. Yellow-brown, suffused with some
black. EPIGYNE : Text-fig. 192, A. MALE PALP : Text-fig. 191, A, B.

OCCURRENCE : In moss and grass, and under stones, usually on high
ground. Recorded only from the more northern English and Welsh
counties, and from Scotland ; rare. Adult in spring and summer.

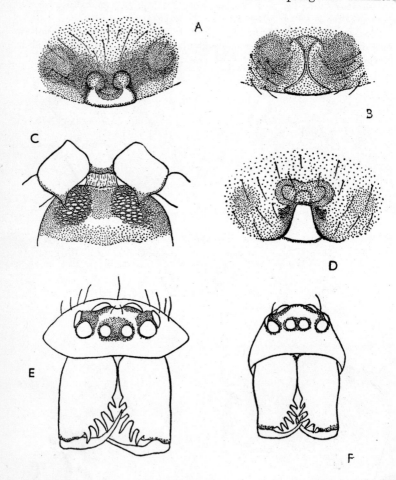

Text-fig. 192.—Epigynes : A, *Rhœbothorax morulus;* B, *Eboria fausta;* D, *E.
caliginosa.*
C, *R. morulus* ♂ : Branchial opercula.
Facies and cheliceræ (♀) ; E, *Donacochara speciosa;* F, *Phaulothrix hardyi.*

67. Genus **EBORIA** W. Falconer 1910.

CHARACTERS OF GENUS. CARAPACE : ♂ : Head not elevated. ABDOMEN : ♂ : Branchial opercula as in *Rhaebothorax*. LEGS : Metatarsus IV without a trichobothrium ; Tm I ca. 0·6. ♀♂ : Tibiæ I–III with two spines (weaker in ♂), tibia IV with one spine ; position of tibia IV spine 0·24–0·30. Metatarsi not much longer than tarsi, with MT I/t I ca. 1·25, MT IV/t IV 1·4.

There are two British species, which are very similar to *Rhaebothorax*, from which they differ slightly in the sex organs, and in the position of Tm I.

Eboria fausta (O. P.-Cambridge).
(Text-figs. 191, C, D ; 192, B)

Sintula fausta O. P.-Cambridge, 1900, p. 30, and 1905, p. 48. *Gongylidiellum faustum* A. R. Jackson, 1911, p. 390. *Rhœbothorax faustus* E. Simon, 1926, p. 456. *Latithorax faustus* Å. Holm, 1943, p. 23.

DESCRIPTION. LENGTH : ♀♂ : about 1·5 mm. CARAPACE : Yellow-brown, with faint striæ radiating from black fovea. ♂ : With some stout hairs in ocular area. EYES : Fairly large. ♀♂ : Posterior medians ca. one diam. apart, and less than one diam. from laterals. ABDOMEN : Grey. Branchial opercula of ♂ with pronounced stridulating ridges, scarcely visible in ♀. STERNUM : Blackish yellow. LEGS : Tm I 0·6. Pale yellow, suffused with blackish. ♂ : Tibiæ I–III with basal spine small, and apical spine longer. EPIGYNE : Text-fig. 192, B. MALE PALP : Text-fig. 191, C, D.

OCCURRENCE : In similar situations and localities to *Rhaebothorax morulus*. There are few records ; rare. Adults in spring and summer.

Eboria caliginosa Falconer.
(Text-figs. 191, E, F, G ; 192, D)

Eboria caliginosa W. Falconer, 1910 (1), p. 83, and 1910 (2), p. 253 ; O. P.-Cambridge, 1910, p. 58.

DESCRIPTION. LENGTH : ♀♂ : 1·8–2 mm. CARAPACE : Yellow-brown to brown, with brown fovea ; ocular area suffused with black. EYES : ♀♂ : Posteriors all rather more than one diam. apart. ABDOMEN : Grey. ♂ : Branchial opercula with stridulating ridges, not quite so pronounced as in *E. fausta*. STERNUM : Yellow to brown, suffused with black. LEGS : Tm I 0·57 (♀), 0·51 (♂). Yellow-brown to brown. EPIGYNE : Text-fig. 192, D. MALE PALP : Text-fig. 191, E, F, G.

The whole spider has a somewhat stouter appearance than *E. fausta*.

OCCURRENCE : In wet moss and grass, in two localities in Yorkshire (Marsden and Scammonden, both at about 1,000 feet), and on Scawfell Pike ; very rare. Adult in early spring.

68. Genus **DONACOCHARA** E. Simon 1884.

CHARACTERS OF GENUS. CLYPEUS : Rather narrow. LEGS : Metatarsus IV with trichobothrium ; Tm I ca. 0·85. All tibiæ with two dorsal spines, but no lateral spines. Metatarsi about twice as

long as tarsi. EPIGYNE: Very similar to that of *Tmeticus affinis*.
MALE PALP: Almost identical with that of *T. affinis*.

There is only one British species, in which the abdomen often has a characteristic pattern (Text-fig. 193, C).

Donacochara speciosa (Thorell).
(Text-figs. 192, E ; 193, A, B, C, D)

Erigone speciosa T. Thorell, 1875, p. 87 (♀). *E. leptocarpa* ibid., p. 88 (♂). *Donacochara speciosa* C. Chyzer and L. Kulczynski, 1891–7, II, p. 323 ; E. Simon, 1926, p. 420 ; A. R. Jackson, 1932, p. 209.

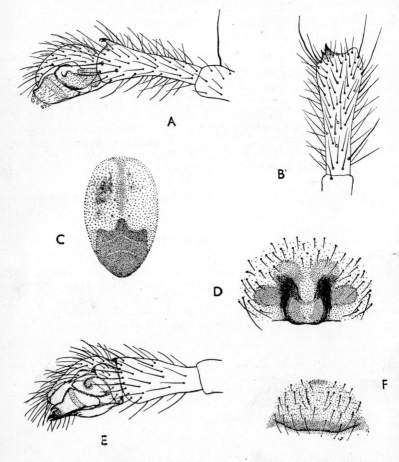

Text-fig. 193.—*Donacochara speciosa:* A, ♂ palp ; B, ♂ palpal tibia (from above) ;
C, abdomen ; D, epigyne.
Leptorhoptrum robustum: E, ♂ palp ; F, epigyne.

DESCRIPTION. LENGTH : ♀♂ : about 3·5–4 mm. CARAPACE : Pale yellow-brown, with some coarse black hairs on head. ABDOMEN : Pale whitish grey with usually a distinct black pattern (Text-fig. 193, C) (sometimes indistinct, particularly in ♂). STERNUM : Pale yellow, with numerous long hairs. CHELICERÆ : Bearing in front a number of minute granules, each with a coarse, downward directed hair. LEGS : Tm I ca. 0·85. Pale yellow. EPIGYNE : Text-fig. 193, D. MALE PALP : Text-fig. 193, A, B ; long and slender, with very small palpal organs ; tibia with small black bifid apophysis.

OCCURRENCE : In very damp places in marshes ; in sewage beds. Frequent locally. Recorded from a few localities in southern England, and from Eire. Adult probably throughout the year.

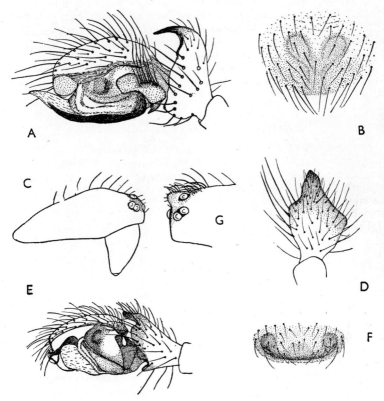

Text-fig. 194.—*Drepanotylus uncata:* A, ♂ palp ; B, epigyne ; C, ♀ carapace. *Phaulothrix hardyi:* D, ♂ palpal tibia (from above) ; E, ♂ palp ; F, epigyne ; G, ♂ head (from side).

69. Genus **LEPTORHOPTRUM** L. Kulczynski 1894.

CHARACTERS OF GENUS. LEGS : Metatarsus IV with trichobothrium ;
Tm I ca. 0·54. All tibiæ with two dorsal spines ; tibia I with an
additional prolateral spine. EPIGYNE : Of simple type. MALE PALP :
With tibial apophysis ; palpal organs small, simple.

There is one British species.

Leptorhoptrum robustum (Westring).
(Text-fig. 193, E, F)

Erigone robusta N. Westring, 1851, p. 43, and 1861, p. 267. *Neriene huthwaiti*
O. P.-Cambridge, 1861, p. 436, and 1879–81, p. 486 ; J. Blackwall, 1861–4, p. 260.
Leptorhoptrum huthwaiti C. Chyzer and L. Kulczynski, 1891–7, II, p. 79.

DESCRIPTION. LENGTH : ♀♂ : about 3–4 mm. CARAPACE : Brown
or yellow brown. EYES : Posterior medians one diam. or slightly
more apart, and ca. 1·5 diam. from laterals. ABDOMEN : Grey to
black. STERNUM : Brown or yellow brown. CHELICERÆ : Robust.
♂ : With a few small warts anteriorly and laterally, each bearing a
bristle. LEGS : Tm I ca. 0·54. Yellow to brown. EPIGYNE : Text-
fig. 193, F. MALE PALP : Text-fig. 193, E.

OCCURRENCE : In damp places ; water meadows, marshes, etc.
Widespread throughout the British Isles, but infrequent in the south.
Adult in summer, autumn and winter.

70. Genus **DREPANOTYLUS** Å. Holm 1945.

CHARACTERS OF GENUS. CARAPACE : Gibbous behind the eyes in
both sexes (Text-fig. 194, C). LEGS : Metatarsus IV without trichobothrium ; Tm I ca. 0·55. All tibiæ with two dorsal spines ; tibia I
has an additional prolateral spine. MALE PALP : Tibia produced
above into prominent curved apophysis, hooked anteriorly and hollowed inside.

There is one British species.

Drepanotylus uncatus (O. P.-Cambridge).
(Text-fig. 194, A, B, C)

Neriene uncata O. P.-Cambridge, 1873 (2), p. 546. *Hilaira uncata* J. E. Hull, 1908,
fig. 2, 3 ; E. Simon, 1926, p. 471. *Drepanotylus uncatus* Å. Holm, 1945, p. 25.

DESCRIPTION. LENGTH : ♀♂ : about 2·5 mm. CARAPACE : Text-
fig. 194, C ; brown or yellow brown, with faint striæ, bearing a median
row of stout bristles ; a few hairs in ocular area. EYES : Posterior
medians rather more than one diam. apart, about 2 diams. from
laterals. ♂ : rather more widely spaced. ABDOMEN : Grey to black,
with many fine hairs. STERNUM : Brown to orange. CHELICERÆ :
Robust. LEGS : Tm I ca. 0·55. Brown to orange brown. Anterior
tibial spines very fine, particularly in ♂. EPIGYNE : Text-fig. 194, B.
MALE PALP : Text-fig. 194, A ; paracymbium with group of stout
spines.

OCCURRENCE : In wet marshes, sphagnum, etc. Widespread throughout the British Isles, but local, and more frequent in the north. Adult in autumn and winter.

71. Genus **PHAULOTHRIX** P. Bertkau 1885.

CHARACTERS OF GENUS. CARAPACE : ♂ : With conical protuberance in ocular area, slightly in front of posterior median eyes (Text-fig. 194, G), with small tuft of hairs behind. LEGS : Metatarsus IV with a trichobothrium ; Tm I ca. 0·85. All tibiæ with two dorsal spines ; no lateral spines. MALE PALP : Tibia with protuberance.

There is one British species.

Phaulothrix hardyi (Blackwall).
(Text-figs. 192, F ; 194, D, E, F, G)

Walckenaera hardyi J. Blackwall, 1850, p. 340, and 1861–4, p. 292 ; O. P.-Cambridge, 1879–81, p. 504. *Phaulothrix hardii* E. Simon, 1926, p. 420.

DESCRIPTION. LENGTH : ♀♂ : about 4 mm. CARAPACE : Brown to dark brown, with faint striæ. ♂ : With small tubercle in ocular area, bearing a number of forward-directed coarse black bristles (Text-fig. 194, G). EYES : ♀ : Posterior medians ca. one diam. apart, rather less from laterals. ♂ : Posterior medians ca. 3 diam. apart, slightly less than one diam. from laterals. ABDOMEN : Black to grey. STERNUM : Brown to dark brown. LEGS : Tm I ca. 0·85. Brown, with numerous long black hairs. ♀♂ : Ventrally (especially on femora and tibiæ) with longitudinal rows of long bristles. ♂ : Legs I and II with a number of black granules ventrally, each bearing a long bristle. EPIGYNE : Text-fig. 194, F. MALE PALP : Text-fig. 194, D, E.

OCCURRENCE : Uncommon, in marshy areas and on high ground. Recorded mainly from northern England, Scotland and Eire.

72. Genus **HILAIRA** E. Simon. 1884.

CHARACTERS OF GENUS. CARAPACE : Broad in front, and smoothly raised behind the eyes (♀), more sharply so in ♂ (less so in *H. frigida*). CHELICERÆ : Robust. LEGS : Metatarsus IV with a trichobothrium ; Tm I 0·6–0·7. All tibiæ with two dorsal spines, those of anterior legs (particularly in ♂) often very thin ; an additional prolateral spine is present on tibia I. Metatarsus IV about 1·4–1·6 times as long as tarsus IV. MALE PALP : With tibial apophysis : palpal organs relatively complex, with large paracymbium.

There are four British species, readily distinguished by the sex organs.

Hilaira excisa (O. P.-Cambridge).
(Text-figs. 195, A, B, E ; 196, E)

Neriene excisa O. P.-Cambridge, 1870, p. 440, and 1879–81, p. 487. *Hilaira excisa* J. E. Hull, 1908, fig. 2, 3 ; E. Simon, 1926, pp. 471, 472. *Hilaira pervicax* O. P.-Cambridge, 1908, p. 173 (♀).

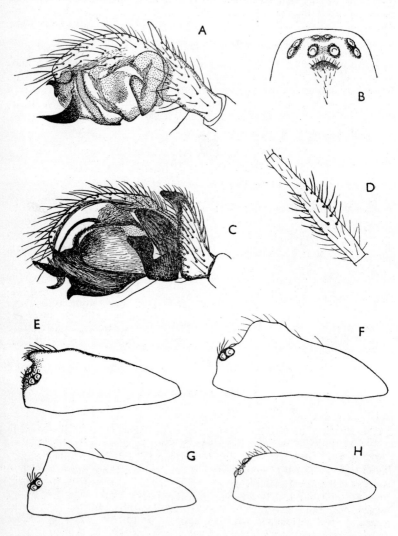

Text-fig. 195.—Male palps : A, *Hilaira excisa;* C, *H. frigida.*
　　Male carapace : B, *H. excisa* (from above) ; E, ditto (from side) ; F, *H. nubigena;*
　　G, *H. pervicax;* H, *H. frigida.*
　　D, *H. nubigena:* Metatarsus I (from above).

DESCRIPTION. LENGTH : ♀ : about 2·5–3 mm. ♂ : about 2·25–2·5 mm. CARAPACE : Brown to dark brown, with faint striæ. ♂ : With slight elevation, clothed in front with short hairs, behind eyes (Text-fig. 195, B, E). EYES : ♀ : Posterior medians about one diam. apart, 1·5–1·75 from laterals. ♂ : Posterior eyes all ca. 1·5 diam. apart. ABDOMEN : Grey to black, with numerous long hairs. STERNUM : Brown, sometimes mottled with black. LEGS : Tm I 0·55–0·6. Yellow-brown. Tibial spines on anterior legs rather fine. EPIGYNE : Text-fig. 196, E. MALE PALP : Text-fig. 195, A.

OCCURRENCE : In damp marshy spots, amongst moss and grass, rushes, etc. Widespread but infrequent, with few records for southern Britain. Adult in August-September.

Hilaira frigida (Thorell).
(Text-figs. 195, C, H ; 196, H)

Erigone frigida T. Thorell, 1872, p. 152. *Hilaira montigena* O. P.-Cambridge, 1911, p. 39. *Hilaira frigida* J. E. Hull, 1911 (2), p. 47 ; J. Braendegaard, 1946, p. 40.

DESCRIPTION. LENGTH : ♀ : 3–4 mm. ♂ : About 3 mm. CARAPACE : Orange to brown, gibbous behind eyes, particularly ♂ (Text-fig. 195, H). EYES : ♀ : Posterior medians ca. one diam. apart, ca. 1·5 diams. from laterals. ♂ : Posterior medians ca. one diam. apart, ca. 2 diams. from laterals. ABDOMEN : Grey to black. STERNUM : Orange-brown, sometimes suffused with black. LEGS : Tm I 0·6–0·7. Orange-brown to brown. Anterior tibial spines in ♂ very fine. EPIGYNE : Text-fig. 196, H. MALE PALP : Text-fig. 195, C.

OCCURRENCE : Found only on high mountains in Britain : Snowdonia, Lake District, Scottish Highlands, Southwest Eire. Locally abundant. Adult in spring and summer.

Hilaira nubigena Hull.
(Text-figs. 195, D, F ; 196, A, B, F)

Hilaira nubigena J. E. Hull, 1911 (2), p. 52, and 1932, p. 104 ; Å. Holm, 1945, p. 28.

DESCRIPTION. LENGTH : ♀ : 3·5–4 mm. ♂ : 3–4 mm. CARAPACE : Deep orange-brown to dark brown, with a few short, forward directed spines in ocular area and behind eyes. ♂ : Carapace raised steeply behind eyes (Text-fig. 195, F). EYES : ♀ : Posteriors practically equidistant, 1·5 diam. apart. ♂ : Posterior medians 1–1·5 diam. apart, and ca. 2 diam. from laterals. ABDOMEN : Black, with sometimes a few ill-defined whitish spots. STERNUM : Orange-brown, faintly reticulated with black. LEGS : Tm I 0·65. Yellow to orange-brown. Anterior tibial spines very fine. ♂ : Metatarsus I swollen basally, bearing towards the middle about 20 stout spines (Text-fig. 195, D). EPIGYNE : Text-fig. 196, F. MALE PALP : Text-fig. 196, A, B.

OCCURRENCE : Killhope Law (Northumberland) in a swampy area. Adult in August-September and possibly later.

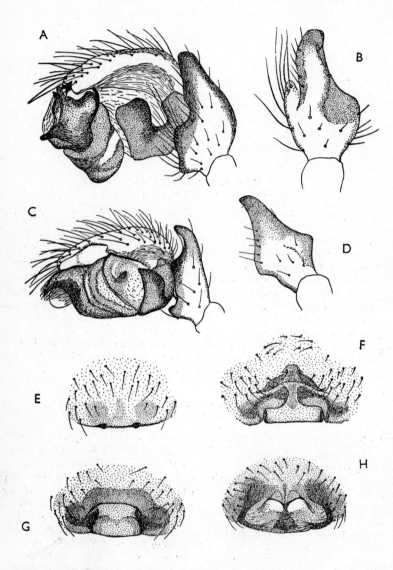

Text-fig.196.—Male palps : A, *Hilaira nubigena;* C, *H. pervicax.*
Male palpal tibiae (from above) : B, *H. nubigena;* D, *H. pervicax.*
Epigynes : E, *H. excisa;* F, *H. nubigena;* G, *H. pervicax;* H, *H. frigida.*

Hilaira pervicax Hull.
(Text-figs. 195, G ; 196, C, D, G)

Hilaira pervicax J. E. Hull, 1908, p. 112 (♂), and 1909 (1), p. 449 (♀). *Hilaira glacialis* var. *thienmanni* E. Schenkel, 1939, p. 107. *H. pervicax* A. Holm, 1945, p. 29.

DESCRIPTION. LENGTH : ♀♂ : 2·5–3 mm. CARAPACE : Pale brown to orange brown, with a few short hairs in ocular area. ♂ : Raised steeply behind eyes (Text-fig. 195, G). EYES : ♀ : Posteriors practically equidistant, 1·5 diam. apart. ♂ : Posterior medians 1·5–2 diams. apart, and 1–1·5 diam. from laterals. ABDOMEN : Greyish-black, with sometimes a few paler spots. STERNUM : Yellow to yellow-brown, faintly reticulated with black. LEGS : Tm I 0·65. Yellow to brown. Tibial spines rather fine. EPIGYNE : Text-fig. 196, G. MALE PALP : Text-fig. 196, C, D.

OCCURRENCE : Amongst moss in a pinewood, Whitfield Fell (Northumberland), at 1,400 feet. Red Tarn, Helvellyn, and Pennines. Adults in autumn and winter.

73. Genus HALORATES J. E. Hull 1911.

CHARACTERS OF GENUS. CHELICERÆ : ♂ : Armed in front with a large cylindrical tubercle, just above outer row of teeth. LEGS : Metatarsus IV with a trichobothrium ; Tm I 0·6–0·7. All tibiæ with two fine dorsal spines, but no lateral spines. Metatarsus IV almost twice as long as tarsus IV. MALE PALP : Tibia with an apophysis. Palpal organs (and epigyne) are somewhat similar in form to those of *Collinsia*.

There is one British species.

Halorates reprobus (O. P.-Cambridge).
(Text-fig. 197, A, B, C)

Neriene reproba O. P.-Cambridge, 1879 (1), p. 196, and 1879–81, p. 431. *Halorates reprobus* J. E. Hull, 1911 (1), p. 581 ; E. Simon, 1926, p. 473.

DESCRIPTION. LENGTH : ♀ : 3–4 mm. ♂ : 2·5–3 mm. CARAPACE : Brown, with faint striæ. EYES : Posterior medians ca. one diam. apart, and 1–1·25 diam. from laterals. ABDOMEN : Grey to black. STERNUM : Yellow-brown. LEGS : Tm I 0·6–0·7. Brown. Tibial spines fine but long. EPIGYNE : Text-fig. 197, C. MALE PALP : Text-fig. 197, A, B.

OCCURRENCE : On salt flats, salt marshes, seashore. Widespread round the coasts, but infrequent. Adults most of year.

74. Genus OSTEARIUS J. E. Hull 1911.

CHARACTERS OF GENUS. ABDOMEN : Reddish, with a black zone posteriorly, around the spinners. CHELICERÆ : ♂ : Armed in front with a strong pointed conical tubercle, bearing a bristle, just above outer teeth. LEGS : Metatarsus IV without a trichobothrium ; Tm I slightly less than 0·5. All tibiæ with two dorsal spines, but no lateral spines. Metatarsus IV almost twice as long as tarsus IV. MALE PALP : Tibia with apophysis.

There is one British species.

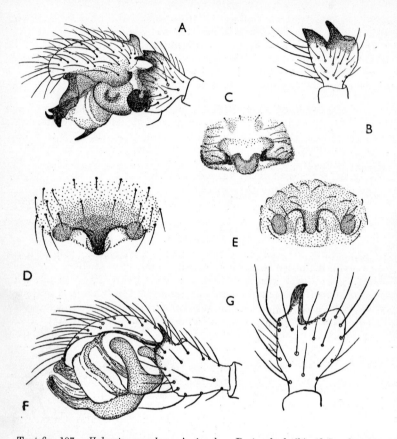

Text-fig. 197.—*Halorates reprobus:* A, ♂ palp ; B, ♂ palpal tibia (from above) ; C, epigyne.
Ostearius melanopygius: D, epigyne ; E, ditto (more from behind) ; F, ♂ palp ; G, ♂ palpal tibia (from above).

Ostearius melanopygius (O. P.-Cambridge).
(Text-fig. 197, D, E, F, G)

Linyphia melanopygia O. P.-Cambridge, 1879, p. 53. *Tmeticus nigricauda* O. P.-Cambridge, 1907, p. 141. *Ostearius nigricauda* J. E. Hull, 1911 (1), p. 583. *Ostearius melanopygius* A. R. Jackson, 1933 (3), p. 27.

DESCRIPTION. LENGTH : ♀♂ : 2–2·5 mm. CARAPACE : Brown, with faint striæ. EYES : Posteriors slightly less than one diam. apart. ABDOMEN : Red, with a small black area at posterior, around spinners. A melanic variety has occurred (A. R. Jackson, 1933 (3), p. 27), in which the abdomen is almost wholly black. STERNUM : Brown, suffused with some black. LEGS : Tm I slightly less than 0·5. Yellow-brown, rather long. EPIGYNE : Text-fig. 197, D. E. MALE PALP : Text-fig. 197, F, G.

OCCURRENCE : On rubbish heaps, sandhills, in gardens, occasionally indoors, in a number of English counties. May have been imported from New Zealand, but seems quite established. Adult in spring to autumn.

75. Genus **HILLHOUSIA** F. O. P.-Cambridge 1894.

CHARACTERS OF GENUS. LEGS : Metatarsus IV without a trichobothrium ; Tm I 0·4. All tibiæ with two dorsal spines ; tibia I with an additional prolateral spine. MALE PALP : Tibia without apophysis. Distinguished from *Porrhomma* by the larger and closer eyes (particularly anteriors), by absence of retrolateral spine on tibia I, and by different form of the ♂ palpal organs and the ♀ epigynes.

There is one British species.

Hillhousia misera (O. P.-Cambridge).
(Text-fig. 198, A, B, C)

Linyphia misera O. P.-Cambridge, 1882, p. 262. *L. turbatrix* idem, 1879–81, p. 454. *Hillhousia turbatrix* F. O. P.-Cambridge, 1894, p. 89.

DESCRIPTION. LENGTH : ♀ : 2–2·5 mm. ♂ : About 2 mm. CARAPACE : Brown or yellow-brown, with faint striæ. EYES : On black spots, and ocular area sometimes suffused with black. ABDOMEN : Grey to blackish, clothed with long hairs. STERNUM : Yellow, reticulated with black. LEGS : Tm I 0·4. Yellow to yellow-brown. Tibial spines fairly long. EPIGYNE : Text-fig. 198, B. C. MALE PALP : Text-fig. 198, A.

OCCURRENCE : In wet, swampy areas, common locally. Recorded from a few localities in England, Wales and Scotland. Adults in spring and autumn.

76. Genus **PORRHOMMA** E. Simon 1884.

CHARACTERS OF GENUS. CLYPEUS : Hairy, particularly ♂. EYES : Variable in size. LEGS : Metatarsus IV without trichobothrium ; Tm I 0·35–0·4. All tibiæ with two dorsal spines ; anterior tibiæ with one prolateral and one retrolateral spine also. Femora I and II with or without dorsal and prolateral spines. Metatarsal spines absent, except in *P. errans*. MALE PALP : With no tibial apophysis.

This genus comprises a very homogeneous group of small spiders. They can be distinguished from one another only by very careful consideration of the genitalia, together with the leg spines and the eyes.

The epigyne consists of a pit, with the anterior edge rounded ; posteriorly there is a little dimple. The form of the internal organs can sometimes be seen faintly through the integument. Some of the species can be distinguished by the form of the pit, as seen by top light with the specimen in spirit, but in some cases it is desirable for reliable identification to clear the epigyne and observe it by transmitted light.

In the male palp (Text-fig. 198, D), the paracymbium differs but little from species to species, and is not a reliable character. The distinguishing characters are seen when the palpal organs are viewed from inside and somewhat below (Text-fig. 202, A). The long, narrow pointed embolus (*s*) projects between two chitinised apophyses : the anterior apophysis (*a*) which is hooked and very similar in all species, and a large chitinised piece with a superior (*b*) and an inferior (*i*)

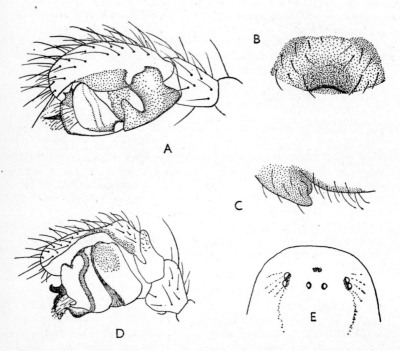

Text-fig. 198.—*Hillhousia miser:* A, ♂ palp ; B, epigyne ; C, ditto (from side) ; D, *Porrhomma pallidum:* ♂ palp ; E, *P. egeria:* Eyes.

apophysis. The embolus itself is a curved chitinised tube with the point directed downwards ; it is bordered below by a small transparent velum, difficult to see, and is accompanied by a membraneous conductor (*c*), irregularly notched on its edges. The distinguishing features are based on the form and disposition of the *embolus* and the *superior apophysis*. It is absolutely necessary to adjust the palps into the exact position for examination.

There are 10 British species, which can be split into four groups with the aid of the leg spines, according to the following key :—

1. Each metatarsus with a spine . . . . *P. errans*
——Metatarsi spineless 2

2. Femur I with two prolateral spines (apart from dorsal ones).
(Eyes very small) . . . . . . *P. egeria*
——Femur I with one prolateral spine 3

3. Femur I with no dorsal spines
P. oblitum and *P. montanum*
——Femur I with one or two dorsal spines

P. microphthalmum, P. campbelli, P. pallidum, P. pygmaeum,
P. convexum and *P. rosenhaueri*

P. oblitum and *P. montanum* are fairly readily distinguished by the sex organs (both sexes) and by their colour.

P. rosenhaueri is recognised at once by its minute eyes or absence of eyes, and by its epigyne (♀). *P. microphthalmum, P. campbelli* and *P. pallidum* are distinguishable from one another and from *P. pygmaeum* and *P. convexum* by their sex organs. *P. pygmaeum* and *P. convexum* can be separated by their eyes, their size, and their epigynes (♀).

This genus has been intensively studied by several authors (F. O. P.-Cambridge, 1894; A. R. Jackson, 1913 ; L. Fage, 1931 ; F. Miller and J. Kratochvil, 1940 (2)).

Porrhomma pygmæum (Blackwall).
(Text-figs. 199, A ; 200, A ; 202, A)

Neriene pygmaea J. Blackwall, 1834, p. 376, and 1861–4, p. 261. *Porrhomma pygmaeum* F. O. P.-Cambridge, 1894, p. 104 ; A. R. Jackson, 1913, p. 35 ; E. Simon, 1926, p. 465 ; L. Fage, 1931, p. 158 ; F. Miller and J. Kratochvil, 1940 (2), p. 165.

DESCRIPTION. LENGTH : ♀♂ : 1·6–2 mm. CARAPACE : Reddish brown to very dark brown, head often suffused with black. EYES : Large ; posterior medians ca. one diam. apart, ca. 1·25 diam. from laterals ; anterior medians practically as large as posterior medians, ca. 0·5–1 diam. apart, and ca. one diam. from laterals. ABDOMEN : Yellowish-grey to black. STERNUM : Brown to dark brown, with blackish margin. LEGS : Tm I ca. 0·35. Orange to yellow-brown. Femur I with one dorsal and one prolateral spine towards apex ; femur II with single dorsal spine. Basal spine on tibia I less than twice diam. of segment. EPIGYNE : Text-figs. 199, A ; 200, A ; small, with pit usually fairly dark (distinction from remaining species in the group). MALE PALP : Text-fig. 202, A.

OCCURRENCE : Damp, marshy places, in undergrowth ; not usually in subterranean localities. Widely distributed throughout the British Isles ; common. Adults in spring and summer.

Z

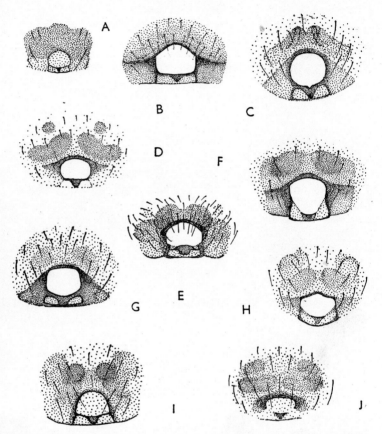

Text-fig. 199.—Epigynes: A, *Porrhomma pygmaeum*; B, *P. convexum*: C, *P. rosenhaueri*; D, *P. pallidum*; E, *P. egeria*; F, *P. campbelli*; G, *P. microphthalmum*; H, *P. errans*; I, *P. oblitum*; J, *P. montanum*.

Porrhomma convexum (Westring).
(Text-figs. 199, B ; 200, B ; 202, A)

Linyphia convexa N. Westring, 1861, p. 137. *Porrhomma proserpina* E. Simon, 1884, p. 360. *Porrhomma thorelli* A. R. Jackson, 1913, p. 36. *Porrhomma proserpina* E. Simon, 1926, p. 466; L. Fage, 1931, p. 158. *P. pygmaeum* forma *proserpina* (?) F. Miller and J. Kratochvil, 1940 (2), p. 167. *P. convexum* Å. Holm, 1944, p. 130.

DESCRIPTION. LENGTH : ♀♂ : 2·25–2·5 mm. CARAPACE : Yellowbrown to very dark brown. EYES : Smaller than in *P. pygmaeum*. Posterior medians slightly more than one diam. apart, ca. 2 diam. from laterals. ABDOMEN : Greyish black, with sometimes a faint pattern of paler bars and spots. STERNUM : Yellow to yellow-brown.

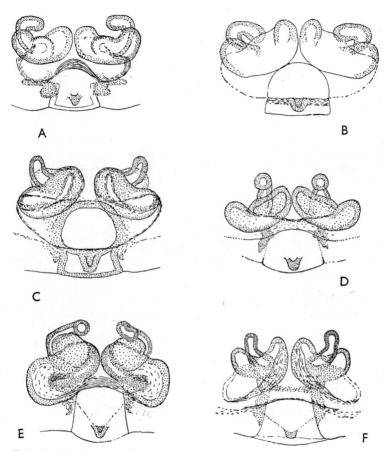

Text-fig. 200.—Epigynes (cleared) : A, *Porrhomma pygmaeum;* B, *P. convexum;*
C, *P. rosenhaueri;* D, *P. pallidum;* E, *P. campbelli;* F, *P. microphthalmum.*

LEGS : Tm I ca. 0·4. Yellow-brown. Spines as in *P. pygmaeum,*
but with occasionally one extra dorsal spine on femur I. Basal spine
on tibia I often greater than twice diam. of segment. EPIGYNE :
Text-figs. 199, B, 200, B ; larger than in *P. pygmaeum,* with pit
usually light in colour. MALE PALP : Text-fig. 202, A.

   This species is usually larger than *P. pygmaeum,* and has relatively
smaller eyes ; the females can be distinguished by the epigynes.

   OCCURRENCE : Cellars, caves, mines, and in buildings. Outdoors
under stones and in undergrowth. Widespread in England, but with
more records from the north ; recorded from Eire, but not Wales or
Scotland.

Porrhomma rosenhaueri (L. Koch).
(Text-figs. 199, C ; 200, C ; 202, C)

Linyphia rosenhaueri L. Koch, 1872, p. 128. *Porrhomma rosenhaueri* L. Fage, 1931, p. 161. *P. myops* A. R. Jackson, 1913, p. 37.

DESCRIPTION. LENGTH : ♀♂ : 2 mm. The identity of this species is uncertain, but it is not *P. myops* Sim. CARAPACE : Yellow-brown. EYES : Usually absent, or evidenced only by pale markings beneath integument ; when visible, very minute in size. ABDOMEN : Pale whitish grey. STERNUM : Yellow-brown. LEGS : Tm I ca. 0·4. Pale yellow-brown, slender. Spines as in *P. convexum*. EPIGYNE : Text-figs. 199, C ; 200, C ; distinguishable from *P. convexum* by shape of dimple on posterior border. MALE PALP : Text-fig. 202, C. Seems almost indistinguishable from *P. convexum*.

OCCURRENCE : Exclusively cave-dwelling. The only recorded locality in the British Isles is in Mitchelstown Caves, Tipperary (Eire).

Porrhomma pallidum Jackson.
(Text-figs. 198, D ; 199, D ; 200, D ; 202, B)

Porrhomma pallidum A. R. Jackson, 1913, p. 38. *P. oblongum* L. Fage, 1931, p. 163. *P. pallidum* F. Miller and J. Kratochvil, 1940 (2), p. 186.

DESCRIPTION. LENGTH : ♀♂ : About 1·7 mm. CARAPACE : Yellow-brown. EYES : Posterior medians 1–1·25 diam. apart, ca. 1·5 diam. from laterals. ABDOMEN : Pale whitish grey. STERNUM : Pale

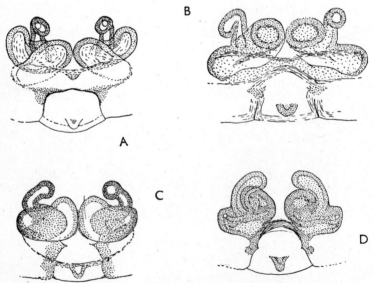

Text-fig. 201.—Epigynes (cleared) : A, *Porrhomma errans;* B, *P. egeria;* C, *P. oblitum;* D, *P. montanum.*

yellow. LEGS : Tm I 0·35. Yellow-brown ; spines as in *P. pygmaeum*.
EPIGYNE : Text-figs. 199, D ; 200, D. MALE PALP : Text-figs. 198, D ;
202, B ; the superior apophysis is short and rather blunt.

OCCURRENCE : In detritus of woods ; on mountains, under stones,
up to 3,000 feet. Recorded from a few English and Scottish counties,
and from Eire, but not Wales. Adults in late summer and autumn.

Porrhomma campbelli F. O. P.-Cambridge.
(Text-figs. 199, F ; 200, E ; 202, D)

Porrhomma campbelli F. O. P.-Cambridge, 1894, p. 108 ; A. R. Jackson, 1913,
p. 44, and 1916, p. 362 ; L. Fage, 1931, p. 165 ; F. Miller and J. Kratochvil, 1940,
(2), p. 180.

DESCRIPTION. LENGTH : ♀♂ : About 2·5 mm. CARAPACE : Yellow-
brown. EYES : Posterior medians ca. one diam. apart, ca. 2–3 diam.
from laterals. ABDOMEN : Grey to greyish brown. LEGS : Tm I
0·3–0·4. Yellow to yellow-brown ; spines as in *P. pygmaeum*.
EPIGYNE : Text-figs. 199, F ; 200, E ; pit elongated and pear-shaped.
MALE PALP : Text-fig. 202, D ; the embolus is broad, and the superior
apophysis turns upwards.

OCCURRENCE : Very rare. Isolated specimens have been taken
under stones, and in a mole's nest. Not recorded from Scotland.

Porrhomma microphthalmum (O. P.-Cambridge).
(Text-figs. 199, G ; 200, F ; 202, G)

Linyphia microphthalma O. P.-Cambridge, 1871, p. 434. *L. decens* idem, 1879–81,
p. 205. *Porrhomma meadi* and *microphthalmum* F. O. P.-Cambridge, 1894, p. 101.
P. microphthalmum C. Chyzer and L. Kulczynski, 1891–7, II, p. 322 ; A. R. Jackson,
1913, p. 41 ; E. Simon, 1926, p. 465 ; L. Fage, 1931, p. 161 ; F. Miller and
J. Kratochvil, 1940 (2), p. 169.

DESCRIPTION. LENGTH : ♀♂ : About 2 mm. CARAPACE : Yellow
to orange-brown, with faint radiating striæ at times. EYES : Posterior
medians ca. one diam. apart (♀♂), and ca. 1·5 (♀) or 2 (♂) diam.
from laterals. ABDOMEN : Grey to grey-brown. STERNUM : Yellow-
brown. LEGS : Tm I 0·35. Yellow to yellow-brown ; spines as in
P. pygmaeum. EPIGYNE : Text-figs. 199, G ; 200, F ; the pit is
almost straight-sided, and rather square in appearance. MALE PALP :
Text-fig. 202, G ; the embolus is broadened at the tip.

OCCURRENCE : Widely distributed, but rare. Amongst undergrowth,
under stones, etc. Recorded from England and southern Scotland,
but not Wales or Eire. Adults in summer and autumn.

Porrhomma errans (Blackwall).
(Text-figs. 199, H ; 201, A ; 202, H)

Neriene errans J. Blackwall, 1841, p. 643; 1853, p. 20, and 1861–4, p. 253. *Linyphia
errans* O. P.-Cambridge, 1879–81, p. 204. *Porrhomma errans* A. R. Jackson, 1913,
p. 34.

DESCRIPTION. LENGTH : ♀♂ : About 2 mm. CARAPACE : ♀ :
Orange-brown, slightly darker on head, which has a number of forward-

directed spines. ♂ : Brown, with broad black radiating striæ ; head blackish, with spines as ♀, but fewer. EYES : Posterior medians ca. one diam. apart, and ca. 1·5 diam. from laterals. ABDOMEN : Yellow-brown. STERNUM : Pale yellow. LEGS : Tm I ca. 0·4. Yellow to yellow-brown. All metatarsi with a dorsal spine, position ca. 0·2. Femoral spines as in *P. pygmaeum.* EPIGYNE : Text-figs. 199, H ; 201, A. MALE PALP : Text-fig. 202, H ; close to *P. convexum.*

OCCURRENCE : Rare ; recorded from six English counties and two counties in Eire. On fences and railings (probably during " ballooning ") and under bark of trees. Adults in spring.

Porrhomma egeria Simon.
(Text-figs. 198, E ; 199, E ; 201, B ; 202, E)

Porrhomma egeria E. Simon, 1884, p. 357 ; F. O. P.-Cambridge, 1895, p. 36 ; A. R. Jackson, 1913, p. 42 ; E. Simon, 1926, p. 462 ; L. Fage, 1931, p. 164 ; F. Miller and J. Kratochvil, 1940 (2), p. 183.

DESCRIPTION. LENGTH : ♀♂ : About 2·5 mm. CARAPACE : Yellow-brown. EYES : Very small (Text-fig. 198, E). Posterior medians 2·5–3 diams. apart, and 4 diams. from laterals ; anterior medians very minute or absent. ABDOMEN : Greyish yellow to white. STERNUM : Pale yellow, with rather coarse hairs. LEGS : Tm I ca. 0·4. Femur I with two prolateral spines apically, and with one or occasionally two dorsal spines ; femur II with one or two dorsal spines only. EPIGYNE : Text-figs. 199, E ; 201, B. MALE PALP : Text-fig. 202, E ; the embolus has a large barb.

The minute eyes, the two prolateral spines on femur I, and the genitalia (particularly of ♂) render this species easily identifiable.

OCCURRENCE : Under stones, on railings, etc., outdoors. In caves, cellars, mines and houses. Widespread but rare outdoors ; frequent in caves.

Porrhomma oblitum (O. P.-Cambridge).
(Text-figs. 199, I ; 201, C ; 202, H)

Linyphia oblita O. P.-Cambridge, 1870, p. 432, and *L. oblonga* p. 433. *L. oblita* idem, 1879–81, p. 215. *Neriene pallipes* idem, ibid., p. 133. *Porrhomma oblongum* F. O. P.-Cambridge, 1894, p. 102 ; A. R. Jackson, 1913, p. 43. *Porrhomma oblitum* A. R. Jackson, 1913, p. 39.

DESCRIPTION. LENGTH : ♀♂ : about 1·5 mm. CARAPACE : Brown to orange-brown, with faint radiating striæ. EYES : Posterior medians ca. one diam. apart, and ca. 1·5 diam. from laterals. ABDOMEN : Grey to blackish. STERNUM : Yellow to brown, faintly reticulated. LEGS : Tm I 0·35–0·4. Yellow to yellow-brown. Femur I with one prolateral spine apically, but no dorsal spine ; femur II spineless. EPIGYNE : Text-figs. 199, I ; 201, C ; similar to *P. pygmaeum,* but rather wider ; the pit is often somewhat darkened. MALE PALP : Text-fig. 202, H ; seems indistinguishable from *P. errans.*

OCCURRENCE : Very rare ; recorded from a few southern English counties only. On low bushes and herbage.

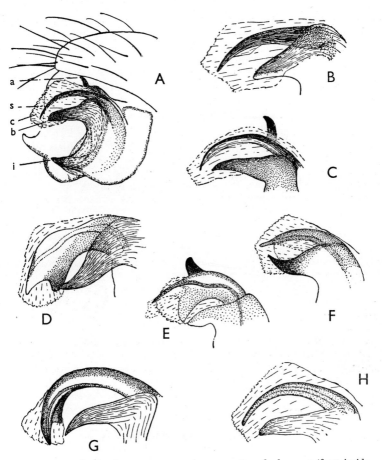

Text-fig. 202.—A, *Porrhomma pygmaeum/convexum* ♂ : palpal organs (from inside, at tip).
Embolus (*s*) and superior apophysis (*b*) of palpal organs (from inside) : B, *P. pallidum;* C, *P. rosenhaueri;* D, *P. campbelli;* E, *P. egeria;* F, *P. montanum;* G, *P. microphthalmum;* H, *P. errans* and *oblitum.*

Porrhomma montanum Jackson.

(Text-figs. 199, J ; 201, D ; 202, F)

Porrhomma montanum A. R. Jackson, 1913, p. 40.

DESCRIPTION. LENGTH : ♀♂ : 1·5–2 mm. CARAPACE : Yellow-brown to brown, with head sometimes slightly darker ; head with a few fine hairs. EYES : Posterior medians ca. one diam. apart, and ca. 1·5 diam. from laterals. ABDOMEN : Pale grey to greyish black. STERNUM : Yellow-brown, reticulated. LEGS : Tm I ca. 0.4. Yellow-

brown to brown. Femoral spines as in *P. oblitum*. Epigyne : Text-
figs. 199, J ; 201, D ; clearly distinguishable from *P. oblitum*. Male
palp : Text-fig. 202, F ; the superior apophysis is curved upwards,
rapidly tapering to a point.

Occurrence : Known in Britain only from a few northern English
counties, North Wales and Scotland ; occurs particularly on mountains.

77. Genus **SYEDRULA** E. Simon 1929.

Characters of Genus. Eyes : Posteriors very large, almost
contiguous (Text-fig. 203, B). Legs : Metatarsus IV without a trichobothrium ; Tm I ca. 0·25. All tibiæ with two dorsal spines, but no
lateral spines. Metatarsi I and II with one dorsal spine. Tarsi I and
II with one dorsal spine. Epigyne : Close to genus *Meioneta*. Male
palp : Tarsus elevated strongly into conical protuberance (Text-
fig. 203, A).

There is one British species.

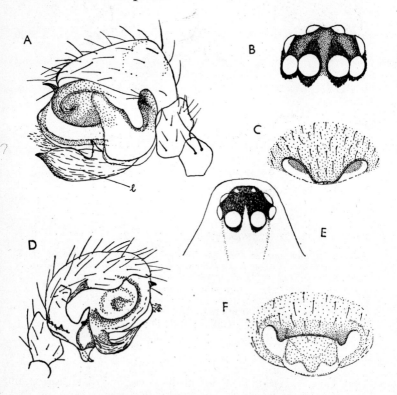

Text-fig. 203.—*Syedrula innotabilis:* A, ♂ palp ; B, eyes ; C, epigyne.
Syedra gracilis: D, ♂ palp (right) ; E, eyes ; F, epigyne.

Syedrula innotabilis (O. P.-Cambridge).
(Text-fig. 203, A, B, C)

Neriene innotabilis O. P.-Cambridge, 1863, p. 8582, and 1879–81, p. 131. *Syedra innotabilis* A. R. Jackson, 1912, p. 124. *Syedrula innotabilis* E. Simon, 1929, p. 536 ; F. Miller, 1947, Tab. 10, figs. 5 and 6.

DESCRIPTION. LENGTH : ♀♂ : 2–2·25 mm. CARAPACE : Brown, with narrow black margin. EYES : Text-fig. 203, B ; posterior medians ca. 0·25 diam. apart, practically touching laterals. ABDOMEN : Grey to black. STERNUM : Brown, sometimes reticulated with black. LEGS : Tm I ca. 0·25. Brown, with metatarsi and tarsi sometimes darker ; spines as described under Genus. EPIGYNE : Text-fig. 203, C. MALE PALP : Text-fig. 203, A ; tarsus strongly elevated dorsally. Lamella (*l*) of characteristic shape.

OCCURRENCE : On tree trunks, in crevices in the bark, and amongst dead leaves near the base of trees. Widespread throughout the British Isles. Adult in summer.

78. Genus **SYEDRA** E. Simon 1884.

CHARACTERS OF GENUS. EYES : Posteriors large, but rather further apart than in *Syedrula* (Text-fig. 203, E). LEGS : Metatarsus IV without a trichobothrium ; Tm I ca. 0·33. All tibiæ with two dorsal spines. Metatarsi I and II with one dorsal spine ; no tarsal spines. EPIGYNE : Quite different in form from that of *Syedrula*. MALE PALP : Tarsus less elevated ; paracymbium with a series of small teeth.
There is one British species.

Syedra gracilis (Menge).
(Text-fig. 203, D, E, F)

Microneta gracilis A. Menge, 1866, p. 233. *Linyphia pholcommoides* O. P.-Cambridge, 1879, p. 212. *Neriene pholcommoides* idem, 1879–81, p. 575. *Syedra pholcommoides* A. R. Jackson, 1912, p. 123. *S. gracilis* E. Simon, 1929, p. 536 ; F. Miller, 1947, Tab. 9, figs. 4–6.

DESCRIPTION. LENGTH : ♀♂ : 1·2–1·3 mm. CARAPACE : Yellow, with darker broad radiating striæ. Ocular area black. EYES : Text-fig. 203, E ; posterior medians ca. 0·5 diam. apart, ca. 0·25 diam. from laterals. ABDOMEN : Greyish yellow to grey. LEGS : Tm I ca. 0·33. Yellow, sometimes suffused with blackish tinge. Dorsal spine on metatarsus I slightly above 0·5. EPIGYNE : Text-fig. 203, F. MALE PALP : Text-fig. 203, D.

OCCURRENCE : Very rare ; amongst moss, grass, detritus, etc. Recorded from a few English counties only.

79. Genus **AGYNETA** J. E. Hull 1911.

CHARACTERS OF GENUS. EYES : Posteriors subequal, practically equidistant. CHELICERÆ : Rather short and feeble ; outer margin with two teeth, inner with one tooth. LEGS : Metatarsus IV with a trichobothrium ; Tm I 0·65–0·9 ; trichobothria sharply bent (Text-fig. 205, B). All tibiæ with two short, fine dorsal spines, but no lateral

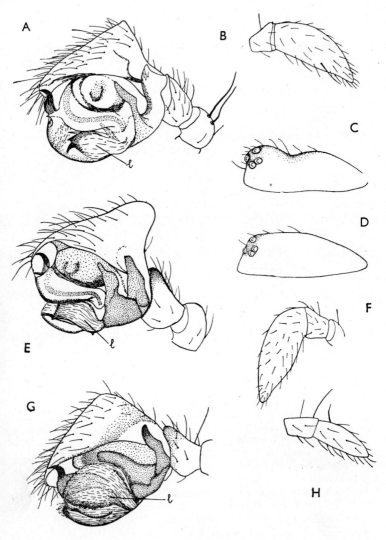

Text-fig. 204.—Male palps : A, *Agyneta subtilis;* E, *A. conigera;* G, *A. decora.*
Female palps : B, *A. subtilis;* F, *A. cauta;* H, *A. ramosa.*
Carapace (female, from side) : C, *A. conigera;* D, *A. ramosa.*

spines. Metatarsi spineless. FEMALE PALP : Tibia and tarsus markedly tumid (Text-fig. 204, B, F), except in *A. conigera* and *A. ramosa* (Text-fig. 204, H). MALE PALP : With tarsus often elevated dorsally. Palpal organs with well-defined *lamella characteristica* (*l*), different in each species.

There are five British species. The males are identified by the form of the *lamella*. The females divide into two groups, depending on the tumidity of the palps :

♀ : Palp strongly tumid . . . . *A. subtilis, A. decora, A. cauta.* .

♀ : Palp not strongly tumid (Text-fig. 204, H). . . *A. conigera, A. ramosa.*

Within these two groups, the females are identified by the epigynes and to some extent by the position of the trichobothria.

Agyneta subtilis (O. P.-Cambridge).
(Text-figs. 204, A, B ; 205, G, H)

Neriene subtilis O. P.-Cambridge, 1863, p. 8584 (♂). *Neriene anomala* idem, ibid., p. 8585 (♀). *N. subtilis* idem, 1879–81, p. 131. *Microneta anomala* W. Bosenberg, 1901–3, p. 149. *Agyneta subtilis* A. R. Jackson, 1912, p. 136 ; E. Simon, 1929, p. 538 ; F. Miller, 1947, Tab. 10, fig. 14 ; Tab. 11, figs. 2–4.

DESCRIPTION. LENGTH : ♀ : about 2·5 mm. ♂ : about 2·25 mm. CARAPACE : Brown, with sometimes faint radiating striæ. ABDOMEN : Grey to black. STERNUM : Yellow-brown to brown, margined with black. LEGS : Tm I 0·75–0·85. Brown or orange-brown, with tibia I and metatarsus I sometimes suffused with dark brown. FEMALE PALP : Strongly tumid (Text-fig. 204, B). EPIGYNE : Text-fig. 205, G, H ; the scape is scarcely bifid at its extremity. MALE PALP : Text-fig. 204, A.

OCCURRENCE : In undergrowth of woods, in grass, etc. Frequent, and widespread throughout the British Isles ; rather commoner in the south. Adult in spring, summer and autumn.

Agyneta conigera (O. P.-Cambridge).
(Text-figs. 204, C, E ; 205, D)

Neriene conigera O. P.-Cambridge, 1863, p. 8583, and 1879–81, p. 132. *Microneta conigera* C. Chyzer and L. Kulczynski, 1891–7, II, p. 86 ; W. Bosenberg, 1901–3 p. 147. *Agyneta conigera* A. R. Jackson, 1912, p. 134 ; E. Simon, 1929, p. 538 ; F, Miller, 1947, Tab. 10, figs. 11–13, Tab. 11, fig. 1.

DESCRIPTION. LENGTH : ♀♂ : about 2 mm. CARAPACE : Brown, with ocular area suffused with black, and with blackish fovea and striæ. ♀ : A definite depression lies between head and thorax (seen in profile) (Text-fig. 204, C). ABDOMEN : Black. STERNUM : Brown, suffused with black (particularly in ♂). LEGS : Tm I ca. 0·65. Brown. FEMALE PALP : Scarcely tumid. EPIGYNE : Text-fig. 205, D. MALE PALP : Text-fig. 204, E ; tarsus blackish, strongly elevated.

OCCURRENCE : Amongst moss, grass, heather, etc., and also on low bushes. Widespread throughout the British Isles, and not uncommon. Adult in spring and summer.

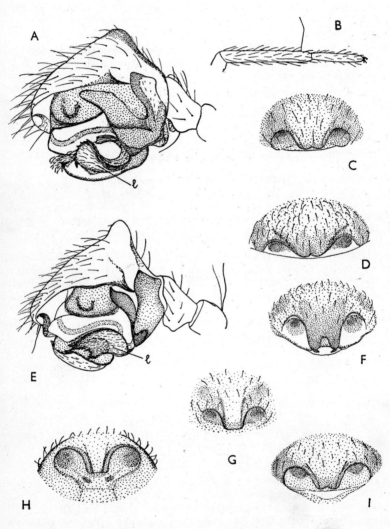

Text-fig. 205.—Male palps : A, *Agyneta ramosa;* E, *A. cauta.*
　Epigynes : C, *A. decora;* I, ditto (more from behind) ; D, *A. conigera;* F,
A. cauta; G, *A. subtilis;* H, ditto (from behind).
　B, *Agyneta:* Metatarsal trichobothrium.

Agyneta decora (O. P.-Cambridge).
(Text-figs. 204, G ; 205, C, I)

Neriene decora O. P.-Cambridge, 1870, p. 438, and 1879–81, p. 492. *Agyneta decora* A. R. Jackson, 1912, p. 135 ; F. Miller, 1947, Tab. 10, fig. 12, and Tab. 12, fig. 1.

DESCRIPTION. LENGTH : ♀ : 2·5 mm. ♂ : 2·5 mm. CARAPACE : Brown, with head suffused with black, and blackish fovea and striæ. ABDOMEN : Black to grey. STERNUM : As *A. subtilis*. LEGS : Tm I ca. 0·9. Brown, with tibiæ and metatarsi I and II suffused with black. FEMALE PALP : Strongly tumid. EPIGYNE : Text-fig. 205, C, I ; the scape is distinctly bifid at its end, particularly when viewed from behind. MALE PALP : Text-fig. 204, G ; tarsus blackish.

OCCURRENCE : Amongst moss and grass. Infrequent, but more records from the north than the south.

Agyneta cauta (O. P.-Cambridge).
(Text-figs. 204, F ; 205, E, F)

Microneta cauta O. P.-Cambridge, 1902, p. 31 (♂). *M. passiva* idem, 1906, p. 89 (♂), and 1910, p. 53 (♀). *Agyneta cauta* A. R. Jackson, 1912, p. 137 ; F. Miller, 1947, Tab. 11, figs. 5–7.

DESCRIPTION. LENGTH : ♀ : 2–2·25 mm. ♂ : 1·8–2 mm. CARAPACE : Brown. ABDOMEN : Grey to black. STERNUM : Yellow-brown. LEGS : Tm I 0·85–0·9. Orange-brown. FEMALE PALP : Strongly tumid (Text-fig. 204, F). EPIGYNE : Text-fig. 205, F ; the scape is strongly cleft at its end (there is some variation here, but it is always distinct). MALE PALP : Text-fig. 205, E ; tarsus suffused with black.

OCCURRENCE : Amongst moss and grass in wet places. Uncommon, but occurs more frequently in northern, exposed situations than in the south ; not recorded from Eire.

Agyneta ramosa Jackson.
(Text-figs. 204, D, H ; 205, A)

Agyneta ramosa A. R. Jackson, 1912, p. 139 (♂), and 1916, p. 361 (♀) ; F. Miller, 1947, Tab. 10, figs. 7–10.

DESCRIPTION. LENGTH : ♀ : 2–2·5 mm. ♂ : 2–2·25 mm. CARAPACE : Brown. Profile (Text-fig. 204, D), cf. *A. conigera*. ABDOMEN : Grey to greyish-black. STERNUM : Orange-brown. LEGS : Tm I 0·85–0·9. Colour as *A. subtilis*. FEMALE PALP : Only slightly tumid (Text-fig. 204, H). EPIGYNE : Scarcely (if at all) distinguishable from *A. subtilis*. MALE PALP : Text-fig. 205, A ; tarsus suffused with black.

OCCURRENCE : Amongst moss in swampy localities ; rare. Recorded from a few English and one Welsh county.

80. Genus MEIONETA J. E. Hull 1920.

CHARACTERS OF GENUS. CHELICERÆ : Dissimilar in the two sexes, being more divergent and attenuated apically in ♂ ; outer and inner borders with 3–5 teeth. LEGS : Metatarsus IV without a trichobothrium ; Tm I ca. 0·25. All tibiæ with two thin dorsal spines ; lateral

spines sometimes present.   EPIGYNES : Similar in form in all the
species (with *M. saxatilis* rather different).   MALE PALP : Tibiæ often
with apophysis or granulations at dorsal apex ; tarsus often gibbous
above.   Palpal organs with well-defined *lamella characteristica*, different
in each species.

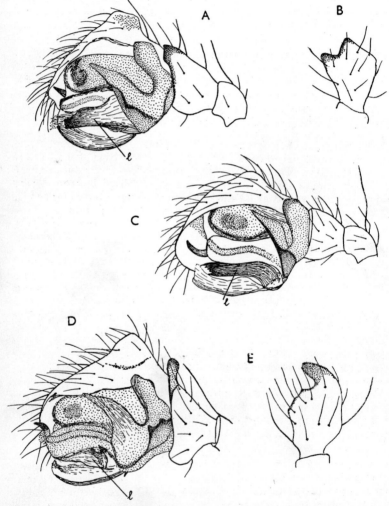

Text-fig. 206.—Male palps : A, *Meioneta rurestris;* C, *M. mollis;* D, *M. saxatilis.*
Male palpal tibiae (from above) : B, *M. rurestris;* E, *M. saxatilis.*

There are six British species, which can be divided into two groups by the tibial spines :—

(i) Tibiæ I and II with a retrolateral spine, approximately level with apical dorsal spine : *M. mollis, M. saxatilis, M. beata.*

(ii) Tibiæ I and II without lateral spines : *M. rurestris, M. gulosa, M. nigripes.*

The male sex can always be identified readily by the form of the *lamella* (*l*). Within group (i), the females can be identified without difficulty by the epigynes. Within group (ii), the females offer some difficulty (see descriptions following).

Meioneta rurestris (C. L. Koch).
(Text-figs. 206, A, B ; 208, A)

Micryphantes rurestris C. L. Koch, 1836, p. 84. *Neriene gracilis* J. Blackwall, 1861–4, p. 256. *N. flavipes* idem, 1861–4, p. 264. *N. fuscipalpis* O. P.-Cambridge, 1879–81, p. 129. *Micryphantes rurestris* C. Chyzer and L. Kulczynski, 1891–7, II, p. 88 ; A. R. Jackson, 1912, p. 126. *Ischnyphantes rurestris* E. Simon, 1929, p. 540 *Meioneta rurestris* F. Miller, 1947, Tab. 9, figs. 9–11.

DESCRIPTION. LENGTH : ♀♂ : 1·8–2·2 mm. CARAPACE : Brown to blackish-brown, with blackish fovea and striæ ; or wholly black. Some bristles in ocular area. EYES : Posterior medians one diam. or less apart, and one diam. from laterals, i.e. equidistant or rather closer to one another than to laterals. Posterior medians equal to or slightly greater than posterior laterals. ABDOMEN : Greyish-black to black. STERNUM : Blackish-brown or black, or yellowish suffused with black. CHELICERÆ : ♂ : Anteriorly with small warts carrying bristles. LEGS : Tm I ca. 0·25. Yellow to yellow-brown. Tibial spines approximately 1·5 diam. long. FEMALE PALP : Blackish, particularly on tibia and tarsus. EPIGYNE : Text-fig. 208, A. MALE PALP : Text-fig. 206, A, B ; tarsus (and sometimes whole limb) black. Tarsus conical above ; tibia with weak apophysis, with granular surface.

OCCURRENCE : Widespread and common throughout the British Isles, in a variety of situations. Adults at all seasons.

Meioneta mollis (O. P.-Cambridge).
(Text-figs. 206, C ; 208, B)

Neriene mollis O. P.-Cambridge, 1871, p. 429, and 1879–81, p. 134. *Linyphia frederici* idem, 1879–81, p. 186. *Sintula aerius* C. Chyzer and L. Kulczynski, 1891–7, II, p. 89 ; W. Bosenberg, 1901–3, p. 150. *Micryphantes mollis* A. R. Jackson, 1912, p. 129. *Aprolagus mollis* E. Simon, 1929, p. 542 ; F. Miller, 1947, Tab. 10, fig. 4, Tab. 9, fig. 15.

DESCRIPTION. LENGTH : ♀ : 1·4–2 mm. ♂ : 1·2–1·5 mm. CARAPACE : Brown, with blackish fovea and striæ. EYES : Posteriors large, with medians 0·5 diam. apart, and slightly more from laterals. ABDOMEN : Grey to black. STERNUM : Blackish, shiny. LEGS : Tm I 0·25–0·27. Yellow to yellow-brown. Tibial spines 1·5–2·5 diams. in length. Tibiæ I and II with retrolateral spine. EPIGYNE :

Text-fig. 208, B. MALE PALP : Text-fig. 206, C ; tarsus and tibia blackish ; tarsus gibbous above.

OCCURRENCE : In woods, in vegetable detritus, etc., in the southern half of the British Isles. Uncommon ; adult in spring and autumn.

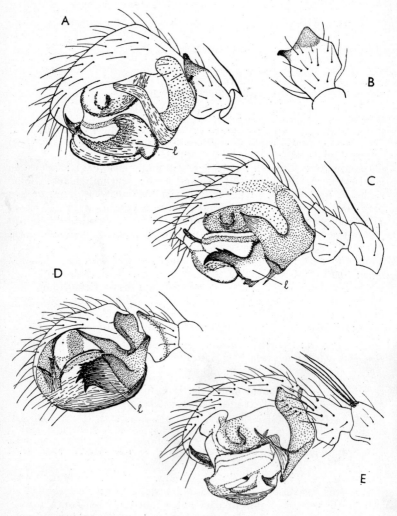

Text-fig. 207.—Male palps : A, *Meioneta beata* ; C, *M. gulosa* ; D, *M. nigripes* ; E, *Microneta viaria*.
    Male palpal tibia (from above) : B, *M. beata*.

Meioneta saxatilis (Blackwall).
(Text-figs. 206, D, E ; 208, E)

Neriene saxatilis J. Blackwall, 1844, p. 183, and 1861–4, p. 262 ; O. P.-Cambridge, 1879–81, p. 124. *Micryphantes saxatilis* A. R. Jackson, 1912, p. 130. *Aprolagus saxatilis* E. Simon, 1929, p. 541 ; F. Miller, 1947, Tab. 10, fig. 2, Tab. 9, fig. 14.

DESCRIPTION. LENGTH : ♀♂ : about 2 mm. CARAPACE : Yellow-brown to brown, with ocular area often suffused with black, and with fovea and striæ sometimes blackish. ABDOMEN : Grey to black. STERNUM : Blackish, shiny. LEGS : Tm I 0·25. Yellow-brown. Tibial spines 1·5–2 diam. in length ; tibia I with retrolateral spine. EPIGYNE : Text-fig. 208, E. MALE PALP : Text-fig. 206, D, E ; tibia with black, rugose curved apophysis ; tibia and tarsus blackish. Tarsus gibbous above.

OCCURRENCE : Amongst low vegetation ; fairly common, and widespread throughout the British Isles. Adult in spring and summer.

Meioneta beata (O. P.-Cambridge).
(Text-figs. 207, A, B ; 208, D)

Microneta beata O. P.-Cambridge, 1906, p. 90. *Micryphantes beatus* A. R. Jackson, 1912, p. 128. *Bathyphantes explicatus* O. P.-Cambridge, 1911 (2), p. 370, and 1912, p. 75. *Meioneta beata* J. Denis, 1942, p. 94. *Aprolagus beatus* F. Miller, 1947, Tab. 10, fig. 1, 3.

DESCRIPTION. LENGTH : ♀ : About 1·75 mm. ♂ : About 1·5 mm. CARAPACE : Brown, with darker fovea and striæ. ABDOMEN : Blackish, with sometimes very faint light chevrons. STERNUM : Brown, with black reticulations. LEGS : Tm I 0·25. Yellow to yellow-brown. Tibial spines 1–1·5 diam. in length ; tibiæ I and II with a retrolateral spine. FEMALE PALP : Tarsus and tibia suffused with black. EPIGYNE : Text-fig. 208, D ; the scape is rather narrower and longer than in the other species. MALE PALP : Text-fig. 207, A, B ; tarsus and tibia suffused with black. Tibia has short apophysis ; tarsus not very gibbous above.

OCCURRENCE : Amongst moss and grass. Rare, but recorded from throughout England and from Scotland.

Meioneta gulosa (L. Koch).
(Text-figs. 207, C ; 208, C)

Erigone gulosa L. Koch, 1869, p. 193. *Neriene sublimis* O. P.-Cambridge, 1879–81, p. 491. *Micryphantes sublimis* A. R. Jackson, 1912, p. 127. *Ischnyphantes gulosus* E. Simon, 1929, p. 539.

DESCRIPTION. LENGTH : ♀ : 1·8–2·2 mm. ♂ : 1·7–1·8 mm. CARAPACE : Yellow-brown to dark brown, suffused with black, and with dark fovea and striæ. EYES : As *M. rurestris*. ABDOMEN : Grey to black. STERNUM : Blackish. LEGS : Tm I ca. 0·22. Brown, suffused with black. Tibial spines 1–1·5 diam. in length. FEMALE PALP : Suffused with black. EPIGYNE : Text-fig. 208, C ; closely similar to *M. rurestris*, but with scape wider, and lateral apertures more oblique. MALE PALP : Text-fig. 207, C ; tarsus gibbous above ; tibia with short apophysis.

AA

The ♀ cannot be distinguished with certainty from *M. rurestris* though there are slight differences in the epigynes and in the position of Tm I. Its identity can be established only by its habitat, and by its association with the ♂.

OCCURRENCE: On high ground (usually above 2,000 feet) in the Welsh mountains, the Lake District, Yorkshire and Scotland. Not uncommon in these situations. Adults in spring and summer.

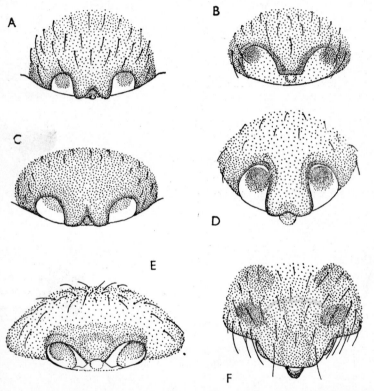

Text-fig. 208.—Epigynes: A, *Meioneta rurestris;* B, *M. mollis;*   C, *M. gulosa ;* D, *M. beata;* E, *M. saxatilis;* F, *Microneta viaria.*

Meioneta nigripes (Simon).
(Text-fig. 207, D)

Microneta nigripes E. Simon, 1884, p. 439. *Micryphantes nigripes* A. R. Jackson, 1915, p. 186 ; J. Braendegaard, 1946, p. 32. *Ischnyphantes nigripes* E. Simon, 1929, p. 541.

DESCRIPTION. LENGTH : ♀: About 2 mm. ♂: 1·75 mm. CARA-PACE : Dark brown. EYES : Posterior medians large, greater than posterior laterals. Posterior medians ca. one diam. or slightly less apart, and ca. 0·5 diam. from laterals, i.e., further from each other than from laterals (cf. *M. rurestris* and *M. gulosa*). ABDOMEN : Black. STERNUM : Black. LEGS : Tm I 0·21–0·26. Dark brown. FEMALE PALP : Dark brown, with tibia and tarsus suffused with black. EPIGYNE : Not distinguishable from *M. rurestris* or *M. gulosa*. MALE PALP : Text-fig. 207, D.

OCCURRENCE : Cairngorm Mountains, Lochnagar, and Conoch Craig, Scotland, above 2,500 feet. Adult in June-August.

81. Genus **MICRONETA** A. Menge 1868.

CHARACTERS OF GENUS. CHELICERÆ : ♂ : Divergent and attenuated apically, being more highly developed than in female. LEGS : Metatarsus IV with a trichobothrium ; Tm I 0·66–0·7. All tibiæ with two rather short dorsal spines ; tibia I with an additional very small prolateral spine. MALE PALP : Patella with a bunch of long spines, directed forwards (Text-fig. 207, E).

There is one British species.

Microneta viaria (Blackwall).
(Text-figs. 207, E ; 208, F)

Neriene viaria J. Blackwall, 1841, p. 645, and 1861–4, p. 255 ; O. P.-Cambridge, 1879–81, p. 127. *Microneta viaria* A. R. Jackson, 1912, p. 132 ; C. Chyzer and L. Kulczynski, 1891–7, II, p. 86 ; E. Simon, 1929, p. 537 ; F. Miller, 1947, Tab. 11, figs. 8–11.

DESCRIPTION. LENGTH : ♀♂ : About 2·5 mm. ; ♂ often larger than ♀. CARAPACE : Yellow-brown or orange-brown. ABDOMEN : Grey to black. STERNUM : Yellow to orange. LEGS : Tm I 0·66–0·7. Orange-brown with femora sometimes rather darker. EPIGYNE : Text-fig. 208, F. MALE PALP : Text-fig. 207, E : 5–6 long spines directed forwards on patella.

OCCURRENCE : In detritus, particularly in woods. Widespread throughout the British Isles, and very common. Adults at most seasons.

82. Genus **MARO** O. P.-Cambridge 1906.

CHARACTERS OF GENUS. Very small, rather pale-coloured spiders. EYES : Fairly large. LEGS : Metatarsus IV without a trichobothrium ; Tm I about 0·4. All tibiæ with two fine spines dorsally (somewhat difficult to see) ; no lateral spines. Legs rather short, with tarsi almost equal in length to metatarsi. EPIGYNE : With scape. MALE PALP : Tibia without apophysis ; paracymbium well developed. The genitalia are Linyphiine in character, and parts of the bulb are homologous with parts of the bulb of *Linyphia* (Å. Holm, 1945, p. 43).

There are two British species, which can be distinguished by the sex organs. The genus seems to be rather close to *Centromerus*.

Maro minutus O. P.-Cambridge.
(Text-fig. 209, A, B, C)

Maro minutus O. P.-Cambridge, 1906, p. 87 (♀) ; A. R. Jackson, 1908, p. 60 (♀♂) ; O. P.-Cambridge, 1908, p. 174. *Maro humicola* W. Falconer, 1919, p. 300, and 1937, p. 3. *Gongylidiellum minutissimum* E. Schenkel, 1929, p. 138 (♀).

DESCRIPTION. LENGTH : ♀♂ : 1·1–1·25 mm. CARAPACE : Pale yellow, with sometimes faint radiating striæ ; ocular area suffused with black. EYES : On black spots. Anterior medians large, about 0·75 diam. of laterals ; anteriors practically touching (ca. 0·25 diam. apart). Posterior medians ca. one diam. apart, and ca. 0·5 diam. from laterals.

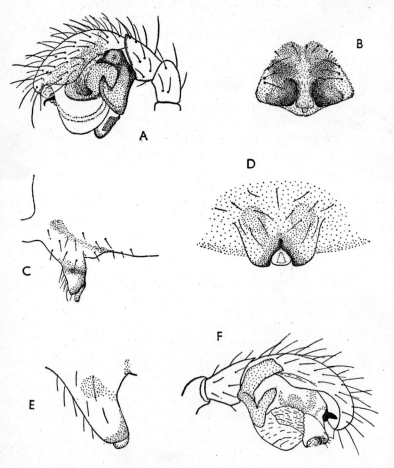

Text-fig. 209.—*Maro minutus:* A, ♂ palp ; B, epigyne ; C, ditto (from side). *M. sublestus:* D, epigyne ; E, ditto (from side) ; F, ♂ palp (right).

ABDOMEN : Pale whitish grey, clothed with fairly long hairs. STERNUM : Pale yellow, sometimes reticulated with blackish. LEGS : Tm I 0·38. Yellow-brown to brown, short and rather stout. Tibia IV apical spine rather short ; close to it is a very long trichobothrium. EPIGYNE : Text-fig. 209, B, C. MALE PALP : Text-fig. 209, A.

OCCURRENCE : Under stones, and in moss, pine needles and detritus. Recorded from a few localities from the south coast to Yorkshire. Adults in autumn, winter and spring.

Maro sublestus Falconer.
(Text-fig. 209, D, E, F)

Maro sublestus W. Falconer, 1915, p. 226 (♀) ; Å. Holm, 1945, p. 43 (♀♂). *Centromerus nanus* E. Schenkel, 1939, p. 109 (♂).

A single ♀ only of this species has been taken in Britain (Wicken Fen, 1914), and was subsequently lost. The descriptions given here are based on Swedish specimens, kindly provided by Dr. Å. Holm.

DESCRIPTION. LENGTH : ♀ : 1·5 mm. ♂ : 1·1–1·2 mm. CARAPACE : Pale yellow to yellow, with faint black striæ. EYES : As *M. minutus*. ABDOMEN : Pale whitish grey, clothed with fine hairs. STERNUM : Pale yellow, reticulated faintly with black. LEGS : Tm I 0·4. Yellow (♀) to yellow-brown (♂), short and rather stout. Apical spine on tibia IV rather short (particularly in ♂), and close to it is a very long trichobothrium. EPIGYNE : Text-fig. 209, D, E. MALE PALP : Text-fig. 209, F.

OCCURRENCE : Wicken Fen (1914).

83. Genus CENTROMERUS F. Dahl 1886.

CHARACTERS OF GENUS. CHELICERÆ : Outer margin with three teeth. In four species (*C. prudens, C. laevitarsis, C. arcanus* and *C. sylvaticus*) the ♂ cheliceræ have a longitudinal row of minute bristles, close to and parallel with the external border (Text-fig. 213, D). LEGS : Metatarsus IV without trichobothrium ; Tm I ca. 0·35. Legs fairly short and stout. All tibiæ with two dorsal spines (except *C. dilutus, C. arcanus, C. persimilis, C. serratus* and *C. satyrus*, where tibia IV has only *one* dorsal spine). Tibia I sometimes with a single prolateral spine. Metatarsi I and II with a small dorsal spine. Femur I (and sometimes II) with one or two spines. EPIGYNE : Usually with scape.

There are 12 British species. The males are often larger than the females. All the species have distinctive sex organs, and are readily identified by this means. The genus is very close to *Syedra*.

⟩(Centromerus sylvaticus (Blackwall).
(Text-figs. 210, A ; 212, A)

Neriene sylvatica J. Blackwall, 1841, p. 644, and 1861–4, p. 254 ; O. P.-Cambridge, 1879–81, p. 129. *Centromerus sylvaticus* C. Chyzer and L. Kulczynski, 1891–7, II, p. 82 ; E. Simon, 1929, pp. 549, 559. *Tmeticus serratus* O. P.-Cambridge, 1907, p. 143 (♀).

DESCRIPTION. LENGTH : ♀♂ : About 2·5–3 mm. CARAPACE : Yellow to orange-brown. ABDOMEN : Grey to black. STERNUM :

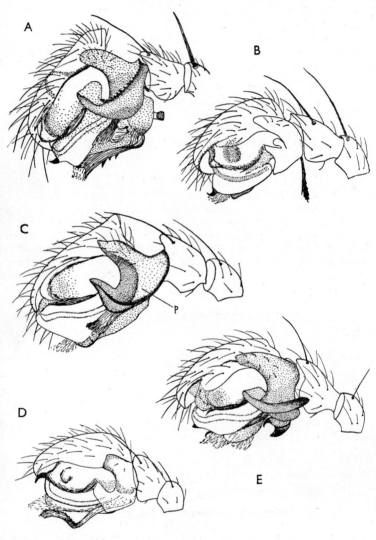

Text-fig. 210.—Male palps : A, *Centromerus sylvaticus;* B, *C. expertus;* C, *C. prudens;* D, *C. dilutus;* E, *C. arcanus.*

Yellow or yellow-brown, finely reticulated with black. CHELICERÆ : ♂ : With longitudinal row of minute bristles. LEGS : Tm I 0·4–0·42. Pale yellow to orange-brown. Numerous erect hairs present, as well as prone ones. EPIGYNE : Text-fig. 212, A. MALE PALP : Text-fig. 210, A ; the paracymbium has numerous teeth along its inner margin. Patella with stout spine.

OCCURRENCE : In moss and grass, particularly in woods. Widespread throughout the British Isles, and common locally. Adults in autumn, winter and spring.

Centromerus expertus (O. P.-Cambridge).
(Text-figs. 210, B ; 212, H)

Linyphia experta O. P.-Cambridge, 1871, p. 429, and 1879–81, p. 203. *Centromerus expertus* C. Chyzer and L. Kulczynski, 1891–7, II, p. 82 ; W. Bosenberg, 1901–3, p. 132 ; E. Simon, 1929, pp. 546, 556.

DESCRIPTION. LENGTH : ♀♂ : 2·5–3 mm. CARAPACE : Yellow-brown. ABDOMEN : Grey to black. STERNUM : Yellow-brown, faintly suffused with black. CHELICERÆ : ♂ : With longitudinal row of minute bristles, less pronounced than in *C. sylvaticus*. LEGS : Tm I 0·4. Yellow-brown to brown. Tibial spines fairly short but stout. EPIGYNE : Text-fig. 212, H. MALE PALP : Text-fig. 210, B ; a slender apophysis, with serrated edge, projects from near base of palpal organs.

OCCURRENCE : Amongst moss and grass, in woods, etc. Widespread but infrequent ; perhaps commoner in south and midlands than in north. Adult in summer and autumn.

Centromerus prudens (O. P.-Cambridge).
(Text-figs. 210, C ; 212, B)

Linyphia prudens O. P.-Cambridge, 1873 (1), p. 538, and 1879–81, p. 456. *Centromerus prudens* E. Simon, 1929, pp. 549, 558. *C. serratus* O. P.-Cambridge, 1907, p. 143 (♂).

DESCRIPTION. LENGTH : ♀♂ : 2·25–2·5 mm. CARAPACE : Yellow to yellow-brown. ABDOMEN : Grey. STERNUM : Yellow-brown, sometimes suffused with black. CHELICERÆ : ♂ : With longitudinal row of minute bristles. LEGS : Tm I 0·35. Yellow to yellow-brown ; spines relatively long and stout. EPIGYNE : Text-fig. 212, B. MALE PALP : Text-fig. 210, C ; paracymbium large and prominent.

OCCURRENCE : In moss, grass, heather, etc. Widespread throughout the British Isles, but commoner in the north than the south, where it is infrequent. Adult in autumn, winter and spring.

Centromerus arcanus (O. P.-Cambridge).
(Text-figs. 210, E ; 212, D)

Linyphia arcana O. P.-Cambridge, 1873 (1), p. 539, and 1879–81, p. 522. *Centromerus arcanus* C. Chyzer and L. Kulczynski, 1891–7, II, p. 84 ; E. Simon, 1929, pp. 547, 554.

DESCRIPTION. LENGTH : ♀ : 2 mm. ♂ : 2–2·5 mm. CARAPACE : Pale yellow to yellow-brown. ABDOMEN : Grey to whitish grey. STERNUM : Yellow, reticulated faintly with black ; sometimes margined

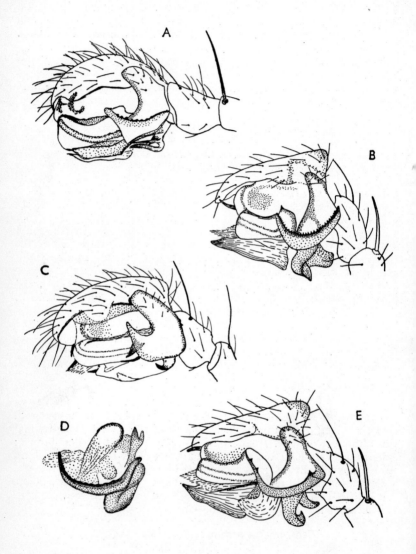

Text-fig. 211.—Male palps : A, *Centromerus incultus;* B, *C. serratus;* C, *C. laevitarsis;* E, *C. jacksoni;* D, paracymbium : *C. subacutus* (♂).

with black. CHELICERÆ : ♂ : With longitudinal row of minute bristles. LEGS : Tm I ca. 0·4. Yellow to orange-brown. Tibia IV with one dorsal spine only. EPIGYNE : Text-fig. 212, D ; scape long and prominent. MALE PALP : Text-fig. 210, E ; paracymbium large and prominent.

OCCURRENCE : Frequent locally on high ground, particularly in the more northern counties ; widely distributed throughout the British Isles. In moss and grass, and in pine needles. Adults in autumn, winter and spring.

Centromerus laevitarsis (Simon).
(Text-figs. 211, C ; 212, E)

Tmeticus laevitarsis E. Simon, 1884, p. 395. *Centromerus emptus* A. R. Jackson, 1907, p. 4. *Tmeticus emptus* O. P.-Cambridge, 1907, p. 140. *Centromerus laevitarsis* E. Simon, 1929, pp. 548, 553.

DESCRIPTION. LENGTH : ♀♂ : 1·6–1·9 mm. CARAPACE : Yellow to yellow-brown. ABDOMEN : Grey to blackish. STERNUM : Yellow, suffused with blackish. CHELICERÆ : ♂ : With longitudinal row of minute bristles. LEGS : Tm I ca. 0·4. Yellow to yellow-brown. EPIGYNE : Text-fig. 212, E ; scape very long. MALE PALP : Text-fig. 211, C.

OCCURRENCE : Only British locality is Oakmere, Delamere Forest (Cheshire), where it was frequent (at least up to ten years ago) in a damp, mossy area in a wood. Adult in autumn, winter and spring.

Centromerus dilutus (O. P.-Cambridge).
(Text-figs. 210, D ; 212, F, G)

Erigone diluta O. P.-Cambridge, 1875 (1), p. 331. *Neriene diluta* O. P.-Cambridge, 1879–81, p. 437. *Lepthyphantes plumiger* F. O. P.-Cambridge, 1892, p. 386. *Sintula diluta* W. Bosenberg, 1901–3, p. 134. *Rhabdoria diluta* J. E. Hull, 1909, p. 583. *Centromerus dilutus* E. Simon, 1929, pp. 546, 553.

DESCRIPTION. LENGTH : ♀♂ : About 1·25 mm. CARAPACE : Yellow to yellow-brown. ABDOMEN : Grey to blackish. STERNUM : Yellow, suffused with some black. LEGS : Tm I 0·3–0·35. Yellow to yellow-brown. Spines rather short and fine ; tibia IV with one spine only. EPIGYNE : Text-fig. 212, F, G ; the slender, colourless scape is often not very visible from below. MALE PALP : Text-fig. 210, D ; a plumose apophysis projects from the base of the palpal organs.

OCCURRENCE : Widespread throughout the British Isles, and very common. In the detritus of woods, and sometimes in moss and grass away from woods. Adults in autumn, winter and spring.

Centromerus incilium (L. Koch).
(Text-fig. 212, C)

Linyphia incilium L. Koch, 1881, p. 53. *Centromerus incilium* C. Chyzer and L. Kulczynski, 1891–7, II, p. 84 ; E. Simon, 1929, pp. 552, 554. *Tmeticus similis* (non Kulczynski) O. P.-Cambridge, 1905, p. 62.

This spider was considered previously (O.P.-Cambridge, 1905, p. 62, and A. R. Jackson, 1916(2), p. 167) to be probably *C. similis* Kulcz.

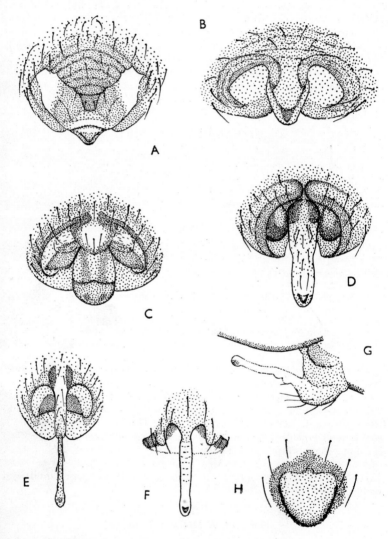

Text-fig. 212.—Epigynes : A, *Centromerus sylvaticus;* B, *C. prudens;* C. *C. incilium;* D, *C. arcanus;* E, *C. laevitarsis;* F, *C. dilutus;* G, ditto (from side) ; H, *C. expertus.*

The recent capture of more specimens, and comparison with examples of *C. incilium* (L. Koch) from the Koch Collection in the British Museum (Natural History), has shown the probable identity of the spider with the latter species.

DESCRIPTION. LENGTH : ♀ : About 2 mm. CARAPACE : Brown to yellow-brown. ABDOMEN : Grey to black. STERNUM : Brown. LEGS : Tm I 0·35. Brown. EPIGYNE : Text-fig. 212, C. The male has not yet been taken in Britain.

OCCURRENCE : A single female, near Balmoral (Scotland). Females in turf on Frilford Heath (Oxfordshire) in March and April 1952 (E. Duffey).

Centromerus incultus Falconer.
(Text-figs. 211, A ; 213, C)

Centromerus incultus W. Falconer, 1915, p. 226 (♀) ; A. R. Jackson, 1924, p. 120 (♂ ?). ? *Centromerus novaki* F. Miller and J. Kratochvil, 1940 (1), p. 60.

The only ♀ has been lost ; its description has been given by Falconer (loc. cit.) ; it is not absolutely certain that the ♂ corresponds with the ♀, but the probability is high.

DESCRIPTION. LENGTH : ♂ : 1·9 mm. CARAPACE : Yellow-brown. ABDOMEN : Grey. STERNUM : Yellow-brown, faintly reticulated with black. LEGS : Tm I 0·36. Pale yellow-brown. Tibia IV with two dorsal spines. EPIGYNE : Text-fig. 213, C (after Falconer). MALE PALP : Text-fig. 211, A.

OCCURRENCE : Wicken Fen (Cambridgeshire) : ♀ in July. Chittering (Cambridgeshire) : ♂ in September.

Centromerus subacutus (O. P.-Cambridge).
(Text-fig. 211, D)

Opistoxys subacuta O. P.-Cambridge, 1891, p. 92 (♂), and 1914, p. 128. *Lepthyphantes patens* O. P.-Cambridge, 1907, p. 139 (♂). *Centromerus subacuta* A. R. Jackson, 1916 (2), p. 166.

DESCRIPTION. Only the male is known, and the unique specimen still in existence is in very bad condition. The whole spider has faded to a pale yellow colour. LEGS : Tm I 0·35. MALE PALP : Distended, and in such a bad condition that nothing very clear could be seen for drawing ; paracymbium (Text-fig. 211, D).

OCCURRENCE : Two males only have been found ; one from moss (Dorset, 1890), and one in the nest of the ant *Acanthomyops fuliginosus* (in Berkshire).

Centromerus serratus (O. P.-Cambridge).
(Text-figs. 211, B ; 213, A)

Erigone serrata O. P.-Cambridge, 1875, p. 325 ; non *Tmeticus serratus* idem, 1907, p. 143. *Centromerus serratus* E. Simon, 1929, pp. 549, 557 ; A. F. Millidge and G. H. Locket, 1947, p. 111.

DESCRIPTION. LENGTH : ♀ : 1·25 mm. ♂ : 1·5 mm. CARAPACE : Yellow to yellow-brown. ABDOMEN : Grey to blackish. STERNUM : Whitish-yellow to yellow. LEGS : Tm I ca. 0·3. Yellow to yellow brown. Tibiæ I–III with two small spines; tibia IV with one spine only. Metatarsal spines very weak (not greatly different from erect hairs). EPIGYNE: Text-fig. 213, A; the opening occupies practically one-half of width of abdomen. MALE PALP: Text-fig. 211, B; the paracymbium is toothed along its inner margin. The sex organs are very similar to those of *C. sylvaticus*.

OCCURRENCE: In pine needles and moss. Known only from the Isle of Wight and Hampshire. Adults in autumn and winter.

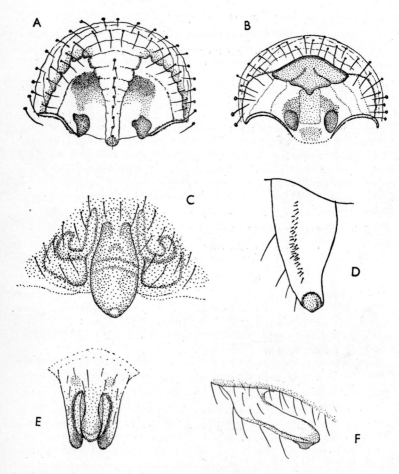

Text-fig. 213.—Epigynes: A, *Centromerus serratus;* B, *C. jacksoni;* C, *C. incultus* (after Falconer); E, *C. persimilis;* F, ditto (from side).
D, *C. arcanus* ♂ : Chelicera (from side and to front).

Centromerus jacksoni Denis.
(Text-figs. 211, E ; 213, B.)

Centromerus satyrus A. F. Millidge and G. H. Locket, 1947, p. 112. non *Tmeticus satyrus* E. Simon, 1884, p. 419. *C. jacksoni* J. Denis, 1952, p. 40.

DESCRIPTION. LENGTH : ♀ : 1·5 mm. ♂ : 1·8 mm. CARAPACE : Yellow to yellow-brown. ABDOMEN : Grey. STERNUM : Pale yellow. LEGS : Tm I ca. 0·3. Yellow to yellow-brown. Spines as *C. serratus*. EPIGYNE : Text-fig. 213, B ; the opening occupies practically one-half of width of abdomen. MALE PALP : Text-fig. 211, E ; the paracymbium has three teeth along its inner margin.

OCCURRENCE : Great Kimble (Bucks) amongst beech leaves, in autumn. Cornwall, Surrey and Sussex, deep amongst beech leaves and detritus.

Centromerus persimilis (O. P.-Cambridge).
(Text-fig. 213, E, F)

Maro persimilis O. P.-Cambridge, 1912, p. 91 (♀). ? *Centromerus strandi* F. Miller, 1937, p. 563.

DESCRIPTION. LENGTH : ♀ : 1·25 mm. CARAPACE : Yellow-brown. EYES : On black spots. Anterior medians ca. 0·5 diam. of laterals, ca. one diam. apart and one diam. from laterals ; posterior medians ca. one diam. apart, and 0·5–0·7 diam. from laterals. ABDOMEN : Dusky yellow. STERNUM : Yellow-brown. LEGS : Tm I 0·35. Yellow-brown, short and rather stout. Tibiæ I–III with two dorsal spines. Metatarsi I and II with one extremely fine bristle. EPIGYNE : Text-fig. 213, E, F.

OCCURRENCE : Known from two localities only, Carlow (Eire) and Northumberland, under stones. Male not known.

84. Genus CENTROMERITA F. Dahl 1882.

CHARACTERS OF GENUS. CHELICERÆ : Outer margin with three teeth. LEGS : Metatarsus IV without a trichobothrium ; Tm I 0·4. All tibiæ with two dorsal spines, lateral spines, and some stout spines ventrally. All metatarsi with one dorsal spine. Femora I and II each with a dorsal and a prolateral spine. MALE PALP : Tibia with a bunch of stout spines or bristles.

There are two British species.

Centromerita bicolor (Blackwall).
(Text-fig. 214, A, D)

Neriene bicolor J. Blackwall, 1833, p. 344, and 1861–4, p. 250. *Linyphia bicolor* O. P.-Cambridge, 1879–81, p. 206. *Centromerus bicolor* C. Chyzer and L. Kulczynski, 1891–7, II, p. 81. *Centromerinus bicolor* E. Simon, 1929, p. 546.

DESCRIPTION. LENGTH : ♀♂ : 3–3·5 mm. CARAPACE : Brown or yellow-brown. ♂ : Head with numerous long forward-directed spines (less obvious in ♀). EYES : Posterior medians one diam. or more apart, and one diam. or more from laterals (cf. *C. concinna*). ABDOMEN : Grey to black. LEGS : Tm I ca. 0·4. Yellow to yellow-brown. Tibia I with a row of 5–6 long spines ventrally ; tibia IV with 5–7 spines ventrally (cf. *C. concinna*). All metatarsi with a spine close to the trichobothrium ; metatarsus IV with an additional pro-lateral and a ventral spine. EPIGYNE : Text-fig. 214, D. MALE PALP : Text-fig. 214, A ; tibia with 12 or more stout plumose spines, set rather close to base (cf. *C. concinna*).

OCCURRENCE : In grass, moss, detritus, etc. Widespread and frequent throughout the British Isles, but less common in the south. Adults most of the year.

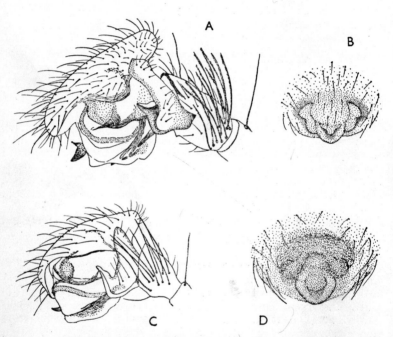

TEXT-FIG. 214.—Male palps : A, *Centromerita bicolor* : C, *C. concinna*. Epigynes : B, *C. concinna* : D, *C. bicolor*.

Centromerita concinna (Thorell).
(Text-fig. 214, B, C)

Linyphia concinna T. Thorell, 1875, p. 29. *Tmeticus concinnus* O. P.-Cambridge, 1886, p. 74. *Troglohyphantes margerisoni* W. Falconer, 1919, p. 297. *Centromerinus bicolor concinnus* E. Simon, 1929, p. 546.

DESCRIPTION. LENGTH : ♀♂ : 2–2·5 mm. Colour as *C. bicolor*, but with CARAPACE usually pale yellow with narrow black margin. ♂ : Head with few rather short spines ; ♀ : Head practically spineless. EYES : Posterior medians less than one diam. apart, and one diam.

or less from laterals (cf. *C. bicolor*). Legs : Tm I ca. 0·4. Less spinose than in *C. bicolor*. Tibia I with 3–4 spines (or less) ventrally ; tibia IV with 2–3 (or fewer) spines ventrally (cf. *C. bicolor*). All metatarsi with a dorsal spine ; usually with no extra spines on metatarsus IV. Epigyne : Text-fig. 214, B. Male palp : Text-fig. 214, C ; tibia with 6–9 stout spines, only slightly plumose, set approximately mid-way (cf. *C. bicolor*) ; palpal organs practically indistinguishable from *C. bicolor*.

Occurrence : In similar situations to *C. bicolor*, and perhaps rather commoner. Adults in autumn and winter.

85. Genus **SINTULA** E. Simon 1884.

Characters of Genus. Legs : Metatarsus IV without a tricho-bothrium ; Tm I about 0·25. Tibiæ I and II with two thin spines ; tibiæ III and IV with one spine. Metatarsi I and II with one dorsal spine (stronger in ♂) (sometimes apparently missing). Metatarsus I scarcely longer than tarsus I. Male palp : Tarsus drawn out basally into long horn-like process.

There is one British species.

Sintula cornigera (Blackwall).
(Text-fig. 215, A, B)

Neriene cornigera J. Blackwall, 1856, p. 233, and 1861–4, p. 273 ; O. P.-Cambridge, 1879–81, p. 430. *Micryphantes corniger* C. Chyzer and L. Kulczynski, 1891–7, II, p. 87. *Sintula corniger* E. Simon, 1926, p. 468.

Description. Length : ♀♂ : 1·5–1·75 mm. Carapace : Yellow to pale brown. Eyes : Anteriors all ca. 0·5 diam. apart ; posteriors all ca. 0·75 diam. apart. Abdomen : Grey to greenish-grey. Sternum : Yellow, suffused and reticulated with much black. Legs : Tm I ca. 0·25. Yellow-brown, with tibiæ I and II suffused with black (some-times heavily in ♂, sometimes absent in ♀). Tibial spines very thin. Epigyne : Text-fig. 215, B. Male palp : Text-fig. 215, A ; the patella has several long black spines. The tarsus is drawn out basally into a long, horn-like process bearing several strong black plumose spines.

Occurrence : In moss, grass, sphagnum, etc., in wet and swampy areas. Widespread, but rare. Adult in autumn and spring.

86. Genus **OREONETIDES** E. Strand 1901.

Characters of Genus. Rather similar to *Centromerus* in general form. Cheliceræ : Outer margin with five teeth. Legs : Metatarsus IV without a trichobothrium ; Tm I 0·36–0·48. All tibiæ with two rather thin dorsal spines ; tibia I with an additional prolateral spine. No metatarsal spines. Epigyne : With a large scape, completely covering the genital aperture.

There are three British species, which are readily distinguished by the sex organs.

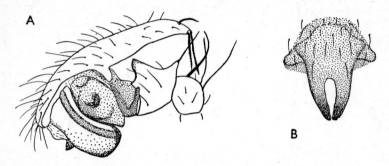

TEXT-FIG. 215.—*Sintula cornigera :* A, ♂ palp ; B, epigyne.

Oreonetides abnormis (Blackwall).
(Text-fig. 216, A, B)

Neriene abnormis J. Blackwall, 1841, p. 649, and 1861–4, p. 286. *Linyphia abnormis* O. P.-Cambridge, 1879–81, p. 207. *Lepthyphantes abnormis* W. Bosenberg, 1901–3, p. 73. *Oreonetides abnormis* E. Simon, 1929, p. 561.

DESCRIPTION. LENGTH : ♀♂ : About 3 mm. CARAPACE : Yellow-brown. ABDOMEN : Grey to black. LEGS : Tm I 0·45–0·48. Yellow-brown. EPIGYNE : Text-fig. 216, B. MALE PALP : Text-fig. 216, A.

OCCURRENCE : In moss, grass, detritus, etc., often in woods ; also on high ground (up to about 2,000 feet) in northern England and Scotland. Widespread throughout the British Isles, and fairly frequent. Adults in late summer and autumn.

Oreonetides firmus (O. P.-Cambridge).
(Text-fig. 216, C, D)

Tmeticus firmus O. P.-Cambridge, 1901, p. 59. *Centromerus firmus* idem, 1908, p. 174. *Oreonetides firmus* E. Simon, 1929, p. 560.

DESCRIPTION. LENGTH : ♀♂ : 1·6–2 mm. CARAPACE : Yellow-brown, with three long spines in median line. ABDOMEN : Grey. LEGS : Tm I 0·36–0·38. Yellow-brown. EPIGYNE : Text-fig. 216, D. MALE PALP : Text-fig. 216, C.

OCCURRENCE : In heather, amongst pine needles, under gorse bushes. Recorded from a number of English counties, from north to south, and from Scotland and Eire, but rare. Adult ♀'s throughout the year ; ♂'s in August–September.

Oreonetides vaginatus (Thorell).
(Text-fig. 216, E, F)

Erigone vaginata T. Thorell, 1872, p. 153 (♀). *Erigone adipata* L. Koch, 1872, p. 263 (♀♂). *Linyphia reticulata* O. P.-Cambridge, 1879–81, p. 521. *Macrargus adipatus* C. Chyzer and L. Kulczynski, 1891–7, II, p. 79. *Oreonetides adipatus* J. E. Hull, 1909, p. 580. *O. vaginatus* E. Simon, 1929, p. 561 ; Å. Holm, 1945, p. 45 ; J. Braendegaard, 1946, p. 34.

DESCRIPTION. LENGTH: ♀♂: 3·0–3·5 mm. CARAPACE: Brown. ABDOMEN: Grey. LEGS: Tm I 0·4. Brown. Tibial spines thin and rather short; tibia I with a series of long inclined hairs ventrally. EPIGYNE: Text-fig. 216, F. MALE PALP: Text-fig. 216, E.

OCCURRENCE: Under stones, on mountains and high ground, in Wales, northern England, Ireland and Scotland. Rare. Adults in late summer and autumn.

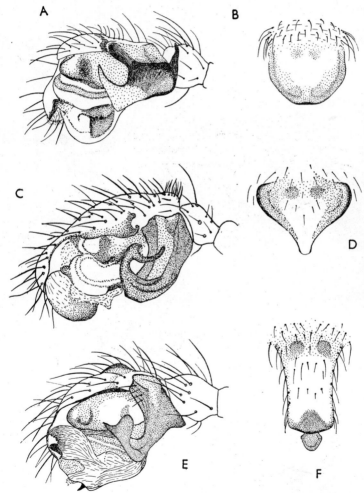

TEXT-FIG. 216.—Male palps: A, *Oreonetides abnormis;* C, *O. firmus;* E, *O. vaginatus.*
    Epigynes: B, *O. abnormis;* D, *O. firmus;* F, *O. vaginatus.*

87. Genus **MACRARGUS** F. Dahl 1886.

CHARACTERS OF GENUS. CHELICERÆ: Outer margin with five teeth ; ♂ : With boss anteriorly. LEGS : Metatarsus IV without a trichobothrium ; Tm I about 0·4. All tibiæ with two dorsal spines ; no lateral spines, and no metatarsal spines. Femora spineless. EPIGYNE : With well-defined scape.

There is one British species, rather similar to *Centromerus* and *Oreonetides*.

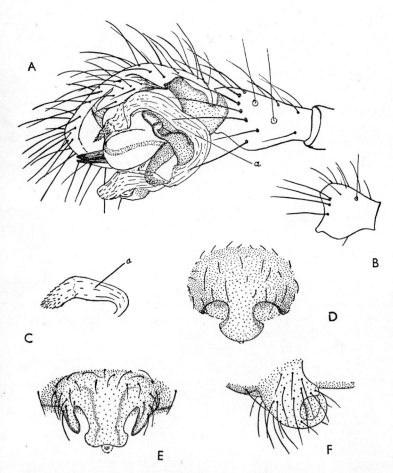

TEXT-FIG. 217.—*Macrargus rufus:* A, ♂ palp ; E, epigyne ; F, ditto (from side). *M. rufus carpenteri:* B, ♂ palpal tibia (from side) ; C, lamella ; D, epigyne.

Macrargus rufus (Wider).
(Text-fig. 217, A, E, F)

Theridion rufum Wider, 1834, p. 223. *Neriene rubripes* J. Blackwall, 1864, p. 287.
N. rufa O. P.-Cambridge, 1879–81, p. 123. *Macrargus rufus* C. Chyzer and L. Kulczynski, 1891–7, II, p. 78 ; E. Simon, 1929, p. 562.

DESCRIPTION. LENGTH : ♀ : 4–4·5 mm. ♂ : 3·25–3·5 mm.
CARAPACE : Yellow-brown to brown. ABDOMEN : Grey to black.
LEGS : Tm I 0·4 (sometimes 0·5 in ♀, when Tm II is then ca. 0·4).
Yellow-brown to brown. CHELICERÆ : ♀ : Rather prominent. ♂ :
Prominent, with a boss just above the outer row of teeth. EPIGYNE :
Text-fig. 217, E, F. MALE PALP : Text-fig. 217, A ; a transparent
process (a) is prominent.

OCCURRENCE : In woods, in moss, grass, dead leaves, etc. Widespread throughout the British Isles, and common. Adult in autumn,
winter and spring.

Macrargus rufus carpenteri (O. P.-Cambridge).
(Text-fig. 217, B, C, D)

Tmeticus carpenteri O. P.-Cambridge, 1894, p. 108. *Macrargus carpenterii* A. R.
Jackson, 1916 (2), p. 168. *Macrargus rufus* var. *minutus* Å. Holm, 1939, p. 19.

DESCRIPTION. LENGTH : ♀♂ : About 2·5 mm. Colour as *M. rufus*.
LEGS : Tm I 0·4. ♂ : Spines weak, particularly on tibiæ I and II.
EPIGYNE : Text-fig. 217, D ; very similar to *M. rufus*. MALE PALP :
Text-fig. 217, B, C ; the palpal organs differ slightly in the apophysis
(a).

OCCURRENCE : A very few, isolated, specimens have been captured :
Scotland, Place Fell (Westmorland).

88. Genus BATHYPHANTES A. Menge 1866.

CHARACTERS OF GENUS. ABDOMEN : Often with a pattern of black
chevrons or bars dorsally. LEGS : Metatarsus IV without a trichobothrium (other trichobothria difficult to see) ; Tm I ca. 0·2–0·25. Legs
rather long and thin. All tibiæ with two dorsal spines ; tibiæ I and II
have in addition one prolateral and one retrolateral spine. Metatarsi
spineless. Femora I–III with a small spine dorsally (except *B. setiger*).
EPIGYNE : With a scape, often elongated.

There are eight British species, which are readily separated by the
sex organs. Only in the case of *B. gracilis* and *B. parvulus* (q.v.)
is any confusion likely to arise.

Bathyphantes dorsalis (Wider).
(Text-figs. 218, A, C ; 220, A, B)

Linyphia dorsalis Wider, 1834, p. 264 ; O. P.-Cambridge, 1879–81, p. 200. *L.
claytoniæ* J. Blackwall, 1861–4, p. 233. *Stylophora dorsalis* E. Simon, 1929, p. 639.

DESCRIPTION. LENGTH : ♀ : 2·5–3 mm. ♂ : 2·5 mm. CARAPACE :
Usually dark brown, often suffused with black, particularly on head
and sides ; sometimes rather lighter. ♂ : Head with some forward-
directed spines. ABDOMEN : Grey to black, with sometimes very faint

broad whitish chevrons. STERNUM : Dark-brown to black. LEGS : Tm I 0·2. Yellow-brown. EPIGYNE : Text-fig. 220, A, B. MALE PALP : Text-fig. 218, A, C.

OCCURRENCE : On low bushes, in undergrowth, etc., in spring and summer. Frequent, and widespread throughout the British Isles.

Bathyphantes concolor (Wider).
(Text-figs. 218, B ; 220, C, D)

Linyphia concolor Wider, 1834, p. 261 ; O. P.-Cambridge, 1879–81, p. 218. *Theridion filipes* J. Blackwall, 1861–4, p. 206. *Stylophora concolor* E. Simon, 1929, p. 640. *Bathyphantes concolor* B. J. Kaston, 1948, p. 131.

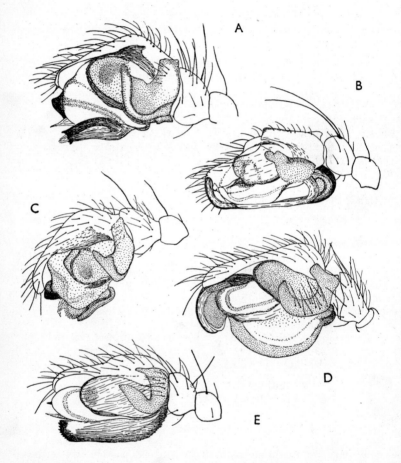

TEXT-FIG. 218.—Male palps : A, *Bathyphantes dorsalis* (from somewhat below); C, ditto (from side) ; B, *B. concolor;* D, *B. approximatus;* E, *B. pullatus.*

DESCRIPTION. LENGTH : ♀♂ : 2·5–2·75 mm. CARAPACE : Brown. ABDOMEN : Grey to black, with no pattern. STERNUM : Yellowish, suffused more or less with black. LEGS : Tm I 0·23–0·25. Yellow-brown. Slender. ♂ : Tibial spines short and inconspicuous. EPIGYNE : Text-fig. 220, C, D ; the scape is very long. MALE PALP : Text-fig. 218, B.

OCCURRENCE : Amongst undergrowth, under stones, etc., in spring, summer and autumn. Widespread throughout the British Isles, and frequent.

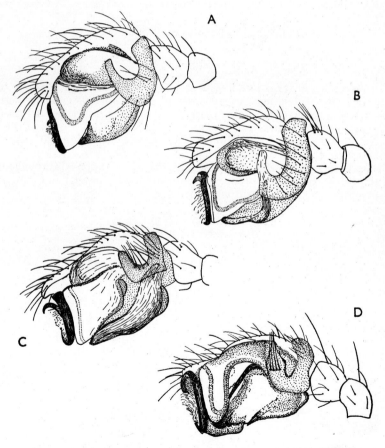

TEXT-FIG. 219.—Male palps: A, *Bathyphantes gracilis;* B, *B. parvulus;* C, *B. nigrinus;* D, *B. setiger.*

Bathyphantes approximatus (O. P.-Cambridge).
(Text-figs. 218, D ; 221, A)

Linyphia approximata O. P.-Cambridge, 1871, p. 424, and 1879–81, p. 199. *Stylophora approximatus* E. Simon, 1929, p. 640.

DESCRIPTION. LENGTH : ♀: 2–2·5 mm. ♂ : 2·5–3 mm. CARAPACE : Brown, with sometimes darker striæ. ABDOMEN : ♀: Ground colour black, but whitish anteriorly, followed by broad white bands or chevrons, often diffuse ; sometimes almost entirely white dorsally. ♂ : Darker, with pattern less clear. STERNUM : Blackish. LEGS : Tm I 0·22–0·24. Yellow brown. EPIGYNE : Text-fig. 221, A. MALE PALP : Text-fig. 218, D.

OCCURRENCE : In wet, marshy areas. Widespread throughout the British Isles, but local. Adult in spring and autumn.

Bathyphantes pullatus (O. P.-Cambridge).
(Text-figs. 218, E ; 220, E, F)

Linyphia pullata O. P.-Cambridge, 1863, p. 8580, and 1879–81, p. 197. *Stylophora pullatus* E. Simon, 1929, p. 640.

DESCRIPTION. LENGTH : ♀♂: 2–2·5 mm. CARAPACE : Brown to dark brown, sometimes suffused with black. ABDOMEN : Black, with white chevrons (sometimes poorly developed) ; sometimes whitish, with a few black chevrons. STERNUM : Brown to dark brown. LEGS : Tm I 0·2–0·25. Yellow-brown. EPIGYNE : Text-fig. 220, E, F. MALE PALP : Text-fig. 218, E.

OCCURRENCE : Amongst grass and heather. Widespread throughout the British Isles, but infrequent ; only one record for Scotland. Adult in spring, summer and autumn.

Bathyphantes gracilis (Blackwall).
(Text-figs. 219, A ; 221, D)

Linyphia gracilis J. Blackwall, 1841, p. 666, and 1861–4, p. 245 ; O. P.-Cambridge, 1879–81, p. 518. *L. circumspecta* J. Blackwall, 1861–4, p. 246 ; O. P.-Cambridge, 1879–81, p. 202. *Bathyphantes gracilis* F. O. P.-Cambridge, 1892, p. 393 ; E. Simon, 1929, p. 641 ; F. Miller, 1947, Tab. 12, figs. 7, 12, 13.

DESCRIPTION. LENGTH : ♀: 2–2·5 mm. ♂ : 1·5–1·75 mm. CARAPACE : Brown. ABDOMEN : Variable ; black or blackish, with white chevrons ; occasionally entirely blackish or grey. STERNUM : Blackish. LEGS : Tm I 0·25–0·3. Pale yellow to yellow-brown. EPIGYNE : Text-fig. 221, D. MALE PALP : Text-fig. 219, A.

OCCURRENCE : Widespread throughout the British Isles, in undergrowth, etc. ; common. A frequent aeronaut. Adult in spring, summer and autumn.

Bathyphantes parvulus (Westring).
(Text-figs. 219, B ; 221, E)

Linyphia parvula N. Westring, 1851, and 1861, p. 135 ; O. P.-Cambridge, 1879–81, p. 210. *Bathyphantes parvulus* F. O. P.-Cambridge, 1892, p. 392 ; F. Miller, 1947, Tab. 12, figs. 15–17. *B. gracilis* E. Simon, 1929, p. 641 (in part).

DESCRIPTION. Size and colour as *B. gracilis*, except that ABDOMEN is normally black or grey, unicolorous. EPIGYNE : Text-fig. 221, E. MALE PALP : Text-fig. 219, B ; distinguishable from *B. gracilis* chiefly by the hairs on the paracymbium.

This spider is considered by some authors to be only a sub-species of *B. gracilis*, but the sex organs appear to be distinct though very close. Intermediate forms may occur.

OCCURRENCE : Less common than *B. gracilis*, but frequent. Adult in spring and summer.

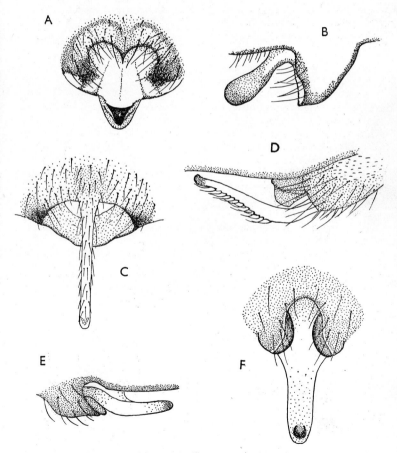

TEXT-FIG. 220.—Epigynes : A, *Bathyphantes dorsalis;* B, ditto (from side) ; C, *B. concolor;* D, ditto (from side) ; F, *B. pullatus;* E, ditto (from side).

Bathyphantes nigrinus (Westring).
(Text-figs. 219, C ; 221, B)

Linyphia nigrina N. Westring, 1851 ; O. P.-Cambridge, 1879–81, p. 198. *Linyphia pulla* J. Blackwall, 1861–4, p. 234. *Stylophora nigrinus* E. Simon, 1929, p. 641.

DESCRIPTION. LENGTH : ♀♂ : 2·5–2·75 mm. CARAPACE : Deep chestnut brown, with paler striæ. ABDOMEN : Blackish, with fairly

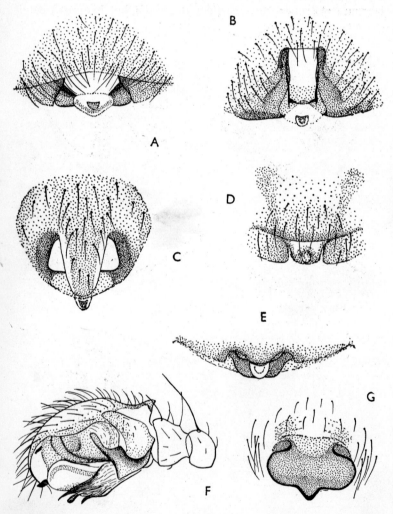

TEXT-FIG. 221.—Epigynes: A, *Bathyphantes approximatus;* B, *B. nigrinus;* C, *B. setiger;* D, *B. gracilis;* E, *B. parvulus;* G, *Pœciloneta globosa.* Male palp: F, *P. globosa.*

sharply defined white chevrons and transverse bars. STERNUM : Brown to dark-brown, suffused with some black. LEGS : Tm I 0·21– 0·23. Yellow-brown. EPIGYNE : Text-fig. 221, B. MALE PALP : Text-fig. 219, C ; paracymbium with several stout bristles.

OCCURRENCE : On low plants, underwood, etc. Widespread throughout the British Isles, and fairly common. Adult in spring and summer.

Bathyphantes setiger F. O. P.-Cambridge.
(Text-figs. 219, D ; 221, C)

Bathyphantes setiger F. O. P.-Cambridge, 1894, p. 91 ; W. Falconer, 1911, p. 283 ; F. Miller, 1947, Tab. 12, figs. 4–6. *B. spretus* O. P.-Cambridge, 1906, p. 76. *B. holnacus* F. Miller, 1937, p. 569. *B. hyperboreus* Å. Holm, 1945, p. 46.

DESCRIPTION. LENGTH : ♀♂ : 1·75–2 mm. CARAPACE : Dark brown (♀) or dark chestnut brown (♂), in either case suffused with black. ABDOMEN : Black, with sometimes ill-defined whitish chevrons dorsally ; occasionally whitish dorsally. STERNUM : Very dark brown to black. LEGS : Tm I 0·27–0·30. Yellow-brown to brown. Femora lack the small dorsal spine present in the remaining species of the genus. EPIGYNE : Text-fig. 221, C ; the length of the scape varies a little. MALE PALP : Text-fig. 219, D ; the paracymbium has a bunch of 3–4 stout spines.

OCCURRENCE : In swampy areas. Widespread in England, but rare ; recorded from Eire, but not from Wales or Scotland. Adult in autumn.

89. Genus PŒCILONETA L. Kulczynski 1894.

CHARACTERS OF GENUS. CARAPACE : Clypeus rather narrow, approximately equal to diameter of anterior lateral eye or 1·5 diameters of anterior median eye (slightly wider in ♂). ABDOMEN : With clear pattern. CHELICERÆ : Outer margin with four rather large teeth. ♂ : Rather more strongly developed, with long fang. LEGS : Metatarsus IV with a trichobothrium ; Tm I 0·75–0·8. Legs long. All tibiæ with two dorsal spines ; lateral spines absent. No metatarsal spines. Femur I with a prolateral spine.

There is one British species.

Pœciloneta globosa (Wider).
(Text-fig. 221, F, G)

Linyphia globosa Wider, 1834, p. 259. *Neriene variegata* J. Blackwall, 1861–4, p. 282. *Linyphia variegata* O. P.-Cambridge, 1879–81, p. 189. *Pœciloneta variegata* E. Simon, 1929, p. 618.

DESCRIPTION. LENGTH : ♀ : 2 mm. ♂ : 1·75 mm. CARAPACE : Yellow-brown, with narrow black margin, a black mark in fovea and black striæ. EYES : On black spots, and with black lines running backwards from posterior eyes. ABDOMEN : Grey and glistening white (or whitish grey) with usually a well-developed black pattern. STERNUM : Yellow, often suffused and margined with black. LEGS : Tm I 0·75–0·8. Yellow-brown, sometimes annulated faintly with

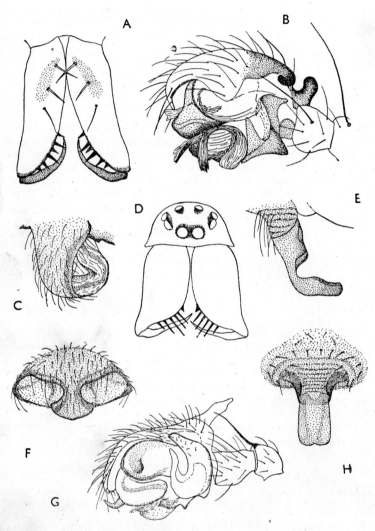

TEXT-FIG. 222.—*Drapetisca socialis:* A, Cheliceræ (from in front); B, ♂ palp; E, epigyne (from side); H, ditto (from below).
Tapinopa longidens: C, epigyne (from side); F, ditto (from below); D, facies and cheliceræ (from in front); G, ♂ palp.

black. EPIGYNE : Text-fig. 221, G. MALE PALP : Text-fig. 221, F ; tarsus produced into small " horn " basally.

OCCURRENCE : Amongst grass, under stones, etc., usually on open land. Widespread throughout the British Isles, and not uncommon, particularly in the more northern counties ; locally abundant under stones at 1,000–2,500 feet in Lake District, Pennines, and North Wales. Adult in spring, summer and autumn.

90. Genus **DRAPETISCA** A. Menge 1866.

CHARACTERS OF GENUS. ABDOMEN : With pattern dorsally. CHELICERÆ : Long, with 5–6 large teeth on outer margin (Text-fig. 222, A) ; fang long and curved. 3–4 conspicuous spines on prolateral face (Text-fig. 222, A). LEGS : Metatarsus IV with trichobothrium ; Tm I 0·95. Legs long. Tibiæ with several spines ; metatarsi with one spine.

There is one British species.

Drapetisca socialis (Sundevall).
(Text-fig. 222, A, B, E, H)

Linyphia socialis C. J. Sundevall, 1832, p. 260 ; J. Blackwall, 1861–4, p. 222 ; O. P.-Cambridge, 1879–81, p. 193. *Drapetisca socialis* C. Chyzer and L. Kulczynski, 1891–7, II, p. 53 ; E. Simon, 1929, p. 567.

DESCRIPTION. LENGTH : ♀ : 4 mm. ♂ : 3·5–4 mm. CARAPACE : Pale yellow, with black margins ; striæ black, broken into blotches. Fovea with brown arrow-shaped mark (directed backwards), and head outlined with black. ABDOMEN : Silvery white at front and sides, with light chevrons on dark mottled ground behind ; the whole giving a protective imitation to lichen-covered tree trunks. STERNUM : Pale yellow, with black margin ; by each coxa there is sometimes a faint black spot. Sometimes entirely dark-coloured. Furnished with a number of long, fine, vertical spines. LEGS : Tm I 0·95, sinuous. Yellow-brown or brown, annulated with black. FEMALE PALP : With a number of long, very strong spines ventrally (particularly on tibia and tarsus). EPIGYNE : Text-fig. 222, E, H. MALE PALP : Text-fig. 222, B ; tarsus with two dark chitinised knobs basally.

OCCURRENCE : On the trunks of trees, especially beeches, and in detritus at the base of trees. Widespread throughout the British Isles, and fairly common, large numbers being sometimes found together. Adult in late summer and autumn.

91. Genus **TAPINOPA** N. Westring 1851.

CHARACTERS OF GENUS. CARAPACE : Clypeus very narrow, not wider than diameter of anterior median eye (Text-fig. 222, D). EYES : Anterior medians larger than remainder. ABDOMEN : With dorsal pattern. CHELICERÆ : With 5–6 large teeth in outer row (Text-fig. 222, D). LEGS : Metatarsus IV without a trichobothrium ; Tm I 0·25–0·3. Legs fairly short and stout. Tibiæ I and II with prolateral and retrolateral spines in addition to dorsal spines. Metatarsi with several spines. Femora with one dorsal spine.

There is one British species.

Tapinopa longidens (Wider).
(Text-fig. 222, C, D, F, G)

Linyphia longidens Wider, 1834, p. 270; J. Blackwall, 1861–4, p. 227. *Tapinopa longidens* O. P.-Cambridge, 1879–81, p. 176; E. Simon, 1929, p. 565.

DESCRIPTION. LENGTH: ♀♂: About 4 mm. CARAPACE: Rather long. Yellow-brown or yellow, with edges suffused with dusky black; faint dusky striæ visible. ♂: With stout curved spines on head. EYES: ♀: Posterior medians ca. 1·5 diam. apart, and one diam. or slightly more from laterals. ♂: Rather more widely spaced. ABDOMEN: Greyish white, with some small shining white patches, and with broad transverse black bars. STERNUM: Brown, with edges

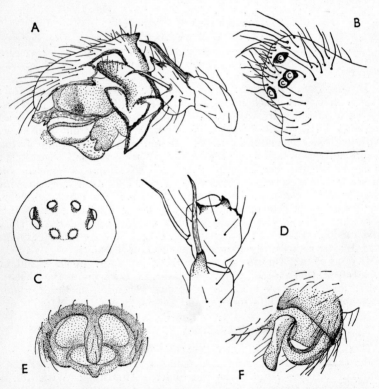

TEXT-FIG. 223.—*Floronia bucculenta*: A, ♂ palp; B, ♂ head (from side); C, facies (♀); D, ♂ palpal patella and tibia (from above); E, epigyne; F, ditto (from right side).

dusky. LEGS : Tm I 0·25–0·3. Yellow-brown. Spines as above.
EPIGYNE : Text-fig. 222, C, F. MALE PALP : Text-fig. 222, G ; tarsus
produced basally into long " horn."

OCCURRENCE : In detritus in woods, in marshy places, and on
open hillsides. Widespread throughout the British Isles, and frequent.
The web is a small white sheet, with a glossy appearance, at ground
level.

92. Genus **FLORONIA** E. Simon 1887.

CHARACTERS OF GENUS. ABDOMEN : With dorsal pattern.
CHELICERÆ : With 5–6 large teeth in outer row. LEGS : Metatarsus
IV without trichobothrium ; Tm I 0·2. Legs long. Tibiæ and
metatarsi with numerous spines. All femora with one dorsal spine ;
femur I with 2–3 prolateral spines in addition.
There is one British species.

Floronia bucculenta (Clerck).
(Text-fig. 223, A, B, C, D, E, F)

Araneus bucculentus C. Clerck, 1757, p. 63. *Linyphia frenata* Wider, 1834, p. 269 ;
J. Blackwall, 1861–4, p. 228 ; O. P.-Cambridge, 1879–81, p. 179. *Floronia frenata*
C. Chyzer and L. Kulczynski, 1891–7, II, p. 51. *F. bucculenta* E. Simon, 1929, p. 566.

DESCRIPTION. LENGTH : ♀♂ : About 4 mm. CARAPACE : Yellow-
brown, with broad dark brown or black margins, or with two broad
dark bands running backwards from the lateral eyes round the carapace,
to the back. ♂ : Head elevated, bearing numerous stout curved
forward-directed spines (Text-fig. 223, B). EYES : All subequal.
♀ : Posterior medians ca. 2 diams. apart, and 1·5 diam. from
laterals ; ocular area with numerous fine hairs. ♂ : Posteriors widely
separated, with medians ca. 3 diams. apart. ABDOMEN : Very
globular (particularly ♀). Greyish, with white spots ; there is a black
band round the front, and two black spots lie transversely about
halfway back, followed by black chevrons ; pattern sometimes obscure.
STERNUM : Dark brown. LEGS : Tm I 0·2. Yellow-brown, faintly
annulated. EPIGYNE : Text-fig. 223, E, F. MALE PALP : Text-fig.
223, A, D ; the patella is drawn out into a conical projection, bearing
a very stout curved spine ; the tibia has a stout curved spine laterally,
and bears dorsally an apophysis with a black point on either fore-corner.

OCCURRENCE : Amongst low vegetation on earthy banks, and in
marshes. Widespread throughout England, but not recorded from
Scotland, and there are few records from Eire ; rare. Adult in summer
and autumn.

93. Genus **TARANUCNUS** E. Simon 1884.

CHARACTERS OF GENUS. EYES : Large and close together, with
posterior medians further from each other than from laterals.
ABDOMEN : With pattern dorsally. LEGS : Metatarsus IV without

trichobothrium; Tm I ca. 0·2 (trichobothria very difficult to see). Legs long. Femora with one dorsal spine. Tibiæ with several spines. Metatarsi with one spine.

There is one British species.

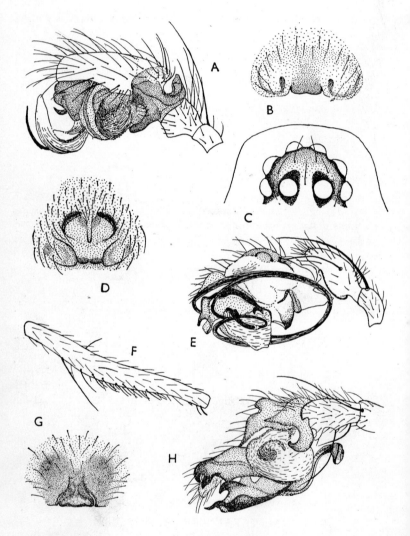

TEXT-FIG. 224.—*Taranucnus setosus:* A, ♂ palp; B, epigyne; C, eyes (from above).

Labulla thoracica: D, epigyne; E, ♂ palp.

Stemonyphantes lineatus: F, metatarsus I (♂); G, epigyne; H, ♂ palp.

Taranucnus setosus (O. P.-Cambridge).
(Text-fig. 224, A, B, C)

Linyphia setosa O. P.-Cambridge, 1863, p. 8578 ; and 1879–81, p. 191. *Taranucnus setosus* E. Simon, 1929, p. 626.

DESCRIPTION. LENGTH : ♀♂ : 2·5–3 mm. CARAPACE : Yellow-brown to orange-brown ; some forward-directed spines in ocular area, particularly in ♂. EYES : Large, close together (Text-fig. 224, C) ; margined with black. Posterior medians further from each other than from laterals. ABDOMEN : Whitish dorsally, with a row of thick black chevrons reaching to sides, which are black. STERNUM : Blackish. LEGS : Tm I ca. 0·2. Long and thin. Yellow to orange-brown. EPIGYNE : Text-fig. 224, B. MALE PALP : Text-fig. 224, A.

OCCURRENCE : Usually in swampy areas, but occasionally amongst heather. Recorded from a number of English counties, but rare. Adult in spring and autumn.

94. Genus LABULLA E. Simon 1884.

CHARACTERS OF GENUS. EYES : Large, all approximately equal in size. ABDOMEN : With dorsal pattern. LEGS : Metatarsus IV without a trichobothrium ; Tm I about 0·25. Legs long. Femora each with a long spine dorsally ; a number of long spines on tibiæ and metatarsi. MALE PALP : Embolus very long, curved into circle.

There is one British species.

Labulla thoracica (Wider).
(Text-fig. 224, D, E)

Linyphia thoracica Wider, 1834, p. 261 ; O. P.-Cambridge, 1879–81, p. 180. *L. cauta* J. Blackwall, 1861–4, p. 220. *Labulla thoracica* E. Simon, 1929, p. 625.

DESCRIPTION. LENGTH : ♀♂ : 4·5–5 mm. CARAPACE : Pale yellow, edged with black, with black marking in fovea, and black wedge-shaped mark behind the eyes. Head with numerous slender forward-directed spines. EYES : On heavy black spots, large, all approximately equal in size, with anterior medians equal to posterior medians. ABDOMEN : Fawn, with some glistening white spots, and a pattern of black spots. STERNUM : Blackish. LEGS : Tm I ca. 0·25. Pale yellow, annulated with black. EPIGYNE : Text-fig. 224, D. MALE PALP : Text-fig. 224, E ; palpal organs very large.

OCCURRENCE : At the base of trees, in hollows of trees, in holes in the ground, in outhouses, etc. Widespread throughout the British Isles, and frequent. Adults in autumn.

95. Genus STEMONYPHANTES A. Menge 1866.

CHARACTERS OF GENUS. EYES : Large and subequal. ABDOMEN : With dorsal pattern. LEGS : Metatarsus IV with a trichobothrium ; Tm I about 0·27. Legs long and thin. Femora each with one dorsal spine ; tibiæ and metatarsi each with several spines.

There is one British species.

Stemonyphantes lineatus (Linnaeus).
(Text-fig. 224, F, G, H)

Aranea lineata C. Linnaeus, 1758, p. 620. *Neriene trilineata* J. Blackwall, 1861–4, p. 279. *Linyphia bucculenta* O. P.-Cambridge, 1879–81, p. 224. *Stemonyphantes bucculentus* C. Chyzer and L. Kulczynski, 1891–7, II, p. 53 ; H. Blauvelt, 1936, p. 159. *S. lineatus* E. Simon, 1929, p. 623.

DESCRIPTION. LENGTH : ♀♂ : 4–5 mm. CARAPACE : Yellow to yellow-brown, sometimes suffused with black, and with narrow black margin ; usually with black mark extending from posterior eyes to fovea. ABDOMEN : Variable in pattern and colour. Yellowish-white, frequently suffused with pink, and reticulated with dark lines. Three longitudinal black bands (often broken into blotches) run almost to spinners. STERNUM : Yellow-brown, sometimes suffused strongly (particularly at edges) with black. LEGS : Tm I ca. 0·27. Yellow-brown, often obscurely annulated. Long, and with numerous spines. ♂ : Metatarsus I fusiform (Text-fig. 224, F). EPIGYNE : Text-fig. 224, G. MALE PALP : Text-fig. 224, H.

OCCURRENCE : In a variety of situations, e.g., hedge bottoms, under stones, in rough grass, heather, bracken, on sandhills. Widespread throughout the British Isles, and generally common.

96. Genus BOLYPHANTES C. L. Koch 1837.

CHARACTERS OF GENUS. CARAPACE : ♂ : Head prominent, with numerous stout spines. ♀ : Head somewhat raised. Clypeus rather concave. ABDOMEN : With pattern. LEGS : Metatarsus IV without a trichobothrium ; Tm I 0·15–0·2. Legs long and thin. Femora without dorsal spines. Tibiæ and metatarsi each with numerous spines. There are two British species.

Bolyphantes luteolus (Blackwall).
(Text-fig. 225, A, B, C)

Linyphia luteola J. Blackwall, 1833, p. 192. *L. alticeps*, idem, 1861–4, p. 226. *L. luteola* O. P.-Cambridge, 1879–81, p. 194. *Bolyphantes luteolus* C. Chyzer and L. Kulczynski, 1891–7, II, p. 52 ; E. Simon, 1929, p. 569.

DESCRIPTION. LENGTH : ♀ : 3·5–4 mm. ♂ : 3–3·5 mm. CARAPACE : Brown, with sometimes a faint black median stripe. ♀ : Clypeus and ocular area with a number of stout bristles. ♂ : Head raised, but not as high as in *B. alticeps*. ♀ : Clypeus concave, but less so than in *B. alticeps*. EYES : ♀ : Anterior medians ca. 0·5 diam. apart, and ca. 2 diams. from laterals ; posterior medians ca. 0·75–1·0 diam. apart, and ca. 1·25 diam. from laterals (Text-fig. 225, B). ABDOMEN : Yellow-brown, with numerous shining white patches anteriorly ; there is a darkish median stripe, and some broken black bars posteriorly. STERNUM : Brown, suffused with black at edges. LEGS : Tm I ca. 0·18. Yellow-brown to brown. Tibiæ I and II each with two dorsal, one prolateral, one retrolateral and several ventral spines. All metatarsi with two dorsal, one retrolateral, one prolateral and one ventral spine. EPIGYNE : Text-fig. 225, C. MALE PALP : Text-fig. 225, A ; the patella has a very stout spine.

OCCURRENCE : In grass, heather, etc., and under stones, often in wet spots. Widespread throughout the British Isles, but much commoner in the north than in the south. Adults in summer and autumn.

Bolyphantes luteolus subnigripes (O. P.-Cambridge).

Linyphia subnigripes O. P.-Cambridge, 1879 (1), p. 204, and 1886, p. 73. *Bolyphantes subnigripes* A. R. Jackson, 1916 (2), p. 164.

DESCRIPTION. The only specimen, a ♀, is in very bad condition. The femora were originally black, but they are no longer even dark. The epigyne is not distinguishable from that of *B. luteolus*, and hence

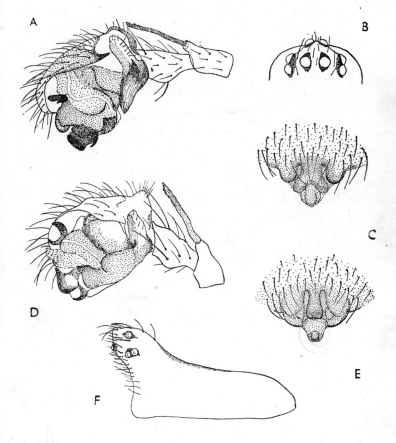

TEXT-FIG. 225.—*Bolyphantes luteolus:* A, ♂ palp; B, ♀ eyes (from above); C, epigyne.
    B. alticeps: D, ♂ palp ; E, epigyne ; F, ♂ carapace.

CC

we are assuming that this is only a colour variety of *B. luteolus*. The capture of further examples would be necessary to decide this point for certain.

OCCURRENCE : A single specimen, near Belfast.

Bolyphantes alticeps (Sundevall).
(Text-fig. 225, D, E, F)

Linyphia alticeps C. J. Sundevall, 1832, p. 261 ; O. P.-Cambridge, 1879–81, p. 515. *Bolyphantes alticeps* C. Chyzer and L. Kulczynski, 1891–7, II, p. 52 ; E. Simon, 1929, p. 568.

DESCRIPTION. LENGTH : ♀ : 4 mm. ♂ : 3 mm. CARAPACE : Brown, with median black stripe, and with edges suffused with black. ♀ : Clypeus very concave ; clypeus and ocular area with a few short hairs. ♂ : Head raised considerably (Text-fig. 225, F), with numerous stout spines. EYES : ♀ : Anterior medians ca. 0·5 diam. apart, and ca. 2 diam. from laterals ; posterior medians ca. one diam. apart, and 1–1·5 diam. from laterals. ♂ : Anterior medians ca. 0·5 diam. apart, and 2·5–3 diam. from laterals ; posterior medians 1–1·25 diam. apart, and ca. 2 diam. from laterals. ABDOMEN : Yellow-brown, with numerous glistening patches anteriorly, and with broken black bars and chevrons posteriorly ; sides blackish. STERNUM : Brown, suffused with black at margins. LEGS : Tm I ca. 0·15. Yellow-brown to brown. Tibiæ I and II each with 2 dorsal, 2 pro-lateral, 2 retrolateral and several ventral spines. Metatarsi with 2–3 dorsal, one prolateral, one retrolateral and one ventral spine. EPIGYNE : Text-fig. 225, E. MALE PALP : Text-fig. 225, D ; patella with a very stout spine.

OCCURRENCE : Amongst pine needles, etc. Found in the more northern counties of England and Wales, and in Scotland, but not recorded from Eire. Infrequent. Adult in summer.

97. Genus LEPTHYPHANTES A. Menge 1866.

CHARACTERS OF GENUS. CARAPACE : Strongly narrowed anteriorly. EYES : Fairly large, on black spots. Anterior medians smaller than posterior medians or anterior laterals. Posteriors normally less than one diam. apart. CLYPEUS : Slightly concave. ABDOMEN : Rather pointed posteriorly (Text-fig. 230, B). With or without a pattern composed of broad black transverse bars on a grey background, interspersed with some silvery white spots (Text-fig. 230, B). LEGS : Metatarsus IV without a trichobothrium ; Tm I 0·13–0·23 (except for *L. obscurus*, which is quite anomalous in this respect). Long and fairly slender. All tibiæ with two or more dorsal spines (usually long) ; tibiæ I and II each with a prolateral and a retrolateral spine ; ventral spines are sometimes present. Metatarsi I–III with at least one dorsal spine ; metatarsus IV may be spineless. EPIGYNE : With a scape, which is usually constricted at the base, then greatly widened and folded under itself and out again, so that the narrow tip appears as a rounded tubercle at the end of the widened, visible part of the

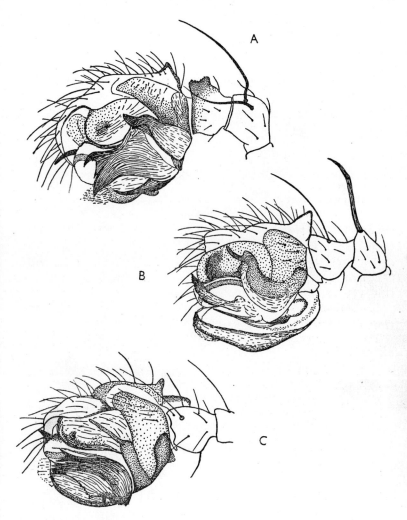

TEXT-FIG. 226.—Male palps : A, *Lepthyphantes nebulosus;* B, *L. minutus;* C, *L. leprosus.*

organ (see H. Zorsch, 1937, p. 857). MALE PALP : The paracymbium (Text-fig. 230, C, *p*) is large, strongly curved, often with one or more chitinised teeth. The *lamella characteristica* (" terminal apophysis " of Zorsch) is large and often conspicuous. The tibia and patella each have a strong spine dorsally. (For a description of the morphology of the male palp of *Lepthyphantes,* see H. Zorsch, 1937.)

The genus contains 20 British species, which can be split up into five groups according to the following key :—

1. Metatarsus I (and usually II) with more than one spine
                                                    Group I

——All metatarsi with only one spine (IV occasionally with
      none)   2

2. Tibia I with strong spines ventrally   .   .   Group V
——Tibia I without spines ventrally   3

3. Tm I 0·85, Tm II 0·4   .   .   .   .   Group II
——Tm I and II ca. 0·2   4

4. Abdomen with dorsal pattern of transverse black bars
                                                    Group III
——Abdomen greyish, with no pattern dorsally (*L. carri*
      occasionally has pattern)   .   .   .   .   Group IV

Group I : *L. nebulosus, L. leprosus, L. minutus, L. alacris, L. whymperi.*

Group II : *L. obscurus.*

Group III : *L. tenuis, L. zimmermanni, L. cristatus, L. tenebricola, L. mengei, L. flavipes.*

Group IV : *L. ericaeus, L. pallidus, L. pinicola, L. insignis, L. angulatus, L. audax, L. carri.*

Group V : *L. expunctus.*

The species within the groups must in general be separated by the sex organs.

Group I

Lepthyphantes nebulosus (Sundevall).
(Text-figs. 226, A ; 227, B ; 228, A)

Linyphia nebulosa C. J. Sundevall, 1830, p. 218 ; O. P.-Cambridge, 1879–81, p. 512 ; C. Chyzer and L. Kulczynski, 1891–7, II, p. 67. *L. vivax* J. Blackwall, 1861–4, p. 221. *Lepthyphantes nebulosus* E. Simon, 1929, p. 578 ; H. Zorsch, 1937, p. 864.

DESCRIPTION. LENGTH : ♀♂ : 3·5–4 mm. CARAPACE : Yellow-brown, with median dark line, bifurcating anteriorly (Text-fig. 227, B). ♂ : Three rows of small bristles radiate forwards from fovea, one median and the others to the lateral eyes. EYES : Anterior medians ca. 0·5 diam. apart, and ca. one diam. from laterals ; posteriors all ca. 0·75 diam. apart. ABDOMEN : Greyish, with transverse black bars. STERNUM : Blackish. LEGS : Tm I ca. 0·13 (difficult to see). Pale yellow or yellow-brown. Metatarsi I with two dorsal spines and several lateral and ventral spines. Legs more spinose than in the remaining species. EPIGYNE : Text-fig. 228, A. MALE PALP : Text-fig. 226, A.

OCCURRENCE : In houses, outhouses, etc. Widespread throughout the British Isles ; frequent in the south, less common in the north. Adults at all seasons.

Lepthyphantes leprosus (Ohlert).
(Text-figs. 226, C ; 228, B)

Linyphia leprosa E. Ohlert, 1865, p. 12 ; O. P.-Cambridge, 1879–81, p. 181.
Lepthyphantes leprosus C. Chyzer and L. Kulczynski, 1891–7, II, p. 67 ; E. Simon, 1929, p. 580 ; H. Zorsch, 1937, p. 861.

DESCRIPTION. LENGTH : ♀♂ : 2–3 mm. CARAPACE : Yellow-brown to brown, with darker striæ and margins. EYES : Anterior medians ca. 0·5 diam. apart, and ca. one diam. or less from laterals ; posteriors 0·5–0·7 diam. apart. ABDOMEN : Greyish, with broad black bars,

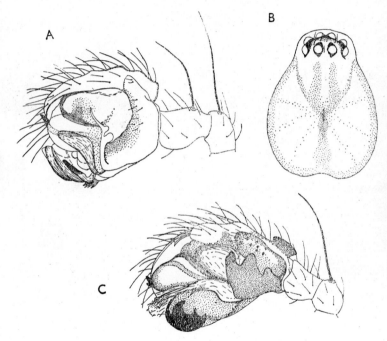

TEXT-FIG. 227.—Male palps : A, *Lepthyphantes alacris;* C, *L. whymperi.*
B, *L. nebulosus:* Carapace (from above).

and black sides. STERNUM : ♀ : Black. ♂ : Brown. LEGS : Tm I ca. 0·2. Yellow-brown to brown. Metatarsi with one dorsal spine and lateral spines ; tibiæ with ventral spines in addition to dorsal and lateral spines. FEMALE PALP : Suffused with black. EPIGYNE : Text-fig. 228, B. MALE PALP : Text-fig. 226, C.

OCCURRENCE : In houses, outhouses, in holes in trees and walls, etc. Widespread throughout the British Isles ; common, but rarer in the north. Adults at all seasons.

Lepthyphantes minutus (Blackwall).
(Text-figs. 226, B ; 228, C, D)

Linyphia minuta J. Blackwall, 1833, p. 191 ; and 1861–4, p. 218 ; O. P.-Cambridge, 1879–81, p. 184. *Lepthyphantes minutus* C. Chyzer and L. Kulczynski, 1891–7, II, p. 67 ; E. Simon, 1929, p. 578 ; H. Zorsch, 1937, p. 858.

DESCRIPTION. LENGTH : ♀♂ : 3–4 mm. CARAPACE : Brown, suffused with black, particularly on radiating striæ. A few hairs in ocular area. EYES : Anterior medians 0·5 diam. apart, and one diam. from laterals ; posterior medians 0·5 diam. apart, and 0·75

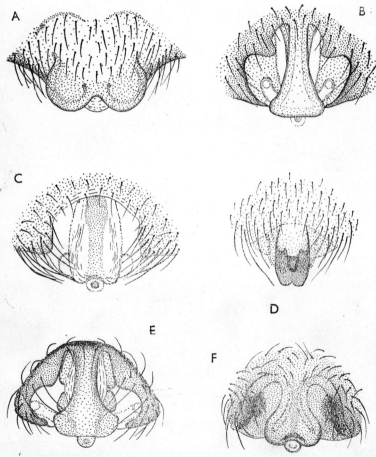

TEXT-FIG. 228.—Epigynes : A, *Lepthyphantes nebulosus;* B, *L. leprosus;* C, *L. minutus;* D, ditto (another specimen) ; E, *L. alacris;* F, *L. whymperi.*

diam. from laterals. ABDOMEN : Grey, with glistening white patches, with broken black bars and chevrons posteriorly, and black sides. STERNUM : Black. LEGS : Tm I 0·19. Brown or yellow-brown. Metatarsi I with one dorsal and two lateral spines. EPIGYNE : Text-fig. 228, C ; a variety has occurred in which the apical half of the scape was very deeply pigmented (Text-fig. 228, D). MALE PALP : Text-fig. 226, B. Spine on patella very stout.

OCCURRENCE : Similar situations to *L. leprosus*. Widespread throughout the British Isles, and fairly common. Adults at most seasons.

Lepthyphantes alacris (Blackwall).
(Text-figs. 227, A ; 228, E)

Linyphia alacris J. Blackwall, 1853, p. 20, and 1861–4, p. 235 ; O. P.-Cambridge, 1879–81, p. 190. *Lepthyphantes alacris* C. Chyzer and L. Kulczynski, 1891–7, II, p. 67 ; W. Bosenberg, 1901–3, p. 76 ; E. Simon, 1929, p. 580.

DESCRIPTION. LENGTH : ♀: 3 mm. ♂: 2·5 mm. CARAPACE : Yellow-brown. ♂ : With several forward-directed spines in ocular area. EYES : ♀: Anterior medians 0·5 diam. apart, and ca. one diam. from laterals ; posterior medians 0·6–0·7 diam. apart, and 0·5 diam. from laterals. ♂ : Eyes rather more widely spaced. ABDOMEN : Greyish, with glistening white spots, and black chevrons and spots. STERNUM : Black. LEGS : Tm I ca. 0·2. Yellow-brown. Metatarsi I with one dorsal spine, two lateral and one ventral spine. EPIGYNE : Text-fig. 228, E. MALE PALP : Text-fig. 227, A.

OCCURRENCE : In woods, in detritus, etc. Widespread throughout the British Isles, but commoner in the north than the south, and generally infrequent.

Lepthyphantes whymperi F. O. P.-Cambridge.
(Text-figs. 227, C ; 228, F)

Lepthyphantes whymperi F. O. P.-Cambridge, 1894, p. 93 ; O. P.-Cambridge, 1894, p. 107, and 1903, p. 164.

DESCRIPTION. LENGTH : ♀♂ : About 3 mm. CARAPACE : Yellow-brown. Head (particularly in ♂) with a number of fairly strong, forward directed spines. EYES : Anterior medians ca. 0·5 diam. apart, and practically 2 diams. from laterals ; posterior medians ca. 0·75 diam. apart, and 0·5–0·75 diam. from laterals. ABDOMEN : Grey, mottled with black. STERNUM : Brown, suffused with black. LEGS : Tm I 0·23. Yellow-brown. Metatarsi with several spines. Tibial spines extra long, up to four times diameter of segment. EPIGYNE : Text-fig. 228, F. MALE PALP : Text-fig. 227, C.

OCCURRENCE : On mountains in the Lake District, Wales, Eire and Scotland. Adults in summer.

Group II
The single species in this group differs from all other Linyphiid spiders studied in having the trichobothrium on metatarsus I in a widely different position from that on the other metatarsi.

Lepthyphantes obscurus (Blackwall).
(Text-fig. 229, A, B, C)

Linyphia obscura J. Blackwall, 1841, p. 665, and 1861–4, p. 244 ; O. P.-Cambridge, 1879–81, p. 188. *Lepthyphantes obscurus* C. Chyzer and L. Kulczynski, 1891–7, II. p. 71 ; W. Bosenberg, 1901–3, p. 78 ; E. Simon, 1929, p. 588.

DESCRIPTION. LENGTH : ♀♂ : About 2·25 mm. CARAPACE : Dark brown to black. EYES : Anterior medians ca. one diam. apart, and rather more from laterals ; posterior medians ca. 0·5 diam. apart, and 0·75 diam. from laterals. ABDOMEN : Black, with sometimes

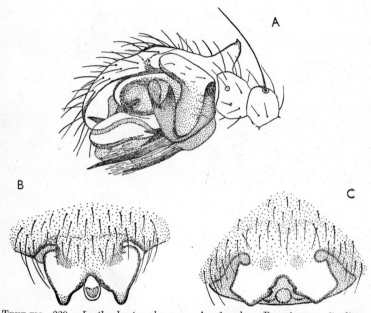

TEXT-FIG. 229.—*Lepthyphantes obscurus:* A, ♂ palp ; B, epigyne ; C, ditto (somewhat from behind).

faint whitish stripes laterally, and faint whitish chevrons posteriorly. STERNUM : Shiny black. CHELICERÆ : Dark brown to black. LEGS : Tm I 0·85, Tm II 0·4, Tm III 0·3. Brown to dark brown. EPIGYNE : Text-fig. 229, B, C. MALE PALP : Text-fig. 229, A.

OCCURRENCE : Widespread throughout the British Isles, but not common. On low plants and shrubs, and in undergrowth. Adult in spring and autumn.

Group III

The males (except *L. cristatus*) in this group can be separated only by a careful comparison of the paracymbia, while with the females careful comparison of the epigynes is necessary.

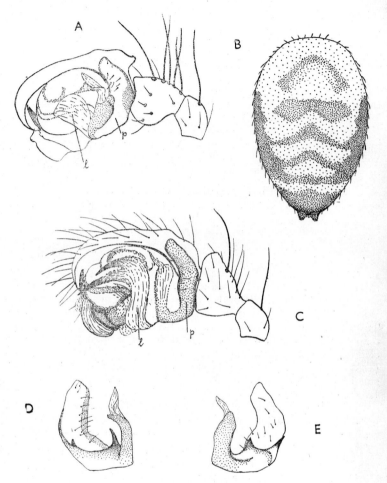

TEXT-FIG. 230.—Male palps : A, *Lepthyphantes cristatus;* C, *L. zimmermanni.*
  Abdomen (from above) : B, *L. zimmermanni.*
  Paracymbia : D, *L. tenebricola* (right palp) ; E, *L. tenuis.*

Lepthyphantes tenuis (Blackwall).
(Text-figs. 230, E ; 232, A)

Linyphia tenuis J. Blackwall, 1852, p. 18, and 1861–4, p. 210 ; *L. tenebricola* O. P.-
Cambridge, 1879–81, p. 185. *Lepthyphantes tenuis* C. Chyzer and L. Kulczynski.
1891–7, II, p. 70 ; W. Bosenberg, 1901–3, p. 82 ; E. Simon, 1929, pp. 589, 594.

DESCRIPTION. LENGTH : ♀♂ : About 2–2·5 mm. CARAPACE :
Yellow-brown, with ocular area suffused with black. EYES : Posteriors
all ca. 0·5 diam. apart. Anteriors almost equidistant, with medians

separated from laterals by ca. 0·5 diam. ; laterals much less than 2 diams. of medians (cf. *L. zimmermanni*). ABDOMEN : With black bars dorsally. STERNUM : Yellow-brown to blackish. LEGS : Tm I ca. 0·2. Yellow-brown to brown. EPIGYNE : Text-fig. 232, A ; distinguishable from *L. zimmermanni* (q.v.) by the greater posterior width of the scape, which virtually obscures the plates (*a*). MALE PALP : The paracymbium (Text-fig. 230, E) has a large conical tooth towards the bottom of the inner margin, and a small tooth about halfway up the basal arm.

OCCURRENCE : In a variety of situations, e.g., in grass, moss, dead leaves ; also a frequent aeronaut. Widespread throughout the British Isles, and common ; probably commoner in the south than the north. Adults at all seasons (at least in the south).

Lepthyphantes zimmermanni Bertkau.
(Text-figs. 230, B, C ; 231, G ; 232, B)

Lepthyphantes zimmermanni P. Bertkau, 1890, p. 10 ; E. Simon, 1929, pp. 591, 595. *L. blackwalli* C. Chyzer and L. Kulczynski, 1891–7, II, p. 70.

DESCRIPTION. LENGTH : ♀♂ : About 2·5 mm. CARAPACE : Yellow-brown, with ocular area sometimes suffused with black. EYES : Posteriors all ca. 0·5 diam. apart. Anterior medians distinctly nearer to each other than to laterals ; medians separated from laterals by more than one diam. ; laterals ca. twice diam. of medians. ABDOMEN : With black bars dorsally. STERNUM : Black or blackish. LEGS : Tm I ca. 0·2. Yellow-brown. EPIGYNE : Text-fig. 232, B ; the scape is narrower posteriorly than in *L. tenuis,* and the plate (*a*) is clearly visible. MALE PALP : Text-fig. 230, C. The paracymbium (Text-fig. 231, G) lacks the large inner tooth of *L. tenuis,* but has a small tooth, directed outwards and backwards, about halfway up the basal arm.

OCCURRENCE : Widespread throughout the British Isles, and generally common, in similar situations to *L. tenuis.* Adults at all seasons.

Lepthyphantes cristatus (Menge).
(Text-figs. 230, A ; 232, E)

Bathyphantes cristatus A. Menge, 1866, p. 121. *Linyphia cristata* O. P.-Cambridge, 1879–81, p. 195. *Lepthyphantes cristatus* C. Chyzer and L. Kulczynski, 1891–7, II, p. 69 ; W. Bosenberg, 1901–3, p. 81 ; E. Simon, 1929, pp. 589, 592.

DESCRIPTION. LENGTH : ♀♂ : 2–2·5 mm. CARAPACE : Yellow-brown. EYES : Posteriors all ca. 0·5 diam. apart. ABDOMEN : With black bars dorsally. STERNUM : Yellow, suffused with black. LEGS : Tm I ca. 0·22. Brown to yellow-brown. EPIGYNE : Text-fig. 232, E ; needs to be distinguished with care from *L. flavipes.* MALE PALP : Text-fig. 230, A ; the tibia has a bunch of stout spines. Tarsus raised into small point posteriorly. Paracymbium with no teeth. Lamella (*l*) is quite distinct from that of the other species in the Group.

OCCURRENCE : Amongst moss, grass, undergrowth, etc. Widespread throughout the British Isles, but not common. Adults at all seasons.

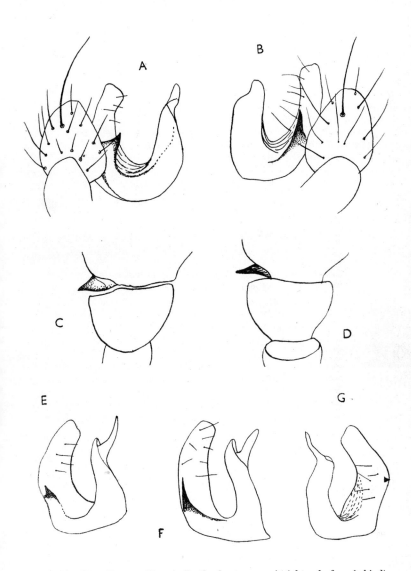

TEXT-FIG. 231.—Paracymbia : A, *Lepthyphantes mengei* (right palp from behind) ;
  E, ditto (right palp from side) ; B, *L. flavipes* (from behind) ; F, ditto (from
  side, right) ; G, *L. zimmermanni* (from side).
  C, tooth on paracymbium, from above : *L. mengei*; D, ditto, *L. flavipes*.

Lepthyphantes mengei Kulczynski.
(Text-figs. 231, A, C, E ; 232, C, D)

Lepthyphantes mengei L. Kulczynski, 1887, p. 320 ; C. Chyzer and L. Kulczynski, 1891–7, II, p. 70 ; A. R. Jackson, 1930, p. 653 ; F. Miller, 1947, Tab. 12, figs. 8–11, Tab. 13, fig. 1. *L. gallicus* E. Simon, 1929, pp. 591, 594. *L. concinnus* Å. Holm, 1945, p. 56.

DESCRIPTION. LENGTH : ♀♂ : 1·5–1·75 mm. CARAPACE : Yellow-brown, with ocular area blackish. EYES : Posterior medians 0·5 to nearly one diam. apart, and 0·5 diam. from laterals. ABDOMEN : With black bars dorsally. STERNUM : Black. LEGS : Tm I 0·2. Pale yellow to yellow-brown. EPIGYNE : Text-fig. 232, C, D ; shows slight variations, but is fairly readily recognisable, though rather close to *L. flavipes*. MALE PALP : The tarsus is suffused with more or less black. The paracymbium (Text-fig. 231, A, C, E) needs to be distinguished with care from that of *L. flavipes* ; seen from the side, behind or above, the tooth is more conical and less acuminate than in *L. flavipes*.

OCCURRENCE : In undergrowth, grass, etc. Widespread throughout the British Isles, and not uncommon. Adults at all seasons.

Lepthyphantes flavipes (Blackwall).
(Text-figs. 231, B, D, F ; 232, F)

Linyphia flavipes J. Blackwall, 1854, p. 178, and 1861–4, p. 247 ; O. P.-Cambridge, 1879–81, p. 517. *Lepthyphantes henricae* C. Chyzer and L. Kulczynski, 1891–7, II, p. 71. *L. flavipes* W. Bosenberg, 1901–3, p. 82 ; E. Simon, 1929, pp. 591, 592 ; F. Miller, 1947, Tab. 13, fig. 2.

DESCRIPTION. LENGTH : ♀♂ : About 2 mm. CARAPACE : Brown to dark-brown, with faint darker fovea and striæ ; ocular area black. EYES : Posteriors all ca. 0·5 diam. apart. ABDOMEN : Black, with ill-defined broad white bars or blotches. STERNUM : Black. LEGS : Tm I 0·2–0·23. Yellow to yellow-brown. EPIGYNE : Text-fig. 232, F ; close to *L. mengei* and *L. cristatus*. MALE PALP : Blackened over its whole length, but particularly on tibia and tarsus. The paracymbium (Text-fig. 231, B, D, F) is close to *L. mengei* : seen from the side, behind or above, the tooth is more acuminate than in *L. mengei*.

OCCURRENCE : In heather, undergrowth, etc. Widespread throughout the British Isles, but not recorded from Wales. Fairly common. Adult at all seasons.

Lepthyphantes tenebricola (Wider).
(Text-figs. 230, D ; 232, G)

Linyphia tenebricola Wider, 1834, p. 267. non *L. tenebricola* O. P.-Cambridge, 1879–81, p. 185. *Lepthyphantes tenebricola* O. P.-Cambridge, 1895, p. 111 ; C. Chyzer and L. Kulczynski, 1891–7, II, p. 69 ; E. Simon, 1929, pp. 590, 592 ; F. Miller, 1947, Tab. 13, fig. 3.

DESCRIPTION. LENGTH : ♀♂ : 2·5–3 mm. CARAPACE : Dark brown, with ocular area blackish. EYES : Posteriors all ca. 0·75 diam. apart. ABDOMEN : Black, with some whitish transverse bars or blotches. STERNUM : Blackish. LEGS : Tm I ca. 0·23. Yellow to yellow-brown. EPIGYNE : Text-fig. 232, G ; resembles *L. tenuis*, but the scape is much wider, the sides forming a smooth curve. MALE PALP : The paracymbium (Text-fig. 230, D) has two large teeth on the inner margin, clearly distinct from *L. tenuis*.

OCCURRENCE : In detritus of woods ; infrequent. Recorded from a number of English counties and from Scotland ; more common in the north than in the south. Adults in spring and autumn.

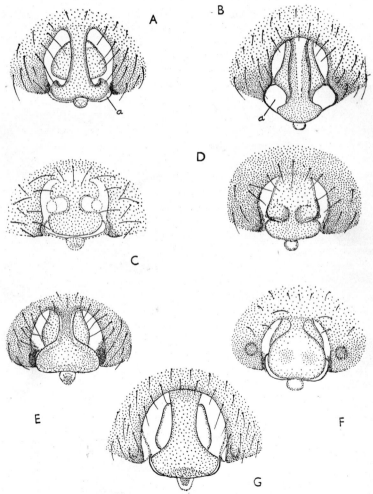

TEXT-FIG. 232.—Epigynes : A, *Lepthyphantes tenuis;* B, *L. zimmermanni;* C, D, *L. mengei;* E, *L. cristatus;* F, *L. flavipes;* G, *L. tenebricola.*

Group IV

The seven species in this group have normally unicolorous abdomens, and fall into two sections depending on the presence or absence of a dorsal spine on metatarsus IV :—

Metatarsus IV spineless—*L. ericaeus*, *L. pallidus*, *L. pinicola* and *L. insignis*.

Metatarsus IV with one spine—*L. angulatus*, *L. audax* and *L. carri*.

The species are readily separated by the sex organs.

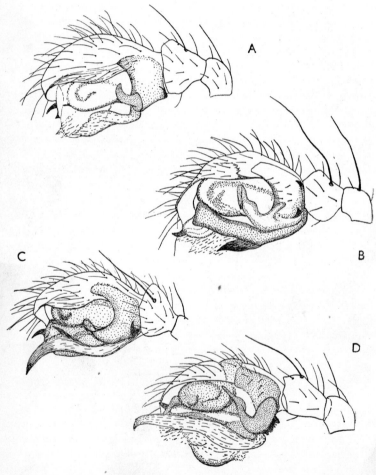

TEXT-FIG. 233.—Male palps: A, *Lepthyphantes ericaeus;* B, *L. pallidus;* C, *L. insignis;* D, *L. pinicola.*

Lepthyphantes ericaeus (Blackwall).
(Text-figs. 233, A ; 235, A)

Linyphia ericaea J. Blackwall, 1853, p. 22, and 1861–4, p. 237 ; O. P.-Cambridge, 1879–81, p. 201. *Lepthyphantes ericaeus* F. O. P.-Cambridge, 1892, p. 390 ; E. Simon, 1929, pp. 605, 615. *Lepthyphantes beatula* O. P.-Cambridge, 1911, p. 52 (♂).

DESCRIPTION. LENGTH : ♀♂ : About 1·5 mm. CARAPACE : Yellow-brown, sometimes suffused faintly with black. EYES : Posterior medians ca. one diam. apart, and ca. 0·5 diam. from laterals. ABDOMEN : Grey to black. STERNUM : Yellow-brown, often suffused

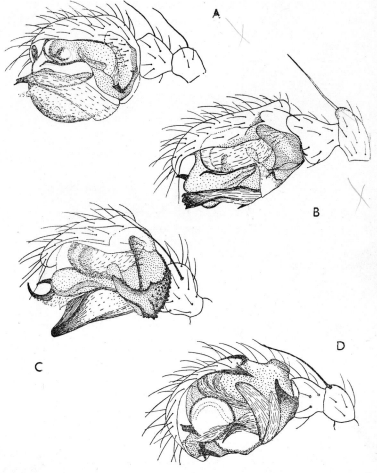

TEXT-FIG. 234.—Male palps : A, *Lepthyphantes audax;* B, *L. angulatus;* C, *L. carri;* D, *L. expunctus.*

with black. LEGS : Tm I ca. 0·17. Yellow-brown. Tibial spines
very long. Metatarsus IV spineless. EPIGYNE : Text-fig. 235, A.
MALE PALP : Text-fig. 233, A.

OCCURRENCE : In heather, grass, etc., usually in dry situations.
Widespread throughout the British Isles, and fairly common. Adults
at most seasons.

Lepthyphantes pallidus (O. P.-Cambridge).
(Text-figs. 233, B ; 235, B)

Linyphia pallida O. P.-Cambridge, 1871, p. 435, and 1879–81, p. 216. *Lepthyphantes
pallidus* E. Simon, 1929, pp. 610, 617. *L. patens* O. P.-Cambridge, 1907, p. 139 (♀).

DESCRIPTION. LENGTH : ♀♂ : About 2 mm. CARAPACE : Yellow
brown. EYES : Posterior medians ca. 0·75 diam. apart, and one
diam. from laterals. ABDOMEN : Grey. STERNUM : Yellow-brown.
LEGS : Tm I ca. 0·17. Yellow-brown. Tibial spines long and stout.
Metatarsus IV spineless. EPIGYNE : Text-fig. 235, B. MALE PALP :
Text-fig. 233, B.

OCCURRENCE : In heather, moss, grass, in marshy ground, under
stones on high ground. Widespread throughout the British Isles, but
infrequent. Adults in spring and summer.

Lepthyphantes pinicola Simon.
(Text-figs. 233, D ; 235, C)

Lepthyphantes pinicola E. Simon, 1884, p. 322 ; F. O. P.-Cambridge, 1891, p. 78
O. P.-Cambridge, 1891, p. 89 ; E. Simon, 1929, pp. 607, 609.

DESCRIPTION. LENGTH : ♀♂ : About 2 mm. CARAPACE : Brown.
EYES : Posterior medians ca. 0·5 diam. apart, and ca. 0·75 diam.
from laterals. ABDOMEN : Grey to black. STERNUM : Shiny black.
LEGS : Tm I 0·23. Brown. Tibial spines long. Metatarsus IV
spineless. EPIGYNE : Text-fig. 235, C ; scape elongated. MALE PALP :
Text-fig. 233, D ; the *lamella* is long and prominent.

OCCURRENCE : On high ground, often among loose stones, in the
more northern parts of England and Wales, and in Scotland (but has
occurred as far south as the Malvern Hills). Adults in summer and
autumn.

Lepthyphantes insignis O. P.-Cambridge.
(Text-figs. 233, C ; 235, D, F)

Lepthyphantes insignis O. P.-Cambridge, 1913, p. 131.

DESCRIPTION. LENGTH : ♀ : 2·5 mm. ♂ : 2 mm. CARAPACE :
Pale brown. EYES : Posterior medians ca. one diam. apart, and
rather less from laterals. ABDOMEN : Pale grey. STERNUM : Pale
brown. LEGS : Tm I 0·17. Pale brown. Metatarsus IV spineless.
EPIGYNE : Text-fig. 235, D, F. MALE PALP : Text-fig. 233, C.

OCCURRENCE : In undergrowth, and in moles' nests. Recorded
only from a few southern English counties ; very rare.

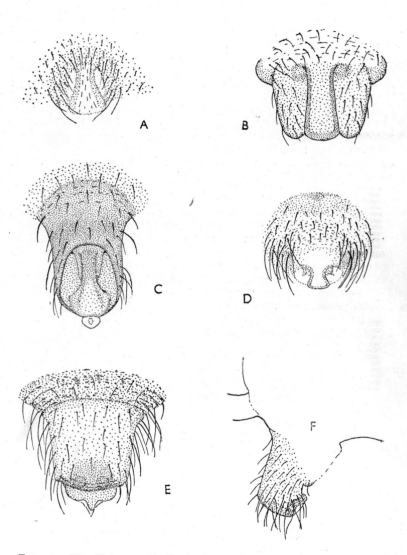

TEXT-FIG. 235.—Epigynes : A, *Lepthyphantes ericaeus;* B, *L. pallidus; C, L. pinicola;* D, *L. insignis;* F, ditto (from side) ; E, *L. audax.*

Lepthyphantes angulatus (O. P.-Cambridge).
(Text-figs. 234, B ; 236, A)

Linyphia angulata O. P.-Cambridge, 1879–81, p. 519. *L. angulipalpis* idem, 1872 (2), p. 536. *Lepthyphantes angulatus* J. E. Hull, 1908, p. 114 ; O. P.-Cambridge, 1908, p. 172. *L. angulifer* E. Simon, 1929, p. 596. *L. lofotensis* Å. Holm, 1944, p. 123.

DESCRIPTION. LENGTH : ♀♂ : About 2 mm. CARAPACE : Yellow-brown to brown. EYES : Posteriors all ca. 0·75 diam. apart. ABDOMEN : Grey to greyish black. STERNUM : Blackish. LEGS : Tm I 0·17 (♂) –0·22(♀). Yellow-brown to brown. All metatarsi with one dorsal spine. CHELICERÆ : ♂ : With large tooth on inner border. EPIGYNE : Text-fig. 236, A. MALE PALP : Text-fig. 234, B ; patella produced into small tubercle anteriorly, bearing a stout spine.

OCCURRENCE : In the north of England, and in Scotland, usually on high ground. Local. Adults in late summer, autumn and winter.

Lepthyphantes audax Sörensen.
(Text-figs. 234, A ; 235, E)

Lepthyphantes audax W. Sörensen, 1898, p. 196 ; A. R. Jackson, 1933 (2), p. 153 ; J. Braendegaard, 1946, p. 29. *L. cacuminum* A. R. Jackson, 1914, p. 118.

DESCRIPTION. LENGTH : ♀♂ : 2 mm. CARAPACE : Pale yellow-brown. EYES : Posterior medians ca. 0·75 diam. apart, and ca. 0·5 diam. from laterals. ABDOMEN : Grey. STERNUM : Yellow-brown, suffused with black, particularly at margins. LEGS : Tm I ca. 0·2. Yellow-brown. All metatarsi with one spine. EPIGYNE : Text-fig. 235, E. MALE PALP : Text-fig. 234, A.

OCCURRENCE : On mountains in the Scottish Highlands, above 3,000 feet. Adult in June-August.

Lepthyphantes carri Jackson.
(Text-fig. 234, C)

Lepthyphantes carri A. R. Jackson, 1913, p. 25 ; O. P.-Cambridge, 1914, p. 127.

DESCRIPTION. LENGTH : ♂ : 2·5 mm. CARAPACE : Orange-brown. EYES : Posteriors less than one diam. apart. ABDOMEN : Grey, with sometimes traces of black bars posteriorly. STERNUM : Yellow-brown, suffused with black. LEGS : Tm I ca. 0·19. Orange-brown. All metatarsi with one spine. MALE PALP : Text-fig. 234, C. The ♀ is not known.

OCCURRENCE : On the bark of trees, in Sherwood Forest (Nottinghamshire). In a jackdaw's nest, Windsor Forest (Berkshire).

Group V
Lepthyphantes expunctus (O. P.-Cambridge).
(Text-figs. 234, D ; 236, B)

Linyphia expuncta O. P.-Cambridge, 1875 (2), p. 251, and 1879–81, p. 512. *Bolyphantes expunctus* J. E. Hull, 1909 (1), p. 446. *Lepthyphantes lepidus* C. Chyzer and L. Kulczynski, 1891–7, II, p. 68. *L. expunctus* E. Simon, 1929, pp. 583, 586.

DESCRIPTION. LENGTH : ♀♂ : 2–2·5 mm. CARAPACE : Yellow-brown with blackish margins. EYES : Posterior medians ca. 0·75 diam. apart and ca. one diam. from laterals. ABDOMEN : Whitish dorsally, with median black dentated stripe anteriorly, and black chevrons and bars posteriorly. STERNUM : Dark yellow-brown. LEGS : Tm I 0·22–0·24. Yellow-brown. EPIGYNE : Text-fig. 236, B. MALE PALP : Text-fig. 234, D.

OCCURRENCE : Scotland. On the trunks and branches of trees (especially pines) ; locally abundant, but restricted in distribution. Adult August and September.

98. Genus **HELOPHORA** A. Menge 1866.

CHARACTERS OF GENUS. ABDOMEN : Usually with no pattern. LEGS : Metatarsus IV with a trichobothrium ; Tm I 0·75. Legs long and thin. Femora spineless. Tibiæ and metatarsi each with several long spines.

There is one British species.

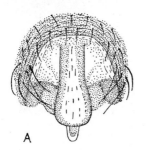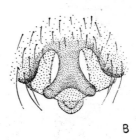

TEXT-FIG. 236.—Epigynes : A, *L. angulatus;* B, *L. expunctus.*

Helophora insignis (Blackwall).
(Text-fig. 237, A, B)

Linyphia insignis J. Blackwall, 1841, p. 662, and 1861–4, p. 238 ; O. P.-Cambridge, 1879–81, p. 219 ; E. Simon, 1929, **p.** 635. *Helophora insignis* H. Blauvelt, 1936, p. 155 ; B. J. Kaston, 1948, p. 126.

DESCRIPTION. LENGTH : ♀ : 3·5–4 mm. ♂ : 3–3·5 mm. CARAPACE : Brown to orange-brown, with very faint striæ. EYES : On black spots. Anterior medians only slightly smaller than posterior medians. Posterior medians one diam. apart, and scarcely more than one diam. from laterals. ABDOMEN : Grey, with sometimes (particularly in ♂) faint black chevrons posteriorly. STERNUM : Brown to dark brown. LEGS : Tm I ca. 0·75. Pale brown to orange-brown. EPIGYNE : Text-fig. 237, B ; the scape is long. MALE PALP : Text-fig. 237, A.

OCCURRENCE : In moss and grass, often in woods, usually in damp places. Widespread throughout the British Isles, but much commoner in the northern parts of the country. Adult in autumn and winter.

99. Genus **LINYPHIA** P. A. Latreille 1804.

CHARACTERS OF GENUS. EYES : Fairly small, widely spaced ; on large black spots. ABDOMEN : With a dorsal pattern. CHELICERÆ : Stridulating striæ not visible in either sex. ♂ : Often long and rather attenuated apically (the cheliceræ show allometric growth : G. H. Locket, 1932 ; G. H. Locket and P. C. Gardiner, 1937). STERNUM :

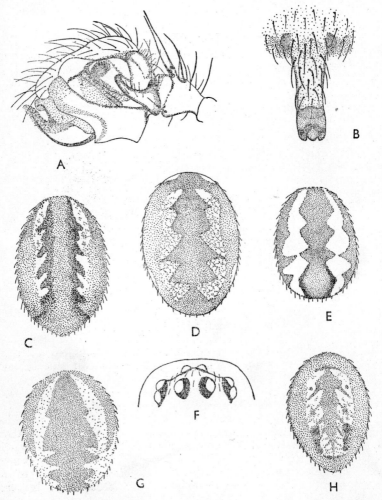

TEXT-FIG. 237.—*Helophora insignis:* A, ♂ palp ; B, epigyne.
   Abdomens (from above) : C, *Linyphia triangularis;* D, *L. pusilla;* E, *L. peltata;*
  F, *L. triangularis:* Eyes ; G, *L. hortensis;* H, *L. impigra.*

Appreciably longer than wide. LEGS : Metatarsus IV without a trichobothrium ; Tm I about 0·2–0·3 (trichobothria difficult to see). Legs usually long, with metatarsi almost twice as long as tarsi. With numerous spines ; one or more on femora. EPIGYNE : Without scape. MALE PALP : Paracymbium very slender and inconspicuous. The palpal organs have been described in detail by H. Blauvelt (1936).

There are nine British species, which can be split into three groups based on the femoral spines :—

Femora I and II spineless . . . . . . *L. marginata*
Femora I each with 4–7 spines (dorsal and lateral)
     L. triangularis and *L. montana*
Femora I with up to 3 spines (dorsal and lateral)
     L. clathrata, L. peltata, L. pusilla, L. hortensis,
          L. impigra and *L. furtiva*

The species can be separated quite readily by the sex organs, and frequently also by the abdominal patterns.

Linyphia triangularis (Clerck)
(=*L. montana* Linn).
(Text-figs. 237, C, F ; 238, A ; 240, A)

Araneus triangularis C. Clerck, 1757, p. 71 ; *A. montana* C. Linnaeus, 1758, p. 621. *Linyphia montana* J. Blackwall, 1861–4, p. 211. *L. triangularis* O. P.-Cambridge, 1879–81, p. 227 ; E. Simon, 1929, p. 633 ; H. Blauvelt, 1936, p. 124.

DESCRIPTION. LENGTH : ♀♂ : 5–6 mm. CARAPACE : Yellow-brown to brown, with darker margins ; median black line extends forwards from fovea, bifurcating behind posterior median eyes (not present in remaining species except occasionally in *L. impigra*). ♂ : A few forward-directed bristles on head. EYES : Anterior medians less than one diam. apart, and ca. 2·5 diam. from laterals ; posterior medians slightly more than 2 diam. apart, and 1·3–1·5 diam. from laterals (Text-fig. 237, F). ABDOMEN : ♀ : Pattern as Text-fig. 237, C. ♂ : A more or less uniform purplish brown folium covers dorsal side, with a few brownish bars posteriorly. STERNUM : Black. CHELICERÆ : ♂ : Greatly elongated, length often ca. 3–4 times width of clypeus (growth allometric). LEGS : Tm I 0·18. Yellow-brown to brown, not annulated. EPIGYNE : Text-fig. 240, A. MALE PALP : Text-fig. 238, A.

OCCURRENCE : On low bushes, grass, etc. Widespread throughout the British Isles, and very common. Adult in late summer and autumn.

Linyphia montana (Clerck).
(=*L. resupina domestica* Degeer)
(Text-figs. 238, B ; 240, B)

Araneus montanus C. Clerck, 1757, p. 64. *A. resupina domestica* Degeer, 1778, p. 251. *Linyphia marginata* J. Blackwall, 1861–4, p. 213. *L. montana* O. P.-Cambridge, 1879–81, p. 225 ; E. Simon, 1929, p. 635 ; H. Blauvelt, 1936, p. 122.

DESCRIPTION. LENGTH : ♀ : About 6 mm. ♂ : About 4 mm. CARAPACE : Brown to dark brown, with darker fovea and striæ, and

median dark stripe (not bifurcated anteriorly) (sometimes indefinite) ;
a few forward-directed hairs on head. EYES : Anterior medians ca.
0·5 diam. apart, and ca. 1·5 diam. from laterals ; posterior medians
1·5–1·75 diam. apart, and rather more than one diam. from laterals.
ABDOMEN : ♀ : With purplish brown folium dorsally. ♂ : A white
blotch on either side anteriorly, followed by a purplish-brown folium
containing some brown blotches and bars. STERNUM : Dark brown.
CHELICERÆ : ♂ : Not greatly developed. LEGS : Tm I 0·25–0·3.

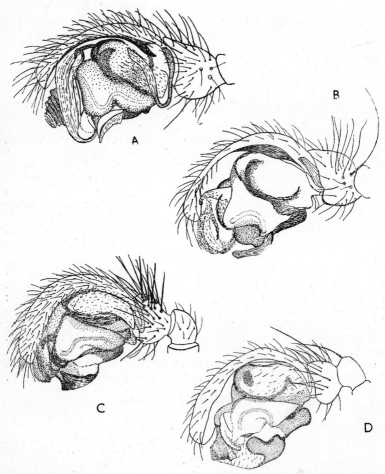

TEXT-FIG. 238.—Male palps : A, *Linyphia triangularis*; B, *L. montana*; C,
L. clathrata; D, *L. furtiva*.

Yellow-brown to brown, annulated with darker brown. EPIGYNE : Text-fig. 240, B ; rather similar to *L. clathrata*. MALE PALP : Text-fig 238, B.

OCCURRENCE : On low bushes, grass, etc. Widespread throughout the British Isles, but much more local than *L. triangularis*. Adult in spring and early summer.

Linyphia clathrata Sundevall.
(Text-figs. 238, C ; 240, D)

Linyphia clathrata C. J. Sundevall, 1829, p. 218 ; O. P.-Cambridge, 1879–81, p. 222 ; C. Chyzer and L. Kulczynski, 1891–7, II, p. 58 ; W. Bosenberg, 1901–3, p. 69 ; E. Simon, 1929, p. 636 ; H. Blauvelt, 1936, p. 96. *Neriene marginata* J. Blackwall, 1861–4, p. 249.

DESCRIPTION. LENGTH : ♀♂ : About 4–5 mm. CARAPACE : Brown to very dark brown, with faint darker striæ ; a few bristles in ocular area. EYES : Anterior medians ca. 0·5 diam. apart, and ca. 2 diam. from laterals ; posterior medians ca. 2 diam. apart, and ca. 1–1·25 diam. from laterals. ABDOMEN : ♀ : A dark purplish-brown folium dorsally. ♂ : Two bright white patches anteriorly, with folium behind containing some blackish bars. STERNUM : Yellow-brown to dark-brown. CHELICERÆ : ♂ : With boss anteriorly, just below clypeus. LEGS : Tm I ca. 0·25. Relatively short and stout. Brown, scarcely if at all annulated. EPIGYNE : Text-fig. 240, D ; rather similar to *L. montana*. MALE PALP : Text-fig. 238, C ; tibia with a cluster of black bristles.

OCCURRENCE : In low undergrowth. Widespread throughout the British Isles, and very common. Adult in spring and summer.

Linyphia peltata Wider.
(Text-figs. 237, E ; 239, B ; 241, A, B)

Linyphia peltata Wider, 1834, p. 256 ; O. P.-Cambridge, 1879–81, p. 229 ; E. Simon, 1929, p. 632 ; H. Blauvelt, 1936, p. 119. *L. rubea* J. Blackwall, 1861–4, p. 217. *Lepthyphantes nigrescens* O. P.-Cambridge, 1912, p. 90.

DESCRIPTION. LENGTH : ♀♂ : 2·75–3 mm. CARAPACE : Brown, with blackish fovea. EYES : Anterior medians ca. one diam. apart, ca. 2 diam. from laterals ; posterior medians slightly more than one diam. apart, and 1·5–2 diam. from laterals. ABDOMEN : ♀ : Text-fig. 237, E. ♂ : Similar, but median band broader and usually not so dentated. STERNUM : Brown to dark-brown. CHELICERÆ : ♂ : Fairly long, but not divergent. LEGS : Tm I ca. 0·2. Pale brown to brown ; not annulated. EPIGYNE : Text-fig. 241, A, B. MALE PALP : Text-fig. 239, B. The whole spider has a fairly slender appearance.

OCCURRENCE : In woods, hedges, etc. ; adult in spring and early summer. Widespread throughout the British Isles, and abundant in places.

Linyphia pusilla Sundevall.
(Text-figs. 237, D ; 239, A ; 241, C)

Linyphia pusilla C. J. Sundevall, 1829, p. 214 ; O. P.-Cambridge, 1879–81, p. 231 ; C. Chyzer and L. Kulczynski, 1891–7, II, p. 58 ; W. Bosenberg, 1901–3, p. 70 ; E. Simon, 1929, p. 638 ; H. Blauvelt, 1936, p. 130. *L. fuliginea* J. Blackwall, 1861–4, p. 216.

DESCRIPTION. LENGTH : ♀ : 3·5–5 mm. ♂ : 3·5 mm. CARAPACE : Brown, with head rather darker. EYES : Anterior medians ca. 0·5 diam. apart and 2–2·5 diam. from laterals ; posterior medians ca. 2·5 diam. apart and ca. 2 diam. from laterals. ABDOMEN : ♀ :

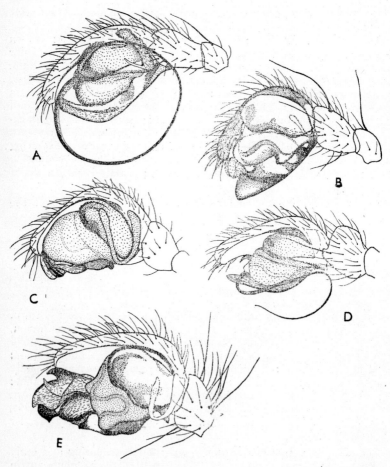

TEXT-FIG. 239.—Male palps : A, *Linyphia pusilla*; B, *L. peltata*; C, *L. hortensis*; D, *L. impigra*; E, *L. marginata*.

Text-fig. 237, D. ♂ : Greyish or black, with a shining white patch on either side anteriorly. STERNUM : Dark brown. CHELICERÆ : ♂ : Fairly long, bearing on sides and behind small warts each carrying a minute bristle (more developed in some specimens than others). LEGS : Tm I 0·2–0·25. Yellow-brown. ♂ : Tibial and femoral spines short, less than one diam. of tibia. EPIGYNE : Text-fig. 241, C. MALE PALP : Text-fig. 239, A.

OCCURRENCE : On low vegetation, grass, etc. Widespread throughout the British Isles, and fairly common. Adult in spring and summer.

Linyphia hortensis Sundevall.
(Text-figs. 237, G ; 239, C ; 240, E)

Linyphia hortensis C. J. Sundevall, 1829, p. 213 ; O. P.-Cambridge, 1879–81, p. 230 ; E. Simon, 1929, p. 637 ; C. Chyzer and L. Kulczynski, 1891–7, II, p. 58 ; H. Blauvelt, 1936, p. 125. *L. pratensis* J. Blackwall, 1861–4, p. 215.

DESCRIPTION. LENGTH : ♀ : 4–5 mm. ♂ : 3–4 mm. CARAPACE : ♀ : Brown, with head sometimes darker brown. ♂ : Chestnut brown, with blackish head, fovea and striæ. EYES : Anterior medians ca. 0·5 diam. apart, and ca. 2 diam. from laterals ; posterior medians ca. 2 diam. apart, and ca. 1·5 diam. from laterals. ABDOMEN : ♀ : Text-fig. 237, G. A narrow white band runs round the sides. ♂ : Practically black, with faint outlines of a folium, and a conspicuous white patch on either side anteriorly. STERNUM : Brown to dark brown. CHELICERÆ : Very dark brown. ♂ : Enlarged (allometric growth) ; with warty granules anteriorly, and a large prominent tooth in outer margin. LEGS : Tm I 0·2–0·25. Yellow-brown to brown, with metatarsi and tarsi sometimes lighter. EPIGYNE : Text-fig. 240, E. MALE PALP : Text-fig. 239, C ; tarsus suffused with black.

OCCURRENCE : In hedges, in low vegetation in woods, etc. (especially by sweeping Dog's Mercury). Widespread throughout the British Isles ; less common than the preceding species, but abundant in local patches. Adults in early summer.

Linyphia impigra O. P.-Cambridge.
(Text-figs. 237, H ; 239, D ; 240, F)

Linyphia impigra O. P.-Cambridge, 1871, p. 422, and 1879–81, p. 578 : C. Chyzer and L. Kulczynski, 1891–7, II, p. 58 ; E. Simon, 1929, p. 638.

DESCRIPTION. LENGTH : ♀ : 4–5 mm. ♂ : 4 mm. CARAPACE : ♀ : Yellow-brown, with dark brown to black head, fovea and striæ. A dark longitudinal streak occasionally bifurcates anteriorly. ♂ : Orange-brown, with blackish fovea. EYES : Anterior medians ca. 0·75 diam. apart, and ca. 2·5 diam. from laterals ; posterior medians 2–2·5 diams. apart, and ca. 1·5 diam. from laterals. ABDOMEN : ♀ : Text-fig. 237, H. ♂ : Black. STERNUM : ♀ : Brown to dark brown, with darker brown or black margins. ♂ : Orange, with black margins. CHELICERÆ : ♂ : Fairly long, with small boss, anteriorly and to side, just below clypeus. LEGS : Tm I ca. 0·22–0·25. ♀ : Yellow-brown, faintly annulated, particularly at apices of segments. ♂ : Orange-brown, not annulated. EPIGYNE: Text-fig. 240, F. MALE PALP: 239, D.

OCCURRENCE: In marshy spots, among reeds and low plants and bushes. Recorded from a number of English counties and Eire, but local. Adult in late summer and autumn.

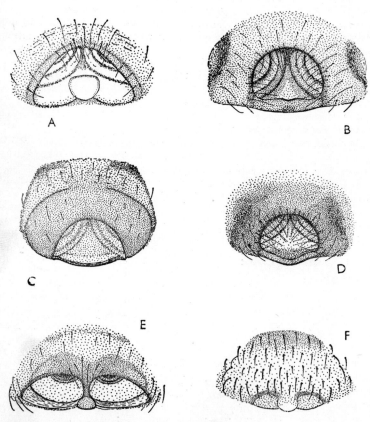

TEXT-FIG. 240.—Epigynes: A, *Linyphia triangularis*; B, *L. montana*; C, *L. furtiva*; D, *L. clathrata*; E, *L. hortensis*; F, *L. impigra*.

Linyphia furtiva O. P.-Cambridge.
(Text-figs. 238, D ; 240, C)

Linyphia furtiva O. P.-Cambridge, 1871, p. 425 ; and 1879–81, p. 223 ; E. Simon, 1929, p. 636 ; H. Blauvelt, 1936, p. 121.

DESCRIPTION. LENGTH : ♀♂: 3·5–4 mm. CARAPACE: Dark brown. ♂: With a few bristles in ocular area. EYES: ♀♂: Anterior medians ca. one diam. apart, and 3 diams. from laterals ; posterior medians 3–4 diam. apart, and 1·5–2 diam. from laterals. ABDOMEN : Similar to *L. clathrata*, but folium less distinct. STERNUM : Dark brown. CHELICERÆ : ♂ : With boss anteriorly, just below clypeus. LEGS : Tm I ca. 0·25. Brown or yellow-brown, not annulated. Relatively short and stout. EPIGYNE : Text-fig. 240, C ; similar to *L. clathrata*, but larger and more prominent. MALE PALP : Text-fig. 238, D ; bristles on tibia less obvious than in *L. clathrata*.

OCCURRENCE : Amongst heather, dry grass, on bushes and low branches of trees. Recorded from the more southern English counties, but rare. Adult in summer.

Linyphia marginata C. L. Koch.
(Text-figs. 239, E ; 241, D)

Linyphia marginata C. L. Koch (3), 1834, p. 127 ; O. P.-Cambridge. 1879–81, p. 523 ; E. Simon, 1929, p. 630 ; H. Blauvelt, 1936, p. 110 ; B. J. Kaston, 1948, p. 122. *L. triangularis* J. Blackwall, 1861–4, p. 212.

DESCRIPTION. LENGTH : ♀♂ : 4·5–5·5 mm. CARAPACE : Brown to orange-brown. ♂ : Head and clypeus with numerous long bristles. EYES : ♀ : Anterior medians ca. one diam. apart, and ca. 2 diam. from laterals ; posterior medians one diam. apart, and ca. 1·5 diam. from laterals. ♂ : Rather more widely spaced. ABDOMEN : With distinct black and white pattern, somewhat variable but often similar to *L. peltata*. STERNUM : Dark brown, with numerous long hairs. LEGS : Tm I ca. 0·15. Brown, not annulated. Femora spineless. EPIGYNE : Text-fig. 241, D. MALE PALP : Text-fig. 239, E.

OCCURRENCE : Recorded only from a number of localities in Scotland.

100. Genus MENGEA F. O. P.-Cambridge 1903.

CHARACTERS OF GENUS. ABDOMEN : With no pattern. LEGS : Metatarsus IV with a trichobothrium ; Tm I 0·7–0·8 (*M. scopigera* has several smaller metatarsal trichobothria in addition to the principal one). Legs long. Tibiæ with several stout spines, including ventral ones. Metatarsi I and II with one spine ventrally or none, and with no dorsal spines ; metatarsi III and IV with more numerous spines. All tarsi with a saucer-like depression (similar to the base of a trichobothrium), position about 0·7–0·8 (Text-fig. 242, E). MALE PALP : Tarsus drawn out basally, and armed at basal tip with a number of stout spines. Paracymbium highly developed.

There are two British species, separated by the sex organs, the eyes and the trichobothria.

Mengea scopigera (Grube).
(Text-fig. 242, B, C, E)

Linyphia scopigera A. Grube, 1859, p. 470. *L. rufa* O. P.-Cambridge, 1879–81, p. 520. *Tmeticus scopiger* idem, 1889, p. 117. *Mengea scopigera* E. Simon, 1929, p. 627.

DESCRIPTION. LENGTH : ♀ : 4–5 mm. ♂ : About 4 mm. CARAPACE : Orange-brown, with faint striæ sometimes visible. EYES :

Posteriors equal in size, and one diam. or slightly more apart. ABDOMEN : Grey. LEGS : Tm I ca. 0·8 ; in addition to the principal trichobothrium, there is a series of 2–3 smaller trichobothria along all the metatarsi. Orange-brown. EPIGYNE : Text-fig. 242, C. MALE PALP : Text-fig. 242, B ; the paracymbium is quite distinct from that of *M. warburtoni.*

OCCURRENCE : In wet, swampy areas (including salt marshes). Recorded mainly from the more northern English counties and Scotland. Common in a few localities. Adults in August-September.

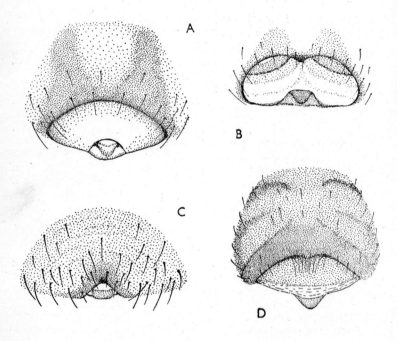

TEXT-FIG. 241.—Epigynes : A, *Linyphia peltata;* B, ditto (more from behind) ; C, *L. pusilla;* D, *L. marginata.*

Mengea warburtoni (O. P.-Cambridge).
(Text-fig. 242, A, D)

Tmeticus warburtoni O. P.-Cambridge, 1889, p. 115. *Centromerus probabilis* idem, 1908, p. 174. *Mengea warburtoni* E. Simon, 1929, p. 627.

DESCRIPTION. LENGTH : ♀: 3·5–4 mm. ♂: 3·5 mm. Colour and form closely similar to *M. scopigera.* EYES : Larger than in *M. scopigera,* and closer together, with posterior medians greater than posterior laterals (particularly in ♀), and less than one diam. apart and less than one diam. from laterals. LEGS : Tm I 0·7–0·73 ;

metatarsi with only one trichobothrium. Usually no spines on metatarsi I and II. EPIGYNE : Text-fig. 242, D. MALE PALP : Text-fig. 242, A ; the tarsus is drawn out basally to a greater extent than in *M. scopigera*, and the paracymbium is quite distinct from that species.

OCCURRENCE : In similar situations to the last (not recorded from Scotland or Wales). Rare. Adults in August-September.

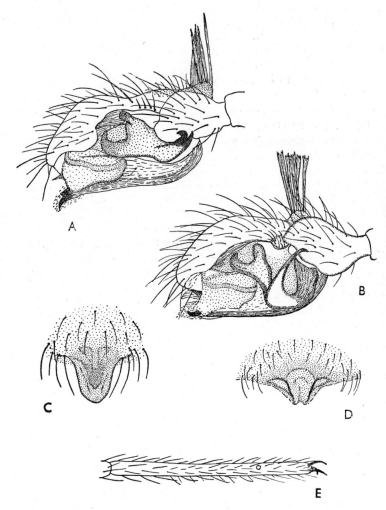

TEXT-FIG. 242.—*Mengea warburtoni:* A, ♂ palp ; D, epigyne.
M. scopigera: B, ♂ palp ; C, epigyne ; E, tarsus I (from above).

II. ADDENDA TO VOLUME I.
and corrigenda (see p. 418)

Since Volume I of the present work was published, a number of species have been found which are new to Britain and which would properly have been described in that volume. The new records are as follows :—

Family GNAPHOSIDÆ.
 Drassodes sörenseni (Strand).
 Zelotes petrensis (C. L. Koch).
 Micaria silesiaca L. Koch.
 Micaria subopaca Westring.

Family CLUBIONIDÆ.
 Scotina palliardi (L. Koch).

Family THOMISIDÆ.
 Xysticus acerbus Thorell.

Family LYCOSIDÆ.
 Pirata uliginosus (Thorell).

In addition to descriptions of these species new to Britain, new or improved descriptions are given of the following : Genus *Dictyna* (female vulvae), *Thanatus striatus* C. L. Koch ♂ (THOMISIDAE), *Euophrys molesta* Camb. ♀ (SALTICIDAE), *Lycosa paludicola* (Cl.) ♂ (LYCOSIDAE).

Genus Dictyna

It has been our intention throughout this work to describe and figure the species in such a way that they can be identified from their external features without the aid of dissections or special methods of preparation. The females of some of the common species of *Dictyna*, however, are not always identifiable with certainty by their external features alone. If the epigynes are cleared, the species are then clearly distinguishable by the characteristic shapes of the internal organs (vulvæ) which then become visible (Text-fig. 251). The clearing may be carried out by soaking the specimens for several hours in a liquid of refractive index of 1.5–1.55 (e.g. phenol containing 5–10 per cent. of alcohol, or clove oil) ; the parts show up more distinctly, however, when the specimens are treated successively with caustic soda and acetic acid in the normal way.

Drassodes sörenseni (Strand).
(Text-fig. 243)

Drassus sörenseni E. Strand, 1900, p. 98. *Haplodrassus lapponicus* Å. Holm, 1939, p. 4. *H. sörenseni* Å. Holm, 1945, p. 63 ; A. Tullgren, 1946, p. 102.

DESCRIPTION. The species, of which a single female has been found in Scotland, is a member of our Group II of the genus *Drassodes* (see vol. I, p. 98). LENGTH : ♀ : 6 mm. CARAPACE : Brownish yellow with faint darker lines radiating from the fovea. ABDOMEN : Greyish brown, with no markings. STERNUM : Coloured as carapace, with a

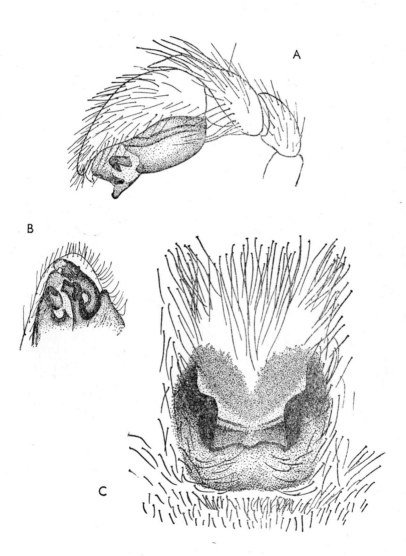

TEXT-FIG. 243.—*Drassodes sorenseni:* A, male palp (side) ; B, tip of male palp (below) ; C, epigyne.

narrow dark borderline. LEGS : Brownish yellow. Tibiæ I and II
with no spines ; tibia IV with no dorsal spine. Metatarsi I and II
each with one pair of ventral spines at about the mid point. EPIGYNE :
Text-fig. 243, C. This is somewhat variable, but that of the British
specimen is clearly recognisable from Tullgren's figure (1946, pl. XVII,
fig. 210) and it has been compared with an authentic specimen from

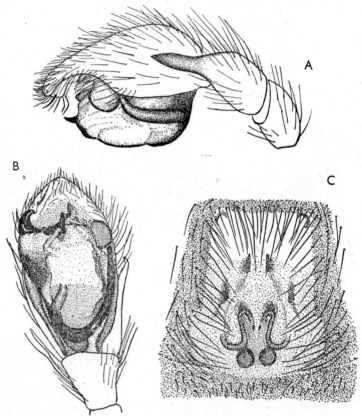

TEXT-FIG. 244.—*Zelotes petrensis:* A, male palp (side) ; B, ditto (below) ; C,
epigyne.

Sweden. MALE PALP : Text-fig. 243, A, B. This is drawn from a
Swedish specimen kindly lent to us by Dr. Å. Holm.

A full description of the species under the name *Haplodrassus
lapponicus* was given by Å. Holm (1939, p. 4), who later (1945, p. 63)
concluded that this was synonymous with *H. sörenseni* (Strand). The
male has not yet been found in Britain.

OCCURRENCE : A single female from Abernethy Forest, where it was found by Mr. A. A. D. La Touche in June, 1948. We are greatly indebted to him for the loan of the specimen, of which this is the first published record.

Zelotes petrensis (C. L. Koch).
(Text-fig. 244)

Melanophora petrensis C. L. Koch, 1839, p. 89. *Prosthesima petrensis* C. Chyzer and L. Kulczynski, 1891–7, II, p. 201. *Zelotes petrensis* E. Simon, 1914, p. 164 ; E. Reimoser, 1937, p. 34 ; A. Tullgren, 1946, p. 210 ; A. F. Millidge and G. H. Locket, 1952, p. 59.

DESCRIPTION. LENGTH : ♀♂ : 6–6·5 mm. CARAPACE, STERNUM and ABDOMEN : Almost uniform black. EYES : Posterior row nearly equal in size and almost equally spaced. LEGS : Femur I with a yellow patch on the retrolateral side. Tibia II with no ventral spine. Metatarsus II with one pair of ventral spines near the base. The

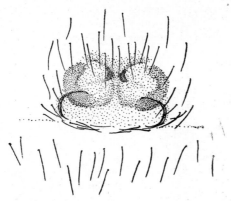

TEXT-FIG. 245.—*Micaria silesiaca*, epigyne.

spider is a typical *Zelotes* in general appearance. EPIGYNE : Text-fig. 244, C. This needs to be distinguished from that of *Z. serotinus* (Vol. I, Text-fig. 58, F). MALE PALP : Text-fig. 244, A, B. (This was drawn from a foreign specimen from the Koch collection.)

OCCURRENCE : Abinger Common and Holmbury Hill (Surrey). April and September, 1949 ; May, 1950. Males in April, 1952.

Micaria silesiaca L. Koch.
(Text-fig. 245)

Micaria silesiaca L. Koch, 1875, p. 4 (♂) ; W. Bosenberg, 1901–3, p. 288 (♂♀) ; E. Reimoser, 1937, p. 94 ; A. Tullgren, 1946, p. 67. ? *M. hospes* C. Chyzer and L. Kulczynski, 1891–7, III, p. 257.

DESCRIPTION. This is a typical *Micaria* in general appearance (see descriptions of other species, Vol. I, pp. 118–123). LENGTH : ♀ : About 4·5 mm. CLYPEUS : About 1·5–2 times diameter of an anterior

EE

lateral eye. EYES : Anterior medians removed from laterals by not more than half a diameter of a lateral. Posterior medians separated by more than twice (nearly three times) the length of one of them. ABDOMEN : The very clear transverse light lines of *M. pulicaria* are in this species replaced by ill-defined transverse bars, widening somewhat on the sides. STERNUM : Dark brown. LEGS : Dark brown, and much more uniformly coloured than in *M. pulicaria ;* patellæ I and II and bases of tibiæ I and II lighter. EPIGYNE : Text-fig. 245.

OCCURRENCE : A female was taken by Dr. A. R. Jackson (who never identified it) in the New Forest in 1936, and another by Mr. A. A. D. La Touche at Beaulieu Road (Hampshire) in June, 1945. This is the first published record of these captures.

Micaria subopaca Westring.
(Text-fig. 252)

Micaria subopaca N. Westring, 1861, p. 336 ; T. Thorell, 1870–73, p. 175. *M. albostriata* L. Koch, 1868, p. 74 ; C. Chyzer and L. Kulczynski, 1891–7, II, p. 259 ; W. Bosenberg, 1901–3, pp. 287, 288 ; E. Simon, 1932, p. 950 ; A. Tullgren, 1946, p. 65.

DESCRIPTION. This species resembles *Micaria pulicaria* (Sund.) (see Vol. I, p. 119) but differs from it in the following respects.

LENGTH : ♀: 2·6 mm. ♂ : 2·3 mm. CARAPACE : With fewer white hairs, mostly in a median line. EYES : The anterior row is not so strongly procurved. (In *M. pulicaria* the anterior margins of the laterals and the posterior margins of the medians lie almost on a straight line). ABDOMEN : A single thin transverse white line, just broken in the middle, lies across the mid point of the abdomen. EPIGYNE : Text-fig. 252, C. This is very distinct. MALE PALP : Text-fig. 252, A, B. The short patella and tibia and the upward-curving tibial apophysis are characteristic. The apex of the tarsus is less pointed, bearing only 2 rather small spines, and projects only a short distance beyond the palpal organs, which lack the hooked central apophysis (see Text-fig. 252, B, and Vol. I, Text-fig. 63, B.).

OCCURRENCE : A male was found by one of us (A.F.M.) in May 1952 on the bark of a Scots pine on Holmbury Hill, Surrey. A female was taken by Mr. A. E. Le Gros at the base of an old oak tree (inhabited by the ant *Lasius brunneus* Latr.), Bookham Common, Surrey, in September, 1952. We wish to thank Mr. Le Gros for making this record available to us and for the gift of the specimen.

Scotina palliardi (L. Koch).
(Text-fig. 246, A, C, D)

Liocranum palliardi L. Koch, 1881, p. 60. *Scotina Paillardi* E. Simon, 1932, p. 945. *Scotina palliardi* E. Reimoser, 1937, p. 85 ; A. Tullgren, 1946, p. 54 ; A. F. Millidge and G. H. Locket, 1952, p. 60. (There is doubt about some of the synonyms given by Simon (ibid, p. 973) : *Agelena gracilipes* Bl. (J. Blackwall, 1861–4, p. 162) and *Agrœca diversa* Camb. (O. P.-Cambridge, 1913, p. 113) are synonyms of *Scotina gracilipes* (Bl.). E. Reimoser (loc. cit.) confuses *S. palliardi* (L.K.) with *Scotina gracilipes* (Bl.).)

DESCRIPTION. LENGTH : ♀: 3 mm. ♂ : 2·5 mm. The general colouration resembles that of *S. gracilipes* (Bl.). CARAPACE : Some

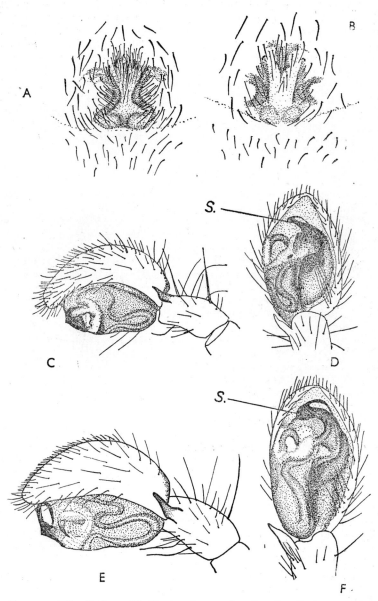

TEXT-FIG. 246.—*Scotina palliardi:* A, epigyne; C, male palp; D, ditto (below).
  Scotina gracilipes: B, epigyne.
  Scotina celans: E, male palp; F, ditto (below).

specimens have marked light longitudinal bands (very much as in
S. celans (Bl.)). LEGS : I and II have the patellæ, tibiæ and metatarsi
considerably darkened. (This has not been noticed in *S. gracilipes*,
but colouration in both species may be variable.) EPIGYNE : Text-fig.
246, A. This is similar to that of *S. gracilipes*, but the seminal ducts
can be seen to approach one another more closely than in that species.
Text-fig. 246, B shows an epigyne of *S. gracilipes* in which the straight
edges of the dark areas at the sides are well developed ; these straight
edges are not always visible, but when they are, they provide a reliable
character for distinguishing the females. MALE PALP : Text-fig.

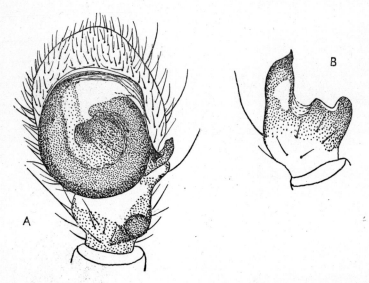

TEXT-FIG. 247.—*Xysticus acerbus:* A, male palp (below) ; B, right palpal tibia
(from side).

246, C, D. This differs from that of *S. gracilipes* in the tibial apophysis,
which is aculeate in *S. palliardi*, and also in the form of the palpal
organs. The latter resemble those of *S. celans* (Bl.) (Text-fig. 246,
E, F), but differ from that species in having the base of the stylus (*s*)
much narrower, and in the disposition of the seminal coils (Text-fig.
246, D, F).

OCCURRENCE : Happy Valley, Box Hill (Surrey), amongst moss and
grass. Mature and immature specimens of both sexes were taken in
May, 1949, 1950, 1951. Three females and one male were found
among specimens of *S. gracilipes* (Bl.) in the Pickard-Cambridge
collection, and had been collected at Bloxworth (Dorset).

Xysticus acerbus Thorell.
(Text-fig. 247)

Xysticus acerbus T. Thorell, 1872, p. 237 ; C. Chyzer and L. Kulczynski, 1891–**7.**
I, p. 96 ; E. Simon, 1932, pp. 832, 833 ; A. F. Millidge and G. H. Locket, 1952, p. 61.

DESCRIPTION OF MALE. LENGTH : ♂ : 5 mm. CARAPACE : The
sides brown, mottled and streaked with yellow ; the pale yellow
central area is almost filled by a blunt wedge-shaped mark which is
brown, mottled with whitish yellow and dark brown blotches. There
are a number of stout spines on the carapace and clypeus. ABDOMEN :
Dorsally dark brown, mottled with pale yellow, with a narrow white
band around the front and sides, and with three or four ill-defined
narrow yellowish-white transverse bars on the posterior half. LEGS :

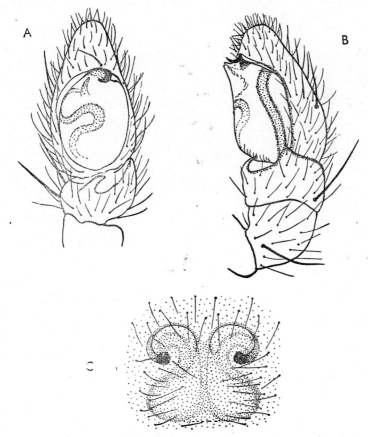

TEXT-FIG. 248.—*Thanatus striatus:* Male palp : A, below ; B, side.
Euophrys molesta: C, epigyne.

Whitish-yellow, mottled and streaked with dark brown and reddish brown ; femora with longitudinal streaks of black dorsally and laterally. MALE PALP : Text-fig. 247, A, B. Coloured like the legs. The palpal organs (Text-fig. 247, A) have no apophyses, and the species falls thus into the same group as *X. luctuosus* (Bl.), *X. sabulosus* (Hahn) and *X. robustus* (Hahn). It differs from these quite clearly in being less deeply coloured, and in the form of the palpal organs. The palpal tibia seen from the side is quite characteristic.

OCCURRENCE : A male at Penrice (Glamorganshire), in 1948, running in short grass in a meadow. Another male at Plaistow (Sussex), in grass on rough ground near a pond by the road side. The female has not yet been found in Britain.

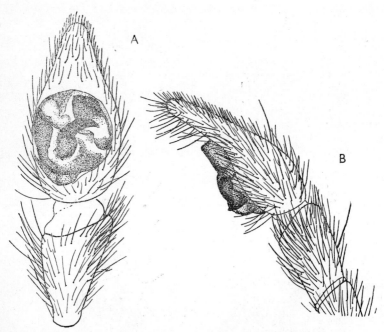

TEXT-FIG. 249.—*Lycosa paludicola:* A, male palp (below) ; B, ditto (side).

Thanatus striatus C. L. Koch.
(Text-fig. 248, A, B)

The female was described in Vol. I, p. 201. Specimens of the male have subsequently been obtained from the Pickard-Cambridge collection (in the Hope Department at Oxford). The male resembles the female in colour (being possibly slightly darker) ; the palp is shown in Text-fig. 248, A, B).

Euophrys molesta O. P.-Cambridge.
(Text-fig. 248, C)

Two females of this species were taken by Mr. A. M. Wild in Cornwall in 1951 ; the epigynes (Text-fig. 248, C) of the fresh specimens were very clearly distinct from *E. frontalis*.

Lycosa paludicola (Clerck).
(= *L. paludicola* Walckenaer)
(Text-fig. 249)

DESCRIPTION OF MALE. LENGTH : About 7 mm. CARAPACE : Very deep brown or black ; the lateral light bands are continuous and have dentated edges. The median light band is dilated behind the eyes, then constricted and, after widening again, tapers towards its posterior end. ABDOMEN : Dark brown, appearing black in living specimens. STERNUM : Dark brown to black ; the light median band, discernible in the female, being here almost always absent or very faint. LEGS : Dark brown ; sometimes very faint annulations can be seen in preserved specimens. MALE PALP : Text-fig. 249, A, B. This is covered with dark hairs. The spider has a characteristic dark colour when alive and this, with its size, makes it distinguishable in the field from *L. amentata* (Cl.), whose markings are somewhat similar.

OCCURRENCE : Near Plaistow (Sussex), in grass by a road side. Mature early in April (and possibly March). The males seem to have a very short season ; none were found early in May (A. F. Millidge and G. H. Locket, 1952, p. 62).

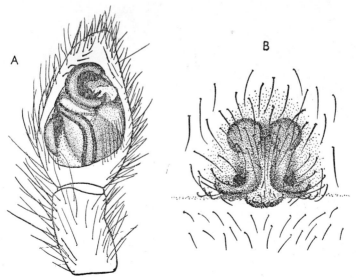

TEXT-FIG. 250.—*Pirata uliginosus:* A, male palp ; B, epigyne.

Pirata uliginosus (Thorell).
(Text-fig. 250)

Potamia uliginosa T. Thorell, 1856, p. 111, and 1872, pp. 344, 346.   *Pirata uliginosus* F. Dahl, 1908, p. 300, and 1927, p. 59 ; Å. Holm, 1947, p. 9 ; E. Duffey (paper in the press).

DESCRIPTION. LENGTH : ♀ : About 5.5 mm. ♂ : About 4.5 mm. The appearance and markings of this species are very close to those of *Pirata hygrophilus* Thor. (Vol. I, p. 289). The carapace markings are not quite so distinct. No annulations were visible on the legs of the specimens examined. EPIGYNE : Text-fig. 250, B. This is quite distinct and enables the species to be identified easily. MALE PALP : Text-fig. 250, A. This needs to be compared carefully with that of *P. hygrophilus* (Vol. I, Text-fig. 139, D).

OCCURRENCE : A number of specimens were captured by Mr. E. Duffey, while engaged in work on spider populations, amongst bracken in a cleared part of Wytham Woods (Berkshire), in the early summer of 1951. We are greatly indebted to him for the specimens he has made available.

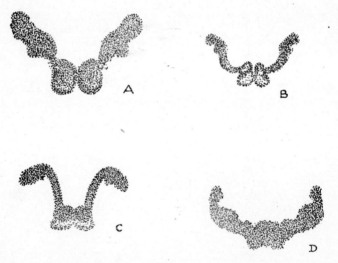

TEXT-FIG. 251. Characteristic shapes of dark regions of vulvae of cleared specimens of *Dictyna* : A, *Dictyna arundinacea* ; B, *D. pusilla*; C, *D. uncinata*; D, *D. major*.

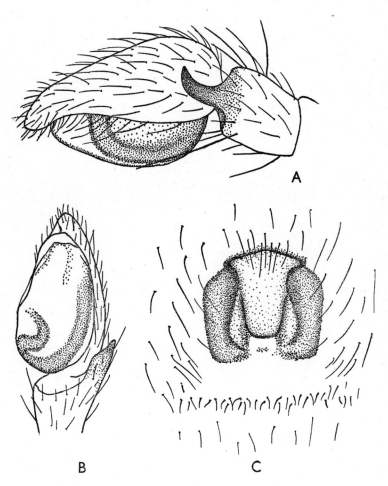

TEXT-FIG. 252.—*Micaria subopaca* : A, Male palp (side) ; B, Ditto (below) ; C, Epigyne.

Corrigenda to Vol. I

p. 41.   Text-fig. 14, last line of legend : for " cb " read " cy."

p. 79.   Text-fig. 38, last line of legend reads : " E, chelicera of *Ischnothyreus velox* ♂.

p. 84.   for " *Dysdera crocata* " read " *Dysdera crocota*."

p. 85.   2nd line from bottom : for " *Harpaetes* " read " *Harpactes*."

p. 155.   Under *Liocranum rupicola ;* 2nd line of synonyms : for " *Liocranum domestica* " read " *Liocranum domesticum*."

p. 265.   Last line : for " E, *L. amentata* " read " G, *L. amentata*."

p. 289.   *Pirata hygrophilus*.   Last line of synonyms : for " *hygrophilus* " read " *hygrophila*."

p. 298.   Bristowe, W. S., 1948.   Reference reads : " Proc. Zool. Soc. Lond. **118** pt. iii, pp. 878–891.

p. 305.   barbipes (Tarentula) : for " 295 " read " 275."

It was suggested to us by Dr. W. J. Gertsch, after seeing our drawings of and description of *Scotophœus blackwalli* (Thorell), that this species belonged to the genus *Herpyllus* N. M. Hentz 1832.   He very kindly sent us specimens of *Herpyllus vasifer* (Walckenaer) and *H. hesperolus* Chamberlin and himself examined our *Scotophœus blackwalli*.   As a result we are all three agreed that this latter species is a *Herpyllus* and should have the name *Herpyllus blackwalli* (Thorell).   Dr. Gertsch also regards the North American *H. pius* Chamberlin as identical with *H. blackwalli* and draws our attention to a paper by Chamberlin (1922, p. 148) where he makes *Scotophœus* synonymous with *Herpyllus*. This paper seems to have been overlooked by European arachnologists. In a recent paper E. Schenkel (1950, p. 38) records *Scotophœus blackwalli* (Thor) (sic.) from San Diego, California.

Dr. Gertsch also suspected from our drawings that the North American *Drassyllus femoralis* Banks was identical with the European *Zelotes rusticus* L. Koch and he sent us a specimen of the former, the examination of which entirely confirms his view.   *D. femoralis* should be added to the synonyms of *Z. rusticus*, which retains its priority of name.

III. DESCRIPTION OF A NEW SPECIES.

The following is an account of a new species which has come to our notice recently.

Clubiona rosseræ n. sp.

(Text-fig. 253, A, B, D)

DESCRIPTION. LENGTH : ♀ : 5·5–6 mm. ♂ : about 4·5 mm. This species belongs to our Group II(*a*) of the genus *Clubiona* (see Vol. I., p. 128) and closely resembles *Clubiona stagnatilis* Kulczynski, from which it may be distinguished by considering :

(*a*) EYES : The posteriors are larger in *C. rosseræ*. Distance between posterior medians : 2·3–2·7 diameters in ♀, 2·1–2·2 in ♂. (In *C. stagnatilis*, the distance is 3·5–5·5 diameters in ♀ ; 2·3–3·2 in ♂.)

(*b*) EPIGYNES : Text-fig. 253, D, E, shows the appearance of these after some days immersion of the spiders in 90 per cent. phenol in alcohol, seen from a little in front.

(*c*) MALE PALPS : Text-fig. 253, A, B, C (see also Vol. I., Text-fig. 65, B). The most striking difference is in the form of the barbed lower arm of the tibial apophysis, and other differences are seen in the ventral views of the palps.

OCCURRENCE : Two pairs were found by the authors when shaking out cut sedge at Chippenham Fen (Cambridgeshire), 23rd September, 1951.

The species is named after my wife, Enid Rosser, in recognition of her help to me while preparing this book.

G. H. LOCKET

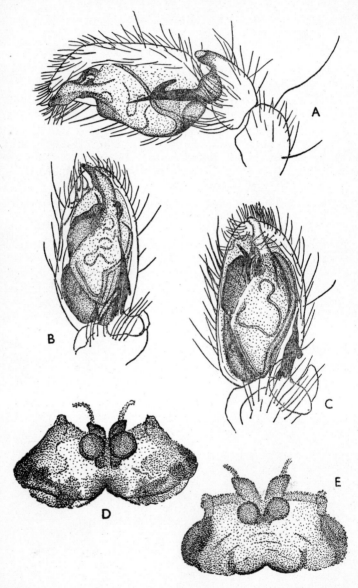

TEXT-FIG. 253.—Male palps : A, *Clubiona rosseræ* (side) ; B, Ditto (below) ; C, *C. stagnatilis* (below).
Vulvæ : D, *C. rosseræ* ; E, *C. stagnatilis.*

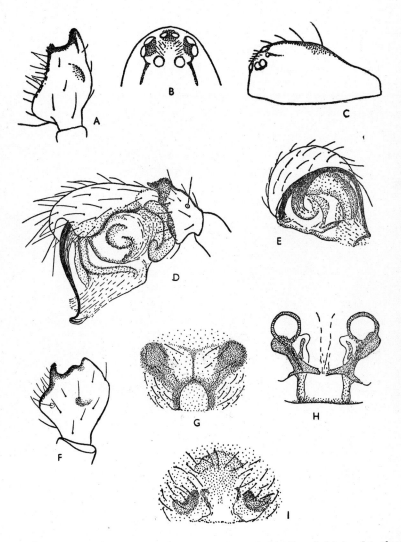

TEXT-FIG. 254. *Tapinocyba antepenultima* : A, ♂ palpal tibia (from behind and to the outside) ; F, do. (from above) ; B, ♂ head (from above) ; C, ♂ Carapace (from side) ; D, ♂ palp (from side) ; E, do. (from in front) ; G, ♀ epigyne ; H, do. cleared. *Hypomma fulvum* : I, ♀ epigyne (fresh specimen).

IV. A CHECK LIST OF BRITISH SPIDERS

Family ATYPIDÆ—
Atypus affinis Eichwald

Family ERESIDÆ—
Eresus niger (Petagna)

Family DICTYNIDÆ—
Ciniflo fenestralis (Stroem)
C. similis Blackwall
C. ferox (Walckenaer)
Dictyna arundinacea (Linnaeus)
D. pusilla Thorell
D. major Menge
D. uncinata Thorell
D. latens (Fabricius)
D. puella Simon
D. flavescens (Walckenaer)
D. viridissima (Walckenaer)
Lathys humilis (Blackwall)
L. stigmatisata (Menge)
Argenna subnigra (O. P.-Cambridge)
Protadia patula (Simon)
Altella lucida (Simon)

Family ULOBORIDÆ—
Uloborus walckenaerius Latreille
Hyptiotes paradoxus (C. L. Koch)

Family OONOPIDÆ—
Oonops pulcher Templeton
O. domesticus de Dalmas
Ischnothyreus velox Jackson
Triaeris stenaspis Simon
Diblemma donisthorpei O. P.-Cambridge

Family DYSDERIDÆ—
Dysdera erythrina (Walckenaer)
D. crocota C. L. Koch
Harpactea hombergi (Scopoli)
Segestria senoculata (Linnaeus)
S. bavarica C. L. Koch
S. florentina (Rossi)

Family SCYTODIDÆ—
Scytodes thoracica Latreille

Family PHOLCIDÆ—
Pholcus phalangioides (Fuesslin)
Physocyclus simoni Berland

Family GNAPHOSIDÆ—
Drassodes lapidosus (Walckenaer)
D. lapidosus macer (Thorell)
D. lapidosus cupreus (Blackwall)
D. pubescens (Thorell)
D. signifer (C. L. Koch)
D. dalmatensis (L. Koch)
D. silvestris (Blackwall)
D. minor (O. P.-Cambridge)
D. sörenseni (Strand)
Herpyllus blackwalli (Thorell)
Phaeocedus braccatus (L. Koch)
Zelotes pedestris (C. L. Koch)

Z. lutetianus (L. Koch)
Z. pusillus (C. L. Koch)
Z. rusticus (L. Koch)
Z. praeficus (L. Koch)
Z. electus (C. L. Koch)
Z. latreillei (Simon)
Z. apricorum (L. Koch)
Z. serotinus (L. Koch)
Z. petrensis (C. L. Koch)
Gnaphosa lugubris (C. L. Koch)
G. occidentalis Simon
G. leporina (L. Koch)
Micaria pulicaria (Sundevall)
M. scintillans (O. P.-Cambridge)
M. alpina L. Koch
M. subopaca Westring
M. silesiaca L. Koch

Family CLUBIONIDÆ—
Clubiona corticalis (Walckenaer)
C. reclusa O. P.-Cambridge
C. subsultans Thorell
C. stagnatilis Kulczynski
C. rosserae Locket
C. norvegica Strand
C. coerulescens L. Koch
C. pallidula (Clerck)
C. phragmitis C. L. Koch
C. terrestris Westring
C. neglecta O. P.-Cambridge
C. lutescens Westring
C. compta C. L. Koch
C. brevipes Blackwall
C. trivialis C. L. Koch
C. juvenis Simon
C. genevensis L. Koch
C. diversa O. P.-Cambridge
C. subtilis L. Koch
Cheiracanthium erraticum (Walckenaer)
C. pennyi O. P.-Cambridge
C. virescens (Sundevall)
Agroeca brunnea (Blackwall)
A. proxima (O. P.-Cambridge)
A. inopina O. P.-Cambridge
A. lusatica (L. Koch)
A. cuprea Menge
Agraecina striata (Kulczynski)
Scotina celans (Blackwall)
S. gracilipes (Blackwall)
S. palliardi (L. Koch)
Liocranum rupicola (Walckenaer)
Zora spinimana (Sundevall)
Z. armillata Simon
Z. nemoralis (Blackwall)
Phrurolithus festivus (C. L. Koch)
P. minimus C. L. Koch

Family ANYPHÆNIDÆ—
Anyphaena accentuata (Walckenaer)

Family SPARASSIDÆ—
  Micrommata virescens (Clerck)
Family THOMISIDÆ—
  Thomisus onustus Walckenaer
  Diaea dorsata (Fabricius)
  Misumena vatia (Clerck)
  Pistius truncatus (Pallas)
  Xysticus cristatus (Clerck)
  X. audax (Schrank)
  X. kochi Thorell
  X. erraticus (Blackwall)
  X. lanio C. L. Koch
  X. ulmi (Hahn)
  X. bifasciatus C. L. Koch
  X. luctator L. Koch
  X. sabulosus (Hahn)
  X. luctuosus (Blackwall)
  X. acerbus Thorell
  X. robustus (Hahn)
  Oxyptila blackwalli Simon
  O. scabricula (Westring)
  O. nigrita (Thorell)
  O. sanctuaria (O. P.-Cambridge)
  O. praticola (C. L. Koch)
  O. trux (Blackwall)
  O. simplex (O. P.-Cambridge)
  O. atomaria (Panzer)
  O. brevipes (Hahn)
  Philodromus dispar Walckenaer
  P. aureolus (Clerck)
  P. aureolus caespiticolis Walckenaer
  P. fallax Sundevall
  P. histrio (Latreille)
  P. emarginatus (Schrank)
  P. rufus Walckenaer
  P. margaritatus (Clerck)
  Thanatus striatus C. L. Koch
  T. formicinus (Clerck)
  Tibellus maritimus (Menge)
  T. oblongus (Walckenaer)
Family SALTICIDÆ—
  Salticus scenicus (Clerck)
  S. cingulatus (Panzer)
  S. zebraneus (C. L. Koch)
  Heliophanus cupreus (Walckenaer)
  H. flavipes C. L. Koch
  H. expers (O. P.-Cambridge)
  Marpissa muscosa (Clerck)
  M. pomatia (Walckenaer)
  Bianor aenescens (Simon)
  Hyctia nivoyi (Lucas)
  Ballus depressus (Walckenaer)
  Neon reticulatus (Blackwall)
  N. valentulus Falconer
  Euophrys frontalis (Walckenaer)
  E. molesta O. P.-Cambridge
  E. petrensis C. L. Koch
  E. erratica (Walckenaer)
  E. aequipes (O. P.-Cambridge)
  E. lanigera (Simon)

  Sitticus pubescens (Fabricius)
  S. caricis (Westring)
  S. floricola (C. L. Koch)
  S. rupicola (C. L. Koch)
  Attulus saltator (Simon)
  Evarcha falcata (Clerck)
  E. arcuata (Clerck)
  Aelurillus v-insignitus (Clerck)
  Phlegra fasciata (Hahn)
  Synageles venator (Lucas)
  Myrmarachne formicaria (Degeer)
  Hasarius adansoni (Audouin)
  Pellenes tripunctatus (Walckenaer)

Family OXYOPIDÆ—
  Oxyopes heterophthalmus Latreille

Family LYCOSIDÆ—
  Lycosa arenicola O. P.-Cambridge
  L. agricola Thorell
  L. agrestis Westring
  L. purbeckensis (F. O. P.-Cambridge)
  L. monticola (Clerck)
  L. tarsalis Thorell
  L. tarsalis herbigrada Blackwall
  L. pullata (Clerck)
  L. prativaga L. Koch
  L. amentata (Clerck)
  L. nigriceps Thorell
  L. lugubris (Walckenaer)
  L. hortensis Thorell
  L. proxima C. L. Koch
  L. trailli O. P.-Cambridge
  L. paludicola (Clerck)
  L. rubrofasciata (Ohlert)
  Xerolycosa nemoralis (Westring)
  X. miniata (C. L. Koch)
  Tarentula pulverulenta (Clerck)
  T. cuneata (Clerck)
  T. barbipes (Sundevall)
  T. fabrilis (Clerck)
  Trochosa ruricola (Degeer)
  T. robusta (Simon)
  T. terricola Thorell
  T. spinipalpis (F. O. P.-Cambridge)
  T. fulvolineata (Lueas)
  Arctosa perita (Latreille)
  A. leopardus (Sundevall)
  A. cinerea (Fabricius)
  A. alpigena (Doleschal)
  Pirata piraticus (Clerck)
  P. hygrophilus Thorell
  P. latitans (Blackwall)
  P. piscatorius (Clerck)
  P. uliginosus (Thorell)
  Aulonia albimana (Walckenaer)

Family PISAURIDÆ—
  Pisaura mirabilis (Clerck)
  Dolomedes fimbriatus (Clerck)

Family AGELENIDÆ
Argyroneta aquatica (Clerck)
Agelena labyrinthica (Clerck)
Textrix denticulata (Olivier)
Tegenaria atrica C. L. Koch
T. larva Simon
T. parietina (Fourcroy)
T. agrestis (Walckenaer)
T. domestica (Clerck)
T. pagana (C. L. Koch)
T. silvestris L. Koch
Amaurobius atropos (Walckenaer)
A. terrestris (Wider)
Cicurina cicur (Fabricius)
Cryphoeca silvicola (C. L. Koch)
Tetrilus macrophthalmus (Kulczynski)
T. arietinus (Thorell)
Tuberta moerens (O. P.-Cambridge)
Antistea elegans (Blackwall)
Hahnia montana (Blackwall)
H. candida Simon
H. nava (Blackwall)
H. helveola Simon
H. pusilla C. L. Koch

Family MIMETIDÆ—
Ero cambridgei Kulczynski
E. furcata (Villers)
E. tuberculata (Degeer)

Family THERIDIIDÆ—
Episinus angulatus (Blackwall)
E. truncatus Latreille
Euryopis flavomaculata (C. L. Koch)
Dipoena erythropus (Simon)
D. prona (Menge)
D. inornata (O. P.-Cambridge)
D. tristis (Hahn)
D. coracina (C. L. Koch)
D. melanogaster (C. L. Koch)
D. torva (Thorell)
Crustulina guttata (Wider)
C. sticta (O. P.-Cambridge)
Asagena phalerata (Panzer)
Lithyphantes albomaculatus (Degeer)
Steatoda bipunctata (Linnaeus)
Teutana grossa (C. L. Koch)
Theridion vittatum C. L. Koch
T. pulchellum (Walckenaer)
T. aulicum C. L. Koch
T. lunatum (Clerck)
T. saxatile C. L. Koch
T. tepidariorum C. L. Koch
T. tepidariorum simulans Thorell
T. sisyphium (Clerck)
T. impressum L. Koch
T. pictum (Walckenaer)
T. simile C. L. Koch
T. varians Hahn
T. denticulatum (Walckenaer)
T. familiare O. P.-Cambridge

FF

T. blackwalli O. P.-Cambridge
T. tinctum (Walckenaer)
T. ovatum (Clerck)
T. instabile O. P.-Cambridge
T. bellicosum Simon
T. bimaculatum (Linnaeus)
T. pallens Blackwall
Enoplognatha thoracica (Hahn)
E. schaufussi (L. Koch)
E. mandibularis (Lucas)
Robertus lividus (Blackwall)
R. arundineti (O. P.-Cambridge)
R. neglectus (O. P.-Cambridge)
R. scoticus Jackson
R. insignis O. P.-Cambridge
Pholcomma gibbum (Westring)
Theonoë minutissima (O. P.-Cambridge)

Family NESTICIDÆ—
Nesticus cellulanus (Clerck)

Family TETRAGNATHIDÆ
Tetragnatha extensa (Linnaeus)
T. pinicola L. Koch
T. montana Simon
T. obtusa C. L. Koch
T. nigrita Lendl
Eugnatha striata (L. Koch)
Pachygnatha clercki Sundevall
P. listeri Sundevall
P. degeeri Sundevall

Family ARGIOPIDÆ
Meta segmentata (Clerck)
M. segmentata mengei (Blackwall)
M. merianae (Scopoli)
M. menardi (Latreille)
M. bourneti Simon
Araneus bituberculatus (Walckenaer)
A. gibbosus (Walckenaer)
A. angulatus Clerck
A. diadematus Clerck
A. quadratus Clerck
A. marmoreus Clerck
A. marmoreus pyramidatus Clerck
A. alsine (Walckenaer)
A. cornutus Clerck
A. sclopetarius Clerck
A. patagiatus Clerck
A. ceropegius (Walckenaer)
A. umbraticus Clerck
A. redii (Scopoli)
A. adiantus (Walckenaer)
A. sturmi (Hahn)
A. triguttatus (Fabricius)
A. cucurbitinus Clerck
A. cucurbitinus opistographus
       Kulczynski
A. inconspicuus (Simon)
A. alpicus (L. Koch)
A. displicatus westringi (Thorell)

Zilla diodia (Walckenaer)
Singa albovittata (Westring)
S. pygmaea (Sundevall)
S. sanguinea C. L. Koch
S. heri (Hahn)
S. hamata (Clerck)
Cercidia prominens (Westring)
Zygiella x-notata (Clerck)
Z. atrica (C. L. Koch)
Z. stroemi (Thorell)
Mangora acalypha (Walckenaer)
Cyclosa conica (Pallas)
Argiope bruennichi (Scopoli)
Theridiosoma gemmosum (L. Koch)

Family LINYPHIIDÆ—
Ceratinella brevipes (Westring)
C. brevis (Wider)
C. scabrosa (O. P.-Cambridge)
Walckenaenra acuminata Blackwall
Wideria antica (Wider)
W. cucullata (C. L. Koch)
W. nodosa (O. P.-Cambridge)
W. melanocephala (O. P.-Cambridge)
W. capito (Westring)
W. fugax (O. P.-Cambridge)
W. polita (Simon)
Trachynella nudipalpis (Westring)
T. obtusa (Blackwall)
Prosopotheca monoceros (Wider)
P. corniculans (O. P.-Cambridge)
P. incisa (O. P.-Cambridge)
Tigellinus furcillatus (Menge)
Cornicularia unicornis
        (O. P.-Cambridge)

C. kochi (O. P.-Cambridge)
C. karpinskii (O. P.-Cambridge)
C. cuspidata (Blackwall)
C. vigilax (Blackwall)
Dicymbium nigrum (Blackwall)
D. tibiale (Blackwall)
Entelecara acuminata (Wider)
E. erythropus (Westring)
E. flavipes (Blackwall)
E. omissa O. P.-Cambridge
E. errata O. P.-Cambridge
Moebelia penicillata (Westring)
Erigonidium graminicola (Sundevall)
Gnathonarium dentatum (Wider)
Tmeticus affinis (Blackwall)
Gongylidium rufipes (Sundevall)
Dismodicus bifrons (Blackwall)
D. elevatus (C. L. Koch)
Hypomma bituberculatum (Wider)
H. fulvum Bösenberg
H. cornutum (Blackwall)
Metopobactrus prominulus
        (O. P.-Cambridge)
Hybocoptus decollatus (Simon)

Baryphyma pratensis (Blackwall)
Gonatium rubens (Blackwall)
G. rubellum (Blackwall)
Minyrioloides trifrons
        (O. P.-Cambridge)
Maso sundevalli (Westring)
M. gallica Simon
Peponocranium ludicrum
        (O. P.-Cambridge)
Pocadicnemis pumila (Blackwall)
Hypselistes jacksoni (O. P.-Cambridge)
H. florens (O. P.-Cambridge)
Oedothorax gibbosus (Blackwall)
Oe. tuberosus (Blackwall)
Oe. fuscus (Blackwall)
Oe. agrestis (Blackwall)
Oe. retusus (Westring)
Oe. apicatus (Blackwall)
Trichopterna thorelli (Westring)
T. mengei (Simon)
Lophocarenum parallelum (Wider)
L. nemorale (Blackwall)
L. stramineum (Menge)
L. elongatum (Wider)
L. radicicola (L. Koch)
Silometopus elegans (O. P.-Cambridge)
S. curtus (Simon)
S. ambiguus (O. P.-Cambridge)
S. interjectus (O. P.-Cambridge)
S. incurvatus (O. P.-Cambridge)
Mecopisthes pusillus (Menge)
Cnephalocotes obscurus (Blackwall)
Acartauchenius scurrilis
        (O. P.-Cambridge)
Trichoncus saxicola (O. P.-Cambridge)
T. affinis Kulczynski
Styloctetor romanus (O. P.-Cambridge)
Anacotyle stativa (Simon)
Evansia merens O. P.-Cambridge
Tiso vagans (Blackwall)
T. aestivus (L. Koch)
Troxochrus scabriculus (Westring)
T. cirrifrons (O. P.-Cambridge)
Minyriolus pusillus (Wider)
Tapinocyba praecox (O. P.-Cambridge)
T. pallens (O. P.-Cambridge)
T. insecta (L. Koch)
T. mitis (O. P.-Cambridge)
T. antepenultima (O. P.-Cambridge)
Aulacocyba subitanea
        (O. P.-Cambridge)
Perimones britteni (Jackson)
Thyreosthenius parasiticus (Westring)
T. biovatus (O. P.-Cambridge)
Monocephalus fuscipes (Blackwall)
M. castaneipes (Simon)
Lophomma punctatum (Blackwall)
Mioxena blanda (Simon)
Saloca diceros (O. P.-Cambridge)

Jacksonella falconeri (Jackson)
Gongylidiellum vivum
              (O. P.-Cambridge)
G. latebricola (O. P.-Cambridge)
G. murcidum Simon
Micrargus herbigradus (Blackwall)
M. subaequalis (Westring)
M. laudatus (O. P.-Cambridge)
Notioscopus sarcinatus
              (O. P.-Cambridge)
Glyphesis cottonae (La Touche)
Erigonella hiemalis (Blackwall)
E. ignobilis (O. P.-Cambridge)
Savignia frontata (Blackwall)
Diplocephalus cristatus (Blackwall)
D. permixtus (O. P.-Cambridge)
D. latifrons (O. P.-Cambridge)
D. adjacens O. P.-Cambridge
D. jacksoni O. P.-Cambridge
D. picinus (Blackwall)
D. protuberans (O. P.-Cambridge)
Araeoncus humilis (Blackwall)
A. crassiceps (Westring)
Panamomops sulcifrons (Wider)
Lessertia dentichelis (Simon)
Asthenargus paganus (Simon)
Caledonia evansi O. P.-Cambridge
Typhocrestus digitatus
              (O. P.-Cambridge)
Collinsia distincta (Simon)
C. holmgreni (Thorell)
Scotargus inerrans (O. P.-Cambridge)
Diplocentria bidentata (Emerton)
Erigone dentipalpis (Wider)
E. atra (Blackwall)
E. promiscua (O. P.-Cambridge)
E. arctica (White)
E. longipalpis (Sundevall)
E. tirolensis L. Koch
E. capra Simon
E. welchi Jackson
E. vagans Audouin
Rhaebothorax morulus
              (O. P.-Cambridge)
Eboria fausta (O. P.-Cambridge)
E. caliginosa Falconer
Donacochara speciosa (Thorell)
Leptorhoptrum robustum (Westring)
Drepanotylus uncatus
              (O. P.-Cambridge)
Phaulothrix hardyi (Blackwall)
Hilaira excisa (O. P.-Cambridge)
H. frigida (Thorell)
H. nubigena Hull
H. pervicax Hull
Halorates reprobus (O. P.-Cambridge)
Ostearius melanopygius
              (O. P.-Cambridge)
Hillhousia misera (O. P.-Cambridge)
Porrhomma pygmaeum (Blackwall)

P. convexum (Westring)
P. rosenhaueri (L. Koch)
P. pallidum Jackson
P. campbelli F. O. P.-Cambridge
P. microphthalmum (O. P.-Cambridge)
P. errans (Blackwall)
P. egeria Simon
P. oblitum (O. P.-Cambridge)
P. montanum Jackson
Syedrula innotabilis (O. P.-Cambridge)
Syedra gracilis (Menge)
Agyneta subtilis (O. P.-Cambridge)
A. conigera (O. P.-Cambridge)
A. decora (O. P.-Cambridge)
A. cauta (O. P.-Cambridge)
A. ramosa Jackson
Meioneta rurestris (C. L. Koch)
M. mollis (O. P.-Cambridge)
M. saxatilis (Blackwall)
M. beata (O. P.-Cambridge)
M. gulosa (L. Koch)
M. nigripes (Simon)
Microneta viaria (Blackwall)
Maro minutus O. P.-Cambridge
M. sublestus Falconer
Centromerus sylvaticus (Blackwall)
C. expertus (O. P.-Cambridge)
C. prudens (O. P.-Cambridge)
C. arcanus (O. P.-Cambridge)
C. laevitarsis (Simon)
C. dilutus (O. P.-Cambridge)
C. incilium (L. Koch)
C. incultus Falconer
C. subacutus (O. P.-Cambridge)
C. serratus (O. P.-Cambridge)
C. jacksoni Denis
C. persimilis (O. P.-Cambridge)
Centromerita bicolor (Blackwall)
C. concinna (Thorell)
Sintula cornigera (Blackwall)
Oreonetides abnormis (Blackwall)
O. firmus (O. P.-Cambridge)
O. vaginatus (Thorell)
Macrargus rufus (Wider)
M. rufus carpenteri (O. P.-Cambridge)
Bathyphantes dorsalis (Wider)
B. concolor (Wider)
B. approximatus (O. P.-Cambridge)
B. pullatus (O. P.-Cambridge)
B. gracilis (Blackwall)
B. parvulus (Westring)
B. nigrinus (Westring)
B. setiger F. O. P.-Cambridge
Poeciloneta globosa (Wider)
Drapetisca socialis (Sundevall)
Tapinopa longidens (Wider)
Floronia bucculenta (Clerck)
Taranucnus setosus (O. P.-Cambridge)
Labulla thoracica (Wider)
Stemonyphantes lineatus (Linnaeus)

Bolyphantes luteolus (Blackwall)
B. luteolus subnigripes
          (O. P.-Cambridge,
B. alticeps (Sundevall)
Lepthyphantes nebulosus (Sundevall)
L. leprosus (Ohlert)
L. minutus (Blackwall)
L. alacris (Blackwall)
L. whymperi F. O. P.-Cambridge
L. obscurus (Blackwall)
L. tenuis (Blackwall)
L. zimmermanni Bertkau
L. cristatus (Menge)
L. mengei Kulczynski
L. flavipes (Blackwall)
L. tenebricola (Wider)
L. ericaeus (Blackwall)
L. pallidus (O. P.-Cambridge)

L. pinicola Simon
L. insignis O. P.-Cambridge
L. angulatus (O. P.-Cambridge)
L. audax Sörensen
L. carri Jackson
L. expunctus (O. P.-Cambridge)
Helophora insignis (Blackwall)
Linyphia triangularis (Clerck)
L. montana (Clerck)
L. clathrata Sundevall
L. peltata Wider
L. pusilla Sundevall
L. hortensis Sundevall
L. impigra O. P.-Cambridge
L. furtiva O. P.-Cambridge
L. marginata C. L. Koch
Mengea scopigera (Grube)
M. warburtoni (O. P.-Cambridge)

V. BIBLIOGRAPHY

ARCHER, A. F., 1950. A study of Theridiid and Mimetid spiders with descriptions of new genera and species. *Alabama Museum of Natural History. Museum paper* 30. pp. 1–40, 4 pls.

—— 1951 (1). Studies in the orb-weaving spiders (Argiopidae): 1. *American Museum of Natural History. Novitates.* No. 1487, pp. 1–52, 82 figs.

—— 1951 (2). Studies in the orb-weaving spiders (Argiopidae): 2. *American Museum of Natural History. Novitates.* No. 1502, pp. 1–34, 78 figs.

—— 1951 (3). "Remarks on certain European Genera of Argiopid spiders." *Nat. Hist. Miscellanea. Chicago Acad. Sci.* No. 84, pp. 1–4, 5 figs.

AUDOUIN, V., 1827. Explication sommaire des planches d'Arachnides de l'Egypte et de la Syrie. (*In*) Savigny, Descr. de l'Egypte, 2nd edit., **22,** pp. 169–434.

BALOGH, J. I., 1934. "Vorläufige Mitteilung über radnetzbauende Pachygnathen" *Folia Zool. Hydrobiol., Riga,* **6** (1), pp. 94–96.

BERTKAU, P., 1890. Arachniden gesammelt vom 12 November, 1888 bis zum 10 Mai, 1889 in San Remo von Prof. Dr. Oscar Schneider, 1890, pp. 1–11. (No journal nor place of origin. See P. Bonnet, "Bibliographia Araneorum" 1945. p. 263.)

BISHOP, S. C., and CROSBY, C. R., 1935. Studies in American spiders: Miscellaneous Genera of Erigoneae. Pt. 1. *Jour. N.Y. Ent. Soc.,* **43,** pp. 217–281. six pls.

—— 1938. Studies in American spiders: Miscellaneous genera of Erigoneae, Pt. II. *Jour. N.Y. Ent. Soc.,* **46,** pp. 55–107, six pls.

BLACKWALL, J., 1833. Characters of some undescribed genera and species of Araneidæ. *Phil. Mag.* (3), **3,** pp. 104–112, 187–197, 344–352, 436–443.

—— 1834. Researches in Zoology, London.

—— 1836. Characters of some undescribed species of Araneidæ. *Phil. Mag.* (3), **8,** pp. 481–491.

—— 1841. The difference in the number of eyes with which spiders are provided. *Trans. Linn. Soc. London,* **18,** pp. 601–670.

—— 1844. Descriptions of some newly discovered species of Araneidæ. *Ann. Mag. Nat. Hist.* (1), **13,** pp. 179–188.

—— 1846. Descriptions of some newly discovered species of Araneida. *Ann. Mag. Nat. Hist.* (1), **18,** pp. 297–303.

—— 1850. Descriptions of some newly discovered species and characters of a new genus of Araneida. *Ann. Mag. Nat. Hist.* (2), **6,** pp. 336–344.

—— 1851. A Catalogue of British Spiders. *Ann. Mag. Nat. Hist.* (2), **7,** pp. 256–262, 396–402, 446–452, **8,** pp. 37–44, 95–102, 332–339, 442–450.

—— 1852. A Catalogue of British Spiders. *Ann. Mag. Nat. Hist.* (2), **9,** pp. 15–22.

—— 1853. Descriptions of some newly discovered species of Araneidea. *Ann. Mag. Nat. Hist.* (2), **11,** pp. 14–25.

—— 1854. Descriptions of some newly discovered species of Araneidea. *Ann. Mag. Nat. Hist.* (2), **13,** pp. 173–180.

—— 1856. Descriptions of three newly discovered species of Araneidea. *Ann. Mag. Nat. Hist.* (2), **17,** pp. 233–236.

—— 1861. Descriptions of several recently discovered spiders. *Ann. Mag. Nat. Hist.* (3), **8,** pp. 441–446.

—— 1861–4. A history of the spiders of Great Britain and Ireland, **1,** 1861, pp. 1–174, pls. i-xii ; **2,** 1864, pp. 175–384, pls. xiii-xxix. *Ray Society, London.*

—— 1869. Description of a new species of *Epeira. Ann. Mag. Nat. Hist.* (4), **4,** pp. 398–400.

BLAUVELT, H. H., 1936. The comparative morphology of the secondary sexual organs of *Linyphia* and some related genera, including a revision of the group. *Festschr. Strand,* **2,** pp. 81–171, eighteen pls.

BONNET, P., 1935. Theridion tepidariorum C.L.K. Araignée cosmopolite : répartition, cycle vital, moeurs. *Bull. Soc. hist. nat. Toulouse,* **68,** pp. 411–414, one pl.

—— 1949. Un point compliqué de nomenclature dans le nom spécifique d'une araignée : cinerea, cicurea ou cicur ? *Bull. Soc. hist. nat. Toulouse,* **84,** pp. 65–72, one pl

BOSENBERG, W., 1901–3. Die Spinnen Deutschlands. *Zoologica. Stuttgart*, **14,** Heft 35 (1), pp. 1–96, pls. i-viii (1901) ; (2, 3, 4), pp. 97–384, pls. ix-xxxvi (1902) ; (5, 6), pp. 385–465, pls. xxxvii–xliii (1903).

BRAENDEGAARD, J., 1932. 3. Araneae. *In* Isländische Spinnentiere. *Göteborg Kongl. Vet. Handl.* (B), **2** (7), pp. 8–36.
——— 1940. I. Spiders (Araneina) from North East Greenland between Lats. 70° 25′ and 76° 50′ N. II. On the possibility of a reliable determination of species of the females of the genus Erigone. *Medd. Grønland*, **125** No. 8, pp. 1–31.
——— 1946. Spiders of East Greenland. *Medd. Grønland*, **121** (15), pp. 1–128.

BRAUN, F., 1931. Beiträge zur Biologie und Atmungsphysiologie der *Argyroneta aquatica* Cl. *Zool. Jahrb. Syst.*, **62** (3), pp. 175–262, 27 figs.

BRISTOWE, W. S., 1931. Notes on the biology of spiders. V. *Theridion ovatum* Cl.,
——— 1944. " A foreign spider *Argiope bruennichi* Scop. established in England. *Ann. Mag. Nat. Hist.* (11), **11,** pp. 829–834, 3 figs.

BROWNING, E., and TAMS, W. H. T., 1944. On the occurrence in Suffolk of a western Mediterranean cavernicolous spider, Meta bourneti Simon. (Araneae : Argyopidae). *Proc. Linn. Soc. London*, **156,** 1943–44, Pt. 2, 15, pp. 95–97, 1 fig., one pl.

CAMBRIDGE, F. O. PICKARD-, 1891. Descriptive notes on some obscure British spiders. *Ann. Mag. Nat. Hist.* (6), **7,** pp. 69–88.
——— 1892. New and obscure British spiders. *Ann. Mag. Nat. Hist.* (6), **10,** pp. 384–397, two pls.
——— 1894. New genera and species of British spiders. *Ann. Mag. Nat. Hist.* (6), **13,** pp. 87–111, two pls.
——— 1895. Notes on British spiders, with descriptions of new species. *Ann. Mag. Nat. Hist.* (6), **15,** pp. 25–40, two pls.

CAMBRIDGE, O. PICKARD-, 1861. Descriptions of ten new species of spiders lately discovered in England. *Ann. Mag. Nat. Hist.* (3), **8,** pp. 428–441, one pl.
——— 1863. Descriptions of twenty-four new species of spiders. *Zoologist*, **21,** pp. 8561–8599.
——— 1871. Descriptions of British Spiders new to Science. *Trans. Linn. Soc. London*, **27,** pp. 393–464, four pls.
——— 1872. Descriptions of twenty-four new species of Erigone. *Proc. Zool. Soc. London*, **1872,** pp. 747–769, two pls.
——— 1873 (1). On British spiders. *Trans. Linn. Soc. London*, **28,** pp. 433–458, three pls.
——— 1873 (2). On new and rare British spiders. *Trans. Linn. Soc. London*, **28,** pp. 523–555, one pl.
——— 1873 (3). On some new species of European spiders. *Jour. Linn. Soc. London*, **11,** pp. 530–547, two pls.
——— 1873 (4). On some new species of Araneida, chiefly from oriental Siberia. *Proc. Zool. Soc. London*, **1873,** pp. 435–452, two pls.
——— 1875 (1). On some new species of Erigone. Part 1. *Proc. Zool. Soc. London*, **1875,** pp. 190–224, three pls.
——— 1875 (2). Notes and descriptions of some new and rare British spiders. *Ann. Mag. Nat. Hist.* (4), **16,** pp. 237–260, one pl.
——— 1875 (3). On some new species of Erigone from North America. *Proc. Zool. Soc. London*, **1875,** pp. 393–405.
——— 1879–81. The Spiders of Dorset. Sherborne, Pt. 1 (1879), pp. 1–235 ; Pt. 2 (1881), pp. 236–625, six pls.
——— 1879 (1). On some new and rare British spiders, with characters of a new genus. *Ann. Mag. Nat. Hist.* (5), **4,** pp. 190–215, one pl.
——— 1879 (2). On some new and rare spiders from New Zealand, with Characters of four new genera. *Proc. Zool. Soc. London*, **1879,** pp. 681–703, two pls.
——— 1882 (1). Notes on British spiders, with descriptions of three new species and characters of a new genus. *Ann. Mag. Nat. Hist.* (5), **9,** pp. 1–13, one pl.

CAMBRIDGE, O. PICKARD-, 1882(2). On some new species of Araneidea, with characters of a new Genus. *Ann. Mag. Nat. Hist.* (5), **9,** p. 259, one pl.

———— 1885. On new and rare British spiders, with some remarks on the formation of new species. *Proc. Dorset Nat. Hist. Field Club,* **6,** pp. 1–17, one pl.

———— 1886. On some new and rare British spiders. *Proc. Dorset Nat. Hist. Field Club,* **7,** pp. 70–78 (sep. 1–9) one pl.

———— 1888. On Walckenaera interjecta, a new spider from Hoddesdon. *Trans. Hertfordshire Nat. Hist. Soc.,* **5,** pp. 18-19, 1 fig.

———— 1889. On new and rare British spiders. *Proc. Dorset Nat. Hist. Field Club,* **10,** pp. 107–138, one pl.

———— 1891. On new and rare British spiders found in 1889–1890. *Proc. Dorset Nat. Hist. Field Club,* **12,** pp. 80–98, one pl.

———— 1893. On new and rare British spiders. *Proc. Dorset Nat. Hist. Field Club,* **14,** pp. 142–164, one pl.

———— 1894. On new and rare British spiders found in 1893, with rectifications of synonyms. *Proc. Dorset Nat. Hist. Field Club,* **15,** pp. 103–116, one pl.

———— 1895. On new and rare British spiders. *Proc. Dorset Nat. Hist. Field Club,* **16,** pp. 92–128, two pls.

———— 1896. On new and rare British spiders obsserved in 1895. *Proc. Dorset Nat. Hist. Field Club,* **17,** pp. 54–63, one pl.

———— 1899. Notes on British spiders observed in 1898. *Proc. Dorset Nat. Hist. Field Club,* **20,** pp. 1–22, one pl.

———— 1900. Notes on British spiders observed in 1899. *Proc. Dorset Nat. Hist. Field Club,* **21,** pp. 18–39, one pl.

———— 1902. On new and rare British Arachnida. *Proc. Dorset Nat. Hist. Field Club,* **23,** pp. 16–40, one pl.

———— 1903. On new and rare British spiders. *Proc. Dorset Nat. Hist. Field Club,* **24,** pp. 149–171, one pl.

———— 1905. On new and rare British Arachnida. *Proc. Dorset Nat. Hist. Field Club,* **26,** pp. 40–74, one pl.

———— 1906. On some new and rare British Arachnida. *Proc. Dorset Nat. Hist. Field Club,* **27,** pp. 72–92, one pl.

———— 1907. On new and rare British Arachnida. *Proc. Dorset Nat. Hist. Field Club,* **28,** pp. 121–148, two pls.

———— 1908. On new and rare British Arachnida, noted and observed in 1907. *Proc. Dorset Nat. Hist. Field Club,* **29,** pp. 161–194, one pl.

———— 1909. On British Arachnida noted and observed in 1908. *Proc. Dorset Nat. Hist. Field Club,* **30,** pp. 97–115, one pl.

———— 1910. On British Arachnida noted and observed in 1909. *Proc. Dorset Nat. Hist. Field Club,* **31,** pp. 47–70, one pl.

———— 1911 (1). On new and rare Arachnids, noted and observed in 1910. *Proc. Dorset Nat. Hist. Field Club,* **32,** pp. 33–54, one pl.

———— 1911 (2). Arachnida. *In* Additions to wild fauna of the Royal botanic gardens. XII. *Bull. Misc. Inform,* **1911,** pp. 370–373.

———— 1912. On new and rare British Arachnida noted and observed in 1911. *Proc. Dorset Nat. Hist. Field Club,* **33,** pp. 70–95, one pl.

———— 1913. On new and rare British Arachnida noted and observed in 1912. *Proc. Dorset Nat. Hist. Field Club,* **34,** pp. 107–136, one pl.

CARPENTER, G. H., 1898. A list of the spiders of Ireland. *Proc. Roy. Irish Acad.* (iii), **5,** pp. 128–210, nine text-figs.

———— 1900. Two spiders new to the British fauna. *Ann. Mag. Nat. Hist.* (7), **6,** pp. 199-204, 15 figs.

CARR, J. W., 1907. New Nottingham spiders and false-scorpions. *Rep. Trans. Nottingham Nat. Soc.,* **1905-6,** pp. 47–48.

CHAMBERLIN, R. V., 1922. The North American Spiders of the family Gnaphosidæ. *Proc. Biol. Soc. Wash.,* **35,** pp. 145–172.

———— and IVIE, W., 1942. A hundred new species of American spiders. *Bull. Univ. Utah.,* **32** (13), *(Biol. ser.,* **7** (1), pp. 1–117.

CHYZER, C., and KULCZYNSKI, L., 1891–97. Araneæ Hungariæ, Budapest, three vols., I, pp. 1–168, six pls. II (1), pp. 1–151, five pls., II (2), pp. 147–366, five pls.

CLERCK, C., 1757. Svenska Spindlar (Aranei Suecici), Stockholmiae, pp. 1–154, six pls.

COMSTOCK, J. H., 1940. The Spider Book. (Revised and edited by W. J. Gertsch.) New York, 1940.

CROSBY, C. R., and BISHOP, S. C., 1928. Revision of the spider genera Erigone, Eperigone and Catabrithorax (Erigoneæ). N.Y. State Mus. Bull. No. 278, pp. 5–73, twelve pls.
—————— 1931. Studies in American spiders : Genera Cornicularia, Para-cornicularia, Tigellinus, Walckenaera, Epiceratacelus and Pelecopsis, with descriptions of new genera and species. Jour. N.Y. Ent. Soc., 39, pp. 359–403, nine pls.
—————— 1933. American spiders : Erigoneæ, Males with cephalic pits. Ann. Ent. Soc. America, 26, pp. 105-172, nine pls.

DAHL, F., 1901. Über die Seltenheit gewisser Spinnenarten. Sitz.-ber. Ges. naturf. Freu. Berlin, 1901, pp. 257-266.
—————— 1908. Die Lycosiden oder Wolfspinnen Deutschlands. Halle. Abh. der Kaiserl. Leop.-Carol. Deutsch. Akad. Naturf., 88 (3), pp. 175–678. (Internal numbering, pp. 1–504, Refs. are to these.) 86 text-figs.
—————— F. and M., 1927. Spinnentiere oder Arachnoidea, II. Lycosidæ s. lat. (Wolfspinnen im weiteren Sinne.) Tierw. Deutsch. Jena. (5th pt.), pp. 1–80, 192 figs.

DAHL, M., 1931. Spinnentiere oder Arachnoidea. VI. 24. Familie : Agelenidæ. Tierw. Deutsch. Jena., 1931, pp. 1–46, 76 figs.
—————— 1937. Spinnentiere oder Arachnoidea. VIII. 19. Familie : Hahniidæ. Tierw. Deutsch. Jena., 1937, pp. 100–114, 33 figs.

DEGEER, C., 1778. Mémoires pour servir à l'histoire des insectes. Stockholm, 1752–1778. Seven vols. (Spiders : Tome 7, pp. 1–950, eleven pls.)

DENIS, J., 1942 (1). Notes sur les Erigonides III. Sur les femelles de trois espèces d'Entelecara. Bull. Soc. ent. France, 47, pp. 91–94, 6 figs.
—————— 1942 (2). Notes sur les Erigonides II. A propos de la femelle de Diplocephalus protuberans (O. P.-Cambr.). Rev. franc. entom. Paris, 9, pp. 82–84, 2 figs.
—————— 1943 (1). Notes sur les Erigonides. VI. Sur Silometopus reussi (Thorell) E. Simon. Bull. Soc. Zool. France, 68, pp. 123–126, 3 figs.
—————— 1943 (2). Araignées du Nord de la France. Bull. Soc. ent. France, 48, pp. 105–108. 3 figs.
—————— 1944. Sur quelques Theridion appartenant à la faune de France. Bull. Soc. ent. France, 49 (9), pp. 111–117, 16 figs.
—————— 1945. Notes sur les Erigonides, X. Remarques sur le genre Entelecara E. Simon avec la déscription de formes nouvelles du genre Plæsiocrærus E. Simon. Bull. Soc. d'Histoire Nat. Toulouse, 80, pp. 203–215, 13 figs.
—————— 1946. Notes sur les Erigonides, IX. La femelle de Cnephalocotes obscurus (Blackwall). Bull. Soc. ent. France, 51, pp. 11–12, 3 figs.
—————— 1947 (1). Notes sur les Erigonides, XI. Les espèces françaises du genre Oedothorax Bertkau. Bull. Soc. Hist. Nat. Toulouse, 82, pp. 131–158, 12 figs.
—————— 1947 (2). Notes sur les Erigonides, XIII. Diplocentria Hull et Mioxena Simon. Bull. Soc. Zool. France, 72, pp. 79–82, 4 figs.
—————— 1948 (1). Notes sur les Erigonides, VII. Remarques sur le genre Araeoncus Simon et quelques genres voisins. Bull. Soc. ent. France, 53, pp. 19–32, 22 figs.
—————— 1948 (2). A new fact about Erigone vagans Aud. and Sav. Proc. Zool. Soc. London, 118, pp. 588–590, 5 figs.
—————— 1948 (3). Notes sur les Erigonides, XVI. Essai sur la détermination des femelles d'Erigonides. Bull. Soc. Hist. Nat. Toulouse, 83, pp. 129–158, 5 figs.
—————— 1949. Notes sur les Erigonides, XVII. Additions et rectifications au tableau de détermination des femelles. Descriptions d'espèces nouvelles. Bull. Soc. Hist. Nat. Toulouse, 84, pp. 245–257. 13 figs.

DENIS, J., 1950.   Araignées de la region d'Orédon (Hautes-Pyrénées).   *Bull. Soc. Nat. Hist. Toulouse*, **85**, pp. 77-113, 46 figs.

——— 1952.   Araignées recoltées en Roumanie par Robert Leruth, avec un appendice sur quelques araignées cavernicoles de Belgique.   *Bull. Inst. roy. Sci. nat. Belg.*, **28**, No. 12, pp. 1–50.

DONISTHORPE, H. ST. J. K., 1927.   The guests of British ants.   London. 1927, pp. 1–244.

EMERTON, J. H., 1882.   New England spiders of the Family Theridiidæ.   *Trans. Connect. Acad. Arts. Sci.*, **6**, pp. 1–86, 24 pls.

FABRICIUS, J. C., 1793.   Entomologia systematica.   Hafniæ, 1792-96.   4 tomes. Aranea, **2** (1793), pp. 407–428.

FAGE, L., 1931.   Araneæ, 5e série, précédée d'un essai sur l'évolution souterraine et son déterminisme.   *Biospelogica*, LV.   *Arch. Zool. Exp.*, **71**, pp. 91–291.

FALCONER, W., 1909.   *Cornicularia kochii* Camb. :   A spider new to Great Britain. With a key to the British Corniculariæ.   *Naturalist, London*, **1909**, pp. 295–298, 332–333.

——— 1910 (1).   A new genus and species of spider (*Eboria caliginosa*).   *Naturalist, London*, **1910**, pp. 83–88, one pl.

——— 1910 (2).   Notes on *Eboria caliginosa* Falconer.   *Naturalist, London*, **1910**, pp. 253–254.

——— 1911.   New and rare Yorkshire spiders.   *Naturalist, London*, **1911**, pp. 283–288.

——— 1912,   The spiders of Wicken, Cambridge.   *Naturalist, London*, **1912**, pp. 310–324, one pl.

——— 1914.   *Laseola erythropus* Sim, with a key to the British *Laseolæ*.   *Naturalist, London*, **1914**, pp. 55–59, one pl.

——— 1915.   The spiders of Wicken, with description of two new species.   *Naturalist, London*, **1915**, pp. 225–230, 10 figs.

——— 1919.   New and rare British spiders.   *Naturalist, London*, **1919**, pp. 295–302, 1 fig.

——— 1937.   *Maro humicola*.   A synonym of *M. minutus* Cb.   *Naturalist, London*, **1937**, pp. 3–4.

——— 1938.   Arachnida *in* The Victoria County History of Oxfordshire.

FORSTER, A., and BERTKAU, P., 1883.   Beiträge zur Kenntniss der Spinnenfauna der Rheinprovinz.   *Verh. naturh. Ver. preuss. Rheinl.*, **40**, pp. 205–278, one pl.

FOURCROY, A. F. DE, 1785.   Entomologia Parisiensis.   Paris, 1785, pp. 1–544. (Aranea, pp. 531–537.)

GERHARDT, U., 1921.   Vergleichende Studien über die Morphologie des männlichen Tasters und die Biologie der Kopulation der Spinnen.   *Arch. Naturg.*, **87**, pp. 78–247, three pls.

GRUBE, A. Ed., 1859.   Verzeichniss der Arachnoiden Liv.–Kur.–und Ehstlands.   *Arch. Naturk. Liv. Ehst. Kurl.*, **1**, pp. 417–486.

GUÉRIN-MÈNEVILLE, F. E., 1838.   Iconographie du Régne animal de Cuvier, etc. Paris, 1829–1844, 3 vols.   Araignées :   **2**, pl. 1–2 :   **3**, pp. 5–9.   (The parts about spiders had probably appeared by 1838.)

HENTZ, N. M., 1832.   On North American spiders.   *Amer. Journ. Sci.*, **21**, pp. 99–122.

HOLM, Å., 1939.   Neue Spinnen aus Schweden.   *Ark. Zool.*, **31** A. (8), pp. 1–38, 17 figs.

——— 1943.   Zur Kenntnis der Spinnengattungen *Rhaebothorax* Sim., *Typhochraestus* Sim, und *Latithorax* n.gen.   *Ark. Zool.*, **34** A. (19), pp. 1–32, 25 figs.

——— 1944.   Revision einiger norwegischen Spinnenarten und Bemerkungen über deren Vorkommen in Schweden.   *Ent. Tidskrift*, **65**, pp. 122–134, 6 figs.

——— 1945.   Zur Kenntnis der Spinnenfauna des Torneträskgebietes.   *Ark. Zool.*, **36**, A.(15), pp. 1–80, 26 figs.

——— 1947.   Svensk Spindelfauna (3).   Stockholm, Fam. 8–10, Oxyopidæ, Lycosidæ, Pisauridæ, pp. 1–48, ten pls.

HOLM, Å., 1950. Studien über die Spinnenfauna des Torneträskgebietes. *Zool. Bidrag. fr. Uppsala*, **29**, pp. 103–213, 26 figs.

—— 1951. The mountain fauna of the Virihaure area in Swedish Lapland. Araneæ. *Lunds Universitets Arsskrift N.F.*, 2, **46**, No. 2, pp. 138–149, 2 figs.

HULL, J. E., 1908. Allendale spiders. *Trans. Nat. Hist. Soc. Northumb.* (N.S.), **3** (1), pp. 110–115, one pl.

—— 1909 (1). Notes on spiders. *Trans. Nat. Hist. Soc. Northumb.* (N.S.), **3** (2), pp. 446–451, one pl.

—— 1909 (2). Northumbrian coast spiders. *Naturalist, London*, **1909**, pp. 283–286, 6 figs.

—— 1911 (1). Papers on spiders. *Trans. Nat. Hist. Soc. Northumb.* (N.S.), **3** (3), pp. 573–590, one pl.

—— 1911 (2). New and rare British spiders. *Trans. Nat. Hist. Soc. Northumb.* (N.S.), **4** (1914), pp. 42–58, 1 fig, one pl. (appeared separately in 1911.)

—— 1920. The spider family Linyphiidæ : an essay in taxonomy. *Vasculum*, **6**, pp. 7–11.

—— 1931. A note on *Diplocentria* and *Lophocarenum* (Genera of spiders). *Vasculum* **17** (1), pp. 7–10, 2 figs.

—— 1932. Nomenclature of British Linyphiid spiders : A brief examination of Simon's French catalogue. *Trans. North. Nat. Union*, **1** (2), pp. 104–110.

JACKSON, A. R., 1905. The genus *Tapinocyba*. *Trans. Nat. Hist. Soc. Northumb.* (N.S.), **1**, pp. 248–261, two pls.

—— 1907. On some rare Arachnids captured during 1906. *Rep. Chester Soc. Nat. Sci.*, **6** (1), pp. 1–8, one pl.

—— 1908. On some rare arachnids captured during 1907. *Trans. Nat. Hist. Soc. Northumb.* (N.S.), **3** (1), pp. 49–78, one pl.

—— 1909. On some rare arachnids captured during 1908. *Trans. Nat. Hist. Soc. Northumb.* (N.S.), **3** (2), pp. 418–439, one pl.

—— 1910. On some arthropods observed in 1909. *Lancs. Nat.* (N.S.), **3**, pp. 17–51.

—— 1911 (1). Notes on arachnids observed during 1910, I. On three additions to the British Fauna. *Lancs. Nat.* (N.S.), **3** (36), pp. 385–392, one pl.

—— 1911 (2). On a spider new to science recently found in Ireland. *Irish Nat.*, **20** (2), pp. 28–31, one pl.

—— 1912. On the British spiders of the genus *Microneta*. *Trans. Nat. Hist. Soc. Northumb.* (N.S.), **4**, pp. 117–142, two pls.

—— 1913. On some new and obscure British spiders. *Trans. Notting. Nat. Soc.*, **60**, pp. 20–49, two pls.

—— 1914. A contribution to the spider fauna of Scotland. *Proc. Roy. Phys. Soc. Edinb.*, **19**, pp. 108–128, two pls.

—— 1915. A second contribution to the spider fauna of Scotland : with descriptions of a new spider of the genus *Clubiona*. *Proc. Roy. Phys. Soc. Edinb.*, **19**, pp. 177–190, one pl.

—— 1916 (1). On some arthropods observed in 1915. I. Arachnida. *Lancs. Nat.* **1916**, pp. 355–364.

—— 1916 (2). On the nomenclature and identity of some little known British spiders. *Ann. Mag. Nat. Hist.* (8), **17**, pp. 163–171.

—— 1924. On new and rare British Spiders. *Proc. Dorset Nat. Hist. Field Club*, **45**, pp. 101–120.

—— 1930. Results of the Oxford University Expedition to Greenland, 1928. *Ann. Mag. Nat. Hist.* (10), **6** pp. 639–656, one pl.

—— 1932. On new and rare British spiders. *Proc. Dorset Nat. Hist. Field Club*, **53**, pp. 200–214.

—— 1933 (1). Results of the Oxford University expedition to Akpatok in 1931. Araneae. *Proc. Zool. Soc. Lond*, **1933** (1), pp. 145–159, 20 figs.

—— 1933 (2). Notes on five species of spiders. *Ann. Mag. Nat. Hist.* (10), **12**, pp. 279–283.

—— 1933 (3). Araneæ in 1932. *Lancs. Chesh. Fauna Comm. Ann. Rep.*, **19**, p. 27.

JACKSON, A. R., 1934. On a collection of spiders made in 1928 by Dr. Sig. Thor in Spitzbergen. *Norsk. Ent. Tidsskr.*, **3** (5), pp. 332-354, 17 figs.

KASTON, B. J., 1948. Spiders of Connecticut. *State Geol. and Nat. Hist. Survey,* Hartford, **70**, pp. 1–874, 144 pls.

KOCH, C. L. (1). 1836–48. Die Arachniden, Nürnberg. (The first two were by C. W. Hahn, 1831, 1834.) 1836, Abt. III, 119 pp.; 1838, IV, 144 pp.; 1839, V., 158 pp.; 1839, VI, 156 pp.; 1839, VII, 130 pp.; 1841, VIII, 131 pp.; 1842, IX, 108 pp.; 1843, X, 142 pp.; 1845, XI, 174 pp.; 1845, XII, 166 pp.; 1846, XIII, 234 pp.; 1848, XIV, 210 pp.; 1848, XV, 136 pp.; 1848, XVI, 80 pp., 562 pls. in all.
———— (2), 1837–50. Übersicht des Arachnidensystems, Nürnberg, Hefte 1–5. 1837, I, 39 pp.; 1839, II, 38 pp.; 1842, III, 131 pp.; 1847, IV, 136 pp.; 1850, V, 104 pp. 30 pls. in all.
———— (3), 1833–1837. Arachniden. (In) Panzer, Faunæ Insectorum Germaniæ initia. Fortgesetz von Herrich-Schaffer, Regensburg, Hefte 111–190. Spiders: 1833, Hft. 119–121; 1834, Hft. 122–127; 1835, Hft. 128–131; 1836, Hft. 134, 137, 138, 139; 1837, Hft. 141.

KOCH, L., 1862. Zur Arachnidengattung Tetragnatha. *Kor.-bl. zool.-min. Ver. Regensburg,* **16**, pp. 79–80.
———— 1868. Die Arachnidengattungen Amaurobius, Coelotes und Cybaeus. *Abh. Naturh. Ges. Nürnberg,* **1868,** pp. 1–15, two pls.
———— 1869. Beitrag zur Kenntnis der Arachnidenfauna Tirols. *Zeit. Ferd. Tirol Voral.* (3), **14**, pp. 149–206.
———— 1870. Beitrage zur Kenntnis der Arachnidenfauna Galiziens. *Jahrb. k. k. Gelehr. Ges. Krakau,* **41**, pp. 1–56.
———— 1872 (1). Beitrag zur Kenntnis der Arachnidenfauna Tirols. Zweite Abhandlung. *Zeits. Ferd. Tirol Voral.* (3), **17**, pp. 239–328.
———— 1872 (2). Apterologisches aus dem fränkischen Jura. *Abh. naturh. Ges. Nürnb.,* **vi**, pp. 127–152, 32 figs.
———— 1875. Beschreibungen einiger von Herrn Dr. Zimmermann bei Niesky in der Oberlausitz und im Riesengebirge entdeckter neuer Spinnenarten. *Abh. naturf. Ges. Görlitz,* **15**, pp. 1–21, one pl.
———— 1876. Verzeichnis der in Tirol bis jetz beobachteten Arachniden nebst Beschreibungen einiger neuen oder weniger bekannten Arten. *Zeits. Ferd. Tirol Voral.* (3), **19**, pp. 221–354.
———— 1877. Verzeichnis der bei Nürnberg bis jetz beobachteten Arachniden, etc. *Abh. Naturh. Ges. Nürnberg,* **6**, pp. 115–198, one pl.
———— 1878. Verzeichnis der bei Nurnberg bis jetz beobachteten Arachniden. *Abh. Naturh. Ges. Nürnberg,* **6**, pp. 1–86, one pl. (a reprint of above).
———— 1879. Arachniden aus Sibirien und Novaja Semlja, eingesammelt von der schwedischen Expedition in Jahre 1875. *Kong. Svenska Vet.-Akad. Handl.,* **16**(5), pp. 3–136, seven pls.
———— 1881. Beschreibungen neuer von Herrn Dr. Zimmermann bei Niesky in der Oberlausitz entdeckter Arachniden. *Abh. naturf. Ges. Görlitz,* **17**, pp. 41-71, one pl.
———— 1882. Zoologische Ergebnisse von Excursionen auf den Balearen, II. Arachniden und Myriapoden. *Verh. zool-bot. Ges. Wien,* **31**, pp. 625–678, two pls.

KULCZYNSKI, L., 1887. Przyczynek do Tyrolskiej fauny Pajeczaków. *Rozpr. spraw. wydz. mat. przyrod. Akad. Umiej.,* **16**, pp. 245–356, four pls.
———— 1891-7. (See CHYZER, C.).
———— 1899. Symbola ad faunam Aranearum Austriae inferioris. *Rozpr. spraw. wydz. mat. przyrod. Akad. Umiej.,* **36**, pp. 64–65, one pl.
———— 1902. Erigonæ Europaeae. Addenda et descriptiones. *Bull. Acad. Cracovie,* **1902** (8), pp. 539–560, one pl.
———— 1905 (1). Fragmenta arachnologica II. *Bull. Acad. Cracovie.* **1905,** pp. 231–250, one pl.
———— 1905 (2). Fragmenta arachnologica, III. *Bull. Acad. Cracovie.* **1905,** pp. 430–440.

KULCZYNSKI, L., 1906. Fragmenta arachnologica, IV. *Bull. Acad. Cracovie*, **1906**, pp. 417-476, two pls.

——— 1911. Fragmenta arachnologica, IX. *Bull. Acad. Cracovie*, **1911**, pp. 12-55, two pls.

LA TOUCHE, A. A. D., 1944. Hampshire spiders, including the description of a new species, *Diplocephalus cottoni*. *Proc. Zool. Soc. London*, **115**, pp. 281-295, 2 figs.

LATREILLE, P. A., 1804. Histoire naturelle générale et particulière des Crustacés et des insectes. Paris, 14, vols., Arachnides, **7**, pp. 144-305, three pls.

LENDL, A., 1886. Species subfamiliæ Tetragnathinarum faunæ Hungaricæ. *Math. Termés. Közlem*, **22**, pp. 119-156, five pls.

LESSERT, R. DE, 1904. Observations sur les Araignées du bassin du Léman et de quelques autres localités suisses. *Rev. suisse zool*., **12**, p. 320, one pl.

——— 1910. Catalogue des invertebrés de la Suisse, Fasc. 3, Araignées. *Mus. Hist. Nat. Genève*, pp. 1-635, 250 figs.

LINNAEUS, C., 1758. Systema Naturæ, Ed. X, Helmiæ, **1**, pp. 1-821.

——— 1767. Systema Naturæ. Ed. XII. Helmiæ, **1** (2) pp. 533-1327.

LOCKET, G. H., 1926. Observations on the habits of some web-spinning spiders. (With some corroborative notes by W. S. Bristowe.) *Proc. Zool. Soc. London*. **1926**, pp. 1125-1146, 4 figs.

——— 1932. Some cases of heterogonic growth in spiders. *Ann. Mag. Nat. Hist.* (10), **9**, pp. 407-419, 5 figs.

——— and P. C. GARDINER, 1938. Further examples of allometric growth in spiders. *Proc. Zool. Soc. London* (A), **107**, pp. 487-498, 4 figs.

LUCAS, H., 1846. Histoire naturelle des animaux articulés. (In) Exploration scientifique d'Algérie, Zoologie, Paris, Tome I (1846), Aranéides, pp. 89-271 (17 pls. in Tome IV).

MARPLES, M. J., 1935. Notes on *Argiope bruennichi* and other Pyrenean spiders. *Journ. Linn. Soc. London*, **39**, pp. 195-202, one pl.

MARPLES, M. J. and B. J., 1937. Notes on the spiders *Hyptiotes paradoxus* and *Cyclosa conica*. *Proc. Zool. Soc. London* (A), **107**, A, pp. 213-221, 2 figs, two pls.

MEADE, R. H., 1861. Description of a new species of spider lately discovered in England. *Ann. Mag. Nat. Hist*. (3), **7**, pp. 20-21.

MENGE, A., 1866-78. Preussische Spinnen. *Schr. Naturf. Ges. Danzig*, N.F., 11 Abteilungen, pp. 1-560, 91 pls.; 1866, Abt. I, pp. 1-152; 1868, II, pp. 153-218; 1869, III, pp. 219-264: 1871, IV, pp. 265-296; 1872, V, pp. 297-326; 1873, VI, pp. 327-374; 1874, VII, pp. 375-422; 1875, VIII, pp. 423-454; 1876, IX, pp. 455-494; 1877, X, pp. 495-542; 1878, XI, pp. 543-560.

MILLER, F., 1937. Neue Spinnenarten (Araneæ) aus der Cechoslovakischen Republik, II. *Festschrift Strand*, **2**, pp. 563-570, 11 figs.

——— 1947. Pavouci zvirena hadcovych stepi u Mohelna. *Acta Soc. cogn. et cons. naturæ. Morav. Siles*, **7**, pp. 1-99, 16 pls.

——— and KRATOCHVIL, J., 1940 (1). Einige weitere neue Spinnen aus Mitteleuropa. *Vestnik c Zoologicke Spolecnosti v Praze*, **8**, pp. 59-72, 6 figs.

——— 1940 (2). Ein Beitrag zur Revision der mitteleuropischen Spinnenarten aus der Gattung *Porrhomma* E. Sim. *Zool. Anzeiger*, **130**, 7/8, pp. 161-190, 13 figs.

MILLIDGE, A. F., 1951. Key to the British Genera of Subfamily Erigoninæ (Family Linyphiidæ : Araneæ) : including the Description of a New Genus (Jacksonella). *Ann. Mag. Nat. Hist*. (12), **4**, pp. 545-562, two figs.

——— and LOCKET, G. H., 1947. On new and rare British spiders. *Proc. Linn. Soc. Lond*., **158**, 1945-6, Pt. 2, pp. 110-118, six figs.

——— 1952. New and rare British spiders. *Proc. Linn. Soc. Lond*., **163** (1950-51), Part (1), pp. 59-78, twelve figs.

MULLER, F., and SCHENKEL, E., 1895. Verzeichniss der Spinnen von Basel und Umgegend. *Verh. naturf. Ges. Basel*, **10**, pp. 691-824, two pls.

NIELSEN, E., 1932. The Biology of Spiders, Copenhagen ; **1** (in English), pp. 1–248, ten figs., 32 pls., **2** (in Danish), pp. 1–725, 426 figs., five pls.

OHLERT, E., 1865. Arachnologische Studien. *Off. Prüf. Schül. Höh. Programm.*, pp. 1–12.

OLIVIER, A. G., 1789. Article : Araignée. (In) *Encycl. Méth. Hist. Nat. Ins.*, Paris, **4**, pp. 173–240.

PALLAS, P. S., 1772. Spicilegia zoologica, Berolini, Tom. I. 10 fasc., 1767–1774. *Aranea*, IX, pp. 44–50, two pls.

PANZER, G. W. F., 1793. Faunæ Insectorum Germaniæ initia. Heft **4**, Regensburg, 1793 (Araneæ, fol. 23, 24).

―――― 1801. Faunæ insectorum Germaniæ initia, Regensburg. Aranea : **74**, fol. 19, 20 ; **78**, fol. 21 ; **83**, fol. 21.

REIMOSER, E., 1937. Spinnentiere oder Arachnoidea, VIII. 17 Familie : Anyphænidæ oder Zartspinnen, pp. 42–44, one fig. ; 18 Familie : Clubionidæ oder Röhrenspinnen, pp. 45–99, 103 figs. (In) *Die Tierwelt Deutschlands*, Jena.

SCHENKEL, E., 1923. Beitrag zur Spinnenkunde. *Verh. naturf. Ges. Basel*, **34**, pp. 78–127, one pl.

―――― 1929. Beitrag zur Spinnenkunde. *Zool. Anzeiger*, **83** (5–8), pp. 137–143, four figs.

―――― 1930. Die Araneiden der Schwedischen Kamtchatka-Expedition, 1920–22. *Ark. Zool.*, **21** A (15), pp. 1–33, 13 figs.

―――― 1939. Beitrag zur Spinnenkunde. *Rev. suisse zool.*, **46** (3), pp. 94–114, seven figs.

―――― 1950. Spinnentiere aus dem westlichen Nordamerika. *Verh. naturf. Ges. Basel.* **61**, pp. 28–92, 34 figs.

SCHOLLMEYER, A., 1914. Argyroneta aquatica. Biologie mit besonderer Berücksichtigung der Atmung. *Ann. Biol. Lac.*, **6**, pp. 314–338, 12 figs.

SCOPOLI, J. A., 1763. Entomologia Carniolica, Vindobonæ, pp. 1–420.

―――― 1772. Observationes zoologicæ. *in* Annus V. Historico-naturalis. *Lipsiæ*, 1772, pp. 70–128 (Aranea pp. 125–126).

SIMON, E., 1872. Notice complémentaire sur les arachnides cavernicoles et hypogés. *Ann. Soc. ent. France* (5), **2**, pp. 473–488, one pl.

―――― 1873. Araneides nouveaux ou peu connus du midi de l'Europe (2nd Mem.). *Mém. Soc. roy. sci. Liège* (2), **5**, pp. 1–174, three pls.

―――― 1874–84. Les arachnides de France. Paris : five Tomes. 1874, **1**, pp. 1–269 ; 1875, **2**, pp. 1–350 ; 1876, **3**, pp. 1–364 ; 1878, **4**, pp. 1–330 ; 1881, **5**, pt. 1, pp. 1–180 ; 1884, **5**, pt. 2, pp. 181–420 ; **5**, pt. 3, pp. 421–885.
(The pages of vol. **6** (of which parts 2–5 were published by L. Berland and L. Fage, after Simon's death in 1924), are numbered continuously throughout, and are referred to by their dates in the text. See E. Simon, 1914, 1926, 1929, 1932, 1937.)

―――― 1879. Arachnides nouveaux de France, d'Espagne et d'Algerie (1 re. Mém). *Bull. Soc. zool. France*, **4**, pp. 251–263.

―――― 1881. Description d'espèces nouvelles du genre Erigone. *Bull. Soc. Zool. France*, **6**, pp. 233–257.

―――― 1914. Arachnides de France, **6**, pt. 1, pp. 1–308, 537 figs.

―――― 1922. Description de deux Arachnides cavernicoles du Midi de la France. *Bull. Soc. ent. France*, **1922** (15), pp. 199–200.

―――― 1926. Arachnides de France, **6**, pt. 2, pp. 309–532, 274 figs.

―――― 1929. Arachnides de France, **6**, pt. 3, pp. 533–772, 300 figs.

―――― 1932. Arachnides de France, **6**, pt. 4, pp. 773–978, 389 figs.

―――― 1937. Arachnides de France, **6**, pt. 5, pp. 979–1298, 527 figs.

SMITH, F. P., 1904. The spiders of the sub-family Erigoninæ. *Jour. Queck. Micr. Cl.* (2), **9**, pp. 9–20, one pl.

―――― 1905. *Anglia hancockii*, a spider new to science. *Jour. Queck. Micr. Cl.* (2), **9**, pp. 247–250, one pl.

SMITH, F. P., 1906. The spiders of the *Diplocephalus* group. *Jour. Queck. Micr. Cl.* (2), 9, pp. 295–320.

—— 1908. Some British spiders taken in 1908. *Jour. Queck. Micr. Cl.* (2), 10, pp. 311–334, one pl.

SÖRENSEN, W., 1898. Arachnida Grœnlandica. *Vid. Medd. naturh. Foren. Kjöbenh.,* 1898, pp. 176–235.

STRAND, E., 1900. Arachnologisches. *Nyt. Mag. Naturv.,* 38, pp. 95–102.

SULZER, J. H., 1776. Abgekürtze Geschichte der Insekten, nach dem Linnæischen System. Winterthur, two vol., 1, pp. 1–274 (Araneæ : 1, pp. 248–254, two pls.).

SUNDEVALL, C. J., 1829. Svenska Spindlarnes beskrifning. *Nova Acta Soc. Sci. Uppsal.,* 1829, pp. 188–219. Also *Kongl. Svenska Vet. Akad. Handl.,* 1829, pp. 188–219.

—— 1831. Svenska Spindlarnes beskrifning. *Nova Acta Soc. Sci. Uppsal.,* 1831, pp. 108–148. Also *Kongl. Svenska Vet. Akad. Handl.,* 1831, pp. 108–148.

—— 1832. Svenska Spindlarnes beskrifning. *Nova Acta Soc. Sci. Uppsal.,* 1832, pp. 171–272. Also *Kongl. Svenska Vet. Akad. Handl.,* 1832, pp. 171–272.

THORELL, T., 1856. Recensio critica Aranearum Suecicarum, quas descripserit Clerckius, Linnaeus, de Geerus. *Nova Acta Soc. Sci. Uppsal.* (3), 2 (1), pp. 61–176.

—— 1869–70. On European spiders. *Nova Acta Soc. Sci. Uppsal.* (3), 7, pp. 1–108 (1869) ; pp. 109–242 (1870).

—— 1870–73. Remarks on synonyms of European spiders. Uppsala, pt. I, 1870, pp. 1–96 ; pt. II, 1871, pp. 97–228 ; pt. III, 1872, pp. 229–374 ; pt. IV, 1873, pp. 375–644.

—— 1871 (2). Om Arachnider fran Spitzbergen och Beeren-Eiland. *Ofvers. Kongl. Vet. Akad. Forh.,* 28 (6), pp. 683–702.

—— 1872. Om nagra Arachnider fran Grœnland. *Ofvers. Kongl. Vet. Akad. Forh.,* 29, pp. 147–166.

—— 1875 (1). Descriptions of several European and North African spiders. *Kongl. Svenska Vet. Akad. Handl.* (N. F.), 13, pp. 3–203.

—— 1875 (2). Diagnoses Aranearum Europæarum aliquot novarum. *Tijdschr. Ent.,* 18, pp. 81–108.

—— 1875 (3). Verzeichniss südrüssicher Spinnen. *Horae Soc. Ent. Ross.,* 11, pp. 39–122.

TULLGREN, A., 1946. Svensk Spindelfauna. 3. Fam. 5–7. Clubionidæ, Zoridæ, Gnaphosidæ. Stockholm, 1946, 141 pp., 21 pls.

—— 1942. Bidrag till kännedomen om den svenska spindelfaunan. I. *Ent. Tidskr.,* 63, Haft. 3–4, pp. 217–234, two pls.

—— 1947. Bidrag till kännedomen om den svenska spindelfaunan. II. *Ent. Tidskr.,* 68, Haft. 3–4, pp. 130–154, 67 figs.

—— 1949. Bidrag till kännedomen om den svenska spindelfaunan. III. *Ent. Tidskr.,* 70, Haft. 1–2, pp. 33–64, 18 figs.

VILLERS, C. de, 1789. Caroli Linnæi entomologia, faunæ Suecicæ descriptionibus aucta. Lugduni, 1789, 4 vol. (Araneæ, 4, pp. 86–130).

WAGNER, W. A., 1900. L'araignée aquatique (Argyroneta aquatica Cl). *Bull. Soc. imp. nat. Moscou.* (N. S.), 15, pp. 61–174, 37 figs., one pl. Also in *Jour. Roy. Micr. Soc.,* 1901, p. 146 ; *Zool. Cent. bl.,* 9, p. 369.

WALCKENAER, C. A., 1802. Faune parisienne. Insectes, Paris. Tome II, pp. 187–250.

—— 1805. Tableau des aranéides. Paris, 1805, pp. i–xii, 1–88, nine pls.

—— 1806. Histoire naturelle des aranéides. Paris-Strasbourg, 1806 (four series of ten plates, with explanatory pages not numbered).

—— 1825. Aranéides. (In) Faune française, etc., Paris, 1825–30, 240 pp.

—— 1837. Histoire naturelle des Insectes aptères. Paris, 1837–47. Four vols., 1, 1837, pp. 1–682.

WESTRING, N., 1851. Förteckning öfver de till närvarande tid Kande, i Sverige förekommande Spindlarten, utgörande ett antal af 253, deraf 132 äro nya för svenska Faunan. *Göteb. Kongl. Vet. Handl.,* 2, pp. 25–62.

WESTRING, N., 1861. Araneæ Svecicæ. *Göteb. Kongl. Vet. Handl.*, **7**, pp. 1–615. (Also Sep. Gothoburgi, 1861, pp. 1–615.)

WHITE, A., 1852. Arachnida *in* Sutherland. Journal of a voyage in Baffin's Bay and Barrow Straights. *London*, 1852, **2**, Appendix, pp. ccvii–ccxi.

WIDER, 1834. Bescreibung der Arachniden. (In) Reuss, A. Zoologischen Miscellen. *Mus. Senck.*, **1**, pp. 195–282, five pls.

WIEHLE, H., 1927. Beiträge zur Kenntnis des Radnetzbaues der Epeiriden, Tetragnathiden und Uloboriden. *Zeits. Morph. Ökol. Tiere.*, **8** (3–4), pp. 468–537, 27 figs., seven pls.

———— 1931 (1). Spinnentiere oder Arachnoidea. VI. 27. Familie : Araneidæ *in Tierwelt Deutschlands*, Jena, **1931**, pp. 1–136, 218 figs.

———— 1931 (2). Neue Beiträge zur Kentniss des Fanggewebes der Spinnen aus den Familien Argiopidæ, Uloboridæ und Theridiidæ. Zeits. Morph. Ökol. Tiere, **22** (2–3), pp. 349–400, 25 figs.

———— 1937. Spinnentiere oder Arachnoidea, VIII. 26. Familie : Theridiidæ oder Hauben-netzspinnen (Kugelspinnen). *Tierwelt Deutschlands*, Jena, **1937**, pp. 119-222, 286 figs.

———— 1939. Die einheimischen Tetragnatha Arten. *N. Act. Leop.* (N. F.), **6** (41), pp. 363–386, 61 figs., two pls.

ZORSCH, H. M., 1937. The spider genus Lepthyphantes in the United States. *Amer. Midl. Nat.* **18** (5), pp. 856–898, six pls.

INDEX

VOLUME II.

INDEX TO FAMILIES, GENERA AND SPECIES